The Man Called Kyril

After graduating from Oxford, John Trenhaile worked as a barrister before becoming a full-time writer. His twelve novels have been translated into over twenty languages. After six years working in Taiwan he spent time in Thailand and Malaysia, and now lives with his wife in Lewes, East Sussex. He has two children, one granddaughter, and a great-granddaughter.

Also by John Trenhaile

The General Povin trilogy

The Man Called Kyril
A View from the Square
Nocturne for the General

JOHN TRENHAILE

THE MAN CALLED KYRIL

CANELO

First published in Great Britain in 1981 by Sphere Books Ltd

This edition published in the United Kingdom in 2022 by

Canelo
Unit 9, 5th Floor
Cargo Works, 1-2 Hatfields
London, SE1 9PG
United Kingdom

A CIP catalogue record for this book is available from the British Library.

Print ISBN 978 1 80032 784 9
Ebook ISBN 978 1 80032 198 4

Printed and bound in Great Britain by Clays Ltd, Elcograf S.p.A.

1

For Vicki, my wife, with love

I am not for the sweetly timid daydreamers

Childish in their complacency.

I am
for those who are willing to fight
not for those who resort to prayer,

For idealists of action!

For those
who have undertaken to change the world…

Yevgeny Yevtushenko, 'Envoys are going to Lenin'

Chapter 1

The blue street lamps were extinguished one by one, conceding the snow-covered streets to the grey half-light of dawn. Across the city dogs spoke to one another, making the most of the early morning stillness before traffic and many human voices gathered to exclude them, but Dzerzhinsky Square was quiet. Nothing moved.

From his vantage point at the tall window the old man had an uninterrupted view of Marx Prospekt and the statue of 'Iron Felicks', who had given the square its name, but that was all. This tickled his sense of irony. The old man, who was paid to do nothing but watch, had nothing to do.

The room was growing lighter.

He turned away from the window and considered his spacious office. He thought he was familiar with it but he had never come to work as early as this; by spending the night there he had gained a new perspective.

The focal point of the room was a large, ornate, old-fashioned desk placed so that the natural light from the window fell directly on to its surface, bare except for a brass inkstand. To the right stood a table with several telephones and a switchboard which the old man could work himself without going through an operator. One of the phones was the 'Kremlevka', direct to the Kremlin, another the ‘Vertushka’, his connection with the Politburo. He often wondered if even those two telephones were safe. But he knew that such things were only relative, that in his world nothing was ever truly secure.

To the left of his desk was another, smaller table for the more mundane requirements of office routine: a diary, paper and pens, two trays, one for outgoing and one for incoming documents. The latter contained such diverse snippets of information as the number of troops currently on the frontier with Pakistan, and the name of the winner of the sweepstake as to the date when the white lines on the British ambassador’s tennis court would first be covered with snow.

One file, more bulky than the rest, lay on the desk awaiting its return to the ‘Out’ tray. His eyes lingered on it for a moment: ‘Masked Shrike’, the oldest of all his many projects and still his favourite. Years ago, quite by chance, he had met a delegate to a Party Congress; now that delegate was local secretary to the communist party of Albania, biding the old man’s time, waiting for orders from Moscow. So many long-term plans, so many projects had evolved in this room, each contained in a master file with the line drawing of a bird on the cover. The achievements of a lifetime…

The old man had read many documents during his lonely vigil, cat-napping between bouts of work. This morning, however, papers no longer interested him. Nor did he care about the quartz clocks ranged on the wall opposite the desk, each showing local time in a foreign capital, nor the priceless Persian carpet, nor the portrait of Yuri Andropov which dominated the wall above the fireplace. At this early hour of greyness and shadows the old man’s whole attention was concentrated on The Chair.

The Chair had become a legend for the men who worked in this building. The initials KGB officially stand for *Komitet Gosudarstvennoy Bezopasnosti* – the Committee for State Security (although within the KGB itself they traditionally represent *Kontora Grubykh Banditov*, or 'Office of Crude Bandits'). As the official name suggests it is a matter-of-fact organisation, not much given to sentimentality or myth. But there are exceptions.

For example, there is The Door. Access to the old man's room on the third floor of 2, Dzerzhinsky Square is normally gained through oak double-doors beside the fireplace. Opposite the desk, however, is another door which seems curiously out of place in such a splendid office. It is made of steel and held shut by twin padlocks. The old man's immediate predecessor, Andropov, hung a curtain over it and in his time the padlocks rusted. The old man did not use the door much either, but he abolished the curtain, wanting his visitors to be able to see what lay behind it.

Within the KGB many stories are told about this steel door. Shelepin, for example, was supposed to have treated it as his regular means of access; during his reign its hinges were oiled once a week. It is also said that, with the exception of the tenant of the large office on the third floor, no one who passes through The Door ever comes back; but these are only stories to frighten children.

The Chair, as it is always simply known, has an altogether different reputation. It is an old, heavy and extremely uncomfortable wooden throne, finely carved and polished to a high reflective shine. No one knows where it originally came from but it is presumed to be a relic of the Tzarist regime, once the property of an autocratic nobleman. Each tenant has his own way of trying to make it comfortable: blankets, cushions, foam rubber... But they all sit in it. No one could ever get rid of The Chair. It has become a symbol. For in it reposes supreme power, control over the daily lives of the citizens of the USSR, power extending into the heart of the Politburo itself. And in the eyes of Soviet law, The Chair is never empty.

Marshal Voldemar Pavlovich Stanov, at 73 the oldest man ever to hold the office of Chairman of the KGB, approached The Chair very slowly and lowered himself into its hard embrace. He laid his head against the carved rest and closed his eyes.

-

When the double doors opened Stanov did not look round. He knew it would be Colonel Yevchenko, his bodyguard and friend. No one who was not expected entered this room. As Yevchenko placed the steaming glass of tea on the desk, Stanov's thin lips compressed briefly in a smile.

'Thank you, Nikolai.'

The old colonel grunted and sat down heavily in the nearest chair. For a few moments neither man spoke.

He's dying, people told Yevchenko, dying and under suspicion. You should get out while you can.

He's old, people said to Stanov (sometimes the same people), old and useless. You should let him go. Have someone young and fit to look after you.

But neither man had so many friends that he could afford to jettison the best.

Stanov finished his tea and sucked the flesh from the thick slice of lemon.

'We must be going, Nikolai. Is it time?'

Yevchenko nodded and hauled himself painfully upright.

'Everything's ready, just like you asked.'

'Nobody suspects I stayed here last night?'

'Just like you asked,' Yevchenko soothed him.

They used the back stairs to the underground car-park, supposedly a fire escape but invariably kept locked 'for security reasons'. Yevchenko had gone to no little trouble to obtain a key without arousing suspicion. Parked close up against the basement door to the stairs was a black Zhiguli, indistinguishable from hundreds of similar vehicles on the Moscow streets. Yevchenko glanced right and left before signalling to Stanov that it was safe for him to leave the shelter of the stairwell.

'You must get down on the floor, old man.'

The endearment, permitted but rarely used, betrayed Yevchenko's anxiety, and Stanov smiled. It was painful creasing his old bones into such a confined space, but he managed it.

'You have the gun?'

In answer Yevchenko pressed a Stechkin into Stanov's hand, then covered him with a blanket.

'I'm going to put some empty salmon boxes over you. Don't worry, they're not heavy.'

Yevchenko took a last look round before settling into the driver's seat. There was no one about. Moments later the car was climbing the ramp to street level.

Notwithstanding his seniority and familiarity to the sentry, Yevchenko had to produce identification before they would let him out. The check was perfunctory, however, and Yevchenko had already begun to accelerate before the barrier was fully raised. When he was cruising comfortably along Marx Prospekt he said softly, 'It's all right.'

There was no reply, and for a mad second Yevchenko wanted to stop and see if Stanov was still alive. He resisted it and drove on. They were going against the rush-hour traffic and in 30 minutes reached the outer suburbs of the city. Yevchenko stopped in a deserted side-street and leaned back over the seat to tug away the boxes and the blanket. Stanov sat up, blinking.

'I said "It's all right" and you didn't reply, I thought...'

'Where in hell are we, Yevchenko? Why have we stopped?'

'I'll drive on, then.'

Yevchenko knew better than to fuss. They completed the journey in silence. A few miles further on the car pulled up outside a block of flats which Stanov eyed with distaste.

'Half-built rubbish. Look at that front area, it's like a building site.'

'You sent him to live there, remember?'

Stanov licked his lips. 'Have you got the file?'

'It's in the flap of the seat in front of you.'

Stanov reached out, but before he could take the folder Yevchenko spoke again.

'I still say you're wrong. Why lie to him? For the last time, think...'

'I have thought.' Stanov's voice was sharp with tension. 'Have I thought of anything else these last two years? And *I* say... and also for the last time... *I* say I will not trust this man with the whole truth. For his sake and for ours, I will not tell him all of what we know. So let there be an end to it.' Yevchenko opened the door and climbed out of the car. From the back seat Stanov noted with approval that in his plain dark overcoat and ordinary shoes Yevchenko might have passed for a civilian; he didn't have 'soldier' written all over him any more. While Yevchenko leaned against the car Stanov opened the file on Captain Ivan Yevseevich Bucharensky and began to read.

Most of the details were so well known to him that he could have recited them from memory. Age 42. Trained at Dietskoye Selo. Specialities: disguise, languages, small arms. Cleared to work for Department 13 of Line F, now Executive Action Department ('Department V'). Twenty years in the field, principally western Europe. Stanov skipped a few pages: he knew there had been several notable successes, no glaring failures, much competent work. Divorced 1971 (no children). Transferred to Centre 1979, Personnel Directorate. A poor fate for an honest worker, therefore a reader of the file must assume that this worker was not as honest as he looked. Stanov pursed his lips. That had been a good move on his part.

He turned up the assessments. Until the transfer to Centre these had been uniformly good; then they became guarded. Bucharensky was a man under a cloud, reasoned the Personnel Directorate; let us not do anything to dispel it.

Then, almost a year ago the sudden demotion; loss of pay; removal to this shoddy apartment. And what must have made it all so distressing to Bucharensky was that there had been not the glimmer of an explanation: not here in his file, not in a personal interview, not anywhere. Just the end of a career. A year ago the assessments simply stopped.

Stanov put away the file. In fact Bucharensky had never been assessed so thoroughly as over the past year. During that time he was under 24-hour surveillance by hand-picked teams who reported daily to Stanov or Yevchenko. Very few lives could undergo that treatment and not show signs of cracking. But Bucharensky had not cracked. As far as Stanov could learn, no word of complaint had passed his lips over the last 12 months. Instead he had stoically endured what must have seemed the worst thing ever to happen to him. Stanov was satisfied. He was about to entrust this man with what remained of his own life.

'He's coming.'

Stanov nodded to show that he had heard and squeezed into the far corner of the back seat. Through the windscreen he saw a man walking towards them, his arms laden with brown paper parcels. The face was familiar to Stanov from numerous photographs. Bucharensky did not look up from the pavement until he was almost level with the car. Then he became aware of Yevchenko standing by the open door.

'Raise arms, please, comrade Captain.'

Bucharensky obediently put down his parcels, lifted his arms and waited while Yevchenko frisked him.

'Get in.'

Bucharensky immediately bent down to obey. Not even the sight of the Stechkin in Stanov's gloved hands caused him to hesitate.

'Good morning, comrade Marshal,' he said carefully. He sat rigidly, staring straight ahead, trying to look as though he were at attention.

'You have been shopping, Captain?' said Stanov, his voice testy.

'Yes, comrade Marshal. It is my free day. I have been saving up...'

His voice tailed off.

'Show me what you have bought, please.'

Bucharensky undid his parcels one by one, careful to preserve the paper for future use. A borodinski loaf, pickled cucumber, herring, a very small bottle of vodka. Stanov raised his eyes from these modest purchases and said, 'You have to save up for such things, Captain?'

For the first time Bucharensky turned his head towards Stanov. 'Yes. Comrade Marshal.'

Stanov nodded. 'Today,' he said, after a short pause, 'we are going on a picnic. Don't worry, we have brought our own food. There are many things I have to say to you.'

Yevchenko took the road to Usovo. In less than an hour they were deep in the wooded hills of the countryside. The car pulled up at the bottom of a steep, muddy track and the three men got out.

'Now,' said Stanov, pulling his overcoat more squarely on to his shoulders, 'we climb.'

Even with the basket which he was ordered to carry Bucharensky found the going easy. For the two old men, however, it was a different story; they puffed and struggled up the gentle incline until by the time the trio reached the top Bucharensky was having to support the combined weights of his elderly companions as well as the hamper.

At the end of the climb they emerged on to a grassy saucer of land set into the hillside, well-protected from the wind by fir trees on three sides, with a dramatic view over the plain across which they had recently driven. This was not a place you would find by accident.

Yevchenko took a thick blanket from the basket and spread it over the nadir of the saucer before sitting down and dispensing tea. Seated on the blanket Bucharensky did not feel cold. At first he found it mildly amusing to watch the two old men bicker over the jars and containers in the huge basket, but once they began to unpack Beluga caviar, and salmon, and fresh river trout and venison his amusement was forgotten and he was conscious only of ravenous hunger. He looked away.

'Eat, Captain. You can't listen on an empty stomach.'

Bucharensky could hardly believe his ears. After a moment's hesitation he took a morsel of trout and began to chew it slowly, restraining an urge to stuff his mouth as full as possible. But even while he ate his mind was alert. Why, he asked himself, why this absurd expedition? Stick followed by carrot? He recognised the technique.

When Stanov judged the moment ripe he said: 'So as not to waste words, Captain, you may take it that your period of disgrace is over. In fact you were never in disgrace. We had to be sure of you, that's all.'

Bucharensky had found an earthenware pot full of apricot jam boiled in brandy syrup. He had cracked the wax seal and was now taking minute teaspoonfuls of the exotic preserve, leaving long, appreciative pauses between each. On hearing these words he nodded.

'I know, comrade Marshal.'

Stanov was enraged. 'How can you know it?'

Bucharensky looked up slowly and stared at Stanov. He spoke with quiet deliberation.

'Because although the KGB often makes serious and foolish mistakes it is too resourceful and too careful ever to make a mistake about the loyalty of one of its own officers, who has served it conscientiously and well.'

Bucharensky put down the spoon and folded his hands in his lap before quietly turning his head away from Stanov's scorching stare.

'I am sorry, comrade Marshal,' he said humbly. 'But I resolved that I would speak those words on the day of my rehabilitation. I did not dream, of course, that I would have to speak them to you.'

Yevchenko broke the ensuing silence by asking curiously, 'Do you really mean that, in spite of all that happened to you, you never doubted that your position was, well… secure? Not once?'

'Often, comrade Colonel, but I knew I had done nothing wrong.'

Stanov eyed him malevolently over his glass of tea.

'So the KGB makes mistakes, does it?'

'Yes, comrade Marshal.'

Yevchenko started to laugh. 'You chose well, old man,' he said. Then Stanov too began to laugh, and after a moment Bucharensky joined in, happy for the first time in twelve weary months.

When they were all serious again Stanov commenced the briefing.

'Tell me, Ivan Yevseevich, tell me how you would defect to the West.'

This question rang coldly in Bucharensky's ears. The more he focused his mind on it the less he liked it. Was there a trap? Should he tell the exact truth? He decided on a middle course.

'I would try to reach a European city with which I was familiar. There I would approach the American embassy. Clandestinely, of course.'

'Of course… I suppose in your case Athens might be an appropriate starting point – you were stationed there for five years.'

'Or Brussels. Brussels for choice, although it is true I have spent time in both places.'

'London perhaps?'

Bucharensky looked up sharply. What did they know about London? But the faces of the two old men showed nothing.

'Certainly. Although London is not as close to Moscow as the other two places.'

'Think about this. We know where you were stationed, it's in your dossier. We would guess where you were probably making for. We would try to stop you.'

Bucharensky nodded unwillingly. The thought had occurred to him, but he was still wary.

'Would you keep to your original plan?'

Bucharensky saw that they were smiling at him. He was not sure how to formulate his reply. Stanov continued: 'I think you would. Because in those foreign cities you, like everyone else who has ever worked abroad, have money, a new personality perhaps, even a safe house. Insurance. Which we don't – officially – know about. Am I not right, Ivan Yevseevich?'

Bucharensky nodded again. There was no hostility in these questions.

'A moment ago we mentioned Brussels. Why is Brussels so important to us, and our finances in particular?'

'The money-route, do you mean?'

'Precisely. What do you know of that?'

'Outgoing money is laundered in Brussels via the Skaldia-Volga factory payroll. Some of it is paid out there, to the Red Brigades and so on. When I was in Belgium, Baader-Meinhof used to benefit, as did ETA. Arms are paid for in Brussels – I remember the panic in '71 when the Dutch seized Ominipol guns at Schipol because it could all have been traced back to the money-route. Then whatever is left goes on to London, Dublin and Belfast where some of it is used to arm and train the Provisional IRA, and then the rest goes to America.' He shook his head. 'That's all I know.'

'Very good. But tell me this – why is it that you, who worked in Europe for 20 years, know so little about the money-route?'

'It was not my business to know. I had no need to know.'

'Precisely. Everything in compartments. Share nothing beyond what you have to. Trust no one.' Stanov paused. 'The KGB is centralised, is it not?'

'So they taught us at spy school.'

'And the consequence is that only a handful of people at its head, six or seven at most, can ever hope to know most of what goes on.'

'Right.'

'So that below this supreme level people can see the most extraordinary things happen without being surprised, because they assume it's no business of theirs.'

'Certainly. I have been in just that position myself, many times.'

'And unless the people at the top are vigilant beyond the norm these extraordinary things may escape their lofty notice?'

This time Bucharensky did not reply. His mind began to race ahead, looking for bolt-holes. Stanov continued.

'Let me now pull together these strands, Ivan Yevseevich, so that you may see the point of all this. Somewhere in the KGB the British Secret Intelligence Service has managed to install a traitor. Putting it at its simplest, we would like you to find him for us. In order to do so you are going to defect to the West, apparently taking with you information of vital importance concerning our money-route and our project-plans. That, at least, is the story for your colleagues.' He paused. 'But some of those colleagues – your superiors, you understand – and the British will be told that you carry in your head the name of the traitor.'

Bucharensky blinked. The alarm bells had been sounding for some time now. He chose his next words as carefully as if his life depended on them, sensing that it might.

'There are many local operatives, comrade Marshal, whose familiarity with the cities you mention and their *referenturas*...'

Behind him Yevchenko methodically started to stack plates. When he had done that he began to toss cutlery into the hamper. The jangling got on Bucharensky's nerves.

'The leak is not in the *referenturas*, Ivan Yevseevich. Those are merely the local offices of the KGB.'

Stanov allowed the silence to develop. For Bucharensky the day had suddenly become cold again.

'Has it ever occurred to you to ask why we are squatting in this isolated spot, having come here in a beaten-up old car, armed, when we might have been sitting comfortably in my office, comrade Captain?'

Bucharensky said nothing. The question had never been far from his mind since the expedition started. Stanov turned to look him full in the face.

'It is because I, Voldemar Pavlovich Stanov, Marshal of the Soviet Union and Chairman of the KGB am, on the express orders of the Politburo, being followed by my own Seventh Directorate!'

Bucharensky looked away and said nothing.

'And they could be right. It could be me. It isn't, but our problem – yours too, now – is that it could be. And on the other side it is just the same. I am convinced that one man, and one man alone, has dealings with this traitor, and that is the Head of the British Secret Intelligence Service himself. You will be flying very near the sun, Ivan Yevseevich.'

He allowed the words to sink in. Yevcheno had finished packing the basket and was listening quietly.

'I will not burden you with the hours of work I have done in order to find this truth; suffice it to say they have been *long*. It is necessary for someone to spread out the whole picture on the table in front of him and go back years; that is the first thing. Only the Chairman can do it. My predecessors either did not bother or were too stupid to understand the results. Perhaps they wilfully refused to credit something terrible, I do not know. But once you have done the groundwork the truth becomes terribly simple, Ivan Yevseevich. It is, in effect, that for the past fifteen years and more we in the KGB,' he waved his hand to embrace everyone, 'all of us, have been missing the point.'

If he expected a reaction from Bucharensky he was disappointed.

'It is all to do with *dezinformatsiya*. For years now we have successfully been feeding false information to the West. On half a dozen important occasions, however, they have either not been completely taken in or have somehow been able to retrieve their position without difficulty. And on three, precisely three and only three occasions of consummate, vital, desperate urgency, they have rejected the information altogether.'

He paused. A cold wind was blowing up from the south-east, strong enough to penetrate even this sheltered spot. Soon it would snow.

'It does not sound much, does it? Nine occasions in all. But Ivan Yevseevich, if you were in my position and could see the Russian lives lost as a result, the man-hours wasted, the advantages thrown away... if you could add up the total damage over the years, you would mourn. And you would want to know who was responsible.'

His face darkened.

'The first two times of vital importance it was made to look as though the information never got through, thwarted by forces of nature beyond the control of the intelligence services concerned. But the last time, a matter of months ago, I was already suspicious and so was able to inspect the scene at once. The message was borne by a man, a man so important to us that only Yevchenko and I knew his name, we thought. But the man died, a week before he was due to attend the OPEC conference and deliver such a blow to the western world as you could not dream of. When I *think*...'

Bucharensky looked at the old man's clenched fists and closed eyes, fascinated. Such things were not meant for his ears.

'There was an avalanche. He was skiing. Eighteen other people died. It was not a natural occurrence. I know it. The members of the Politburo know it. Nothing has been said openly. But we require answers.'

Bucharensky broke silence at last.

'How soon?'

'The beginning of July.'

Bucharensky nodded. Nearly six months. Here was something practical at last, something within his province.

'If by then the answer is not known I shall be replaced. I tell you this because I want you to be under no illusions: the Politburo has spelled out the consequences of failure very clearly.'

He lowered his voice, so that Bucharensky was not sure whether he was supposed to hear, or if the old man was talking to himself.

'Believe me, you are the last, the very last chance. I have tried everything. For months at a time I have concentrated on each of these six or seven candidates for the role of traitor. Nothing! I have kept them under constant surveillance: they can't shit without me knowing the colour and consistency. I have laid false trails. I have fed them lies. I have sent each of them abroad and had them watched. Let me show you...' He snapped his fingers and Yevchenko handed him a file. 'This is the record of what I have done. Look at it!'

Bucharensky took the thick file. He read it quickly, skimming whenever possible, astounded at the extent of the operation, the time, the thoroughness, the lengths to which Stanov had gone not only to prevent the subjects from knowing that they were being watched, but also to keep this same information from the men detailed to do the watching. Can this be happening, he asked himself over and over again, here in the headquarters of the KGB? The whole machine turned in upon itself... it was unreal. When he had finished he stood up and walked to the edge of the clearing to stand with his back to it, staring into the forest.

Eventually Stanov called to him.

'Nothing has worked. And every time I fail I go back to the Politburo and they say: what now, Voldemar Pavlovich?'

The old man raised his eyes to Bucharensky's face.

'How long have I been Chairman of the KGB, Ivan Yevseevich?'

'Eight years, comrade Marshal.'

'And in that time, how many sleepers do you think I have put to bed, in how many countries? How many plans? How many networks laid? How many long, slow fuses have I lit?' He laughed suddenly. 'Why don't I just retire? Why don't I go away and let someone else sort it out? I could, you know. That's what my *friends* in the Politburo say! Well, I shall tell you, Ivan Yevseevich, I am not about to see a lifetime's achievements thrown into the garbage pit. Albania!' He clapped his fists to his forehead and closed his eyes. 'When I think of the plans I have prepared for that benighted little country! How near we are!' His eyes opened. 'Do you think I am going to leave that *now*? Give it to some buffoon who instead of gently prising the fruit from the tree would wait for it to rot on the bough and then trample on it when it fell? No! On July 1st I shall still be here, Chairman or dead.'

His voice became a whisper. Bucharensky leaned forward, hypnotised.

'It will be my last duty to the Soviet Union. To root out this traitor. And to save the KGB from… Kazin.'

At the sound of the name everything fell into place for Bucharensky. Kazin, the Party theoretician and member of the Politburo, a civilian without either knowledge or experience of the KGB, a man thirsty for blood and the purification of another purge, or so it was rumoured in Dzerzhinsky Square.

Other memories, other rumours came flooding back. 'Stalin's baby', that is what they used to call Kazin, and for years he had wondered why. Was it because when late at night they came to take the Monster to bed they would find him sitting beside the fire, Kazin kneeling at his feet? Or did some deeper, less savoury mystery lie concealed beneath the ironic phrase? Whatever the answer, the primal influence on Kazin's character was not in doubt. He was Stalin's man, would be to the last… and he was one of Nature's survivors.

For years he had been Stanov's sternest critic, baying for reforms and a more flexible approach to the modern techniques of espionage and internal security. Now the Politburo was dangling his opportunity in front of his eyes: either Stanov succeeded or the Chairmanship of the KGB would pass from his hands into Kazin's. Bucharensky shut his mind to it. It must not happen. No one could count himself safe under Kazin. It *would* not happen.

Stanov was speaking again.

'Someone near the top of one of the departments, here in Moscow. Someone who has been so careful for so long, someone with the nerve, the insolence and the rank to say to the West: I will not help you every time, I will not be your lackey, but when it is a matter beyond life or death, a matter of your survival, *then* I will help you. No matter what it costs, I will be there…'

For a while the three of them sat in silence, each engrossed in his own thoughts. Stanov spoke again.

'Let me tell you about the two occasions when this man acted, Ivan Yevseevich. The first was in Mexico, in 1971. Perhaps you know the story… 'Nuthatch', the operation was called. The man Gomez who was controlled by Nechiporenko from the *referentura*, it was his job to proclaim the *Movimiento de Acción Revolucionaira*. Everything was ready after years of work: explosives, arms, money. It could have set South America alight. It was brilliant… and it failed. Gómez was arrested. Five of our best agents were expelled. Total humiliation, not a voice was raised to help us. Then there was London. September 24th, 1971, 105 Soviet agents expelled from the United Kingdom. Lyalin "defected". The whole of Department V in Europe, Asia and Africa devastated at a stroke. Pavlov in Montreal, General Vladimirov in Helsinki, Yevdotev in Bonn… the list was endless.'

'I remember.' Bucharensky could not help himself. 'We were all called in. No one was left on the streets. For days we waited in the embassy cellar, crowded round the telex machine. It was like the end of the world. But what is this to do with a traitor in Moscow?'

'Lyalin did not defect. It was a blind. He was tortured until he had told all he knew and then he was killed by SIS. He was the only agent in Europe to carry the names of the others in his head. His visit to England was supposed to be a total secret. But they knew he was coming. And they knew what even Lyalin himself did not know: that he had been doctored in such a way as to be allergic to scopolamine derivatives. The first injection of a conventional truth-drug would have killed him. But they used a massive dose of Pentothal instead. Do you begin to see? On both occasions our oh-so carefully prepared disinformation was utterly without effect. The British knew the truth.'

Bucharensky nodded.

'It was then that I first began to concentrate my suspicions on England. Such a sensational coup did not occur in a vacuum. By jettisoning the other NATO-pact countries from the scope of the inquiry many things at once became clear. We are looking for a man with a peculiar affinity for England, perhaps someone who harbours a personal relationship with the Secret Intelligence Service. I need to provoke this man – and quickly – into betraying himself. For this I have chosen you, Captain Bucharensky.'

'I shall be honoured, comrade Marshal.'

His voice was vibrant, and as he heard it Stanov's hopes rose. The gamble had paid off. Here was a man he could trust, and it had not after all been necessary to reveal exactly how near 'Masked Shrike' was to fulfilment and for that reason how desperately Stanov needed to be back in complete control by 1st July. Perhaps it was not impossible after all…

'Good. Then suppose the following. An officer of the KGB has fallen out of favour. Let us call him… Kyril. Everyone recognises the smell and keeps well away from him. Then one day, without warning, he is promoted full colonel, taken from his lowly quarters and installed in an apartment in the Sivtsev Vrazhek district, supplied with his own chauffeur-driven Chaika and assigned to Marshal Stanov as his personal assistant in charge of co-ordinating liaison between the Main Directorates.'

'Since for all practical purposes there is no liaison between the Main Directorates,' Yevchenko broke in, 'everyone will be suspicious at once.'

'Now this Kyril is a taciturn man,' Stanov continued, 'not given to gossip, and so his colleagues must speculate as best they can – and they do. Soon the news is all over Centre; soon it has reached London.

'Then one day Kyril simply disappears. The lure of the West has proved too strong. Money, a new life… and now that he is an important man he is worth something to the British and their precious MI6.'

His voice became sharp.

'And it is known that while in London on an earlier tour of duty this Kyril formed an attachment to a woman. A woman who never married after he left her, possibly a woman who waits…'

Bucharensky closed his eyes. He could see her face so clearly, hear her voice, feel her hands cupping his face.

Vera. *They knew.*

'Do you see now, Captain, why I have chosen you for this mission? Anyone with access to your dossier will at once assume that you are making for only one possible destination – London. So much for the first, "official" version of your defection. But there is another story, one so secret that it circulates only in the very highest echelons of Dzerzhinsky Square – that Kyril has managed to uncover the name of a traitor within the Organs. Can it be true? Apparently yes, because within the hour the Chairman of the KGB has personally given the order: find this man, find him at all costs, for here is no ordinary defector. Find him *alive* and bring him to me *alive*; the fate of our country depends on it, for as well as knowing this traitor's identity he has stolen one of our most sensitive plans. What will happen then, Ivan Yevseevich?'

Bucharensky thought for a moment.

'The traitor will alert the British.'

'Yes. And then?'

'Every KGB agent in the world has been detailed to find the defector… MI6 will try desperately hard to get to him first, to protect their source from disclosure and to retrieve this mysterious plan.'

'I believe so. The "plan", of course, is nothing but an added bonus, a lure. But the important thing is that none of this can happen in isolation. The traitor must act. Yevchenko and I will be watching closely to see who jumps. As of that moment Kyril will become a priceless commodity to both sides.' Stanov smiled a wintery smile. 'He will have to be quick on his feet. Many people all over the world will urgently wish to talk to him.'

'But comrade Marshal, where is Kyril to go?'

'To Athens. At least at first. Then on to Brussels and London. You remember what you said earlier: if you were going to defect you would try for certain cities where you had… assets. All former fieldmen have such assets, it is well known. Kyril is no exception. He must show himself to both sides while at the same time evading them. A message will go from our embassy in Athens to Moscow, and the head of the Eighth Department of the First Main Directorate. I shall be watching, for I will know Kyril's movements to the nearest half-hour. I will give him a detailed itinerary, to which he must stick *without fail*. If anything goes wrong – if that vital message from the embassy is delayed, or distorted, or slanted – then I may have found the source of the leak.'

'I am sorry, comrade Marshal, I do not understand.'

'The leak in our organisation, the traitor, will, I believe, have a first loyalty to the British in a case of this importance. Besides, he will be anxious to protect himself, and there MI6 will be far better placed to help, for unlike the KGB they will not necessarily have orders to take Kyril alive. So the traitor will not pass on the alert to KGB Athens, even though it emanates from the Chairman himself, without first ensuring that England has a head start on his own men. And he will not pass on anything *from* Athens until he is sure that MI6 is there ahead of us. He is off-balance, his life is in danger, he may do irrational things. If he does, I shall see.'

Stanov leaned forward to place a hand on Bucharensky's shoulder.

'You are Kyril. I do not underestimate the danger, comrade Captain. You must make sure that you are seen but not captured, not once but three times.'

Bucharensky looked him in the eye and smiled.

'And the traitor,' he said lightly. 'What will he do all this time, eh? Watch with a kindly eye while I slip across Europe, ready to expose him if I fall into the wrong hands?'

Stanov released his shoulder.

'You are right. It has to be said. At first he will be uncertain. That is when he will make mistakes and I hope to catch him out. But suppose he can survive the first dreadful forty-eight hours. He recovers his nerve. He begins to make survival plans. The British... want you alive or dead, but if the "project plan" which you are reputed to have stolen is attractive enough, better alive. The Russians, the traitor's own men... they certainly want you alive. But he, he needs you dead, and very quickly, for if M16 are not quick enough, and Kyril falls into *my* hands, and talks, then for him there is only a bullet in the Lubianka cellars. So every time you escape, the traitor's confidence in MI6's ability to stop you will weaken and the chances increase that he will panic and send an executioner after you, to kill you before you can be unmasked. But if he does try to kill you we shall hear of it, and that in itself will help us in our task of pin-pointing the traitor.'

'No back-up, no emergency stand-by?'

'Nothing. Every KGB officer in the world will have orders to hunt you down. So will every SIS agent. One of them maybe more than one, will have orders to kill you.' He hesitated. 'There may come a time when SIS decide to liquidate you before you are captured by us, purely in order to maintain the secrecy which protects the traitor. I hope not. I hope that if I can convince the British that you are carrying one of our most cherished project-plans, they will delay for as long as possible in the hope of interrogating you alive. But… well.'

'And if I get to London?'

Stanov sat back. Bucharensky could hear him sucking his teeth. The seemingly innocent question appeared to have cast a blight over the briefing.

'Ivan Yevseevich, I am going to tell you a secret. I do not want to. But it is necessary.' Stanov paused. Bucharensky could not begin to imagine what was coming.

'Scattered throughout the world there are a handful of men who report only to me. They are not members of the KGB at all, not as you know it. They owe only one loyalty: to the Chairman. To me. They are in touch with no embassy, no *referentura* holds their files. But in their own way they are more powerful than even the KGB residents.'

Bucharensky saw that Stanov was watching him out of the corner of his eye. He was at a loss to know what to say. Such irregular agents went entirely against the whole underlying philosophy of the bureaucratic machine. To employ them was to open oneself to a charge of treason.

'A valuable weapon,' Bucharensky ventured cautiously. 'As long as things go well.'

Stanov nodded. 'You come very quickly to the point, Captain. One of these agents in England is called Loshkevoi.' He smiled wryly. 'Kazin says I play it too much by the book. I don't. In fact if he knew about Loshkevoi, and others like him, who are nothing to do with any book, he would be screaming for my head even louder than he is at present. And in a way he'd be right, because I can no longer trust Loshkevoi. He has been… diverted. There is interference. Subtle, but noticeable.'

Bucharensky raised troubled eyes to Stanov's face. The Chief had gone out on a limb, and as a result who knew how many lives were in danger. Stanov read his thoughts.

'As you say, Captain, a valuable weapon when things go well.' He grunted, then: 'Find Loshkevoi,' he said abruptly. 'He poses as a descendant of White Russian emigrés, running a garage in South London. The address will be in the phone book. Find him and make him talk. Be careful, because he's a powerful man. No one knows more about the money-route than Loshkevoi. He's supposed to be my direct liaison with the Provisional IRA: banker and adviser in one. So he has both money and thugs at his back; look out for yourself. But you *must* get him to talk, for either he knows who the traitor is or he can give you clues to his identity. I'm sure of it.'

'But how can you be sure?'

'The pattern is there. All signs point to England as being the traitor's first loyalty. The life has gone out of my most gifted, trusted agent in England. That by itself would suggest that the one we seek is using Loshkevoi as a pawn. But there is more.'

Stanov hesitated, as if trying to recall some long lost detail, to pierce an invisible veil.

'You remember the events of 1971 in London? The September Massacre, we called it then. I was still a Deputy Chairman only, but already Loshkevoi was established. He was to attend a secret meeting with Lyalin. But he never attended that meeting. Instead the British were at the appointed place. Oh, Loshkevoi had a good enough alibi at the time. He was supposed to have been involved in a car accident. I had the records looked up, and it was true, so I thanked my stars that Loshkevoi himself was not ambushed and taken. But suppose the traitor had arranged for the records of the accident to be faked? You see? Make no mistake, Captain: the ultimate goal and purpose of your mission is to find a way into Loshkevoi's head. Oh, I don't play down the importance of your race across Europe…' Stanov gazed into the distance and his voice fell. 'I see you as a rapidly moving, highly-charged magnet, sometimes attracting others to you, sometimes repelling them, but always, always, always forcing them to *move* and be *seen* to move. It is inconceivable that the British will not seek to open new channels of communication with their precious source when they learn that you are carrying his name, and once they do I can hardly fail to detect them. All that…' Stanov flicked his fingers dismissively.

'But if you can find Loshkevoi and make him talk…'

Stanov paused and nodded with heavy emphasis.

'…We shall have the name, comrade Captain. I am convinced of it. I know it. All that matters. *The name!*'

The long speech was over.

Bucharensky thought about his instructions. As far as he could see they led to inglorious and inevitable death. As an experienced field officer he reckoned his chances of reaching London at less than ten per cent. But… it was somehow attractive. Anything was better than the crippling desk-work in Moscow, the loneliness, the deprivations; after the year he had just endured Hell itself could not be worse. He would see he drank some good wine, smoked a few packs of decent cigarettes before the end. Perhaps he could spin it out a bit; after all, he had spent most of his adult life evading the Americans and the British; also the French, the West Germans, the Dutch… and he knew his brothers in the KGB so well, oh so very well: how they thought, and acted, and reacted. Perhaps it was not impossible. Perhaps he would get to Brussels at least. And there was Vera, always Vera…

Besides, he had no choice. Better make the best of it.

'When do we start?'

Stanov exhaled a long breath.

'Tomorrow. Report first thing to the Voyentorg – they have a colonel's uniform ready for you. Then move into the new apartment, we will see you have everything you need. Take the rest of the day off. Dine somewhere expensive. Book a seat at the ballet. Kick a few arses. Make enemies. Don't worry, I'll back you. Act as a new member of the *nomenklatura* should.' Stanov nodded to Yevchenko. 'Give him the stuff.'

Yevchenko pulled a thick leather wallet from his overcoat.

'We are giving you this now so that you will be able to leave at a moment's notice if you have to. Guard it carefully. Four American Express cards, each in a different name. Travellers' cheques, $10,000. Letters of credit in Athens, Brussels and London. Four passports, all with valid visas. Back in the car, 200 rounds of ammunition.'

'Gun?'

'This…' Stanov thrust the Stechkin into Bucharensky's hand and smiled. 'Why do you think we brought it?'

'Credit limit?'

'None. Although we want you also to use money and arms you have left for yourself in Greece, Belgium and London. Everything must look as far as possible as though you are genuinely defecting.'

Bucharensky took a deep breath and nodded.

'We anticipate that if you reach London you may have to buy a house. It is the only way you can hope to protect yourself, and you will need a secure base in order to interrogate Loshkevoi effectively. Pay cash if you can, or next best thing, banker's draft or whatever. Don't rent; buy.'

Bucharensky was still in the grip of astonishment.

'But comrade Marshal... I could simply disappear with all this.'

'You could,' observed Stanov drily. 'In some ways you would be no worse off: evading the Intelligence services of East and West. Only then it would be for the rest of your life. We would never forget you... Kyril.'

Bucharensky laughed. 'I can assure you I had no intention...'

'I did not think you had. Next. No ciphers, no drops. Your isolation from Centre will be absolute and immediate from day one. You will be beyond our reach until the operation is brought to an end. Understood?'

'Understood.'

'One way or the other, matters should be settled by July 1st.' He hesitated. 'If Colonel Yevchenko and I should then be dead, papers will automatically be sent to the First Secretary of the Communist Party of the Soviet Union, informing him of all we know and commending you to him as a brave and loyal officer. He may believe it, he may not; that is a chance you must take.'

Stanov rose awkwardly to his feet, waving aside Bucharensky's offered arm.

'There is much more to tell you in the way of detail. Your briefing will be long and thorough, but all that can wait. I'm tired and it's getting cold out here. Any more questions?'

Bucharensky stood deep in thought for several moments.

'One thing. You are going to put it about that I have stolen a valuable project-plan. If you're going to make that stick it'll have to be one I'm in direct contact with in my new job, and something attractive to the West, a plan the loss of which would scare the hell out of the Politburo as well as my colleagues. And… well.' He hesitated, suddenly aware of his thought's true destination. 'It would increase the chances of SIS's deciding to capture me alive if that plan were important, really big.'

Stanov laughed.

'In my safe is supposed to be the only extant copy of Operation "Sociable Plover".' Noting Bucharensky's startled expression he added, 'It is the name of a bird, comrade Captain… or Colonel, as I must call you now. The file consists of about five hundred single-spaced pages and has attained "blue status", which, as you know, means that only one copy can be in circulation at any time. When you go, that file goes too.'

'And what is this… Sociable Plover?'

'Nothing. It does not exist. But your colleagues – yes, and the British too – will be told that it is something we have been working on since the War, that it sets out in precise and minute detail the connection between the KGB and organised, world-wide terrorism: the history, the financing, including the money-route, the co-operation, proposed joint operations, everything, including the names of key agents, the numbers of secret bank accounts, the locations of Soviet-financed and run training centres, and much more. Can you imagine what the loss of such a file, if it existed, would mean?'

Bucharensky gaped at him. For a hostile intelligence agency the prospects would be irresistible. Mossad, for example, could use the information to wipe out the PLO as an effective Middle East force. The CIA could expose the KGB to the world as an utterly unscrupulous, manipulative gang of thugs, no better than the murderers they financed. Soviet foreign policy would be set back years. Countless trusted officers of the KGB would at best be rendered useless and at worst be exterminated as a result of such a file falling into the wrong hands.

If Stanov could make his officers, and SIS, believe that Kyril was carrying such a priceless weapon, they would turn the world upside down in their search for him.

Stanov and Yevchenko were starting off down the path. Bucharensky picked up the hamper and followed them, his mind still reeling under the impact of what he had been told.

'The possessor of Sociable Plover,' said Stanov over his shoulder, 'could either dominate or effectively eradicate world terrorism, as he pleased. Its "loss" will make those vultures in the Kremlin shit their pants.'

Chapter 2

The telephone made a noise like a clock about to strike the hour. Royston's hand lifted the receiver before the bell could ring while the rest of him was still struggling up to the surface of a deep sleep.

'Do you recognise the voice?'

Royston fought for bearings in his personal history. His sick daughter had cried in her sleep. Night ops, and the enemy were coming. The burglar downstairs making off with the silver. Special Branch at the door…

'I said, do you recognise…?'

'Yes, I know who you are.'

Royston was awake in the bedroom of the house in Sheen, his wife beside him, still asleep, his children grown up, the past dead. Cold sweat on his back and a less than steady hand were now the only links between him and the unquiet world beneath the surface.

'For God's sake, man, do you know what time it is?'

'Later than you think.'

Royston held his watch up to his eyes before realising that the caller intended this for a warning.

'What is it?'

He was fully awake now.

'Meet me in exactly twenty-five minutes at the junction with the South Circular. My car, not yours. Don't be seen if you can help it.'

A click heralded the purr of the free line. Royston swung his legs out of bed and went to stand by the window, partly out of professional instinct to see if there were watchers in the street, but mainly because he wanted to know what the weather was doing. In the glare of the white street lamps the pavements glistened with drizzle. He sighed and quietly began to put on his clothes, while Jenny, his wife, slept on.

As well as being wet it was cold outside, typical March weather, and as Royston hurried along with his head down he prayed that Bonham wouldn't be late for the rendezvous. About half a mile from his house a phone-booth stood at the junction of the South Circular Road with a side-street. It took him eight minutes to reach it, allowing for an elementary detour to shake off any tails. From the shadow of the booth he had an uninterrupted view of the main road and of the street down which he had come. Both were empty. In the few minutes he had to wait he saw only two cars, both travelling west. Royston's dark mac and brown suede shoes, shrouded in the angle where the phone-booth met the wall, made no impression on their headlights.

Bonham was late. To divert himself Royston tried to devise stories that would satisfy the curiosity of a hypothetical policeman on the beat who chanced to find him leaning against the wall, wrapped up in a shabby old gardening mac. The ideas wouldn't come. Royston looked at his watch. Bonham was three minutes overdue. 'Exactly', he had said, when appointing the rendezvous.

Something was wrong.

For the first time Royston felt a stab of real curiosity about Bonham's mysterious phone call. It wasn't like him to use the telephone. It wasn't like him to be late, either.

Royston wanted to walk up and down, a process which helped him think, but resisted the impulse. Somewhere in London, something which affected Royston was happening without him. And it had gone wrong.

He was about to step from the shadows and damn the risk of being detected when he saw the lights of the car. The driver was coming up the long arm of the 'T' to the South Circular Road, the engine labouring in second. As Royston raised his head the front nearside indicator began to flash. The car idled to the junction and he saw it was Bonham's. Two steps took him across the pavement and in through the passenger door, already ajar; as he pulled it shut after him the driver revved the engine to drown the noise of the slam and engaged gear. A hidden observer might have seen Royston enter the car, provided he hadn't blinked at the crucial moment.

Bonham went gently through the gears, travelling east, and for a while there was silence.

'Whatever it is that keeps Five awake at nights,' said Royston eventually, 'it had better be bloody important.'

Without waiting for a reply he took a portable electric razor from his mac pocket and began to shave, tracing progress with his fingertips. Royston's pointed, angular face was not well suited to electric shaving. As a young man his skin had been too sensitive; now, in his early fifties, the skin had slackened, making it hard for the rounded shaving-head to cut close inside the folds of the worry-lines.

'There's some aftershave in the dash,' said Bonham, and Royston wrinkled his nose.

'Yes,' he said. 'I can smell it. Is that why you're late? Been shaving, had you?'

'Another phone call. Sorry.'

'Exactly, you said. Twenty-five minutes exactly.'

Bonham moved his hand and the indicator warning-light glowed. As the car swung right Royston saw the locality sign reflected in the beam of the headlamps. Battersea, Clapham, Balham. He suddenly realised that Bonham was driving very carefully, well within the statutory limit. The tingle of apprehension which Royston had first experienced outside the phone-booth was refining itself into a state of permanent unease.

He put the razor back in his pocket. 'Where's the fire?'

For a moment Bonham said nothing, but continued to concentrate on the road ahead. Then he turned to look at his passenger, just for a second, and in the reflected glow of the orange standards Royston saw that Bonham seemed older than his 45 years.

'Does the name Loshkevoi mean anything to you? No? We rather thought not. A couple of years ago the Special Branch raised a query on him. For the owner of a used-car-cum-garage business in Balham he was taking some pretty funny trips abroad. They ran the usual checks. Seems the Revenue weren't too happy about some of his trading accounts, but nothing else showed up. They put a note in the file and let it pass, you know how it is. Interested?'

Royston grunted. He had pushed back the passenger-seat and was now sprawled out as far as the Rover's limits would allow, his eyes level with the glove compartment. He was finding it hard to stay awake, or so Bonham must have thought, because now he raised his voice.

'Earlier tonight we took a look at Loshkevoi's business premises. There was some evidence of handling stolen cars...'

'Some evidence...?'

The irony sounded through the drowsiness in Royston's voice, and Bonham smiled.

'The police said "some". I didn't press it.'

Another grunt from Royston.

'I went round myself. We had all night. Loshkevoi is currently assisting the police with their inquiries, and likely to be so for at least another eight hours. No one else lives over the shop, so we didn't have any worries. What fun. An armoury, for a start. Automatic weapons. Grenades. Hand guns. And rifles.'

'So Loshkevoi's a terrorist.' Royston sounded bored. This wasn't his line.

'With Kalashnikov AK-47s? American FC-180s? A pretty well-equipped terrorist, wouldn't you think? But you haven't heard it all yet. We found approximately fifty-thousand pounds in hard currencies. Passport blanks. Secret compartments in some of the cars, large enough to hold a man. And a radio set, tuned to a short-wave band which we've been monitoring off and on for the past ten years. Without any great success, I may say. A band where the messages are invariably in code and the code-pattern is unmistakably Russian.'

Royston pulled his chair forward again and struggled upright.

'You're telling me,' he said softly, 'that you've uncovered a KGB treasurer... an armourer...'

'Yes.'

'...Who's been lying low, undetected, for... how many years?'

'He came here in 1944, when he was still in his teens, claiming to be a refugee from north Italy. Son of White Russians fleeing the glorious revolution by a neck, drifting from place to place, you know the sort of thing. He had papers that fitted; then. We're checking it out.'

'More than thirty years late,' mused Royston. His unspoken conclusion hovered between the two men like an accusation.

'We're unlikely to find very much,' agreed Bonham. 'I know. That's where you come in. Here we are.'

He swung the car on to the forecourt of a large garage. Royston got out and looked around. Some dozen cars were stationed to one side of the pumps, each with a fluorescent orange price-sticker on the windscreen. Above his head and all down either side of the forecourt tiny red and white flags fluttered and flapped in the breeze. By the light of the nearest street lamp he read this week's Special Offer plastered across a fluorescent green board: half a dozen 'tumbler type' glasses. Royston had seen a hundred places just like it and never turned his head.

'Come on.'

With an uncomfortable start Royston realised that Bonham had silently materialised beside him and was hissing in his ear. The garage looked shut up and deserted. Bonham took him by the forearm and guided him through the darkness until Royston sensed an obstacle across their path. Bonham knocked quietly, using what was obviously a prearranged tattoo. A thin line of light appeared in front of the two men, turned into a rectangle, became an open door. Bonham hustled Royston through and an unseen hand closed it behind them.

The interior of what Royston now realised was a large workshop had a dreamlike quality about it. The only lighting was provided by a muted red glow from lamps strung round the walls at head level. Royston could hear muffled hammering in the far corner, and quite close to where they were standing a steady stream of white sparks illuminated the masked face of a welder.

'They're clearing up,' explained Bonham. 'All nice and tidy for the morning. He had this knack of building the stuff into cars, you see.'

'He's never going to fall for that,' muttered Royston. 'He'll know.'

'Of course he will.' Bonham's voice was tired but patient. 'That's the point. We're going to sweat him, aren't we?'

Royston frowned. 'You mean… you're going to leave the stuff lying around?'

'Of course. Then perhaps we might find out what chummy's up to.'

Royston had not hitherto credited MI5 with such imagination. The idea appealed to him, despite the risk.

'You'd better just hope that the Minister doesn't find out,' he said grudgingly.

'That's why I was late,' Bonham replied casually. 'That other phone call I mentioned, remember? Ever tried to get the Home Secretary in the middle of the night? Don't. That's my advice to you.'

'He actually wore it?' Royston sounded incredulous. Bonham did not answer. Instead: 'Come over here,' he said. 'I told them to leave this one open for you.'

He led the way down the steps of an inspection pit. As Royston's foot touched bottom a torch flashed in his eyes.

'Who's this?'

'This is the guest I told you about, Superintendent. I'll even sign him in the club book, if you like.'

There was a moment of uneasy silence. Royston stood perfectly still and did not try to hide his eyes from the glare of the torch.

'It'll have to go in my report, Mr Bonham.'

'No it won't, Superintendent.' The torch was suddenly extinguished, and Royston was aware of whispering close by. Bonham must have sounded convincing, for when the torch came on again a few seconds later the beam was directed to the side of the pit.

'The brickwork looks new,' said Royston.

'We're waiting to hear from Forensic on that.' The superintendent's voice was a shade less hostile. 'Six months is my guess.'

'Look at this,' said Bonham. The beam of the torch centred on a large cavity in the side of the inspection pit. Bonham put in his hand and withdrew it holding something heavy. Royston took it from him and with a tremor of excitement recognised an FC-180. The barrel felt cold and slightly damp. His fingers played with the trigger while his thumb, guided by instinct, found the switch to the laser sight. A thin red beam of light darted along the barrel. Royston turned the gun on end and looked up at the ceiling of the workshop. Thirty feet above their heads the red beam flickered across the corrugated iron, its focus still no bigger than a fivepenny-piece.

'Amazing.' Royston was slightly shocked to hear the awe in his own voice. 'Amazing.' Almost reverently he handed the automatic rifle back to the superintendent, who wiped it with a handkerchief before replacing it in its hiding place beyond the wall.

'You say there are more of them?'

'Forty in all. Another forty Kalashnikovs. British SLRs. Mr Loshkevoi appears to do business internationally.'

'And you're just going to leave it all here…'

Royston shook his head, dumbfounded by the audacity of it. Suddenly he had had enough of the suffocating, oily darkness. He wanted to breathe fresh air. 'Let's go up,' he said.

Back on the workshop floor he took a last look round, while the superintendent gave orders for bricking up the cavity in the pit wall. The operation seemed to be winding down; the welder had finished and somebody was starting to unsling the first of the several ropes of red light-bulbs which adorned the walls.

'Come outside,' said Bonham, and Royston steeled himself for the pitch. Publicly the secret services enjoyed an unparalleled degree of mutual trust, co-operation and brotherly love. That was the official version. On the ground, in the undergrowth, it was different.

'Smoke?'

They were sitting in the Rover again. Royston accepted the proffered cigarette and inhaled gratefully, holding the smoke deep in his lungs.

'I suppose you're wondering why I brought you here.'

Royston said nothing.

'I wanted to convince you. I wanted you to see for yourself that we're not joking. Think about that. If you merely saw the photographs, heard about it in a briefing, would you believe it?'

Royston was forced to shake his head.

'We badly need someone on the inside, Michael. Someone who can get close to Loshkevoi, what is it you call it? "Befriending", isn't it? We want to borrow a P.4. A lawyer. The best.'

As Bonham said 'best' Royston launched into his prepared speech.

'You are well aware that P.4 is attached to MI6, furthermore that it operates solely and exclusively beyond the seas, beyond the jurisdiction of Five.'

'And you know that's a load of shit.'

Bonham's quiet voice was as controlled as ever but Royston could hardly mistake the anger in it. He registered, not for the first time, that heads were going to roll over Loshkevoi. In the operational files of the domestic security service tonight's find must represent a failure of monumental proportions. For Royston it was a seller's market.

Bonham paused, as if conscious that his self-control was less than perfect. When he resumed his voice was still tired but all emotion had been shaded out of it.

'I could name you every occasion on which P.4 has worked in England over the past eighteen months. There are seven of them. All illicit. All without ministerial knowledge or sanction. The psychiatrist who treated a certain Member of Parliament for the two months immediately before he shot himself, that was one of yours. Not very good at his job, it seems. The architect who designed the security chambers in the basement of Sheikh Ab' A' Man's house in Cumbria. Are you telling me a copy of those plans isn't sitting in the safe at Vauxhall Bridge Road? Shall I go on? What about a certain highly respected venereologist in Wimpole Street...'

'My, my,' said Royston. 'You have been working hard.'

'Hard enough. Well? Do we get our lawyer? Or do I go back to my office and prepare a regretful report stating that certain irregularities have come to light in MI6's conduct of one of its key sectors?'

Royston stubbed out his cigarette and said nothing for a moment, reasoning that it would do Bonham no harm to sweat a little.

'What's in it for me, then? Apart, of course, from avoiding the consequences of your burn.'

'What do you want?'

'A lift back to Vauxhall Bridge Road, for a start. By the way,' he continued, as Bonham turned the ignition key, 'congratulations on finding out where MI6 has its London HQ. I always knew you people in Five were bright.'

Bonham braked hard to avoid a police Scimitar manoeuvring off the forecourt without lights, and swore.

'I want to know everything you know. Same day, same *hour.* Got it?'

'Yes.'

'Say "agreed".'

'Agreed.'

'That's better.'

'So long as it works both ways.'

'What?'

'Somewhere out there in your world, the world beyond the seas, there's a man listening for that transmitter. You'll be looking for him. If I know anything about the way you work, and I do, before nine a.m. this morning there won't be a single out-station from Seville to Sydney which hasn't been set to work on Loshkevoi's name. I want to know what you find out. I have a *need* to know.'

Royston thought about it. 'All right,' he said at last. 'I buy that. Now listen. There's rules, see? One. My man has to be protected at all times. Two. He reports only through me, right? You go near him and two things will happen very quickly: he'll shut up like an oyster and I'll post him to Katmandu on the next flight. Three. It's your job to get Loshkevoi to pick my lawyer out of the hat. If he wants another solicitor, that's tough.'

'All agreed.'

'Good.'

Traffic was beginning to pick up. Bonham passed several cars and cut in front of a lorry in order to make a left on to Vauxhall Bridge. Royston smiled to see how the standard of driving had declined since leaving Balham.

'Where's chummy being held?'

'Lavender Hill nick.'

'Right. This is the name. Sculby. S-c-u-l-b-y, Laurence. Got it? He'll be in the Law List.'

'Sculby,' muttered Bonham, and Royston knew relief when he heard it. The car drew up outside London Station. Royston got out and stood on the pavement, a hand on the car's roof, his head bent to Bonham's level. Bonham wound down the window a fraction.

'Thanks,' said Royston. 'Be in touch.'

As station chief Royston was able to go through the fandangle of electronic alarms without assistance, the only man who could. He went first to the cellars to reassure the duty officer, then to the first floor where they kept the Personnel files. Equipped with Sculby's bulky dossier he made his way upstairs to his office on the second storey.

It was an undistinguished room, hardly a fit place in which to enjoy the summit of a career. The wiring had originally been installed when the building was erected in the '20s; the light-switch was a nipple set in a round twat, easy to find with the fingers in the dark. Royston momentarily closed his eyes against the flashing white neon (which at least was new), waiting for the noisy hum which meant the strip-lighting had settled down. When he opened his eyes nothing had changed since yesterday. All was as it should be. The yellow net curtains, in need not just of a wash but of outright replacement; the bulbous, old-fashioned radiator under the stone window-sill; leather-covered dining-room chairs strategically positioned to cover holes in the threadbare grey carpet; upturned tin-lids still full of dog-ends. But the desk was brand new Ryman's, as was the swivel-chair behind it, and the green press-button telephone stood out brightly against the heavy black scrambler. Give it another year or two, thought Royston to himself, as he always did on coming in first thing, and I'll have renewed everything.

If they haven't renewed me first.

Royston dumped the file on to the desk and sat down in his swivel-chair, thinking that he was not often presented with a tailor-made opportunity for disposing of a subordinate as troublesome as Sculby. It was an ill wind… He opened the dossier's cover, read a few words; then the events of the night overtook him; he rested his elbows on the desk and placed his head in his hands.

They had caught up with Loshkevoi at last, then. For the past ten years not a day, not an hour had gone by without Royston wondering whether somewhere, out there in the London suburbs, a man was walking up to Loshkevoi with a warrant card in his left hand while he kept his right firmly closed over the gun in his pocket. He had envisaged the scene over and over again. The variations were infinite. Now at last it had happened. From where he was sitting Royston bleakly reviewed the possibilities, starting with merely inconvenient and going methodically through to bloody catastrophic; although if he had been sitting in the club to which his superiors had, after years of baulking at his polytechnic education, finally elected him, sipping port and watching his vowels, he would doubtless have described the worst in more prosaic terms. A bit of a bore, perhaps. Or: a singularly unattractive prospect.

But whatever the language, Royston didn't mean to spend the twenty declining years of his life in prison if he could help it.

Chapter 3

To Bucharensky's astonishment, Stanov's office was locked on the outside. He struggled to get his breath back while Yevchenko fumbled with the keys. At last the double doors burst open.

Bucharensky thought the old man was dead. He sat slumped in The Chair, eyes closed, one arm flung awkwardly across his chest, and the room smelled terrible. At the sound of Yevchenko closing the doors, however, Stanov stirred and mumbled as if in pain.

On the desk in front of him lay a sheet of paper. Green stripe on blue flimsy. Flash signal. Urgent.

'What… time?'

Stanov's speech was slurred. He seemed to have trouble in recognising Bucharensky. Yevchenko looked at his watch.

'Seven.'

Bucharensky was trying to read the upside-down signal. Something about 'arrest'…

'Were… you… sleep, colonel. A… pologise.'

'It's nothing, comrade Marshal.'

Stanov indicated the signal with a slight movement of his head. His voice echoed with plaintive surprise, the voice of a man faced with some outrageous breach of the rules.

'It's happened 'gain. Sure of it. Betrayed.'

The race through the darkened streets, the motorcycle escort, the howling sirens, Yevchenko's grim silence… everything fell into place. The smell Bucharensky had noticed earlier when he first came in. Human sweat. Terror. But only here, in this room. Outside, no one knew. Yet.

'It's time for you to go.'

The old man seemed to be only half in this world. His wide-eyed stare missed Bucharensky's eyes by inches. Kyril's heart contracted as he read the signs. A stroke. Not serious, perhaps, certainly not fatal, but a stroke nonetheless. The security-empire which was all he had ever known since he was a boy was teetering on the brink of the abyss. Outside, somewhere in the city, Kazin was waiting. Had he heard?

An icy hand seemed to clutch Bucharensky's heart. He knew the KGB. Kazin had heard.

'We are not ready.'

'I know.' The arm draped across the old man's chest shuddered in a feeble gesture of despair. 'Nothing… prepared. Your detailed schedule…'

He tried to rise, sank back, made his greatest effort yet.

'You must leave… today. Mus' talk… soon. Not now… tired… sleep…'

Yevchenko took Bucharensky roughly by the arm and hustled him out before closing the double doors behind them. Bucharensky opened his mouth to speak but Yevchenko laid a forefinger to his lips.

'He is right. You must go. Leave everything to me. But for the moment you have seen nothing. You know nothing. You have just arrived. Keep in character. Run a lightning check. Give out a few weeks' detention all round for inefficiency. Make them hate you more than ever before. *Go.*'

Bucharensky swung on his heel and made for the lift. After only a few steps, however, he was arrested by a croak from Yevchenko.

'The diary!'

Bucharensky froze. The old colonel came quickly to his side.

'Is it up to date?'

'Yes. I finished it last night. A piece of luck, that.'

They spoke in rapid whispers, their faces close to the wall, but even so Bucharensky looked nervously around. This diary was the linchpin of Stanov's plan. It lay concealed in a drain in the grounds of Bucharensky's new apartment-block, not so well hidden but that the KGB would find it when they ransacked the place after his 'defection'. It purported to be the daily record of Kyril's slow awakening to the presence of a traitor in KGB headquarters in Dzerzhinsky Square. On the third floor. The generals' floor...

It was the record of someone identified only as '*Lisa*' – the Fox. Bucharensky and Stanov between them had devised this pseudonym for the traitor, and it was through the pages of the diary that the KGB must be made to hunt.

'It is in its proper hiding-place?'

'Yes. I always replaced it myself, it was never kept in the flat.' Bucharensky could not keep the anxiety from his voice. 'Will it work, d'you think?'

'How could it not?' Yevchenko sounded surer than he felt. 'You stood at Stanov's elbow all this time. Closer even than I did. He is old and sick. Your sharp eyes would see many things that escaped his, that is what they will assume. And you would not be the first to keep a written record, evidence for later. "Who is Lisa?" they will ask. All except one. The one who knows who "Lisa" is...'

Bucharensky was unconsciously clutching the lapels of Yevchenko's tunic, almost pleading for his reassurance.

'The traitor will see through it... He will realise that it is a trap, we do not know his real name...'

'No! Did the old man and I not help you write that diary? Did we not dictate every sentence, every word? It has our blood in it, that book! There is more than enough to convince the traitor that you really know. Listen to me...'

Yevchenko took Bucharensky's arms and shook them free of his coat. Their suppressed tension was beginning to find expression in raised voices.

'You were almost certain of the identity of the traitor. Then, you were sure but you lacked final proof. All this is plain to anyone reading the diary. *It will work!*'

In the silence that followed they could hear only their own laboured breathing. Bucharensky gave Yevchenko one last, imploring look, straightened his uniform and, without another word, marched off down the corridor.

The old colonel was right: he must act true to form. It was the start of the morning shift and to the great misfortune of those who were yawning their way on duty in KGB headquarters, Colonel Ivan Yevseevich Bucharensky had unexpectedly arrived.

In the office of the Chairman, Stanov remained slumped helplessly before the cable which lay on his desk. 'ORIOLE' ARRESTED, it read. NEST SEARCHED + PRODUCT FOUND + ASSIST AGAIN ASSIST + URGENT URGENT URGENT

-

'I, Victor Gregory Loshkevoi, wish to make a statement...'

The Russian sat at the rickety table which took up most of the floorspace in the tiny cell, forehead resting on his hands. The black writing at the head of the ruled A4 sheet coiled before his tired eyes. He desperately wanted to sleep but knew that he must keep awake. A statement. The one thing he did not wish to make. He had proved it by saying nothing at all for six hours while they worked on him in shifts, always going over the same ground, again and again, until at last they had left him alone with his exhausted, over-stimulated thoughts, and a sheet of paper on which someone had already written the words, 'I, Victor Gregory Loshkevoi, wish to make a statement...'

Keys jangled down the corridor and stopped outside his cell. Loshkevoi spread his fingers and through the gap saw the grille swing open to admit a pair of official-looking dark blue legs.

'This is what you asked for earlier.'

A second sheet of paper landed on top of the first. Loshkevoi screwed up his eyes in concentration. A list. Names.

'Solicitors. They all do Legal Aid work if you're short.'

Loshkevoi slowly raised his head. The voice was young. He saw it belonged to a fresh-faced constable in shirt-sleeves. Seeing him look up, the boy – to Loshkevoi he was a mere boy – smiled. Loshkevoi immediately lowered his gaze in the only defence he had against the insidious psychological warfare of love – and – hate.

'Cuppa tea?'

A cracked mug of reddish-brown liquid was deposited at Loshkevoi's elbow. He ignored it.

'That one's pretty good.' The young constable jabbed a thumb at the last name on the list. Loshkevoi said nothing.

'They're all okay. Except him.'

Again the jab. Through half-closed eyelids Loshkevoi read the name. Sculby.

'Claims he's never lost a case in this court. Way he operates, I'm not surprised, meself.'

With more jangling of keys the constable let himself out. He was about to clang the grille to when he seemed to hesitate.

'Seriously,' he said. 'Do yourself a bit of good. You have that Mr Roberts. He's all right, he is. One of the boys. Know what I mean?'

As the keys clanked back down the corridor Loshkevoi nervously fingered the list while he strove to concentrate. The police obviously wanted to see Roberts on the case. The other names meant nothing to Loshkevoi. His head was going round and round with sheer fatigue. I, Victor Gregory Loshkevoi, wish to make a statement…

Never lost a case… not surprised…

'Sculby,' he said aloud.

Chapter 4

When the phone rang shortly after six, Laurence Sculby had already been up for an hour. From his chair at the desk the double-bed was visible through the half open bedroom door, and in it the sleeping form of Judy, his current. Some men would have found that a distraction. Not Sculby.

At ten o'clock he was due to attend the West London Coroner's Court for the start of what promised to be a very long inquest. Most of Sculby's time over the past few months had been spent preparing for this case. He was deeply committed to it. A naked girl in his bed did not even begin to compete.

David Sanson had been a card-carrying member of the Communist Party and fully paid-up member of the TGWU. He was employed as a driver by a medium-sized firm of hauliers. Shortly before Christmas the drivers at the firm's Acton depot went on strike over threatened redundancies. Sanson did not work at the Acton depot but that did not prevent him from joining the picket line. At 7.30 a.m. on the first day of the strike there was trouble. Sanson died, his head staved in by a violent blow which a number of witnesses might (or might not) have seen delivered by the baton of a mounted policeman. The baton could not now be found. The dead man's fiancée had retained Sculby to attend the inquest.

It was right up his street, but even by his standards it was a plum. At 28 Sculby already had a reputation for being a 'difficult' lawyer with an impeccable pedigree of left-wing activism going back to his years as an undergraduate at the London School of Economics. On two occasions the police had lodged formal complaints with the Law Society's Professional Purposes Committee in connection with his conduct of criminal litigation. Neither complaint had been upheld, but relations between Sculby and the police were strained to breaking-point. No one on the inside was surprised when Sculby's name began to be mentioned in the same breath as Sanson's. No one doubted that Sculby would do the case as vitriolically as if his own brother lay buried in the cemetery, and several times more efficiently.

So when the phone rang shortly after six and Sculby lifted the receiver to hear Royston say, 'I'm having the Sanson case adjourned', he knew a moment of black, uncontrolled rage so powerful that he couldn't speak. The sheer bloody-minded effrontery of it struck him dumb.

'Oh you have to be joking' was all he could say, at first.

'I'm sorry, Laurie. I know how much it means to you.'

Judy, roused by the sound of Sculby's voice, was getting up. She stood naked in front of the dressing-table, combing the long blonde hair which cascaded almost to the cleft of her buttocks, and Sculby didn't even notice.

'*Meant* to me. That's a laugh. *You* said when I told you I'd got the Sanson papers, *you* said it was the best fucking thing that we'd had in years. Run it for all it's worth, you said. Do it so as they'll never forget you, in Fleet Street or anywhere else, and now all of a sudden it's a pious bleat about what it meant to *me*. Jesus Christ, Michael, who the hell do you think I am?'

'I've said I'm sorry...'

'Well fuck that for a laugh. What about that woman out there who thought she was going to a wedding and ended up going to a bloody funeral? She's *paying* me, do you realise that?'

'We pay you...'

'That's different. That is totally different. That is so totally irrelevant...'

Judy came out of the bedroom, fully clothed, and picked up her handbag from the floor. She tried to catch Sculby's eye, failed, shrugged and went out to the kitchen.

'I'm adjourning it,' Royston was saying. 'I'm not sacking you, am I, for Christ's sake? I'm not taking you off the case.'

'Well I won't adjourn it.'

'But the police have already said they'll ask for an adjournment anyway.'

'And I'll oppose it.'

'Coroner won't, though.'

And Royston sniggered, a loathsome sound which echoed in Sculby's ears long after the call was over. The lawyer was aware of the coffee grinder going and Terry Wogan in the background. The snigger made him feel suddenly futile.

'I see,' he said dully. 'Well, if that's how it is.'

In his anger he had stood up. Now he sat at the desk and tried to think productively. Judy put her head round the door, saw him slumped over his papers, shrugged again and disappeared. A moment later the front door slammed loudly. Sculby, a connoisseur of early-morning door slams, was not unduly worried.

'That's how it is,' confirmed Royston. 'So ring up the office and get somebody sent down to agree an adjournment, all right? And believe me, I wouldn't ask you if it wasn't important.'

'Sanson was important,' said Sculby. He was no longer using the harsh, hectoring tone employed by trades union leaders to state the terms on which 'the lads' would settle. 'His fiancée was important. To themselves. And me.'

There was a short silence. When Royston spoke again his voice, too, had changed.

'But that's what it's all about, isn't it, Laurie? Giving up when it matters most...'

Sculby swallowed. 'You promise this is only a delay.'

'Yes. But something's come up and I need you. Now do I have you, Laurie?'

'Yes.'

'Good. It may come to nothing, I can't tell. All I want you to do for the moment is be available. Just that. You may get a phone-call about a character called Loshkevoi. I'll spell that...'

Sculby picked up the pencil he had dropped on the floor in his earlier rage and wrote down the name.

'He's being done for handling stolen cars. I've arranged for your name to be fed to him. He may bite, he may not. If he does, stick with him. Do your level best for him, no holds barred. I want that man to love you, Laurie. I want him to see in you the dead father, long-lost brother and innocent child he never had, all rolled up in one. Okay?'

'And if there's no phone-call?'

'Then forget it. You don't try to contact him. I'll be in touch.'

Royston hung up. Sculby replaced the receiver on its cradle. He realised he was hungry.

Judy had left a note for him propped against the coffee-grinder: something about the Albert Hall and two tickets.

He screwed it up and threw it in the trash without trying to decipher it further, then made himself some toast and black coffee, which he carried back to the living-room and proceeded to bolt. While he was still chewing the last mouthful of toast he dialled the home number of one of his partners and tersely explained that on account of an overnight development he wouldn't be in a position to fight the Sanson case after all, and he wasn't going to be in before lunchtime. The partner promised to arrange for an adjournment by consent.

No sooner had Sculby replaced the receiver than the phone rang.

'Is that Mr Sculby?'

'Speaking.'

'Mr Laurence Sculby, the solicitor?'

'Yes.'

'Detective-Sergeant Fitzgerald, Lavender Hill police station here. I am telephoning on behalf of one Victor Gregory Loshkevoi. He has been charged with handling stolen property, contrary to section 22 subsection…'

'Yes, I'm familiar with it, Sergeant. Go on.'

'He wishes to retain you as his solicitor to act for him in preparing his defence.'

It amused Sculby to hear the undisguised hostility in Fitzgerald's voice. 'When's he coming up?'

'Ten o'clock this morning at Lavender Hill Magistrates' Court.'

'I'll be there. You're not going to try to attach any stupid conditions to bail, I suppose?'

'We shall oppose bail.'

'You'll do what?' scoffed Sculby, but the line was dead. He stared at the receiver as if seeking confirmation that he had heard correctly, and shook his head. The filth never ceased to amaze him.

He took a cab all the way from Kilburn to Clapham, knowing that Royston would pay. He spent the journey sunk in depression, staring vacantly out of the window. This was his daily grind. Most of his time-sheets recorded visits to obscure magistrates' courts on the outer fringes of London in buildings never designed for the purpose, where he would trade cigarettes and sometimes larger favours with bored policemen while together they engaged in the most common of legal practices – waiting for something to happen. Today should have been different.

He was at Clapham by half-past nine. For Sculby, the worst moment always came on entering the cell. Each one looked alike: brick walls painted dark green to chest height and pale green thereafter; a dark stripe round the room at the level where a man's head would leave a grease-mark if he sat long enough; a table and a chair. Through the narrow doorway Sculby saw these familiar things and unconsciously squared his shoulders.

Loshkevoi was sitting at the table, head in hands. At the sound of Sculby's entry he rose to his feet and retreated until he was standing with his back to the far wall.

'Mr Loshkevoi?' breezed Sculby. 'I'm a solicitor, my name's Sculby, and I'm here to see what I can do for you. As an arrested person charged with an indictable offence you have certain rights, one of which is to apply for bail…'

Sculby continued with his easy-going, reassuring speech, reminding Loshkevoi of his rights, outlining the cash limits for Legal Aid, inquiring about his client's means. But underneath he was troubled. Loshkevoi had a bad smell to him. He was tall and thick-set and fit-looking, obviously a man to have on your side in a fight if at all possible, and his neatly trimmed black beard gave him the appearance of one who has secrets to hide. Fatigue would account partly for his haggard look, but there was more to it than that. Someone had got to Loshkevoi. He was running scared.

Sculby paused, so as to give his latest client a chance to speak. Loshkevoi muttered something incomprehensible. He seemed dazed.

'I'm sorry?'

'I said I'm… I have committed no offence. I do not…' Loshkevoi shook his head from side to side. 'I do not know what is happening to me. I am in your hands, Mr Sculby.'

The deep bass voice was hoarse with strain.

'Let's take it a step at a time, shall we? Bail, that's the first thing. Let me explain about court procedure…'

Loshkevoi's case was called on first. A detective-sergeant outlined the charges and asked for an adjournment pending further enquiries. Sculby formally stated that his client would plead not guilty and reserve his defence; he had no objection to a remand, provided it was on bail.

'Sergeant?'

'I oppose bail, Sir. We have reason to believe that further offences may be committed and evidence destroyed if bail is granted.'

'I protest!'

Sculby was on his feet. The stipendary magistrate raised his hand. 'All in good time. Anything else from the police?'

'No, Sir.'

'Now, Mr Sculby…'

'Sir, I would respectfully remind you of the provisions of the Bail Act. My client has no previous convictions. He is prima facie entitled…'

The magistrate listened stoney-faced for five minutes while Sculby said everything he could think of on Loshkevoi's behalf. Then:

'The prisoner is remanded in custody for seven days.'

Behind Sculby there was a sudden commotion. Loshkevoi was standing in the dock, his hands grasping the rail in front of him, while two policemen struggled to restrain him. He had hurled himself forward with such violence that his body was bent almost double over the bar of the dock. The subdued man whom Sculby had interviewed in the cells was gone; in his place was a frenzied, white-faced maniac.

'Get me out!'

Sculby's jaw dropped. He looked helplessly from the bench to the dock, and back again. 'Be quiet,' he hissed. 'You'll do yourself no good.'

'Sculby, I'm telling you…' Loshkevoi's voice was a bare croak. '*Get me out.*'

'Take him down,' said the magistrate.

Chapter 5

While Sculby was shaving that morning, the government communications centre at Cheltenham finally cracked the runaway code.

They called it the runaway code because transmissions invariably disintegrated into repetitions of the same group of letters, then of one letter, then silence. It was only two weeks old, and for most of that time it had been sitting in the SIS computer, subjected to millions and millions of electronic operations designed to analyse its mysteries.

The print-out of the latest message together with a copy of the key were finally delivered at about eight o'clock on the morning after Loshkevoi's arrest. Shortly after nine, Telecommunications reported a worldwide transmission emanating from Moscow, destination all embassies and consulates. The monitors sat up. This was unusual. They were using the runaway code. Fingers began to tingle. The message was sent to Computer Operations under a red flag. Less than an hour after the transmission had ceased 'C' was being dragged from a meeting to inspect the product.

He arrived back in his office to find it unusually crowded. The head of the Inquisition was there, together with the Director of Planning and the Chief of Staff. Sir Richard Bryant put on his gold-rimmed half-spectacles and read the cable lying on his desk.

REDFIRE + COL IVAN YEVSEEVICH BUCHARENSKY DESERTED MC 03 MARCH + CASENAME KYRIL + BELIEVED SEEKING BRITISH CONTACT VIEW DEFECTION + POSSESSION TOPMOST SECRET DOCUMENTS + POSSESSION IDENTITY SIS CONTACT MC + ALL STEPS NEUTRALISE SHORT SHUTDOWN + SECURE PRIMEMOST + REDFIRE END ++

'Redfire' was the most urgent classification a Soviet transmission could carry. Two of the men present in C's office had never seen one.

'I don't understand this,' said C. 'What is the meaning of "shutdown"?'

'Execution,' explained the head of the Inquisition. 'They want him alive.'

'I see.' Bryant pondered the explanation. 'Hardly surprising, in the circumstances. What do you have on this... Bucharensky?'

'The file is coming across from Registry. Meanwhile we have a photograph for you.'

The Director of Planning turned to the IBM console that was built into the side of C's desk and tapped out some figures, while the Chief of Staff drew the curtains. A picture was flashed on the far wall. They all turned to look at the face of the one the Russians called 'Kyril'; sad but friendly, the kind of man your child could safely talk to in the park. From the darkness C spoke.

'Find out the colonel's movements. Seize him alive by any means possible.' He paused, so as to give his next words greater emphasis. 'You are to regard this as a major emergency. I am prepared, if absolutely necessary, to risk a diplomatic incident. But bring him to me, alive, here, in one piece. If you all manage to achieve nothing else for the next twelve months, at least do this and do it *soon*.'

Chapter 6

Sculby was surprised to find his secretary still in the office. She ought to have gone to lunch long before.

'You shouldn't have waited,' he said.

Betty eyed him over the sheet of paper which she was feeding into her typewriter.

'I had to. Guess who's in there.'

Sculby did not need to guess. Royston was the only 'client' who regularly came in at lunchtime without an appointment. It upset the routine when he called because the office in Milward Street was small; only Sculby and his secretary worked there, so that one of them always had to be around if a stranger was present. The other seven partners in the firm of Sculby O'Connor & Co worked in plush City offices with a pretty receptionist to protect them from the outside world. Sculby preferred Whitechapel, though. He liked being the boss.

'What is it this time?'

'Says it's the kids. She's threatening to take them with her and go off with that karate instructor.'

Sculby nodded morosely. The advantage of his secretary was that she pried.

'Rough morning?'

He nodded again.

'Want a quickie before you go in?'

'No. I've had a couple.'

'Yes, I thought so.'

This time Sculby smiled. 'Shows, does it?'

Betty grinned at him and started to type. Sculby removed his macintosh and hung it on one of the cheap metal hooks provided for the use of clients. The only other garment on the rack was a faded, thin overcoat, the pockets of which overflowed with soiled kid gloves and an old scarf.

'Don't wait any longer. See you at two-thirty. Oh, leave me a line through, will you?'

'Okay then. Bye.'

As Betty picked up her bag and made ready to lock up she heard the beginning of Sculby's usual opening remarks before the office door closed behind him.

'Now then, Mr Royston, what can I do for you? Cold day, isn't it, sorry to hear from my secretary...'

Royston stood up as Sculby entered. The two men shook hands formally.

'Good of you to see me without an appointment, Mr Sculby.'

'Not at all, some things won't wait, will they? If you'll just hang on a minute...'

Sculby began to shuffle papers across the untidy desk, trying to replace chaos with a semblance of order. When he was tired of that he sat back in his chair and gazed across the mess at Royston, as if expecting him to say something. Sensing this, Royston opened his mouth to speak, but Sculby held up a hand. For a moment they sat there, frozen, silent, until afar off they simultaneously heard the sound of the street door closing and the clink of keys.

Sculby loosened his tie, undid the top button of his shirt and pushed with his feet against the desk until he was able to rest his legs on the top and slump back in his chair. For a moment he did nothing except raise his hand to his forehead and massage it gently. It helped to ease the muzzy pain which the gin he had drunk earlier had done nothing to alleviate.

'My God, Michael, I don't want any more mornings like that one.'

Royston smiled. 'How'd you get on?'

'Oddly. It's all on tape. Which reminds me…'

Sculby stood up and went to fetch the briefcase which he had let drop to the floor on entering the office. 'Here.'

Royston picked up the tape. 'Anything to interest me?'

Sculby didn't answer at once; instead he took a long, cool look at the man sitting opposite him. On the whole he liked Royston. He was an excellent control, one who worked in full sympathy with his agents. But in six years of emphatic co-operation Royston had never learned that there were some questions which couldn't be answered, at least not in the same language as the questioner used.

'He's crazy. And he scares me witless.'

Royston sat back in his chair and thought about that. He knew that what Sculby had just told him might be exaggeration born of nerves. But it might be streetwise instinct. And you didn't ignore that.

Royston tossed the little cassette in the air, caught it and pocketed it.

'Tell me,' he said softly.

Sculby quickly ran through the morning's events.

'When I found him in the cells afterwards the surgeon was about to stick a needle in him. I stopped that, of course. It seems he thought as long as he shut up and didn't incriminate himself he'd get bail. That's all he cares about, for the moment. When it didn't happen he couldn't take it. That's a hell of a frightened man you've got yourself there, Michael. Says he's innocent, it's a fit-up. Fair enough. I can't do any more until I've seen the police depositions. I suppose it's no use asking you what's going on?'

Royston was silent for a moment.

'What are you going to do now?'

'Go to the judge in chambers.'

'Come again?'

'Get bail. You appeal against the magistrate's decision by going to a High Court judge sitting in private, in chambers.'

'I'm only guessing,' said Royston, 'but I think you may find the police don't oppose on appeal.' Noting Sculby's sour look he added quickly, 'It was nothing to do with me that Loshkevoi didn't get bail. Five are still clearing up, that's all.'

'Five are cunts,' said Sculby. 'And you're another' hung unspoken in the room between the two men. 'What happened to my inquest, anyway?'

'Never mind that for a moment. I'm going to tell you all you need to know, Laurie.' Royston drew his chair closer to Sculby. 'And not a word more. That's for your own protection. Last night, Five found a whole heap of arms and other stuff on Loshkevoi's premises. We're leaving them there, pretending we haven't noticed anything, in the hope he'll lead us up the line. This handling charge is just to give us something on him for now. You understand? All you've got to do is worm your way into his confidence. When I give the word, you'll be the one to make the pitch. Safety in exchange for hard information, that'll be the name of the game. And for now that's all you need to know.'

Royston stood up, and Sculby realised he wasn't going to learn any more.

'You're all right for cash on this one?'

Sculby nodded. 'Loshkevoi's loaded.'

'Then I'll be off.'

Sculby was overtaken by a burning desire to score over Royston, something, anything…

'Just one thing, for when you next come, Michael. That coat outside, the suit you're wearing… they're all great, no one would think you weren't a client. But those shoes…'

In spite of himself Royston had to look down.

'…It's not that they're filthy. Quite a lot of my clients have dirty shoes. But you don't see that much suede on Milward Street, Michael. Hope you don't mind me mentioning it.'

While Royston was formulating a reply the phone rang.

'Hello… hold on, please.'

Sculby held his hand over the receiver and frowned across at his companion. 'For Christ's sake, who knows you're here…?'

Royston snatched the instrument from Sculby's hand.

'Hello… yes.'

Sculby watched curiously. Royston's mouth had developed a tic. Suddenly he went very white.

'He did… *what*?'

Chapter 7

Kyril stood frozen at the centre of a huge, intricate web. Silence and shadows had isolated him completely from the tangible world outside. Only tiny tingling sensations on the extremities of the strands which he had woven round himself revealed that he was still alive. First his hearing went, worn out with the strain of listening for sounds which did not happen. Now his sight was failing with the short winter twilight. Soon all the systems of his body would shut down, night would come, and he would be dead…

He shook himself angrily. *Think.*

From his vantage point on the bedside chair he could see the old-new skyline of Athens through the broad tunnel of his bedroom: a maze of aerials and high-tension cables linking the uneven roofs, beyond them a hill topped by stately ruined columns. Earlier in the afternoon the hillside had been the colour of washed sand; now it was ground ginger; soon it would become black, indistinguishable from the surrounding night.

By standing on the chair he was able to look down into Kaningos Square without approaching the window. The two men were still there, talking, every so often directing a swift glance towards the hotel. One of the men operated a souvlaki stall with some pretence to efficiency; Kyril acknowledged that the Athens *referentura* had improved its standards over the last nine years. In some ways.

The hotel had been unnaturally silent for more than an hour. None of the usual sounds rose from the kitchen, no porter whistled aimlessly as he carted crates of empty, rattling bottles through the hall. They were inside, then. Somewhere in the corridor, in the room next door, on the terrace above him, men were waiting patiently for the next move.

Kyril's heart beat faster than usual and his palms were sweating, but he could detect no signs of internal panic. The old training still held. It was not as though anything which had happened today was unexpected; Stanov had promised him all this. But Kyril had left it so very late. He had slipped up, once. Nothing in his impassive face or his quiet, controlled movements disclosed that he had been thrust willy-nilly into the most nerve-wracking crisis of his career.

Below him in the dusty square, one of the two men detached himself from the souvlaki stall and began to walk towards the hotel. A three-wheeler van hooted aggressively; the man faltered, advanced again, and was lost from Kyril's sight.

–

It was not the city he remembered. More cracked walls, dirt, empty building-sites. Fewer taxis. No quick 'deals' by virtue only of having the language. The smell, that was the same: hot oil, carbon monoxide, red dust, air-cured tobacco, wine. Salt, a dash of the sea. Everything else was changed.

The friendly lorry-driver had dropped him in Omonia Square and watched for a moment of amusement as the 'German teacher', doing Greece on the cheap off-season, withstood the first shock of downtown Athens. The hooting, hustling roar of the cars hurtling five abreast down the broad avenues, the vendors, the crowds... the first point of familiarity, of contact: a man dressed in a grey, short-sleeved shirt over black slacks, an attaché case under his arm, stopping to buy Papastratos cigarettes at the kiosk. Kyril's eyes began to focus. Suddenly he knew where he was.

-

He shifted his weight gingerly on the chair and stood still again, listening. Nothing disturbed the eerie quiet of the hotel. With the thumb of his right hand he eased the safety-catch of the Stechkin to 'off' while at the same time his forefinger curled round the trigger, testing the pressure. He forgot he had once had to learn that simple movement in far-off days when it still seemed clumsy and unnatural. Only his body and its well-trained muscles remembered.

By turning his head a fraction he could see part of the corridor through the skylight over the door. No awkward shadows. No diminution of light. No sounds. Nothing.

Through the window the far hillside had dissolved into a smoke-laden mist. Nightfall was minutes away. Neon lights flickered outside and a Greek boy shouted before gunning his motorbike and zooming down a side-street. Kyril could hear bazouki music coming from a nearby taverna. Athens was changing into its evening attire. The siesta was over. Soon there would be enough noise in the street to mask any unpleasantness which might occur on the upper floor of a small hotel.

He had selected this hotel from working files on possibly useful 'stations', buildings recognised by the KGB as having operational potential but not yet tested by them. The 'Silenus' occupied a narrow site in one corner of the triangular 'square', with its tiny patch of green in the centre and a mish-mash of cafés spilled on to the pavement. The hotel overlooked a busy intersection with excellent sightlines and ready access to neighbouring apartment-blocks at the rear. In March he was able to obtain a top-storey room at the front without difficulty, paying for a day's lodging in advance. He allowed himself one hour in the roof-top open bar, already balmy in the pre-spring, drinking Hellas and smoking Benson & Hedges, before lunch and a short rest. Then work.

It was the first chance he had had to think since leaving Moscow. He discovered he quite enjoyed his role – for the moment. It could not last, of course: sooner or later he would find an executioner on his tail, someone determined to see he did not fall into the hands of his own side alive, and then the fun would be over, but for the present he could cope. A magnet, that was what Stanov had called him, and the image appealed to Kyril. Everything depended on him. If he snapped his fingers on the street somebody, somewhere, perhaps thousands of miles away, knew about it and acted accordingly. Kyril liked that. In its way it represented more power than he had ever known.

He wondered whether they had found the diary yet. They should have done. Would it fool anyone? Kyril shook his head, the old doubts returning. Would the traitor fall into the trap of believing that a comparatively junior officer like Ivan Bucharensky had discovered his secret when all others had failed? He might. Kyril appreciated the possibility. If his nerves were already on edge, if he were sufficiently near the brink, then the diary might just instil a doubt… and it would have served its purpose.

After lunch he lay on his bed for an hour, but could not sleep. The weather was mild and overcast. He took a taxi to the intersection of the two main arteries, Leoforas Alexandras and Vassilissis Sofias, then walked slowly south along the latter until he had passed the American embassy. He kept going. After a while Vassilissis Sofias became Vassileos Konstantinou, and he turned right into Stisikhorou, which took him behind the Russian embassy before pointing the way back towards his hotel. One last call, the Odos Stadiou branch of the National Bank of Greece, there to collect his nest-egg from the deposit-box where it had languished for the past nine years, and he was ready to go home. It was a long route but Kyril did not hurry; he wasn't used to walking and his feet ached. Even at the end, when he realised with a stab of unease that the KGB were ahead of him and on either side, he did not break his stride.

For the next half hour he enjoyed himself, glad to be back in the old game again. Stores with rear exits, taxis stuck in traffic-jams, entrances to the subway; all the techniques came flooding back. As he entered his hotel he was smiling at the ease with which he had shaken off the tail. The rest of the schedule was easy: collect his things, make for the station, double-check for tails, hitch a lift, change cars every three miles for the first leg of the journey, then… disappear. He was still smiling when he took a final glance out of the window of his bedroom, and saw the two men outside, waiting.

Kyril held his luminous-faced watch up to his eyes. He could hear nothing, but his instincts now told him that between his room and the stairs someone waited: unseen, soundless, but there.

He padded across to the telephone and lifted the receiver. A room-waiter would disrupt anyone loitering, or at least identify his precise location. Becoming impatient he jiggled the cradle up and down. Nothing. They weren't answering.

Kyril took a fold of skin from his forefinger between his teeth and bit, not so hard that the pain distracted him but enough to pump the blood a little faster, sharpen his reflexes. Now he was ready.

He felt along the bottom seam of his rucksack. Tucked into a fold of the lining, as if to save it from a casual thief, was a thin platinum cigarette-lighter. He unscrewed the fuel cap and extracted an inch-long bullet-like tube from the lighter. He placed it carefully on the bed. Then he began to pile things over it: his German passport, detected by the feel of its cover and the embossed lettering; the American Express card with a notch in the left-hand corner; a letter of credit also with a notch in the left-hand corner, all now expendable. He pulled the bedspread over the little pile. As an afterthought he placed on top of that a newspaper which he had bought that morning, and his room key.

He shouldered the rucksack, tightening the straps until they would go no further. He did not need light to tell him that he had forgotten nothing; his memory was as sharp as ever.

For the moment all was still in the corridor. Kyril padded over to the sash window and eased it up, silently cursing the noise made by the heavy counter-weight chains. Other ears must have heard it too, for suddenly a shadow flitted across the strip of light from the oriel. Kyril didn't wait to investigate.

Once on the narrow ledge outside his room he turned to face the wall and scrabbled upwards with crooked fingers. Sure enough, there was the parapet, above it the open-air terrace bar where he had sat drinking earlier in the day. He hauled himself quickly upwards. The two men in the square might see but he didn't care any longer; it could even be turned to his advantage.

Below him he could hear voices in the bedroom he had just left. He glanced quickly around. The bar was unlit and deserted; nobody wanted to drink out in the open on a March night in Athens. Kyril grinned. Two men at least in the bedroom, talking increasingly loudly in Russian. Very careless. He would advise Stanov to shake out the Greek Resident on his return…

Kyril held up the slim platinum lighter and flicked the lever. The impulse leapt forth. There was a muffled boom as the silver nitrate and potassium bomb exploded on the bed in the room below, a scream and a sudden waft of hot air over the parapet. Kyril smiled and pocketed the lighter. Suddenly he froze. A hand was coming over the edge, garishly illuminated by a flashing neon sign above. Before he could move a man was up on the ledge of the bar, crouched low in order to minimise the target. His other hand was coming up level. Kyril knew what was in it.

For a split second he deliberated. The assassin's hold was precarious; if Kyril could only get close enough he could push him over the edge. But that meant running into range. In the dark, with a hand gun, the chances were that the man would miss a target moving away from him.

Before the split second was up Kyril was pivoting on his toes and racing for the far end of the terrace.

Earlier that day he had stood on this very spot, calculating distances, some professional part of him alive to potential danger. Kyril knew that five metres separated the terrace from the roof-top of the adjacent building and there was a drop of one and a half metres to allow for as well. His stride never faltered. Using every scrap of momentum he could gather he sped along the patio until, at the far end, he hopped on to the low ledge and propelled himself into the darkness. A whirl of light far below him, a sick feeling in his stomach and then his right knee and left forearm crashed into concrete, the breath went out of him and he lay there, winded but alive.

The 'ping' of the bullet roused him. He rolled rapidly to one side, seeking desperately for cover. Another 'ping' – the gunman was using a silencer, bad for accuracy but still dangerously close. A third 'ping' spattered concrete chips over his head; at the same moment he saw the skylight and launched his way towards it, praying for a soft landing. A second before impact he punched forward with both hands, letting them take the brunt of the broken glass and protect his head. Another sickening fall into darkness, then a soft bump and scream, this time a woman's. A dim bedside light went on. He had landed on top of a girl, very beautiful he noticed – and not alone. Details began to penetrate: bare breasts, a hairy chest... surely not the girl's, no *not* the girl's...

'*Lipomai, kyrie. Kalinikta sas.*'

Kyril fled. One or two curious heads peered out of partly opened doors as he emerged on to the landing. He ran uncaring until he was down the stairs and out the back door among the dustbins, a passageway ahead of him, and escape.

He was in a side-street, dimly lit and deserted. Nothing moved. He did a swift damage-check. It was bad. Blood everywhere, crystals of splintered glass, a knee that was beginning to seize up in spasms of pain. Hide? No... He had to get out of town while the evening crowds still thronged the streets, then he could rest.

It was a long, painful night. Several times he nearly blundered into the bright lights of a busy avenue, and once he thought he was being followed. It was an illusion, but after the scare he put on more speed. Dawn found him on the road to Aharne, well away from any route he could be expected to take, bruised and shaken but alert. His wounds had been bathed in cold spring water; a clean shirt and a new identity from the rucksack had done wonders.

He consulted his map. Athens Station had tried to stop him, but he had got away. There was no doubt in his mind that they had not intended him to escape completely. From now on the schedule would be tight. If he was to arrive in Brussels in accordance with Stanov's carefully timed plan he would have to cut corners, take chances.

He looked up sharply. Far off to the south he could see a cloud of reddish dust rising from the road. It was a local delivery van.

Kyril hesitated for only a moment, then folded the map, shouldered his burden, stepped on to the highway and lifted his thumb.

As the cloud of dust grew closer his tired brain began to register details. An old van coated with layers of grease and grime, its gear-box crunching... typically Greek. No, not typical. Something was different.

Kyril lowered his thumb. He had to make a quick decision. The van was okay, he told himself, desperate to believe it; nothing was wrong.

The windscreen was just a black rectangle. Soon he would be able to see the driver.

The windscreen…

Suddenly he knew what was wrong. Every Greek driver plasters the inside of his windscreen with brightly coloured postcards, slogans, trinkets… this van had none of them.

Kyril flung himself off the road and began to run.

'Stand still!'

The van had drawn up by the side of the road. Kyril did not look back. Not even the sound of an English voice made him falter.

'I'm warning you…'

Kyril began to weave right and left. Already some part of him knew it was hopeless. He was miles from the nearest cover. When the first spray of bullets hit the ground within inches of his racing feet he stumbled, fell and lay perfectly still.

Chapter 8

On the first floor of the Royal Courts of Justice in the Strand there is an area called the Bear Garden. Anyone who needs to ask his way to it will probably never get there, for, as with members' clubs, newcomers normally arrive only in the company of old hands. The Bear Garden consists of two large, high-ceilinged rooms connected by a short corridor, and in some ways it resembles not only an exclusive club but also a medieval palace ante-room. The setting is much the same: heavy wooden tables with carved chairs and benches along the walls, dusty portraits of old men clad in flowing, scarlet robes, even a gallery at one end; and the rooms are thronged with gossiping, conniving courtiers ready to present their petitions, make their requests. But there the resemblance ends. The carpet is twin to that in Royston's office, the air is heavy with cigarette-smoke and the twentieth-century princelings who occupy the seats of power wear dark grey suits.

Leading off the short corridor which connects the two main rooms is an office known as 'Room 98'. Here a judge of the Queen's Bench Division of the High Court sits daily to hear matters within his jurisdiction, including applications for bail, and it was from Room 98 that Laurence Sculby emerged at four o'clock on the day after his meeting with Royston.

'Wasted brief fee,' murmured the young barrister who followed him.

'Nah,' said Sculby. 'Worth every penny.'

The barrister laughed uneasily.

'"I've read the affidavit, Mr Gyddon, I don't see the police, order as asked, two sureties in the sum of five hundred pounds." I wasn't exactly overworked, was I?'

'Beautiful bit of advocacy,' said Sculby. 'Lovely touch, Spence. I'll just have a word with the judge's clerk and we'll get that order down to Brixton tonight. Then first thing tomorrow, he's out.'

'That's fast,' said Spencer Gyddon. 'I'm surprised you got in front of the judge so quickly, Laurie. How do you do these things?'

Sculby winked. 'Trust me,' he said.

'I do,' said Gyddon as Sculby turned away from him and started towards the stairs. 'I think,' he added under his breath.

At eleven o'clock next morning, formalities complete, Sculby met Loshkevoi at Brixton jail. To the lawyer's surprise his client looked in better health, and he remarked on the fact. 'Sleep,' replied Loshkevoi. 'Fourteen hours at a stretch, Mr Sculby. I needed it. Nothing else to do, anyway.'

'Please call me Laurie,' murmured Sculby. 'Everyone does.'

'Victor.' Loshkevoi held out his hand and grasped Sculby's in a painful squeeze. 'You do a fine job, Laurie. What next?'

'I expect you want to get home, see to things…'

'For that I have a manager. He's been in charge two days, another couple of hours won't break him. All I want right now is to beat that fucking charge. You excuse my language, please.'

Sculby's grin widened. 'S'long as you'll excuse mine. Tell you what. There's a nice little Italian place up the hill. I'll buy you lunch.'

'It's on me.'

Sculby put a friendly arm round Loshkevoi's shoulders. 'Argue about it over the coffee,' he said.

Loshkevoi made a good lunch. Sculby wondered if he always ate that much or if prison had sharpened his appetite. Only when the coffee came, and they were well into the second litre of Soave, did the two men begin to talk seriously.

'I come from Italy, you know. Years back. The food travels well, even here it's good.'

'What part of Italy?'

Loshkevoi raised suspicious eyes to Sculby's face and evidently decided the question was innocent, for he replied 'Bergamo'.

'Why'd you leave?'

'The war.'

Loshkevoi swilled down half a glass of wine and wiped his beard with his napkin.

'I was a boy then. My father was killed, my mother went missing. There were plenty like me, wanted in Russia by the Bolsheviks. I made friends with the right captain, he took care of everything.' Seeing Sculby's look of puzzlement he added, 'Sure I slept with him. I'm not bent, you understand. But rather that than a bullet in the neck. Illegal, too: it gave me a hold over him. Too late to do anything about that now, eh?'

'I hope so,' said Sculby thoughtfully. 'Why do you think they'd have sent you to Russia?'

'It's where we came from. My parents, I mean. They drifted from place to place. In Bergamo my father was mechanic. He taught me. So, I come here with a trade.'

Sculby reached for his briefcase and pulled out a notebook. 'Tell me a bit about yourself. Married?'

'No. You get yourself a wife, you got overheads. I select the company I want, when I want.'

Sculby grinned. 'Me too.'

'I'm starting to like you, Laurie.' Loshkevoi lit a thin, black cigar and offered the pack to Sculby. 'Smoke?'

Sculby hesitated only a second. He was trying to give up, but Royston said to make an effort. All in the line of duty... 'How long have you had your own business?'

'Ten years. I bought it off my boss when he retired, did it up a little. Jaguars, that's my speciality. The occasional Daimler, maybe. Your Fords and Vauxhalls...'

Loshkevoi made a heavy gesture of dismissal with the cigar. Sculby found his diction curiously irritating. A mixture of styles, it sounded put on, but the lawyer was coming to realise that it wasn't.

'You haven't got a regular solicitor?'

'Never needed one. Except when I took over the business, but that was years ago and I didn't like him anyway.'

'No previous? Convictions, I mean... ever been in trouble with the police before?'

'No.'

'Straight up.'

Loshkevoi's head was sunk on to his chest. At Sculby's question he lifted his eyes and subjected the solicitor to a long stare.

'Straight up?'

'Sorry. But I have to know. You'd be surprised the number of people who tell you they've no form when they have.'

'Laurie, I deal in used cars. *Nothing* surprises me.'

They haggled amicably over the bill. Loshkevoi overrode his lawyer, and paid. Outside the restaurant Sculby said, 'I'll give you a lift. My car's just round the corner.'

It took less than 15 minutes to drive to Loshkevoi's garage. Sculby watched him scuttle inside the workshop, waving a hand to the man in the cashier's booth. Nobody seemed surprised to see him. Sculby hung around as long as he decently could but in the end had to drive away without being any the wiser about his client's affairs.

Loshkevoi closed the sliding doors of the workshop.

'Sammy!'

A bald, fat man emerged from behind an XJ6 wiping his hands on an oily rag.

'Vic... Didn't expect to see you. The Old Bill was here yesterday, give the place a right going-over.'

Loshkevoi brushed him aside.

'Half day. Come on lads, I'm shutting up.'

The man called Sammy stared at the gaffer in puzzlement.

'Yer wot?'

'We're closed until eight tomorrow morning.'

'How'd you get on, boss?'

A young mechanic had slid from under a jacked van and was grinning up at Loshkevoi from the floor.

'Button it, Kelly. Go home.'

Other men in overalls began to appear from the hidden recesses of the shop. No one tried to argue. Within minutes Loshkevoi had the place to himself.

For a while he did nothing but stand with hands on hips, treating every inch of the walls and ceiling to a minute scrutiny. He started with the bottom left-hand corner of the rear wall and worked horizontally along the line of bricks before, at the end of the row, lifting his gaze a fraction and working back over the second line of bricks the way he had come. It took a long time for him to be convinced that nothing had apparently changed. But of course, the ferrets would have taken photographs before they began, and replaced everything in order afterwards.

Only after he had satisfied himself by this superficial visual inspection did Loshkevoi go in search of a crowbar and a torch.

Once inside the inspection pit he peered closely at the wall. It all looked the same. He began to hack at the bricks. Inside the cavity the light-sensitive cell attached to the ultra fast camera concealed by MI5 picked up the first flash of Loshkevoi's torch. At once the shutter began to operate, 90 times in the first minute, then a pause of a minute, followed by a further 90 exposures. As the last frame of infra-red film passed the shutter the camera automatically switched itself off. When the film was retrieved and developed Loshkevoi would be identifiable on approximately two-thirds of the shots, which was more than the makers of the camera claimed for it.

Chapter 9

It had been a week of frenetic activity in Dzerzhinsky Square. By the time the weekend came all the heads of the First Main Directorate wanted to do was get away. The two generals drove down to Zhukovka on Friday afternoon, before the traffic built up. Because he was going with Michaelov, Povin had dismissed his own driver until Monday morning with orders to report to the dacha at eight a.m., ready for work. The man was pleased but not surprised. Most senior KGB officers who were also bachelors (there were not many) insisted on staffing their holiday retreats with chauffeurs, cooks and bottle-washers, but Colonel-General Stepan Ilyich Povin was not among them. He preferred the simple life: books, records, a little vodka and his own company were all he wanted.

Unfortunately, however, it was the first weekend of the month, so he was bound by convention to dine with his superior Michaelov and his wife Nadia. Privately Povin thought little of Nadia, who was a bore, and would have liked to break this convention if he could, but he was a good-natured man and he sensed that his visits helped the Michaelovs, in a funny sort of way. So month in and month out he did his duty on the first Friday, always vainly hoping that illness or the exigences of the service might intervene to save him.

But nothing that happened in Dzerzhinsky Square, not even the defection of a traitor like Bucharensky, ever seemed sufficiently serious in Michaelov's eyes to warrant the breaking of a social engagement.

On arrival in Zhukovka Povin managed to dredge up a smile and the hug which was the very least required by such a longstanding friendship as theirs, before delivering himself of his presents.

'Stepan Ilyich, you really should not do this…'

'It is nothing, nothing. My contribution to the feast, eh?' Michaelov caught Povin's eye and surreptitiously tapped his throat – the Russian way of saying 'Drink?' Povin smiled and nodded. Once he was closeted with his chief in the study, and Nadia was safely ensconced in her culinary domain, he could relax.

'The usual?'

'Please.'

Povin watched while Michaelov poured a generous tot of petrovka, the brown vodka which goes so well with milk mushrooms. He had been addicted to it ever since officers' school at Ryazan.

'Still nothing for you?'

Michaelov shook his head dolefully.

'The doctor… aah! Sometimes I'm tempted, but then Nadia always reminds me of what happened last time.' Povin nodded sympathetically. His chief suffered from ulcers. Alcohol was forbidden. The last time Michaelov broke the embargo and drank cognac, the surgeons only just managed to save his life. Nadia, thought Povin, would be unlikely to forget.

'But to go back to what I was saying in the car…' Michaelov sat down opposite his deputy and lit a 'papirosy', a vile, sweetly scented cigarette consisting of a cardboard tube half-filled with tobacco. They were manufactured for him specially by the makers of 'Novostj', a popular brand obtainable in Moscow. It was a joke in Dzerzhinsky Square that you always knew where old Michaelov was by the smell.

'…Stanov was a fool to have compiled "Sociable Plover" in the first place. All that information collected together in one place…'

'Maybe.'

'You're still not convinced?'

'I just wish I could be sure he'd ever compiled it in the first place, that's all.'

'What do you mean?'

'Oh, nothing really. But if it's gone, why hasn't it surfaced by now? How explain the fiasco in Athens? And the trick he played on the British – what do you make of that?'

Michaelov shrugged. 'Don't talk to me about Athens. What a balls-up. But Bucharensky's another idiot, thank goodness.'

'Not such an idiot as Stanov for trusting him in the first place.'

'You're right, Stepan. So much for double-oh-seven-eight.'

Povin downed the last of his vodka and made a face.

'That one was a born loser. I've always said so. The Administrative Organs Department of the Politburo was never going to release its hold on our appointments, I don't give a damn what Kazin's supposed to have said. It's all a myth.'

'Well if it wasn't before, it is now,' Michaelov assented. 'They'll never let Stanov forget it was he who recommended Bucharensky for promotion. Chairman's Order

0078 won't be promulgated in our lifetimes. Here, give me your glass.'

'Make it a tumbler,' said Povin gloomily. 'I tell you, Valery, if we don't catch up with Bucharensky soon, we're going through The Door, you and I. Is there anything new on the diary?'

These innocent-sounding words seemed to lower the temperature in the room by several degrees. 'The Diary' was a sensitive subject among KGB officers of general rank; this was the first time since its discovery that Povin had summoned up the courage to talk to his chief about it, and on reflection he realised that it might have been more tactful to avoid the subject so soon after mentioning The Door.

'Forensic say it's genuine.'

Michaelov addressed the wall, busying himself with drinks.

'The paper and ink were official issue, but the pen was Bucharensky's own. His handwriting. Stanov's enjoying this, you know. He likes having us all on a plate. There are times I almost think he wrote that bloody diary up himself...'

As Michaelov handed Povin a fresh drink the door behind them burst open and he turned round, startled, the glass in his hand forgotten. In the doorway stood a lanky, long-haired blonde girl. Povin blinked. She was wearing thigh-tight faded jeans, obviously from the West, and a denim jacket. It took him a second to recognise Olga, the Michaelov's eldest daughter. She nodded carelessly in his direction, then said: 'Where are the car keys, father?'

Michaelov straightened his shoulders and barked: 'Olga! More to the point, where are your manners? Come here at once, say hello to General Povin.'

From the mulish look which crept across the girl's face Povin judged that she would refuse outright, and was mildly surprised when she obeyed. She approached the sofa where he was sitting and said, 'Good evening, Stepan Ilyich. It's good to see you. How are things?'

'Very well, thank you, Olga. You?'

'Yes, well. Father… the keys. Please.'

Michaelov felt in the pockets of his uniform. 'Here. But remember, don't be back late.'

'Yes, yes. G'night, Stepan.'

The girl bounced out of the room without acknowledging her father. Povin turned an inquiring eye towards Michaelov in time to catch the baffled look on his face.

'A concert. It all started with this Elton Jahn… John?'

'John,' confirmed Povin.

'Now it's every Friday. Underground, of course. I've asked Stupar to tell his boys to be damn careful who they pull in tonight.'

Povin nodded approvingly. What father would not do as much for his daughter?

'All the same, I don't mind telling you… it's tough, being a parent these days. They get harder to control. What can I do?'

Michaelov pulled a gun-metal cigarette case from the pocket of his coat and lit up. Povin's nose wrinkled; after years of working with this man he still couldn't help it. Despite his doctor's warnings Michaelov had proved unable to cure himself of the nicotine habit, and continued to smoke his revolting cigarettes.

Povin smiled at Michaelov, who commanded the First Main Directorate of the KGB and was responsible for the Soviet Union's entire foreign intelligence system.

'The young are so difficult to manage, Valery. Don't let it worry you. She'll grow up soon.'

Before Michaelov could reply Nadia summoned them to table, and the subject was closed. Povin knew from hard experience that you did not discuss the children in front of Michaelov's wife.

The evening passed off quietly, as usual. Povin declined a lift home and set out through the pine woods shortly before midnight. It was very cold; the snow squeaked under his feet. Above him a white moon sailed in a cloudless sky devoid of any threat; tomorrow would be fine.

As he trudged homewards his thoughts kept returning to the dacha he had just left – what would become of Olga, he wondered? In five years, say: a brilliant scientist devoted to the service of the State... or a dissident, in exile, or worse... on the archipelago. Povin let himself in through the back gate of his own house and began to trot up the path.

The empty house, solitude, had never worried him. The woman who came twice a week to look after his dacha in winter had left the stove piled high with wood, so that his place was warmer than the Michaelovs'. He poured himself a last glass of his favourite petrovka and switched out the lights. From his chair by the window he could look out across the Moscow river, winding like a snake through the snow-laden pine trees that fringed his spacious property. In the moonlight everything looked still and peaceful.

But Povin's inner mood was rapidly losing touch with the tranquil surroundings. It had been an effort to appear calm in front of the Michaelovs. Now he was a desperately worried man. For the past few days he had pushed everything to the outer fringes of consciousness while he strove to concentrate on the immediate problems of office. Once the pressure was off, however, he could no longer delay facing the harsh realities of his situation. The truth was appalling. But he had to keep calm. Panic was a short-cut to the grave.

Something had to be done to stop Bucharensky. And the quicker the better.

Povin put down his glass on the table beside him and eased himself on to his knees. Praying was not as simple as it used to be.

-

He had started his career in the KGB by being assigned to what is now the Fifth Direction of the Fifth Main Directorate, which oversees the practice of religion within the Soviet Union. At first the prospect had bored him. Then he was instructed to infiltrate a Ukrainian sect of the Russian Orthodox Church, and overnight his life had changed. He came away from the first meeting, held in a darkened cellar with someone on the door to listen for the guards, shaken out of his old complacency. To run such risks, merely in order to join with a few others in a demonstration of faith… there had been a Red Army officer there, his head bowed with the rest of them, also a local Peace Committee leader. Something kept Povin from reporting their presence. A few days later his superior, Major Oblensky, called him into his office. When Povin faced him across the table the major's eyes were cold.

'The other night you attended a meeting of the Krinsky Square sect. Captain Mitkov of the 16th Airborne Division was there. So was Rudolf Maximov, from the

Peace Committee. Yet you did not report these matters. Why not?'

Povin stammered. 'I did not recognise them, comrade Major.'

'Don't make it sound worse than it is already,' said Oblensky coldly. 'You're in deep.'

Even at that moment Povin had no regrets. He looked stubbornly at the floor.

'Lesser men might have been finished by this.' Oblensky was speaking again. 'Fortunately for you, Povin, your family is too well connected for me to take the steps I originally had in mind. I'm transferring you to other duties.'

He nodded curtly. The interview was at an end. As Povin laid his hand on the door handle Oblensky fired his parting shot.

'Stay away from religion, Povin.'

It was advice he had persistently ignored ever since. He sometimes wondered what had happened to Major Oblensky who one day, like so many other people, simply wasn't around any more. Shortly after that he had met Michaelov and struck up a friendship with him; ever afterwards Povin had advanced smoothly under the benign influence of his own highly placed Party family and the man who was destined to become Russia's chief foreign spymaster. It was all God's work, Povin had no doubt of it. With growing power and rank he had more time to read and think, greater freedom of movement and expression. It was no secret that the elite frequently discussed among themselves subjects which were officially taboo and Povin was soon in a position to talk over his innermost doubts and convictions with others of like mind. There were more of these than he had ever suspected. When one day

Povin simply began to think of himself as a Christian, he was acknowledging something which had in fact occurred long before.

So that night Povin stayed on his knees for a few minutes, praying for Oblensky, as always, and for Michaelov and his family and all the nameless others in general who impinged on his consciousness: the prisoners in the camps, the poor, the helpless... the words of the ancient Orthodox prayer came readily to his lips: '...for those under trial, or condemned to the mines or bitter labour in exile...'

There were so many to pray for. But chief among them tonight was Povin himself.

Next day he was up early, ready for his expedition to the Khruschev Store.

Most people did their shopping in Zhukovka at the large, single-storey complex which was the nearest thing the Soviet Union had to a supermarket. If your face didn't fit you didn't get in, but most of the high-ranking officers, ministers, scientists and artists who were allowed to live in the region were well-known there. Even though Khruschev had officially ceased to exist, his name lingered on with this shop, the Khruschev Store. Inside, the white hygienic shelves were always well-stocked with fresh dairy products, meat and fish; to the left, as you entered, were racks of men's and women's clothes shipped from France and Italy, while at the far end, by the checkout, stood rows and rows of fine French and German wines. Everything sold cheaply; this was a state-subsidised store. It was an almost classic demonstration of the theory that all are equal but some are more equal than others; the poor and unconnected weren't allowed in, but one afternoon Solzhenitsyn and Rostropovich had stood in line to buy tomatoes while behind them Molotov waited patiently to pay for Scotch and cigarettes.

The stores are presided over by a woman known to her customers only as Mother Kerenina. She has survived every purge, every change at the top, every reversal of policy; she knows all her customers by their patronymics; her stock of good-humour is boundless. This morning as Povin entered the store Mother Kerenina was dusting down a huge stack of tins piled up by the door.

'Ah Stepan Ilyich,' she cried, her eyes lighting up at the sight of him. 'How are you?'

The hug he gave her was warmer than the one he had given Nadia the night before.

'Very well. Good to be back.'

'You like my latest line?'

She waved a proud hand in the direction of the tins. Povin peered closer.

'Gravlaks! Is it any good?'

She shrugged. 'As good as tinned stuff ever can be. I suppose you'll want herring, Stepan Ilyich.'

'Please.'

'Over there, in the ice cabinet. Deep frozen, I'm afraid, but good quality.'

He wandered over to inspect the recently delivered 'catch'. Suddenly he became aware of someone standing by his side.

'If you pick that stuff over any more, Stepan Ilyich, it will be unfit for human consumption.'

He looked up to find the laughing face of Stolyinovich close to his own. Povin grinned.

'Capitalist. You'll be wanting me to cook it for you next.' They embraced affectionately. Povin was very fond of the pianist and had all his records in his Moscow apartment. Since Stolyinovich had been granted his own dacha the two men spent much time together – Povin had shyly sought the other man out to declare his admiration and respect, stayed for a drink, then for dinner and overnight. They had even gone into a kind of partnership: on his frequent trips to play in the West Stolyinovich bought up as many Deutsche Grammophon records as he could, the aim being to equip and maintain a jointly financed music library.

'Anyway, why aren't you in some western paradise, you idle wretch. Not sunning yourself in the south of France, eh?'

'Not yet. But I go tonight. So here I am, getting in my herring for the journey.'

'It will go off. Besides, you can buy herring anywhere.'

'Ah, but not like this. And I have a freezer pack; it is filled with some kind of chemical, don't ask me what, but it stays cold until I can get it into my hotel fridge.'

Povin shook his head indulgently. 'One of these days, Pyotr, I shall get the boys to work you over at the airport.'

Stolyinovich flicked a contemptuous finger. 'I go through Vnukovo now. Your boys don't get a look in.'

Povin chuckled. He knew that the distinguished pianist had recently won the right to use the V.I.P. airport on the other side of Moscow. 'Still,' he said, 'you'd be surprised at what the hidden x-ray cameras show up at Vnukovo.'

He made no secret of his job to Stolyinovich, had told him long ago that he was the Deputy Director of the First Main Directorate. His friend even knew his speciality: England and Ireland.

'I can guess. Pornography and state secrets.'

'More or less.'

'And in my case, herring. Now tell me, Stepan, which should I choose. What about that fellow, eh? He looks nice and plump.'

Povin studied the freezer-shelf where he had himself been rummaging a moment before. 'I should take... *that* one.'

'You are sure?'

Povin nodded and moved away, as if uninterested. Stolyinovich followed him on his round of the shop, talking excitedly about his coming trip to Stockholm. When at last their bags were full they stood for a minute in the slush outside the store, reluctant to part.

'Come to lunch.'

'I can't old friend. I have an early flight. I must practise. Then I must sleep.'

Povin nodded resignedly. 'Go safely, then.'

Stolyinovich smiled and nodded. Povin stood on the steps and watched him until he was out of sight, carrying the frozen herring which was addressed to the head of the Secret Intelligence Service, London.

Chapter 10

Kyril rolled over very slowly and lay on his side. He could hear footsteps approaching over the stony soil of the roadside waste. Suddenly they stopped, and Kyril raised his head to see a very young man, scarcely more than a boy. He was flushed and breathing heavily: more from nerves than exertion, Kyril guessed. The machine-pistol looked awkward in his hands, and Kyril noted that his captor was unused to firearms.

'You're English,' he said.

The boy jumped at being addressed in his own language. He was standing about four feet away, as if not sure what to do next. His lips were dry and he continually flicked a stray lock of hair out of his eyes. His patent nervousness alarmed Kyril.

'And you're Colonel Bucharensky,' the boy replied. 'Get up. Keep your hands where I can see them, nice and easy.'

If he meant to sound confident he failed. This boy puzzled Kyril greatly. He was hardly twenty and his inexperience showed in everything he did. His obvious lack of control over the situation made the Russian feel faintly ridiculous. He stood up slowly and dusted off his clothes.

'But I was looking for you. The KGB ran me out of Athens…'

'Yes, yes, we know all about that.'

By now it was fully light. If the boy dithered much longer a bus full of schoolchildren would come along, with everyone ooh-ing and aah-ing. The image brought a smile to Kyril's lips.

'Here... put these on.'

Kyril's smile faded. The boy had produced a pair of handcuffs.

'Look, I'm on your side, see? I'm looking for SIS. Don't you understand? I'll come quietly, because I want to.'

'Shut-up. Now listen. Put on the right bracelet and snap it shut.'

Kyril stared at him. This was going wrong.

'*Do it!*'

Kyril hesitated no longer. The gap between them was too great for heroics and he didn't like the way the boy's finger kept tightening and loosening on the trigger. His throat was dry. With every second that passed his options narrowed.

He snapped the bracelet shut.

'Now... get in the other side. Move!'

Keeping a healthy distance between them, the boy covered Kyril while he walked round the front of the van and sat sideways on the passenger seat, leaving the door ajar.

'Put the other cuff through the handle.'

On the inside of the door was a metal grip attached to the frame by two screws. As he fitted the cuff through the narrow gap Kyril cautiously tested the handle's strength. The screws were firm.

'Now put on the other bracelet and close it.'

Kyril tried to swallow and failed. His throat had a dry, wooden feel to it. This couldn't be happening. He had evaded the might of the KGB and now this boy...

'*Get in!*'

This hysterical boy. Kyril swung his legs off the road, ignoring the fiery pain which radiated through his injured knee, and sat in the passenger seat.

'Close the door.'

Kyril obeyed numbly, hearing another chance disappear with the click of the closing lock. Now he was squeezed up against the door, his hands incapacitated. The boy went round to the driver's side, got in, and tucked the machine pistol away between him and the door.

Kyril began to calculate. They could not be more than ten kilometres from the centre of Athens. At this time of day the roads were still quiet: during the time it took for the boy to pick him up and immobilise him not a single car had passed in either direction. Assuming no breakdowns or hold-ups, they should make good speed. He had a quarter of an hour in which to act. Maybe less.

Think.

The boy started the car, reversed in a three-point turn, and started off towards the south. The engine sounded rough but was obviously still a long way from total collapse.

Make friends. No... Rattle him.

'I don't have to tell you that I could kill you now,' he said quietly. The boy's hands tightened on the wheel and he shifted angrily in his seat. The van swerved.

'Shut up.'

Kyril let the silence develop. The gear-lever was a stalk on the steering-column. The floor of the van between him and the driver was flat.

'I don't want to hurt you. You're just a kid. Forget what they told you at Gosport. We don't murder kids.'

The front seat was a single bench. The boy had to sit close to his prisoner. Kyril began to gauge distances, rearranging his body slightly so that he was facing more to the front.

The boy took his left hand off the wheel and let it stray to the gun by his side.

'And if I want you to be silent, I can make you be silent.'

It sounded childish. It wasn't. Kyril knew he had pushed the boy to the limit. He turned still further and stared at the youthful profile. The driver's skin was greasy and pocked with acne; he had nicked himself while shaving and cut off the head of a spot, which still oozed. And suddenly it clicked, the solution to the mystery which had eluded him since he first heard the boy speak. An adventure. Fresh from England, he had read the telex and decided to come out alone, on the off chance. The great game. Kudos, promotion, the love of pretty women… Kyril saw it all, and cursed himself for not realising before. It was so many years since he had had to deal with this phenomenon, he thought it was extinct. The amateur in a world long ago grown professional. The maverick attempting the impossible feat, unaided, when only iron discipline and subjugation of self enabled a man to stay alive at all. And with this poignant recognition there came for Kyril a second of unspeakable sadness.

He was still looking at the boy. By lowering his eyes a fraction he was able to see a long jack-handle thrust under the driver's seat! It was the one thing he had been seeking, the one thing he still lacked: a lever.

'Stop looking at me like that.'

Kyril stole a glance at the road. It was flat and a sturdy-looking hard shoulder gave directly on to unfenced fields. Say 40 kph. A bend coming up…

'It's your day off, today,' said Kyril gently. 'Isn't it?'

As the boy turned to snap at him he swung his legs up, clenched the ankles together and, catapaulting backwards against the door to give himself every last available ounce of force, he pounded his feet into the boy's trunk above the spleen.

The breath went out of the driver's body in a long groan and he slumped over the wheel, his face hidden from view.

The van slowed as the boy's foot came off the accelerator. Kyril shut his eyes and prayed for a soft landing. The van lurched off the road, bumped over stony ground for what seemed a long time and finally stalled. The horn was sounding continuously.

Kyril opened his eyes. He was in one piece. His shoulders ached where they had thudded against the door but that was nothing. His first thought was for the boy. His arms were hanging down on either side of the wheel; Kyril was glad he couldn't see the face. He kicked again at the body, managing to dislodge the head from the horn-button, and it fell to one side.

Kyril raised himself up and cautiously peered out. They had come to rest about 20 metres from the road on rocky, untilled ground. Anybody seeing the van from the road would assume an accident had occurred and come to investigate. He must work fast.

He sat upright and wrenched the door handle. No result. He tried again, throwing the whole weight of his body away from the door, towards the boy. Still no good.

Kyril took a deep breath and exhaled it while counting to ten. Steady pressure, maybe that would do it.

After a couple of minutes he gave up. The muscles of his forearms ached beyond endurance and the metal cuffs were starting to chaffe his skin. A tag of skin had already flaked away from his right wrist, leaving a rough square of red flesh in contact with the metal.

The jack.

Kyril twisted his body round so that he was half lying on the front seat, his feet on the floor beneath the steering-wheel. By scrabbling with his heels he was able to shift the handle a little. Another kick and the handle was out from under the seat.

Kyril paused to get his breath. He must stay calm. Don't look out of the window to see who's coming. Don't waste energy. Concentrate on that handle, nothing else.

Kyril squeezed his feet together, the handle between them, and lifted his legs. At once the handle clashed with the steering wheel and fell. He tried again, straining to see what he was doing. This time he managed to negotiate the handle round the wheel. The sweat was running down his face. His injured leg throbbed with pain and his body had begun to tremble with muscular effort.

Kyril twisted until he was lying on the seat, his knees pulled up to his chest, the jack handle dangling between his clenched heels. To his horror he saw that the handle was slipping. He squeezed his feet more tightly together and commenced the most difficult phase of the whole operation.

The chain connecting the handcuffs was about three inches long, allowing him some play but not much. Somehow, using only his feet and, in the last second, his manacled hands, he had to lodge the shaft of the jack handle between the metal grip and the door to which it was fastened.

Kyril pulled his knees up even further into his chest and spread them slowly while keeping his feet clenched together. The van's roof was low but by twisting his body he could just manoeuvre the handle until it was above his head. A loud gasp was forced from him as the crippling effort began to tell. Let him not get cramp, for the love of Lenin. He stretched up his hands to the very limit of the chain. It was now or never. He would have to flick the handle with his feet and pray that it dropped close enough to his hands for him to catch it as it fell. There would be only one chance. If he fluffed it the handle would drop to the floor, permanently out of reach.

Kyril relaxed his legs slightly, took a deep breath, and jerked violently backwards, separating his heels as he did so. The handle grazed his shoulder, fell to one side, out of reach of his left hand and came to rest in his right.

Kyril closed his eyes and did nothing for a while. Relief had drained him of oxygen, he had trouble breathing. When his body was more or less back to normal he entered on the final stage.

With short, jerky movements he was able to insert his newly acquired lever between the door and the metal grip. By sliding his right hand up the shaft as far as it would go he gained the necessary purchase. The second heave wrenched the handle from its screws, and he was free.

Kyril sat up and looked around. There was some traffic on the road but so far no one had stopped. Kyril turned his attention to the boy. The key to the handcuffs must be somewhere. He searched rapidly and found it in the top pocket of the driver's shirt. Now he had no option but to examine the face.

As he pushed the body aside the boy groaned. He was still alive!

Kyril sat back in amazement. The kick had been meant to kill. Maybe the awkward angle had robbed his effort of some of its efficacy...? He shook his head. Perhaps he had spoken the literal truth. There were more important things to do than murder children.

Kyril shouldered his rucksack and struck out for the road. Someone would rescue the boy before too long. Now the important thing was to hitch a lift.

He had lost valuable time when every second was precious. Somehow he would have to catch up on schedule, only now SIS would have a score to settle and he could no longer hope for an easy ride to England.

He needed time in which to rest and heal, and that in turn meant he needed a secure base. He would somehow have to get to London... and Vera...

For the second time that day Kyril stood on the road to Aharne and lifted his thumb.

Chapter 11

Royston's car swung into the filling-station at the foot of the 20-storey glass and concrete office block which houses the international headquarters of the British Secret Intelligence Service. A ramp led downwards to a steel shutter which rose at his approach. Royston parked neatly and extinguished his lights. He walked to the lift, inserted a thin plastic wafer into a slot, and pressed the 'call' button. After a short wait the doors opened to reveal two hefty young men in shirtsleeves, pistols tightly holstered to their thighs.

They went all the way to the top floor. Once out of the lift it looked like any other big modern office; the clatter of typewriters mingled with the sound of people talking on the phone and the distant clang of filing-cabinets. C's personal assistant was a pot-plant enthusiast, and there was a long-running office scandal about the personnel director's relationship with one of the typists.

Today, however, Royston was not in tune with his surroundings. He never looked forward to his weekly meeting with 'the chief' and this morning his nerves were on edge from lack of sleep. One topic of conversation was going to dominate the discussion: Bucharensky. Royston had problems enough at the moment. Kyril was a subject he would have liked to avoid.

The first thing he noticed was a dead fish lying on a wooden board which took up the place of honour in the middle of C's desk.

As he advanced slowly into the huge room familiar details began to impinge on him: the thick curtains at the windows, threaded with fine-spun lead wire, the lush carpet, the smooth air of affluence which pervaded the place like a perfume. Above C's head was the usual picture of the Queen. And in front of him was the fish. C raised his eyes from it when Royston had almost reached the outer edge of the desk and treated him to a long, appraising look before returning his attention to the platter in front of him. For several moments no one spoke.

'In Russia they have a saying...'

C's voice, addressed to the fish rather than to Royston, was quiet and cold. Royston could not imagine it ever being raised for any purpose whatsoever, a voice devoid of passion, love or anger.

'... "A fish rots from the head".'

C picked up a knife which Royston had not noticed before and delicately prised away the upturned eye of the fish. Royston watched as if hypnotised. With the sharp point of the knife C eased a tiny black spot from the eye and held it aloft. A man standing behind his left shoulder bent down and took the knife from C's hand, the black spot still impaled on its tip, before quickly leaving the room. C raised his eyes to Royston's face.

'The pupil. A microdot.'

C turned his head slightly.

'Take it away.'

Another man standing behind C's right shoulder removed the board and the remains of the fish, leaving Royston alone in the room with C.

'I want to talk to you about that microdot. But not now. Let them decode it. Deal first with the routine material.' Royston spoke from memory. In the next half-hour the two men covered a lot of ground without taking notes or referring to files. At last there came a break in the conversation and C sat back.

'Bucharensky.'

Royston stiffened. 'Anything new?'

'You received the report from Head of Athens Station?'

Royston nodded. He could still recall the sense of crippling unreality which came over him as he took the phone from Sculby's hand and learned of Kyril's defection from Moscow Centre. That was days ago. A lot had happened since then, including Athens.

'What will they do with the boy?'

'We shall pay for his hospitalisation, then get rid of him.'

Royston shook his head. It scared him to think that other such 'heroes' might lurk in the lower echelons of the Service, perhaps in his own Station. Trying to take Bucharensky alone was on a par with inviting a rattlesnake into bed with you.

'The Soviets would still have us believe that he is defecting, but if that is so a pretty mess he is making of it.'

'But if the boy scared him off...'

'Perhaps. Do you think he is coming here?'

Royston made a face. 'I haven't thought about it,' he lied. 'I only know what I've read on the float, a Russian defector wants to make contact with us. But he doesn't have to come to London to do that.'

C sighed. 'I'm sorry about this,' he said. 'But the remainder of this conversation is to be most secret. I'm going to have to ask you to sign a minute in blank.' Seeing

Royston twist uncomfortably in his chair he added, 'If it's any consolation to you, I had to sign just such a minute myself in Number Ten last week. I know how it rankles.'

Royston nodded reluctantly.

'Of course.'

C was about to speak again when the door opened without a preparatory knock. Royston recognised the man who earlier had taken the knife from C's hand. He advanced to the desk and laid a single sheet of paper before C, who scanned it rapidly before once more raising his eyes to Royston's face. He waited until the messenger had left the room, then said: 'You are aware, I think, that some years ago we managed to install a certain source in Moscow Centre?'

Royston knew a moment of utter stillness, a second of silence and light.

'Source Nidus.'

'Correct. Nidus and I have certain common interests, the nature of which I need not trouble you with. As a result a contact was made of a… personal kind. No one else is aware of his true identity. We speak to each other quite outside the usual channels of communication. You follow me?'

Royston nodded.

'The microdot you saw earlier, of which this…' C tapped the sheet of paper, '… is a translation, emanated with Nidus. His message puts beyond doubt certain matters of which I have felt reasonably sure for some time now.'

C sat forward and folded his hands on the desk in front of him.

'Bucharensky is going round all his old haunts. He's on the money-route. He is supposed to be carrying as bait a plan which is tied into world terrorism, including the IRA. In London, where he was once stationed, he formed an attachment with a girl called Vera Bradfield. And he's coming here. He's coming here *soon.*'

C hesitated.

'I have given instructions to Brussels station that if Kyril is indeed on the money-route, and turns up there, they are to leave him strictly alone. It would be a waste of time when he is so obviously coming to London. As head of London Station the principal burden of neutralising Bucharensky therefore now falls on you. I have to tell you – although I regret it greatly – that Bucharensky is, or may be, aware of Nidus's true identity.'

Royston swallowed. The silence unreeled itself like empty tape off a spool. It seemed to him that in a weird kind of way the whole of his life had hitherto been but a preparation, a training, for this moment and what was to follow.

C's cold eyes bored into Royston's own.

'You realise what the Planners will tell me.'

'Oh yes,' Royston replied gloomily. 'If we can't catch him damned quickly we'll have to kill him, won't we. Otherwise we run the risk that the KGB might kidnap him, and then they'll know Nidus, too.'

'You had better make a start with the Bradfield woman. Bucharensky has another lead, however. Somebody called Loshkevoi is apparently...'

Royston looked up sharply.

'Say again?'

'Loshkevoi. The name is familiar to you?'

Royston felt like a traveller who desperately wants to reach some high ground in order to learn where he is.

'It's difficult. I don't want to burden you... We have an operation at the moment involving Loshkevoi.' Royston hesitated, conscious of C's narrow gaze. Both men were well aware that C could not compel Royston to disclose operational details against his will. The 'need to know' convention had long ago become an inflexible rule.

'Five are receiving unofficial assistance...'

C held up his hand and Royston was inwardly relieved; almost by accident he had found the right words to curb the chief's curiosity.

'Tell me only this. Does the operation involve keeping this Loshkevoi under constant saturation surveillance?'

'It does.'

'So that if Bucharensky comes into close proximity with him we may reasonably suppose that we shall know it?'

'Beyond doubt.'

C nodded curtly. 'Good. Because I tell you this, Royston. The KGB have as their number one priority the arrest of Bucharensky. If he should fall into their hands no explanation or apology will be acceptable in the place where I was recently required to sign my own minute in blank.'

C stood up and moved away from his desk, the interview at an end. As Royston went through the door he heard his chief say:

'We are too old to live on social security, you and I.'

Royston's face set hard. It was a true thought. Roubles, perhaps, but not the dole.

Chapter 12

It took Kyril two days to reach Brussels. In western Europe it is easy to cross frontiers undetected and he did not have to show a passport once. On the evening of the second day he lay up in Mont-St-Jean, just below Waterloo, keeping out of sight and catching up on his sleep. His plan looked good, because it was simple. He had learned from his experiences in Athens. Skip the famous 'hidden assets', for a start; the KGB would be watching the banks. Instead take the bus to the centre of Brussels, an anonymous face in the morning rush. A quick walk to the Boulevard du Regent, home of the American Consul-General, where the KGB would not expect to see him but where they would be maintaining their usual skeleton watch. Tram to the Gare du Midi, as if to take the Ostende train, shake any tail at the station, with a fallback along the route at some local stop before heading north to Holland, and Breskens, where Kyril could make his own, very private, arrangements for a passage to England. Speed was the essence of success: once he stepped off the bus in the morning rush hour he would not stop moving until he reached the coast at nightfall. As a kind of insurance policy he had started to grow a beard and altered his hairstyle; the reports flowing back to Centre from Athens would bear little resemblance to his present appearance.

But it did not work out like that.

He stepped off the bus in the Gran' Place, another tourist doing Belgium in the low season, a stranger wrestling to get his bearings in a foreign city. He slowly unshouldered his pack and rummaged for a street-map, his eyes darting hither and thither in search of watchers. There were none, but he did not expect them. The regulars would be monitoring the places they always monitored, every day, without imagination or flair. And on the boulevards, in the squares, along the bustling streets… there would be one irregular killer, the man sent to assassinate Kyril before he could put a finger on the traitor…

He pushed the thought out of his mind. He had to make a move. Innocent tourists did not spend the whole day in the Gran' Place, they saw sights. He folded his map like a man who has made up his mind and moved off in the direction of the Rue Royale.

The killer was not there, not yet. That would come later, in England.

Keep moving. Never present the same profile twice. Hug crowds. Stay away from the edge of the road… Extracts from his training lectures, years old. 'If you are lucky you will hear the very high-pitched song of the bullet, somewhere between a whine and a hum. You must learn to identify it. There is no sensation to equal it. Your life will change…'

Stay with people. No alleys, no side-streets, no short-cuts down deserted passages. Do everything lawfully. No jaywalking, nothing to justify an 'arrest' by someone who might be a genuine policeman but probably was not.

He took it slowly, changing direction every few blocks and varying his pace to suit the flow of pedestrians on either side. After a while he knew he had company.

He frowned. That was bad luck. For the next ten minutes or so he studied the pattern while ostensibly continuing to drift aimlessly along the boulevard. There were two of them; a young girl with a dog and a man in soldier's uniform. They were good at the job but to Kyril's experienced eye it stood out a mile that they had been programmed by KGB instructors. He shrugged. Better them than the British.

Something about the tail pattern told Kyril that they were not sure of his identity, not yet. For a second he agonised, longing to pack it in and break for the coast but knowing it was wrong. Moscow Centre – and Stanov – had to be certain that he had arrived in Brussels.

He was nearing the Boulevard du Regent.

'Pardon me, can I ask you something…?'

The lilting, unmistakably American drawl caused Kyril to look up sharply and see a woman planted squarely in his path, street-plan fluttering in her hand. Mid-West, middle-aged; bespectacled; lost… harmless.

As he prepared a few words of French with which to give her the brush-off he felt a tap on the shoulder and instinctively wheeled round before his conscious mind could stop him. In the same second the 'lost' American tourist clamped herself to his side, suddenly developing a grip of steel; the second agent took up an identical stance on Kyril's right; a car screeched to a halt and all four doors burst open. He had a sudden confused vision of the crankshaft case rushing towards him, his chin jarred on the floor and for a second he passed out. Then a blanket was thrown over his head and he was suffocating. He screamed, but the noise was stifled in the heavy folds of material enveloping his head. He panicked and began to struggle, but strong hands held him down. His heart was pounding in his chest and a terrible roaring filled his ears. The more he struggled the worse it became.

Kyril knew the first seconds of the rough disengagement of death. Then he was pulled upright and the blanket was snatched from his head. He gasped for breath. He could see nothing, his eyes were blurred. His heart-beat began to lessen. Slowly his head cleared. The car was racing along a broad avenue, the sun was shining, the radio was playing pop music. Kyril swayed, grabbed the front seat to steady himself and was sick. Someone exclaimed and opened the window to let out the smell. Another man tossed him the blanket and indicated that he should wipe up the mess.

'Sorry about that, fella,' he said. 'But you were looking kinda lost back there. Guess I'd better introduce myself. Nat McQueen, CIA.' He grinned. 'You made it, buddy.'

For a few moments Kyril covered his confusion by bundling up the pile of vomit in the blanket. He did not speak until he was quite ready.

'Am I glad I found you. The KGB had me staked out back there.'

The man called McQueen laughed. He sounded pleased with himself.

'That soldier guy was so excited when he saw you he almost wet his pants. But you were okay. We'd look after you.'

Kyril inspected his face. The man seemed honest enough. He turned to look at the passenger on the other side of him and recognised the 'tourist'. When she smiled at him he smiled back, and settled down in his seat, feeling the other two relax as he did so. The tension was fast draining out of the situation. He was supposed to be defecting to the West with precious documents, and he had made it…

Inside, however, he was seething. In all their calculations he and Stanov had completely overlooked the CIA. With benefit of hindsight Kyril couldn't understand how they could have made such an incredible mistake. The British worked on a shoe-string, their resources abroad were minimal. What could be more natural than for them to ask the CIA to lend a hand, with their superior technology and limitless manpower? Or perhaps… no, surely not, *surely* the CIA wouldn't decide to take a hand anyway, without consulting SIS? Kyril closed his eyes and tried to see through the countless possible permutations.

But not for long. Escape: that was the important thing. Progress was fast; with every second his chances of making a break diminished. Soon they would be in open country and then he was finished.

Kyril stole a glance out of the window. The car was travelling north-west along the Avenue de la Reine, towards Laeken. Soon they must cross over the Bassin Vergote. There was a chance… but a mortally dangerous one. Kyril quietly ground his teeth.

Make friends. Put them off their guard.

'Where are you taking me, please?'

'One of our airbases. There's a plane coming for you. This time tomorrow you'll be in Washington.'

Kyril allowed a look of anxiety to play over his face.

'You say a plane is coming. Can't we leave at once, please? How long must we wait?'

'Not long. We didn't know where you were going to show up, see? Planes have to be cleared in advance; this is some of the most crowded airspace in the world. Don't worry, fella. We'll take good care of you.'

'Please, you do not understand. My life is in danger. They have orders to kill me.'

'Don't worry.' McQueen's voice was reassuring. 'No one's out to kill you, buddy-boy. They just want your hide back in Moscow. Once we get to where we're going they haven't a chance in hell.'

'Where are we going?'

McQueen smiled but did not reply. By now Kyril was almost fawning on him.

'Please… when we get there, let's stay in the open. Guard me as much as you like, but don't coop me up, eh?'

'Okay, fella. Why'ncha just relax and enjoy the ride?'

Kyril sat back slowly. His lips were dry. They had almost reached the long, low bridge over the neck of the Bassin Vergote. Every agent is taught how to throw himself from a rapidly moving vehicle. No agent ever does it willingly.

There was the bridge.

Kyril shut his eyes and drew a deep breath.

'Are we being followed?'

The driver glanced in his rear-view mirror and shook his head.

Kyril swivelled in his seat and pretended to stare out of the back window.

'That red Fiat… I've seen it before today. The registration's the same.'

McQueen and the woman turned to look. In the same instant Kyril hurled himself at the nearside door and flung it open, pitching forward with all his might. He had a glimpse of the road coming up at an ugly angle, a tremendous shock ran the length of his spine, then he was rolling in the dust, over and over… Through a red haze he made out the steel bridge wall. Somehow he was on his feet, not only upright but running. Confused noises behind him… toot of a barge's siren below… let, oh let there be clear water…

After the shock of the initial icy plunge he seemed to go down and down for ever. He couldn't move. For an eternity of time he hung suspended in a cold, thick, muddy-brown mixture of sewage and oil; then he was rising, very slowly, the sky above lightened, and suddenly his head broke water and he could no longer put off the increasingly painful business of struggling to stay alive.

He heard McQueen shout 'Get him!', and knew he had been spotted. Kyril trod water, desperately looking round for help. His rucksack was weighing him down, his strength was deserting him. He had drifted about 50 metres from the bridge. Opposite him a long line of barges was slowly travelling north on the way to Antwerp; the leading tug's siren was the last sound he had heard before hitting the water. The end barge was almost past him now. Attached to it by a painter was a small dinghy, scarcely big enough to hold a man. Kyril struck out for it.

At first he seemed to make no impression at all on the water. Invisible ropes attached to his pack were pulling him down, down… He began to panic. The last barge was well past him now, and he was still several metres from the dinghy. He thrashed hard and was rewarded with a mouthful of wash from the tug. Choking and spluttering he fought to keep his head above water. Surely he must be moving. No one could struggle as hard as that and not move…

His fingers scraped on something solid. The boat… It was passing him, going away out of his reach. *No!* He scrabbled desperately for a hold, got it… and next second almost let go as the momentum of the convoy picked him up and swept him onwards towards Antwerp, towards the sea.

He dragged himself out of the water with slow, laborious movements, and looked back. A small crowd of people had gathered on the bridge, among them McQueen and the anonymous American woman. They made no move to follow him. It would have been hopeless in any case. Kyril was passing through a Gehenna of bleak, dock badlands, where such few roads as there were ended in cul-de-sacs, crumbling warehouse walls, railway sidings… he turned to face the front and saw no signs aboard the tug that anyone had noticed him.

As the convoy chugged onwards beneath a cold, stony sky Kyril lay down on the bottom of the dinghy and fell into an exhausted sleep.

Chapter 13

From his rocking-chair in the little conservatory beyond the kitchen Povin could see across the Moscow River to the pine-clad slopes of the hills opposite. The sun had gone half an hour ago and it was nearly dark. The general, hovering between wakefulness and sleep, could just hear the strains of the B flat minor sonata quietly played by Stolyinovich.

The music stopped. A moment later the pianist's hand descended on to Povin's shoulder and he opened his eyes.

'That was very nice, Pyotr. Thank you.'

Stolyinovich drew up a chair and sat by Povin's side.

'Thank God for Chopin.'

Povin raised his eyebrows. 'God, Pyotr Ivanovich?' he said, with mild reproof. Stolyinovich was about to protest when Povin held up his forearms, crossed, and spread them with a sudden chopping movement, his lips set in a tight line. Stolyinovich was appalled.

'*Here?*'

Povin nodded and placed a finger on his friend's lips. 'In the office, too,' he whispered gently. 'Things are bad. I'll tell you sometime. Not now.'

Stolyinovich stood up and moved restlessly to the window. Povin's words disturbed him. When generals were under suspicion, who was safe?

'You've done it well,' he said to the glass. 'Champagne, caviar, fresh strawberries even. You must be broke.'

'No. It comes from the club.'

'What! You mean the KGB pays for all this at subsidised rates?'

Povin shrugged. 'Of course. We all do it. Tonight it's my turn. Did you see the oysters?'

Stolyinovich laughed. 'Stepan, I congratulate you on your sagacity and resource. Look, your first guest is coming. Lights on the hill... let's have some music.'

As Stolyinovich went back to the day-room Povin hauled himself out of his rocking-chair and stretched. He knew without seeing it that the car coming up his drive belonged to Michaelov. Nadia was ill, and her husband had promised to look in on Povin's party for a short while on his way home from the office. Michaelov did not know this, but it was Nadia's illness that had prompted Povin to give a party in the first place.

As Povin passed through the day-room Stolyinovich was beginning some Mendelssohn. Povin's driver was doubling up as doorman this evening; the general went across the hall to find him helping Michaelov off with his greatcoat. The two officers greeted each other warmly. As they entered the day-room Povin, to his horror, heard Stolyinovich weave a phrase from the Khovantschina March into the melody of the Albumblatt. But if Michaelov noticed, he said nothing about it. Instead, he offered the pianist the kind of perfunctory bow which their difference in social function and standing required, and Stolyinovich gravely reciprocated.

'Stepan, a quick word...'

Povin ushered his chief through into the little conservatory, closing the glass-panelled door behind them.

'News?'

Michaelov shook his head despondently.

'No. We've missed him, Stepan. I've got Belgium crawling with men, they couldn't have failed to find him if he was still there. Kyril's given us the slip.'

'So it's London,' mused Povin. 'And Sociable Plover…?'

'Not a ripple.'

Povin smiled. 'I'm really beginning to think it never left Stanov's safe.'

'You said that before and I laughed. Now I'm not so sure. But why, Stepan? Why go to all that trouble to fake a theft?'

Povin bit his lip. He seemed on the point of telling Michaelov something, then changed his mind.

'Let me at least offer you some tea.'

They went back through the kitchen and into Povin's dining-room. Two large tables laden with food were set against the far wall, and at the sight of them Michaelov's eyes widened.

'When you said a small party I didn't realise you meant a feast.'

'Look at this.' Povin beckoned to one of the servants, supplied by the KGB along with the food. The man came up smiling, a dark green bottle in his hand. Povin took it from him and passed it to Michaelov.

'See what Pyotr Ivanovich brought me back from France.' Michaelov looked at the marc. He looked at the year. And he sighed.

'Just a little drop in the tea,' murmured Povin. 'What d'you say?'

'In the *tea*!' Michaelov was outraged. Povin saw him hesitate and held his breath. 'A thimbleful in a glass. Just to taste, you understand.'

'Of course. A glass at once for General Michaelov!'

His chief took a cautious sip. 'Magnificent,' he said. 'The best brandy I ever tasted.' He knocked back the tiny glassful of spirit and wiped his moustache with the back of his hand. 'Well,' he said reluctantly, 'I must be getting back to Nadia.'

'Of course. How is she, by the way? I should've asked earlier.'

'On the mend.'

'I think I'll have a glass of this myself, Valery, since you say it's so good. I won't offer you another, I know how it is with your health.'

'I've been feeling much better lately, as a matter of fact.'

'I'm glad to hear that, Valery.'

There was an embarrassed silence. Povin appeared suddenly to realise the consequences of what his chief had said.

'Oh, but then why not have another little glass? For the road. I'll join you.' Povin waved away his chauffeur, who was standing nearby with Michaelov's coat in his hands. 'Sit down, do.'

'Thank you, Stepan. I won't stay long but it does a man good to get out of the house now and then.'

'I've always said so. Pyotr...' Povin leaned over the back of his chair and called through the doorway. 'Play us something cheerful, something jolly.'

'There's this little song they taught me in France, comrade General. But it's blue, does that matter?'

Michaelov slapped his leg. 'The bluer the better!' Stolyinovich launched into an obscene ditty about some

French soldiers who come home on weekend leave and discover that all the girls in their village have signed on at a nunnery. As Michaelov leaned forward, straining to catch the words, Povin used the opportunity to top up his glass unobserved.

'Lights in the drive, comrade General.'

'Thank you. Stay here, Valery, and listen. I've got to see to new arrivals. There's quite a crowd coming tonight, you know most of them. Excuse me...'

On his way to the front door Povin beckoned his driver. 'Tell General Michaelov's chauffeur to go home and come back later,' he said. 'Much later.'

–

By midnight Povin had reduced Michaelov to the precise state of intoxication he intended. It was no easy task. A slight miscalculation and his chief would either have fallen asleep or, worse, had another seizure and been carted off to the nearest hospital.

He had deliberately invited a lot of people to this party, most of them drawn from Moscow's artistic sub-culture. By the time he lent Michaelov his shoulder in order to help him into the conservatory the mood of the evening was maudlin. Stolyinovich, who for some reason was now minus his shirt, poured out love songs in a tear-laden baritone to an admiring audience, mostly women, one of whom was sobbing her heart out. Three quarters of the food had disappeared and the champagne had given out in favour of neat vodka. Only with great effort had Povin managed to keep Michaelov on brandy.

He closed the door and slipped the lock before turning round to find Michaelov already slumped in the rocking-chair, his eyes closed. Povin took the brandy bottle from his chief's fingers and swilled down a large tot. He was sweating profusely.

'Listen, Valery...'

'Wassup. Wassermatter?'

Michaelov's head tilted backwards and he began to rock to and fro, a look of astonished delight on his face. ''S moving, Stepan, y'room's moving. Dja know?'

'Are you feeling all right?' Oh Christ, Povin was thinking, don't let him pass out on me, not yet. 'Valery, old friend, I have to tell you something. I should've told you earlier, I nearly did, only I lost my nerve. Kazin...'

'Warrer 'bout him?'

'He was here. This afternoon.'

Michaelov stopped rocking. Povin watched anxiously as the first stages of cerebral activity manifested themselves on his coarse features.

'Wha'... why?'

'To see if I knew what was going on. What Stanov is up to. And he wants to get his hands on a copy of Bucharensky's diary.'

Michaelov raised his hands to his temples. 'What 'ja tellim?'

'I said that the diary was impossible, out of the question, and as for anything else I had to ask you. He won't talk to you directly because he knows Stanov is having you watched.'

'*What!*'

'Valery, we're in deep trouble, you and I.' Povin squeezed his hands together and went to kneel by Michaelov's side. His chief's face was flushed with drink but his eyes were no longer vacant. He looked like a survivor again.

'Kazin says Stanov is on the way out… well, we always knew that. But he's plotting something and using Bucharensky to see it through.'

Michaelov's eyes widened in sudden comprehension.

'Sociable Plover… it always was a fake, just like you said.'

'But not in the way I originally thought. At first I couldn't believe that Stanov was such a fool as to compile the plan. But he did. It exists. It's the theft that's a fake.'

Michaelov was rocking to and fro, his head still in his hands.

'And this traitor, the British source in the KGB the diary talks of…'

'It's *our* source in London that Kyril knows. He's carrying *Royston's* name. And he's going to use it to buy Stanov a place in the sun!'

Michaelov staggered up from the chair and started to blunder about the room, hands still clapped to his forehead.

'Fools,' he cried. 'Why didn't we see it?'

'Ssh, *please*, Valery. It's only a theory. But we have *got* to act. Do you realise what the loss of Royston would mean to us. *Do you?*'

Michaelov stopped in mid-stride and turned very slowly to face his deputy.

'What?'

Povin chose his next words with care, infusing them with every ounce of sincerity he could command.

'For us, it would finish England for the next ten years.'

There was a pause. The sentence seemed to percolate very slowly into Michaelov's deeper consciousness. When at last he was quite satisfied he understood his deputy he raised his head and stared into Povin's eyes.

'An executioner. We must liquidate Bucharensky before he can do any more damage. An executioner, it's the only way...'

Povin gnawed his lip. 'It's a hell of a risk.'

'Yes, but... hey, wait a minute.' Michaelov's mind was by now functioning almost normally. 'This is all rumour. Why can't Kazin come out with it in the open? Why talk to you?' His voice had a sudden edge of suspicion in it. 'Why not come to see me? I'm the First Deputy Chairman of the KGB.'

'I've explained all that. Kazin's anxious not to endanger you by being seen in your company. We all know what Stanov thinks about Kazin, and if he thought you were associated with him in any way...'

'But what proof do we have? Kazin is asking us to disobey a Chairman's personal order and he won't even put it in writing...'

'He gave me... this.' Povin slowly held up a key. Michaelov squinted at it. 'What's that?'

'An earnest of the Politburo's good faith. It's a key to Stanov's blue safe.'

Michaelov's eyes bulged. 'You're kidding! That's impossible. Not even the First Secretary of the Party has the right to ask Stanov to open the blue safe.'

'Who said anyone had asked?'

Michaelov seemed about to retort, then fell silent. He was overwhelmed.

'Kazin says that inside the safe we'll find Sociable Plover. He's seen it. He's seen it *since* Kyril defected.'

Some of the colour drained out of Michaelov's face.

'It'll mean trouble if we're caught.'

'I know. In effect we'd have to burgle the Chairman's office. But Valery... think what it would mean if Kazin is on the level. We know that there is only one copy of Sociable Plover! According to Stanov – the only person officially in a position to know – Bucharensky has taken it. If it really is in the blue safe, all the time…'

Two murderous sparks burned at the back of Michaelov's eyes.

'Then we'll know Kazin's telling the truth… and if he's telling the truth, Stanov is himself… a…'

'We've been on the wrong track with Bucharensky, all along. He's just a pawn. He doesn't know anything, Stanov lied to him, told him any old thing… The famous diary. A fake. Stanov's doing. He told Bucharensky what to write.'

'But why?'

'To divert suspicion from where it belongs – with him!' There was silence while the two generals sombrely contemplated the significance of Povin's revelation.

'You work late at night, Valery, everyone knows it. You won't cause any suspicion. Take a look one weekend, when it's quiet. And if it's there…'

'Kyril's a dead man.'

Povin played his last card.

'Perhaps we should wait, Valery. Maybe we ought to try to take Kyril alive, like Stanov says…'

'And risk blowing the whole KGB operation in England sky-high! Are you out of your mind?'

'But there's no proof…'

Michaelov's face set into a mask of angry malice. He knocked aside Povin's hand and stomped out to the kitchen. 'Proof! No time like the present… Where's my car?' Provin signalled through the doorway and his chauffeur nodded.

'It's coming, Valery. Can you manage alone? You've got the key?'

He helped his chief on with his coat. From the dayroom he could hear the strains of a lugubrious cossack song with Stolyinovich leading a ragged chorus. 'Go safely,' he murmured.

As if struck by this farewell Michaelov paused in midstride and turned to face Povin, who was surprised to see how serious his chief's face had suddenly become.

'And you Stepan... you go safely also. This Kazin...' He seemed to falter over his next words.

'...He's dangerous. A killer. He'd slit your throat, or mine, with his own hands and never think twice. Watch your back.'

Michaelov was many bad things but no coward. Povin looked uneasily away, and it was not until the First Deputy Chairman of the KGB was seated in the back of his official car that he began to relax.

This slight chill apart, he reckoned he had judged it perfectly. Michaelov was now sufficiently sober to run rings round the night watch at Dzerzhinsky Square while at the same time operating in the grip of a manic obsession. Povin stood on the steps and watched his car wind down the hill towards the river, and the road to Moscow, until the tail-lights were lost from view.

Back in the day-room the party was all but over. Most of the guests were asleep. Seeing Povin in the doorway, Stolyinovich stood up abruptly, leaving the music in the middle of a bar, and came over to him. A woman protested before consoling herself with a swig of vodka from the bottle in her hand.

'It's hot in here,' murmured Povin, loosening his collar. The room was oppressive with smoke and the heat of many human bodies. 'Let's go for a walk. Bring that...'

He indicated an unopened bottle of petrovka standing on a nearby table. Stolyinovich obeyed, laughing. Outside in the hall they pulled on their boots and Stolyinovich donned his outrageous heavy mink coat, the gift of a besotted admirer high up in the Kremlin. The pianist stuffed Povin's bottle of petrovka in one of its huge pockets and a bottle of brandy for himself in the other, and the two men set off.

Stolyinovich was hard-pressed to keep up with Povin, who strode vigorously up the hill behind the dacha as if he was on a route-march. Before long Stolyinovich found himself well away from the beaten track, almost up to his knees in snow, with Povin so far ahead that he was scarcely visible in the white moonlight. 'Stepan,' he panted. 'For God's sake…'

At the sound of his voice Povin stopped and waited for his companion to catch up. Stolyinovich found him resting with his back against a tree, hands held to his eyes. He reached out to touch him but Povin sensed the movement and shied away.

'No,' he cried hoarsely, and Stolyinovich checked himself. Were they tears that he heard rattle in Povin's throat? Surely not.

'Stepan,' he said cautiously. There was no reply. 'Stepan, what's the matter?'

Povin turned to face the tree, resting his head on his arms crossed against the bark, and Stolyinovich heard him take half a dozen slow, deep breaths. The pianist was by now thoroughly alarmed. He looked around. He had no idea where they were or what the time was. Povin was acting entirely out of character. This could take some explaining if they were found.

'I… I'm all right now.'

'Stepan, what is it?'

Stolyinovich could not keep the fear out of his voice. If Povin cracked now... he forced the thought quickly out of his mind. What could have happened to reduce him to this miserable state?

Povin raised his head and moved away from the tree.

'Vodka.'

Silently Stolyinovich handed him the petrovka bottle, and Povin drank. When next he spoke his voice was firmer.

'You remember what I told you earlier... Things are none too easy just now.'

'What... tell me?'

There was a long silence while Povin wrestled with the temptation to make a clean breast of everything to his friend.

'Remember always, Pyotr, that what you don't know you can't tell them. I don't feel I'm trusted any more, that's all. And I... well, I've been used.'

'Used?'

'Stanov used me to pass on a... a certain message, last week. As if I were a dirty *schpick* learning the ropes in some Godforsaken embassy in the Third World. He did it to see how I reacted.

'To see if I was loyal,' he added, under his breath.

Stolyinovich chuckled and Povin gave him a hurt look. 'You think that's funny.'

'I'm sorry. It's just that I and, well, you know, the people I talk to... we assume that kind of thing happens all the time in your job.'

There was silence while Povin thought about that. 'Yes. It's true. In a way. Oh Pyotr...' Povin suddenly came close to Stolyinovich and laid his hands on the pianist's coat. '...Pyotr, am I going mad, do you think?'

This time Stolyinovich laughed out loud. He was beginning to feel reassured. To him the question was itself a proof of sanity.

'Sometimes I wonder if I am,' Povin went on. 'I look around me at what goes on, at the people who give the orders and the others who carry them out and I ask myself, what am I *doing* here?'

'But Stepan, we've been through all this before.' Stolyinovich's voice was gentle. 'You know that God places some of us in a position where we can only do good by stealth. It's His will for us. He knows what it costs.'

'Does he? Is there not to be an accounting, Pyotr Ivanovich? And when it comes, what am I to say?'

Povin moved away from his friend and spread his arms in a hapless gesture of appeal.

'How many Jews have I... *I*, Pyotr Ivanovich... exiled to starve? Look out there!' Povin flung his arms wide. 'What do you see?'

Stolyinovich hesitated. 'I see... darkness. The forest...'

'And I see barbed wire. Hundreds and hundreds of miles of it. Watch-towers. Dogs. Kalashnikov machine-guns. *Camps*, Pyotr. How many godly souls rot on the archipelago tonight because of me?'

Again that strange wet rattle in Povin's throat.

'Stepan, *Stepan*.' Stolyinovich shook Povin roughly, his former fears returning. 'For the love of Christ! Pull yourself together. You're over-reacting. You forget yourself.' He glanced uneasily about him. 'Even here... you forget yourself, who you are.'

Povin's head lolled forward on to his chest and for several moments there was silence.

'I am sorry, Pyotr. You should not have had to put up with that.'

Povin's voice was calm, unnaturally so. Once more the lid was on and screwed down tight. Stolyinovich felt awkward.

'No, it's good to let loose once in a while. I'm sorry, Stepan, I should have listened, I...'

Povin dusted some snow off his friend's coat.

'It's nothing. Let's go back.'

He moved away; then, sensing Stolyinovich's reluctance to leave it there, he stopped.

'Don't worry, Pyotr. I really am all right.' He paused. When he spoke again his voice was sad, almost reproachful. 'You're not in any danger. You never were.'

Hearing these words Stolyinovich looked away, ashamed. They went down the hill more slowly than they had come up, Povin seemingly reluctant to go home. When they were in sight of the house, almost at the boundary fence, Povin stopped.

'Do you ever wonder...?'

'Eh?' Stolyinovich's thoughts were far away and he was confused by this unexpected arrest of their steady progress down the hill.

'Do you ever ask... how far you would... how far you *could* go... to save yourself? Do you?'

Stolyinovich, failing to plumb the depths of this question, said nothing.

'Would you kill, Pyotr?'

'I don't know, Stepan.'

'But... *could* you?'

There was a long silence.

'Yes. I believe so. If it meant... no pain.'

For a while this seemed to content Povin, for he said nothing. But he had not quite finished with Stolyinovich. 'Do you ever feel that… we could do more?'

'More?'

'For the things we believe in.'

Stolyinovich fought to stifle his impatience. Although, like Povin, he was a Christian he was content to accept his lot in life without questioning overmuch. God had done well by him. He showed his thanks by rising early and practising for eight hours a day to perfect his divine gift. He was very tired, and the events of the last half-hour had drained him of resilience.

'Stepan, we've been through that before. Remember how it goes? "God has plans for you, plans for good and not for evil"? You do His will in your daily life as far as you can. Sometimes I help you, I'm your secret messenger, and that's my part. We get by.'

'I wonder… You don't know what I've had to contend with over the years, Pyotr. No one does. And sometimes I think to myself: you'd suffer less if just once in your life you came off the fence and did the whole of what you believed in…'

'You'd suffer for less time,' agreed Stolyinovich wearily. 'They'd take you down to the Lubianka cellars and shoot you within the week.'

Povin shook his head and remained silent. But as he turned in at the gate of his house some troubled instinct warned Stolyinovich that the general was taking the first steps towards conscience, towards choice, an instinct so strong, and with consequences so terrible, that the pianist was seized with a sudden irresistible urge to reach out and stop him.

Chapter 14

Sculby pulled on to the forecourt of Loshkevoi's garage and switched off the engine. He had been expecting to find at least the pumps still open, it was only eight o'clock, but everywhere was shut up and deserted.

'We can't figure it out,' Royston had said to him earlier that day. 'Chummy seems to have gone to pieces.'

He's not the only one, thought Sculby. The Sanson inquest was in a mess, he had an intolerable backlog of paperwork and to cap it all he had spent the day arguing at Marylebone County Court in an unsuccessful attempt to save a client from being committed to prison for contempt of court. Royston was the last straw. His face was drawn and there were dark rings under his eyes. Sculby thought he looked tired and ill. So when Royston told him that Loshkevoi had gone to pieces, Sculby thought that that made three of them.

'He shuts up the garage at five or six and goes on the bottle. But that's not all. He keeps futzing up to this road in Clapham and hanging around, as if he's supposed to be meeting someone, then loses his nerve and goes home again. We've got a pretty good idea who it is, too. Woman name of Bradfield, Vera Bradfield.'

'Who's she?' inquired Sculby.

'Never mind. But we're interested in that, Laurie. *Very* interested. Go and see him. Try to find out what's going on, will you.'

Sculby rifled through his 'In' tray. 'You might be in luck, at that. I seem to remember the depositions coming in a while back... oh yes, here we are. Regina v. Victor Gregory Loshkevoi. I suppose I could always make an appointment to go and see him.'

'You do that.'

Royston stood up and Sculby walked with him to the door. 'You look all in,' he remarked cheerfully, and Royston made a face.

'I've not been sleeping too well.'

'Early night, then.'

'Fat chance. It's my wedding anniversary today.'

'Congratulations.'

Royston grunted. 'She's expecting to be taken out to dinner. That's thirty quid down the drain for a start. Then there's the taxi...'

Sculby grinned. 'Think of all the years you've been coming here for a "divorce", Michael. Just say the word and I'll make it for real.'

But now, sitting in his car on Loshkevoi's forecourt, he didn't feel like laughing. It was bitterly cold, and he pulled up the collar of his overcoat even for the short walk from the car to the entrance to Loshkevoi's flat. He pushed the bell-button and waited for the whine of the entry-phone. Nothing happened. Sculby began to feel uneasy. Loshkevoi had sounded strange on the telephone when he had rung earlier to make the appointment; as if he'd been drinking, perhaps. Sculby tried again. This time the buzzer sounded and the latch of the door clicked back. Loshkevoi obviously didn't care to find out who was calling.

Inside the door some narrow stairs led straight up to the first floor. Sculby found himself in one of the most depressing living-rooms he had ever seen. The only lighting was provided by a single table-lamp half obscured by a dark brown shade. The predominant colour of the wallpaper and the furnishings was deep, dark red; the materials struck the eye as heavy and substantial.

'Hi, Laurie.'

Loshkevoi was lying across the sofa, apparently watching a portable television. Sculby looked again and saw that the picture was of the forecourt where he had stood a moment ago. It seemed a lot of expensive trouble to go to over a tiny flat in one of the poorer quarters of London.

Loshkevoi was holding a remote-control unit; he flicked a switch and the picture dissolved into darkness.

'That's neat.'

'Thank you. I like gadgets… mechanical things. You wanna drink?'

Sculby examined his client carefully. It was impossible to say how much Loshkevoi had drunk before his arrival, but the lawyer sensed that it was a good deal. The effects showed only in the slow, ponderous movements of Loshkevoi's body, and speech that was faintly slurred. To Sculby, it was rather like encountering the real Loshkevoi in a dream: everything was fuzzy at the edges.

'Thanks. Gin.'

'Help yourself. Over there…'

A large, heavy mahogony table carried a wide selection of bottles. Sculby poured himself a drink and looked in vain for tonic.

'Don't you have any mixers?'

'Never touch the stuff. Water in the tap if you want.'

Loshkevoi gestured vaguely in the direction of a door and Sculby went through to find himself in the kitchen. There everything was at sixes and sevens. Loshkevoi couldn't have washed up anything for at least a week. Sculby negotiated his glass round a pile of dirty dishes in the sink and added some water to the neat spirit, trying to avert his eyes from the globules of cold fat floating on the surface of the nearest plate.

'At least we know what the police are going to say now,' he called. 'It doesn't add up to much. I reckon we're going to win this one without too much trouble, Victor.'

Loshkevoi seemed not to be paying attention. Sculby went back into the living-room and poured a couple of drops of Angostura into his glass. He looked around for a chair. There was only one, opposite the sofa, and he flopped down into it. A spring had broken, allowing him to sink down further than he expected, and causing him to spill his drink.

'I've got the depositions here. We can go through them if you like.'

Loshkevoi waved a hand. 'Later. Cheers.'

They drank.

'Would you mind passing me the bottle, Laurie. Vodka.'

Sculby obliged. Loshkevoi poured himself a generous treble and then appeared to forget about it.

'These charges,' he said. 'A joke. A fraud. What's that expression? To do with cards...' He rubbed a hand across his face. 'Trumped up.'

'Could be. It's pretty flimsy stuff. It's there, but only just. But why would anybody do that to you?'

Loshkevoi rested his glass on the floor and sat up, placing his head in his hands and his elbows on his knees. Sculby heard him sigh.

'Oh… all kinds of reasons. You get to make enemies. There's a lot of trouble I could make for a lot of high-up people in this city, you know?'

Sculby sipped his drink and said nothing. It was a sentiment which most of his clients expressed at one time or another, but if Royston was involved it just might be true.

'Sometimes I think I'd trade it all for a little peace and quiet. You know what I mean? Another name.' Loshkevoi paused and sighed again. 'Somewhere warm, where it don't rain too often. A little money as well, maybe.'

Sculby raised his eyebrows. 'You'd have trouble finding a buyer if that's your price.'

'No.' Loshkevoi seemed to talk to himself rather than to Sculby. 'There's plenty of people in this country who'd pay my price, Laurie. Aach…'

He stood up, putting out a hand to steady himself on the arm of a chair.

'Life used to be simple. Y'know? Uncomplicated. There can only ever be one boss, Laurie. S'right, isn't it? One boss…'

Sculby shifted uneasily in his seat.

'Forget it. Just forget I said anything, will you?'

Loshkevoi was standing by the window. Sculby saw him pull the edge of the curtain aside a fraction and peer out.

'I tell you want I need… I need a woman.' He giggled. 'I fancy a night out. Coming, Laurie? It's on me. There's a massage joint round the corner. Anything you want. Hand job. French. Even a screw. Nice girls, they are. Cheap.'

He was swaying slightly, his back still turned to Sculby.

'…Or maybe we could go and see Vera… sweet little, pretty little Vera B.'

Sculby stood up, not quite sure whether he had heard correctly. 'Who?'

'Vera, Vera, Vera B.'

Then Loshkevoi did the most extraordinary thing. With slow, elephantine movements he knelt down in front of the window, as if about to pray: first one leg, then the other. Having done that he paused, as if not sure what to do next. Sculby moved forward uncertainly.

'Victor…?'

As if in response to some unspoken command reflected in Sculby's voice, Loshkevoi keeled over to the left and began to snore.

At first Sculby was so taken aback that he couldn't do anything. When he recovered from his initial surprise he went over to where Loshkevoi was lying and arranged him more comfortably, placing a cushion from the sofa under his head and loosening his collar. Then he stood up, wondering what to do next. He realised that there was nothing he could do.

He took his glass out to the kitchen and left it on the dresser. Then he let himself out quickly, pausing for a second at the top of the stairs for a last look at this curious room the colour of blood, before descending to the forecourt and getting into his car.

French, Loshkevoi had said. Even a screw. Maybe Judy would be free tonight…

Sculby drove away in search of a phone-box.

Chapter 15

Stanov stood in his favoured position by the tall windows, looking out over the square. From the other side of the room Colonel Yevchenko watched him curiously. For once the chief was unsure. Yevchenko could tell from the way he twisted his steel-rimmed spectacles this way and that, unconscious of what he was doing.

The office was hermetically sealed against the outside world. Somewhere in the same building men monitored transmissions, typed reports, kept the machinery grinding away. They might have been on another planet. In the office of the Chairman of the KGB no word had been spoken for twenty minutes.

'Where is he? Where *is* he?'

Yevchenko kept silence. Stanov had asked the same question with a variety of emphases many times that day. Kyril had been kidnapped by SIS in Athens and given them the slip, so much was certain. Stanov's contacts in the KYP, the Greek Intelligence Service, could help no further. After that the veil came down until Bucharensky showed up in Belgium.

'If he ever got out of Brussels, where the hell did he go?'

Stanov continued to stare out into the darkness while Yevchenko pulled a heavy, cork-covered flask from his inside pocket and poured two generous tots of vodka. The heating was turned low in the evenings now; one of many spending-cuts ordered by the Politburo. He tossed down his drink and poured another.

'Vodka.'

Stanov turned away from the window and absent-mindedly collected his drink. After a moment's indecision he wandered across to The Chair and sat down so that he could face Yevchenko over the desk.

'It's going wrong, Nikolai,' he said abruptly. 'None of our people put a foot wrong over Athens. The Eighth Department's completely in the clear. I was watching every move they made. It's the same with Brussels. The Fifth Department's clean, too. The traitor *has* to be elsewhere.'

Yevchenko shrugged. He had had enough of this. He wanted to go home.

'One thing is sure, old man. There is nothing you… any of us… can do.'

Stanov nodded glumly. 'I agree. But things are very tight now. Today…'

He compressed his lips and for a while said no more. Yevchenko knew that the Politburo had met that morning. For Stanov life was becoming progressively more tense.

'They took some convincing over Sociable Plover. At first they flatly refused to believe it ever existed, but I had to tell them it did, of course. Then they wouldn't accept that Bucharensky hadn't got it with him – or at the very least, a copy. I had to show them the original – I ask you, Nikolai, a blue file leaving this office! – and explain about the paper, how it shows up if it's so much as touched by human skin, but even then they weren't really convinced. Kazin said…'

Stanov tailed off, got a grip on himself again.

'...That man is a trial to me, Nikolai.'

Yevchenko grunted but said nothing. Stanov mused, his sunken eyes glittering dully in the poor light. Since the day of his stroke the illness was fast increasing its hold on him.

Privately Yevchenko doubted whether he would ever see July 1st, and for the hundredth time reminded himself that if he did not make plans soon it would be too late.

'Suppose, Nikolai... Stanov's voice rose barely above a whisper. Yevchenko had to strain to hear the words that followed. 'Suppose we find this... this one we are looking for.' He looked up slowly. 'What should we do with him?'

'Kill him. Torture him until we're sure he's told us all he knows, then...'

Yevchenko drew his finger across his throat. Stanov nodded slowly, like a man who wants to convince himself.

'Perhaps. But suppose we could persuade him to work for us again, just for a little while, eh, Nikolai? Perhaps he has a wife, a child?'

'Turn him, you mean. A dangerous game, that.'

'Dangerous... But deadly, if properly used. Does it not appeal to you, the thought that we might be able to undo some of what this traitor has done? Think of the store of trust he has built up over the years.'

But Yevchenko was still doubtful. He signified as much by raising from his seat and saying, 'Time to go. Tomorrow I'll tell you what I think. Now, we go home.'

Stanov placed his hands on the desk-top and used them to lever himself painfully upright.

'Sometimes Nikolai, I even wonder if you weren't right about Bucharensky. If I'd told him a little more of the truth...'

Yevchenko shrugged with obvious annoyance.

'It seemed so pointless, that's all. I thought you were being devious for the sake of it. We both know that Loshkevoi isn't the answer. The traitor won't have revealed himself to a slug like that. If Kyril ever does manage to interrogate him, he'll be wasting his time.'

'But I had to give him a goal, Nikolai. Something for Bucharensky to work towards, take his mind off the knowledge that he was really only a moving target, put up for the sole purpose of drawing fire. Surely you can see that? And you're wrong about Loshkevoi. Have you seen his latest report?'

Stanov began to rummage about on his desk. Suddenly his hand fell on what he was looking for and he held it up to the light, eyes squinting.

'It's crap. Loshkevoi's gone adrift. Why, he was drunk when he wrote this, he had to be. He knows something. I feel it in my bones. He may not know it all, but *something...*'

'You could be right.'

Yevchenko hated dithering. He wanted to go home to his warm appartment and have dinner, preceded by a drink, several drinks. His flask was empty.

'What's happening in A2?'

Yevchenko ground his teeth.

'Every one of our executioners was still accounted for as of five o'clock this evening. Nothing suspicious. If "*Lisa*" means to send somebody after Bucharensky...'

'If!'

To Yevchenko's horror Stanov sat down again.

'Put yourself in *Lisa*'s position. What facts does he know?'

Yevchenko said nothing.

'First. Because of the diary it is possible that Kyril knows, or may know, his true indentity. Second. He knows that I have issued a personal order; return Kyril to me alive. Third. He knows that down in the cellars here they can be very persuasive. If Kyril is caught the traitor must reckon that he will talk. So, Nikolai… knowing all these facts, what would *you* do, eh?'

'Then why hasn't he done it already?'

Stanov lowered his eyes.

'I don't know,' he said after a pause. 'Perhaps because he's clever. Perhaps… because like us he doesn't yet know where Kyril is going to end up.'

He rose, and Yevchenko helped him on with his overcoat, now several sizes too large for him. As the Colonel stepped aside for his chief to pass through the double-doors he heard the old man mutter:

'But where is he? *Where?*'

Chapter 16

One o'clock in the morning. Sculby floated on the surface of sleep, half-conscious of the wind that drove down the street outside while scattered images from the day competed for attention behind his sore eyelids. He was distantly aware of being cold; that same night Judy had broken off relations for the third time, calling him (among other things) a self-opinionated pseudo-Marxist, and the wind's sough made the lawyer doubly conscious of the empty space by his side.

He tugged the crumpled duvet over his shoulders, tried yet another position and pretended that he was at the beginning of a dreamless night's sleep.

The undersheet was saturated with sweat from his naked body. He threw himself across to the other side of the bed and in desperation began deep-breathing exercises… one, two, three, in, one, two, three, four, five, out; one, two, three…

He started to go under. Judy was waiting for him, long blonde hair unleashed from its tight bun to cascade around her waist. She was so real that Sculby could see the little scar which fascinated him, a thin, blue line on the slant across her left breast… she turned her back to him and bent forward slowly, soft buttocks parting. Now she was on her knees. With one hand she reached back to caress the long strands of hair away from her supple back and over her neck.

Sculby moved in his sleep and awoke, sharp pain in his bladder causing him to lose the erection at once. He stumbled, cursing, to the bathroom. Everything in his familiar flat had suddenly grown a point or a sharp edge.

As he slumped back on the bed he fought to stifle his thoughts, but it was no good. That afternoon he had been wrestling with a point of Social Security law. Sculby was one of the very few people who knew anything about it, though that wasn't saying much. The client had been denied a benefit to which she was entitled but there was a time limit for an appeal, he couldn't remember how long. Sections, subsections and paragraphs floated before his tired eyes. He felt sick, nauseous with lack of sleep. The answer to his problem was there, in the regulations… it had to be there…

Time passed. Slowly, very slowly, Sculby's hyperactive brain released its hold and he sank into a proper sleep.

The telephone rang five times before he could bring his jolting heart back under control. As he lifted the receiver his imagination supplied the illusory clicks and hums which signalled that in the telephone-tapping centre at Ebury Bridge Road tape-recorders had automatically switched on, activating the voice analysers which would determine whether the caller was known to MI5 or the Special Branch. Until lately he had resignedly tolerated surveillance as part of the price he had to pay for his cover as a standard-bearer for the Left. But recently he was becoming increasingly resentful of the all-seeing, all-hearing eyes and ears of The State. Sculby struggled upright in bed and strove to concentrate. 'Laurie… you know who this is, don't you?'

Sculby was about to acknowledge his awareness of Royston's identity when the latter said, 'Don't bother to confirm. Don't say anything. Just listen. I have to see you within the hour. Drive to Shepherd's Bush tube station. Park under the bridge leading to the shopping-centre and wait.'

'Hang on… Where will you be? For God's sake…' But the line was dead.

Sculby replaced the receiver and swung his legs off the bed, annoyed and vaguely ill at ease. Royston had hardly ever contacted him at home before in all the years of their association. Now this call came out of the blue in the middle of a winter's night… Sculby checked the time. Two a.m.

Afterwards he found it odd that he had never thought to deny Royston's request, roll over and go back to sleep.

Royston was waiting for him in the shadows of the footbridge over the road. As he saw the white Ford Mexico with its distinctive broad red stripe he stepped to the edge of the pavement and waved. Sculby squelched to a halt, and for a second Royston listened, hearing only the rain and the scrape of the car's noisy wipers across the windscreen. There was no tail. All was well.

'Do me a favour, Michael,' said Sculby as he got in. 'Take this and give it a wipe.'

Royston accepted the duster and removed the accumulated condensation from the inside of the windows.

'Which way, squire?'

'The Goldhawk Road. Make for the M4: plenty of traffic going the same way, even at this time of night, and keep to thirty. At least you weren't followed.'

Sculby's vague feeling of uneasiness increased. Something about Royston's clipped instructions conveyed urgency and more than that… a kind of warning.

'Followed? Why on earth should I be?'

Royston did not reply at once. When he spoke again it was with a question of his own.

'How long have we known each other, Laurie?'

'Six years.'

For the next mile or so there was silence in the car while the two men recalled their memories of that time.

'Somewhere in England,' Sculby's tutor had written, 'a tailor is even now perfecting a three-piece suit in clerical grey which will fit this young man to a "T". All you have to do is wait outside the shop until he's ready to buy it – which will be soon.'

Royston had believed it, then. From the very first moment he met Sculby he disliked him, but he never doubted that he would be good at the job. The tutor was right: Sculby was ready for conversion to High Toryism and faith in the Establishment. What Royston had failed to bargain for was Sculby's delighted attachment to his chosen cover as a leftwinger. It was, as the lawyer never hesitated to point out, the perfect logical choice: a simple extension of his wayward youth lived in a world where no one really believed that the leopard changed its spots. But when his 'cover' began to take the form of moving against the Special Branch, stirring up feeling against the police, that kind of thing, Royston's assessment abruptly changed. It irked a man who had fought his way up the post-Philby ladder the hard way, to see this arrogant coxcomb having it all so easy at the expense of the sovereign state. His dislike of Sculby deepened in direct proportion to the lawyer's increasing store of experience and consequent usefulness.

Sculby, on the other hand, admired and quite liked Royston. The role of secret agent appealed to him more than to most people; that was his nature. Whenever he passed on to Royston some piece of information which a client had confided in him, it never failed to send a delicious thrill down Sculby's spine. For him, the rules of conduct and etiquette imposed by his profession did not begin to compete with the well-being and future safety of his country. And it was Royston who had shown him how best he could serve, Royston his control, mentor, perhaps even friend. Certainly they were on the best of terms. If only he wouldn't insist on being quite so smug about his lower-middle class upbringing, it wasn't as if we were all still living in the sixties…

'I ask,' said Royston, 'because I'm afraid I've unwittingly got you into something, Laurie. Something messy. And we've never done that with you before. So you see, we've got to find out how to play it from now on.'

In the silence which followed, Sculby was uncomfortably aware of his heart beating faster than usual.

'Messy…'

He tried to make it sound neutral but the little stab of fear must have showed in his voice, for at once Royston said by way of confirmation, 'Dangerous, yes.'

Sculby concentrated on making a left turn. Only when he had completed the manoeuvre successfully did he say, 'You mean… professionally? It could affect my career?'

'It could affect your life. Danger of death.'

Sculby was startled into a new awareness of his surroundings. He suddenly realised that he was exceeding the speed limit and applied the brakes, using too much pressure. Royston swore.

'Careful. I don't want us attracting any attention. Nice and easy, now.'

'Sorry.'

They had reached the start of the M4. At a sign from Royston Sculby took the inner carriageway.

'Keep your speed down to a steady fifty.'

It had stopped raining. Sculby switched off the wipers.

'While you drive I'm going to tell you where we're at, Laurie. But before I do I've got to say this. I can't force you to do anything against your will. Equally, I can't promise you anything fancy if you decide to stay in the game. So what we've really got to decide tonight, you and I, is whether you're the same man who joined up with me six years ago, or whether things are different now. D'you follow?'

Sculby's mouth was dry. He opened his mouth to say 'Yes', but only a squeak came out and he had to clear his throat quickly, hoping that Royston hadn't noticed.

'Mind if I smoke, by the way?'

'Give me one, will you,' Sculby muttered.

Royston lit two, keeping one for himself and placing the other between Sculby's lips. Then he took a deep drag and began.

'I'll tell you only what you need to know. When I've finished, if you don't want to go on with this, you simply forget it. Understand?'

Royston stole a look at Sculby. In the orange glow of the sodium lamps which lit the centre divide of the motorway it was impossible to see the colour of his face, but the lawyer's eyes were staring fixedly at the road ahead and Royston had a feeling he was white.

'Yes.'

'Then there's a high-ranking defector on the run from the KGB. A colonel, no less. Everyone knows him simply as Kyril. That's not his real name, it's what the Russians call a casename. Kyril is coming to London. He used to work here, years ago. He's probably got money put away somewhere, and in any case he may want to do a deal with SIS. Now this Kyril used to have a girlfriend in London.'

Royston took a deep drag on his cigarette and exhaled it slowly, relishing the momentary uplift.

'She's called Vera Bradfield.'

Sculby said nothing. Royston allowed the information to work in him for about a mile, then continued.

'Something else we know about Kyril is that he urgently wants to talk to Loshkevoi.'

The car swerved slightly and Royston grimaced.

'Take it easy, Laurie. We don't know why he wants to, and we'd dearly like to. Now you know why we're all so interested in your client.'

London Airport dropped away to the left, lurid oasis in a desert of darkness. Sculby kept the car going at a steady fifty, navigating by reference to the chain of orange lamps which stretched away from him to the horizon.

'We would like nothing better than to talk to the Bradfield woman. But we can't. The chances are that she is sympathetic to Kyril and the last thing we want to do is put the wind up the people he's due to visit. On the other hand, by leaving her alone we run the risk of passing up valuable information about Kyril's time of arrival in this country and what his plans are. We can't afford to talk to her. And we can't afford not to.'

Royston allowed Sculby a long pause in which to digest this latest chunk of information. He was not an angler, but he understood the angler's need for patience.

'Why not just concentrate on Loshkevoi?' Sculby asked. 'Pull him in. Give him a right going over.'

'Because Loshkevoi is sensitive. We're holding our breath with you in there as it is. And in any case, Kyril is unlikely to give Loshkevoi advance warning of his plans: quite the contrary. Whereas the same can't be said of Vera Bradfield.'

Royston waited until he was sure that Sculby wasn't going to speak again.

'This is the pitch, Laurie. We'd like you to make an appointment with this woman, go to visit her. Say that you have a client who's mentioned her name. From what you told me about the other night, that's virtually true anyway. See how she reacts when you name Loshkevoi. Pretend to be doing your best for an unco-operative client. Loshkevoi's coy about her and won't talk, but in the exercise of your professional duty you feel obliged to follow up every possible lead, that kind of thing. Try to see if the spare bed's made up. Find out whether she's expecting visitors. Whether she's nervous, afraid even. While you're in the house, plant a bug, something we can monitor. You're a solicitor, she'll never suspect you.'

'You've thought it all out, haven't you,' said Sculby. 'Have MI5 gone on strike, or something? I thought they employed lads dressed up as telephone engineers to do that kind of thing. You don't need me.'

Royston could hear the anxiety in the lawyer's voice. Was he nerving himself up to a refusal?

'Kyril is MI6 material. You know the rules, Laurie: no inter-service poaching. Five have no need to know about Kyril, so they're out. This is strictly London Station territory. P.4 is the only executive arm we have which isn't obliged to operate exclusively beyond the seas. So it's you or nobody, I'm afraid. You see, Laurie, you're uniquely placed. That's the trouble.'

It had begun to rain again. Sculby switched on the wipers. One of them was sticking badly: zink-zonk, zink-zonk…

'You said it was dangerous.'

'If Kyril does visit the Bradfield woman he's going to find out about your appearance on the scene. And it isn't going to take him long to discover that you're connected with the only other person he wants to see: Loshkevoi. That's going to make you a very interesting proposition to Kyril. He's going to want to know where you stand.'

The noise of the wiper was getting on Royston's nerves. Zink-zonk, zink-zonk.

'The chances are that he'll pay you a visit. And if he does, well, then you're going to carry the standard, Laurie. You'll have to play him for all you're worth, using your wits. No one can help you. I can't back you up. I've just got to trust you to do the best you can for us. Because we want Kyril. We want him more than we've ever wanted anyone in the six years I've known you. But he has to come willingly, of his own accord, if he's to be the slightest use.'

The car breasted a slight rise and Sculby saw that there was less than a mile of sodium lighting left. After that came darkness.

'What do you want me to do?'

'Make friends. Play him along. With your lefty leanings that shouldn't be too difficult…' Royston checked himself, wondering if he had gone too far. Sculby said nothing.

Zink-zonk, zink-zonk.

Ahead of them the darkness was coming up with terrifying speed.

'But whatever you do, however it goes, you must say one thing. You must work a phrase into the conversation. "For love of the motherland." Just that. It has a special meaning, has done for years. It enables sleepers who've been adrift from Moscow Centre for a long time to identify themselves as members of the KGB. That's what you've got to do, Laurie, if you're to make Kyril swallow it. Nothing less will do. Make him believe you're on his side. Make him talk to you. Find out what the hell is going on...'

Zinz-zonk, zink-zonk.

'...But take care. I said it was dangerous and I meant it. Kyril has killed. Not once, but many times.'

The last link in the chain of orange sodium which had lit the car's progress from London loomed up, flashed by, was gone.

Chapter 17

As soon as he saw the house Kyril knew that he had found exactly what he was looking for. The short, grey-brown terrace was over-shadowed by a high railway embankment at a point where Queenstown Road veered round to the left, the gap between the frontage of the end house and the soil being blocked off by a brick wall twice the height of a man. That was the first thing to strike him as he stood in the shelter of the broad railway bridge, listening to the hollow roar of the trains overhead. There was no back entrance, so anyone who wanted to approach otherwise than by the street would have to brave either the wall or the trains and the live rail above. The location was as near perfect as he could hope for. Apart from providing him with a secure base, the house was within easy reach of the people he wanted to see. This had to be the place.

Kyril curbed his mounting excitement. No over-hasty decisions, no false starts. For now he was living by one golden rule: he would be seen only when he wanted to be seen, and for the rest of the time he was invisible.

Kyril had been doing a lot of thinking since he left Athens. The more he considered Stanov's briefing the less he liked it. What had seemed clear-cut and straightforward in Moscow appeared rather more nebulous under a watery, slate-grey London sky. For the moment he was concerned only with self-preservation.

Kyril opened a flap in the side of his rucksack and rummaged through the wadge of agents' particulars. Early inspection was recommended. Kyril agreed.

He looked up sharply, distracted by a sudden movement. The board advertising a long lease of the first floor maisonette was fixed to the wall of the end-of-terrace house. From the adjoining front gate a young woman and a child were emerging: the next-door neighbours. Kyril weighed them up from the shadows of the bridge. One reason why he chose this area was that he knew it well from his spell of duty in 1974 as part of the London team, and the woman gave Kyril a familiar, 'good' feeling. She was running to fat and looked neglected; possibly a single parent making do on too little money. Friendly but not nosy. Typical Battersea.

The kind of woman who would hear a scream in the night and roll over with a shrug, reasoning that it was none of her business, and anyway, she had enough problems of her own...

Kyril nodded slowly. He was not going to find anything better.

-

At first, Mr Williams thought it was just another routine legal transaction. His very good friend Mr Simmons, partner in a well-known firm of Estate Agents, rang up to say he was passing along a client who wanted to buy No 703 Queenstown Road, Battersea. Mr Williams raised his eyebrows. The property had been on the market at £15,000 for months, but no one wanted to buy. It was a Victorian house, nestling in the shadow of a railway embankment, which had long ago been divided into two flats, one up and one down. The freehold was owned by the upper tenant, who had died in the spring. The executors were anxious to dispose of the whole house but money was tight and no one was interested in a rundown end-of-terrace dwellinghouse subject to a controlled tenancy of the downstairs part. Mr Williams' draft contract had lain in a file, unopened, for most of the summer and autumn. The prospect of a purchaser pleased him no end. It would be a simple transaction, for title was registered, and then he could wrap up the estate of the deceased owner once and for all.

Something in the estate agent's voice led Mr Williams to ask a few more questions.

'Well, it's just that the client's very… odd.'

'Odd?'

'Yes. Scruffy. Not the sort of person who usually pays cash.'

'Cash?'

'Yes. Banker's draft, already made out to bearer. But he's not the sort of chap to have a banker, if you know what I mean.'

'Is he a foreigner?'

'Don't think so. Sounds frightfully British.'

Mr Williams grunted. 'Anyway. Plenty of time to sort things out. Local searches are taking four months at the moment, you know. Which solicitor is acting for him?'

At the other end of the line there was a chuckle. 'Don't think I'll say any more, old man. You'll meet him soon enough. You see, he's under the impression that you're acting for him. Bye now.'

Mr Williams replaced the receiver with a frown. It was most improper for the same solicitor to act for both parties in a conveyancing transaction. There were exceptions, but the Law Society held strong views on the matter. He would have to be very firm with Mr... (he consulted his notes)... Mr Webb.

Fifteen minutes later there was a commotion in the outer office, a disturbance which ended when Mr Williams' secretary flung open the door to admit the firm's latest client. Mr Williams shot upright, upsetting his swivel-chair. Advancing towards him was a tall, solid-looking man, his face half-obscured by a thin growth of beard. Mr Williams looked into his eyes and felt momentary reassurance. This did not look like an assailant. The face was genial and full of life, the look of a man of the world who had earned his experience the hard way but kept his humanity.

'Mr Webb?'

'Mr Williams. Such a pleasure to meet you, sir, the gentleman at Kelly Stimpson's said how well you looked after clients, I'm afraid we've never met but I'm sure you'll find we get on like a house on fire. May I sit down? Thank you. Now this property.'

'Seven hundred and three Queenstown Road?'

'As you say, Mr Williams, the Queenstown Road house. Do you have a contract for me to sign? Only I'm very busy today and it's quite essential for me to have possession by this afternoon. I propose to pay by banker's draft made out to bearer, of course you'll want to telephone the bank. I don't mind waiting. Such a pleasant office.'

Mr Williams drew a deep breath. This was going to take time.

'The first thing I must tell you, Mr Webb, is that you'll obviously need your own solicitor.'

Kyril smiled bleakly. As far as he was concerned, this was not going to take any time at all.

'I appoint you,' he said. 'I will pay your fees before I go.'

'But the professional impropriety...'

'Have your secretary type up a legal waiver. I'll sign it.'

'Local searches... inquiries of the local authority...'

'Forget it. I'm a gambling man. The upstairs is vacant, yes? That's all I need to know.'

Mr Williams was flummoxed. In front of him he saw a man, a nice enough man he was sure, lounging in the best chair. He noticed one or two details. The man's clothes were shabby and travel-stained. By his side was a large rucksack, the kind of thing Mr Williams' children carried when they hitched-hiked around Europe. The clothes had a foreign look about them, although the quality was there all right. Mr Webb wore no tie; evidently a habit, for Mr Williams could see a sunburned triangle of skin between the folds of his collar.

'I'm afraid I must ask you to wait a minute, Mr Webb.'

'Of course. Can I possibly have a cup of tea, d'you think?'

Once 'Mr Webb' had been dealt with by handing him over to the secretaries Mr Williams closed the door of his office and drew the telephone towards him.

Five minutes later he sat back, a look of puzzlement on his face. He had spoken personally to the manager of the bank at the branch whence Mr Webb's draft emanated. It was perfectly above board. For good measure Mr Williams had requested the manager to call him back, when he had again confirmed that there was nothing suspect about the draft. Then Mr Williams had phoned his contact in the Law Society, who had hummed and hawed and finally said that it should be all right as long as Mr Webb was prepared to sign a waiver, as he suggested.

Mr Williams took out the draft contract and studied it. Everything was in order. He had a power of attorney to sign it on behalf of the executors, who lived abroad. Vacant possession could be given that day. He sat in silent thought for a minute, before flicking down a switch on his intercom and asking his receptionist to show Mr Webb back in.

–

When he was through with Williams Kyril went down to Dawsons, the builders' merchants at Clapham Junction, and worked his way through a long and expensive shopping-list before returning to the house. Once he had let himself in he contented himself with making a thorough inspection while waiting for Dawsons to deliver.

It was a solid house with few signs of neglect or decay; the impression which he had formed on his quick walk-through with the agent was accurate.

The doorbell rang. Kyril clattered down the uncarpeted stairs to take delivery of his order, tipping the driver generously enough to prevent resentment but not so lavishly as to cause him to stick in the man's mind.

Kyril took his coat off and set to work. He had given himself plenty of time to get established before he need reveal himself on the streets of London. There was no particular hurry.

Kyril had never owned a house before. The thought that it was his to do as he liked with, that he was accountable to no one, quickened his interest and made the prospect of hours of physical labour somehow less daunting. As he bored the first hole in the wooden window-frame he began to whistle quietly to himself, a cheerful air which he had inherited from his father, who had learned it from his father before him.

First he dealt with the outer defences. All the windows were sealed with bonded adhesive and angle-brackets fastened to the frame. The single drain-pipe at the rear he treated with anti-burglar paint and a wrapping of barbed wire. The chimneys were already bricked up, so Kyril didn't waste time on them, but he secured the hatchway to the roof-space with double iron bars let into the woodwork.

Then he began to seal off the interior. The main front room he designated his headquarters, that and the tiny kitchen leading off. All the other rooms were fastened with the same bonded adhesive, double bolts on both sides of the frame, and padlocks. The front door at the foot of the stairs he fitted with a padlock, double bolts and a new Yale deadlock. When he had finished he bundled up all the keys to the various locks he had bought, with the single exception of the key to the front door, put them into a small canvas bag and slipped out for a quick trip to the nearby river, glad of the excuse for some fresh air. He waited only long enough to see the bag sink beneath the slimy water before returning to the house.

Next came the really heavy work. At the head of the stairs was a door leading into the main room. Kyril hadn't touched it. Now he knelt by the door, on the inside, testing the floorboards. A padsaw would do for the initial incision, and that he had, but for the main task he was going to save a lot of time by using a power-saw. That meant another shopping trip.

It was getting late, but Kyril didn't worry. That was one of the reasons why Battersea, attracted him, an aspect which reminded him of Moscow: he was living in a cash economy. On the street outside his house brand new Jaguars were parked side by side with cement-dusty builders' vans and the front halves of articulated lorries; men in dirty jeans came home at six o'clock and emerged half an hour later dressed in good quality suits, their equally well-dressed wives or girlfriends on their arms. Kyril liked that. He knew there were little shops open where normally you would not even expect to find trade premises, shops down quiet alleys, or in the basement of a terraced house. Within 20 minutes he had found what he wanted, a second-hand Black & Decker, haggled with the shopman, relishing the sound of his own voice again, struck a bargain and paid cash. On his way home Kyril stopped in a 'Mini-Mart' and bought bread and tea from the morose Asian proprietor, again enjoying the brief touch of human contact.

Darkness had fallen, but the street was noisy and Kyril had no compunction about using the power-saw. Let the neighbours complain, much he cared. Besides, it was necessary to make the downstairs tenant aware of him.

At nine o'clock Kyril broke off for a scratch meal and a smoke. He didn't eat much. The bread felt damp to the touch and tasted of nothing while at the same time coating his mouth with a faintly acidic, bilious substance. He thought with regret of a borodinski loaf, coarse and brown and liberally sprinkled with caraway seeds. Kyril sighed. There was nothing like that in England.

After he had eaten he lay down on an old mattress which he had picked up in the market earlier and looked through the black oblong of the window at the sky. Quite close to his house, though not so near as to be uncomfortable, a lamp-standard cast a garish orange glow into the room. Despite its softness this glow brought Kyril no comfort. It made him afraid. He propped himself up on one elbow and tried to analyse the feeling.

So far he was undetected; no one knew where he was. That was fine. Why, then, be afraid? Kyril drew deeply on his cigarette. It was something to do with the area... he had come to the end of his journey now, there was nowhere else to go. Except home. And Kyril felt exposed. He was at the centre of a web fringed with terraces of crumbling property, a tangled labyrinth of high streets and main streets and cross streets and side-streets, all leading to him, in the centre, alone. Kyril remembered how as a boy his father would take him fishing on a Sunday afternoon, the sun glinting on the river as it wound down from the Urals, the sound of birdsong, the feel of a clean wind on the skin. He smiled. His father... there was a good man. But he had died, as had Kyril's mother; his wife left him, there were no children. He was in London, at the cold centre of a concrete maze where the sky was always grey and the rain never washed the grime from the stained, forbidding walls which hemmed him in.

The rain. A thin drizzle had begun to fall, coating the window-pane with a dirty mixture of lead, carbon-monoxide and filth. For a second Kyril thought of the stalacmites in the caves in the mountains above his childhood home: there too, the moisture never washed anything away, never cleansed, never purified, it merely added stone to stone, drop by drop.

Somewhere out there was another world, in which Stanov plotted desperately, the Athens *referentura* fought to cover its tracks, the KGB combed Brussels, then Belgium, then all of western Europe. But it was not his world any longer. He had no means of knowing what went on there. How much did SIS know? Had Stanov succeeded in exposing the traitor? Precisely *how much* danger was Kyril in, and how immediate was that danger…?

The last question was easy to answer. If the diary had any effect on the traitor at all he must try to eradicate Kyril. He could not afford to run the risk that Stanov might get to him first and make him talk. Now that Kyril was stationary, the peril was immediate. He put that question aside as answered and went on to something else.

Loshkevoi.

This aspect of his mission had begun to trouble Kyril greatly. Before, he could ignore it. Now, at the end of the road, it must be faced.

Stanov had lied about Loshkevoi.

A high-ranking traitor was not going to reveal himself to one of Stanov's irregular agents. It went against all the rules of the game. So what was the point of telling Kyril that Loshkevoi held the key? To divert him from something else, perhaps? But why do that? What was this mysterious something that Kyril ought not to know?

Should he try to see Loshkevoi anyway? Should he leave him strictly alone? Assuming he did meet Loshkevoi, what then?

Why had Stanov lied?

He extinguished his cigarette and stood up, shaking off these doleful thoughts. Action. He had been putting it off for long enough.

It was time to meet the neighbours.

He spent a few moments hanging the drapes at the window, all he would ever need in the way of curtains.

Then he went out by the front door and immediately turned left, so that he was facing the entrance which belonged to the downstairs tenant. Halfway up the frame glowed an illuminated bell. Kyril peered closer. 'Trumper', that was all the sliver of cardboard said. It could mean anything. The estate agent had spoken of 'old Mr Trumper' and called him 'a nice old man', but there might be other occupants; Kyril didn't trust agents. Well, there was only one way to find out. Kyril pressed the bell.

For a long while nothing happened. At last Kyril heard the sound of shuffling movement on the other side of the door, together with a tapping noise he couldn't identify.

'Who's there?'

A male voice. Breathless. Frightened. Old.

'It's your neighbour from upstairs. Ian Webb. I've come to say sorry about all the noise.'

There was a long pause.

'What did you say your name was?'

'Webb. Ian Webb.'

There was an indistinguishable sound; the speaker could have been saying 'Go away', or 'Wait a mo', or any one of a number of things. Kyril gnawed his lip. The last thing he wanted was to have to break in. But suddenly the door opened, and Mr Trumper was revealed.

'You'd best come in, then. It's a wet night.' The voice had lost some of its terror. 'Sorry about you waiting, and that, but it's the kids, see? Rotten little buggers, some of them. I thought it was them.'

Kyril took in the white stick, the staring, vacant eyes. The old man was blind.

He stepped over the threshold, feeling and hearing the cold click of lino under his feet. The only light came from a single naked bulb halfway down the passage. As Kyril followed the stooped form of the old man towards the back of the draughty house he began to notice details, take measurements with his eyes. It ought to be possible, the layout was the same as in the flat above…

'Come in here, it's warmer.'

'Here' was a small scullery leading to the kitchen. Such warmth as there was came from a paraffin stove which gave off more stench than heat. Kyril wondered how the old man managed without setting the place alight. As if in answer to his thought Trumper said, 'Don't trouble about me, I can see a bit. Find yourself a chair and sit yourself down.'

Kyril looked round. The only vacant chair was a moth-eaten pouffe with its stuffing beginning to come out of a tear in the side. He lowered himself onto it gingerly.

'I'm glad you came. I appreciate that. I wondered what all the banging was.'

The old man had awkwardly let himself down into his own chair, a few inches away from the stove. Presumably he was used to the poisonous atmosphere. The only light in the room came from the same bulb in the hall: a shaft of yellow fell through the open door between the two men, illuminating neither of them. Kyril blinked and struggled to get his bearings.

'Things were in a state upstairs. I only moved in today.'

'I'll bet they were. I'll bet they were.'

The old man spoke very slowly, and with obvious effort. Although Kyril could not see him he was gaining an increasingly powerful and detailed impression of Mr Trumper. In his late seventies, probably; breathing poor; partially sighted; bronchitic… Kyril thought he could detect the dead smell of cheap pipe tobacco somewhere, strong and black, but doled out sparingly.

He was incredibly frail. Too frail to live long.

'The old couple upstairs, the Walkers... he died, then she died, you see. That's how it was.'

Kyril nodded sympathetically and said 'ah'.

'She was always untidy but when he died she went to pieces. It's been empty for ever so long.'

'Ah,' said Kyril again. 'Cigarette?'

Trumper sighed and shook his head. 'No thanks. I used to but I've given it up. Doctor's orders. He's another bugger, an' all.'

'Does the doctor come often?'

'Does 'e hell. There's nobody comes now. My daughter and her husband, they live in Canada. They never write to me and I never write to them. Since my wife died there's nobody calls.'

'But... there must be somebody. The people from the Council, now, what about them?'

'What? Welfare, d'you mean? Social Security?' The old man cackled, caught his breath and choked. Kyril waited patiently for the fit to end. 'Don't make me laugh.'

Kyril had a sudden vision of himself, at the end of his life, like this. Alone, in a damp flat without light or heat. He leaned forward and peered at Trumper. He seemed to be wrapped up in layer upon layer of wool, like an advertisement for a jersey manufacturer.

'You shouldn't have to live in a place like this. Wait 'til I'm fixed upstairs. It shan't be long now. Then you must come and visit.'

'That's good of you, that is. Kind, I call that. I don't mind about the noise. It's your home now. You've got to get it fixed. Don't worry about me, the noise tells me you're up there, and I like that. It's been lonely since the

Walkers. You'll like it here, you will really. You can't beat south of the river, that's what I say.'

Kyril sat back slowly. He hadn't meant it to be like this.

'I wanted to ask you a favour.'

'Ask away.'

'I keep a bit of money in the flat. I'm worried about thieves. I've bought some of that non-dry paint and barbed wire and I've treated the drainpipe outside. Would you mind if I did the downstairs half of the pipe as well?'

Trumper seemed not to grasp what he was saying.

'It's to stop them climbing up,' Kyril explained. 'Burglars.'

The old man cogitated awhile, then chuckled.

'You do what you like,' he said. 'Suit yourself. Want a cup of tea?'

Kyril swallowed. To his annoyance his hands had begun to shake, not so as to be noticeable to anyone else, but *he* knew.

'Thanks,' he said. 'Thanks a lot.'

The old man prodded the floor with his white stick, as if to check that the wood was still safe, then levered himself up from his chair. Kyril was halfway off the pouffe in order to help him but the old man waved him back. 'No.' His voice was very firm. Kyril knew pride when he heard it. In a sudden fit of disgust he clenched his hands together and squeezed hard.

Trumper awkwardly changed his stick from one hand to the other, and Kyril realised that he relied on it for support as well as to warn people of his infirmity. The vision of his own life's end came back to Kyril. For a moment he lacked the energy to push it away, and instead he stared at it, appalled.

'D'you take sugar?'

With a start he realised that Trumper had gone into the kitchen.

'No, thank you. And no milk either,' he added mechanically.

'No milk?' Normally the old man's querulous voice would have brought a smile to Kyril's lips, but now they remained set in a dead straight line.

'The only other person I ever knew who didn't take milk in his...'

Trumper looked up from the stove, surprised to find Kyril by his side. His visitor made no more noise than a shadow on the wall.

'Can I help?'

Kyril was thinking, it would be an easy thing to dispose of the body: two dustbin-liner bags over the feet, two more over the head, and all these houses had cellars. Why, then, not do it now?

No. Trumper's death would be unnecessary. He was worrying needlessly. When the time for action came the old man must take his chance, but for the moment he presented no threat.

Kyril fished out a cigarette, saying 'Do you mind?'

'You suit yourself.'

Kyril held the cigarette to the gas flame. Why was it necessary, all of a sudden, to use both hands? To check the trembling which he had noticed earlier?

Kyril observed his body's latest phenomenon with detached interest. Tension. That was all. His body and brain had been aligned for the kill; now the order was rescinded it took both a little while to adjust.

The old man had finished making the tea. Kyril accepted a cup and sipped the strong, black liquid. It was good: not as good as in Moscow but unmistakably restorative and refreshing. He felt the tension of the kill begin to drain away.

'Come and sit yourself down,' said Trumper.

But suddenly Kyril couldn't face any more. He put his cup on the sideboard and said, 'I must go. Really. It's been a long day for me.'

Trumper seemed to understand his abrupt change of mood for he said, 'Right you are. I won't keep you. But I hope you'll come down again.'

'I will. Soon.'

He wearily climbed the stairs to his own part of the house, remembering to bolt the front door behind him. Tomorrow, he said to himself, I shall finish. The hole in the floorboards will be completed and then concealed, leaving only a thin float of plaster between me and the flat below.

I will begin my preparations for entertaining Loshkevoi. And I shall see Vera again.

He was standing in the middle of the main upstairs room, the mattress in front of him. His mind couldn't function any more.

Tomorrow, said Kyril to himself…

Tomorrow, I shall…

His head was spinning round and round. The wall opposite rippled up and down, backwards and forwards.

Tomorrow I shall conquer the world.

Kyril knelt on the mattress, lay down, and slept.

Chapter 18

Sculby was having a dream.

On this, the first occasion, the details of the dream were unclear, although it was destined to recur, night after night, until at last everything was plain.

Sculby knew he was in Russia, in the middle of Red Square, exposed and alone. All around him men were marching, rank upon rank of goose-stepping soldiers, passing before him from right to left, from left to right, sometimes away from him, at others towards him. A great ceremonial occasion, May Day perhaps. The sun was shining brightly, throwing the scene into sharp relief, but it was very cold in Red Square, cold enough to make the cheeks burn.

A solitary figure detached itself from the marching men. An officer, identifiable by his drawn sword. He began to cross Sculby's field of vision from right to left, the white blade swinging in the crook of his arm. Details started to emerge: highly polished cavalry boots, an immaculate uniform… suddenly the officer executed a left turn towards Sculby, who looked for his face and found only shadow cast by the officer's stiff, peaked cap. He came closer; soon Sculby would be able to see clearly, and he knew he would recognise this man as someone he had known for many years past, someone he was anxious to avoid, an enemy. Sculby wanted to run and found he couldn't move a muscle, not even to raise a hand against the oncoming threat. But when the officer was only a few feet away and the shadow cast by his cap was starting to lift, all the bells of the Cathedral suddenly tolled so that Sculby looked away, startled…

Sculby picked up the alarm dock and threw it across the room. It went on ringing. He staggered out of bed, cursing his failure to switch it off first. His head was throbbing: too much Chianti the night before. A heavy grey feeling of dread, its source as yet unidentifiable, pervaded the flat.

Sculby sat down by the window and put his head in his hands.

The night before, he had arranged to take Judy out to dinner in an attempt at reconciliation. But the Registrar of the Haywards Heath County Court sat after hours at Sculby's request, so he was late at the restaurant, and thereafter the evening went from bad to worse. The double bed remained in single occupation.

Sculby picked up the newspaper from the mat and inspected his post. Recognising his mother's handwriting he made a face and thrust the letter, still unopened, into the pocket of his dressing-gown.

Well why *don't* you go to see them more often? he asked his face in the shaving-mirror. Is that *such* an unreasonable question to ask? His mother was fond of underlining key words.

Then Sculby remembered why the day was bleak. He had an appointment to see Vera Bradfield at 9.30.

–

She went to the front door with the solicitor's letter in her hand, as if that short, courteously phrased missive could somehow guarantee protection from the hand that had written it.

'Miss Bradfield?'

'Mr Sculby?'

They spoke simultaneously and smiled the same half-rueful, half-resentful smile.

'Come in.'

She decided not to turn her back but stood aside to let him pass, recoiling a little. She did not much like Mr Sculby, with his pebble-lensed glasses and cynical mouth. There seemed to be a lot of him in her tiny hallway: obviously the kind of man who liked to fill all the available space.

'In here?'

'No.'

She had to reach across Sculby to pull shut the door of the spare bedroom, recognising in him the sort of person who deliberately chooses the wrong room in order to make his presence felt. Something in the way he refused to budge while she dealt with the door suggested that the mistake was her fault.

'I'm very busy this morning. In here, please…'

She ushered him into the workroom and pointed to the typewriter.

'…I've got a deadline to meet. For a manuscript. Can you make it fast?'

She had been looking forward to his visit. It should have made an interesting break in an otherwise dull routine. But already she wanted him to go.

Sculby took a notebook out of his briefcase and opened it at a blank page. He looked everywhere but at what he was supposed to be doing. Vera sat down at the typewriter, keeping the wooden screen of the table between her and the lawyer's roving eyes.

'You must think this is very odd, Miss Bradfield. I'm most grateful to you for agreeing to see me at all.'

He had a nice voice; she conceded that. But he wasn't really grateful.

'One of my clients is a Mr Victor Loshkevoi. Does that name mean anything to you?'

She shook her head. 'I've been racking my brains ever since I got your letter, Mr Sculby, but I've never met anyone of that name.'

For a while he said nothing but merely looked at her, so that she was reminded of the Social Security inspector who called to see if she was living with a man. She pushed the memory hastily away.

'It means nothing to me. Really.'

After another short pause Sculby began to tell her about Loshkevoi, keeping to the truth as far as possible and trying to make it sound convincing. Vera's attention wandered; it didn't seem a very interesting story that he was telling her. She decided that Sculby was unlikely to be married: any woman worth her salt would have tried to do something about the ragged tie, grimy cuffs, and unkempt, overlong hair. But perhaps he had a wife, and she was meek and ineffectual? It seemed improbable. His type nearly always married a forceful, strong-willed woman and then proceeded to row with her in public. Vera knew. She had seen such men often, even gone out with one or two.

'So there it is, Miss Bradfield…'

Suddenly she wished he wouldn't call her that, and knew it was time to get rid of him.

‘I’m sorry,’ she said abruptly. ‘You’ve been wasting your time. I can’t imagine where your client picked up my name. I do freelance typing work and I advertise in the South London Press, he may have seen it there. But apart from that, I can’t help you. And quite frankly, I think you should confine your inquiries to him.’

Sculby smiled and put away his notebook. He seemed as relieved as she was that the interview was over, and not at all disappointed at the outcome. She rose to her feet with him and waited while he placed his briefcase on the table in order to close it properly. The latch seemed to be sticking.

‘Well, goodbye then. I’m sorry to have taken up your time.’

Now he really was sorry, she decided. In the hall he looked around.

‘Nice flat you’ve got. Best part of Clapham, this. Quiet.’

‘I think so.’

‘It makes a difference having the other room. I do a lot of conveyancing, you know. Space. That’s what people want these days.’

‘It’s too much for me, really. I never have anyone to stay…’

Vera checked herself. Careful.

He walked to his car and she watched at the front door until he had driven away. As she closed the door she noticed that the same man who had been there yesterday was sitting in a car opposite, reading a newspaper. Was it really the same man? The car was different, surely… Vera hesitated. Could it be burglars, seeing who lived where and what was worth taking? You read a lot about that kind of thing these days…

She sat down at the typewriter and rattled a sheet of paper into the carriage with unnecessary violence. 'Honestly, Vera,' she said to herself. 'You'll be seeing Reds under the bed next.'

Chapter 19

The KGB 'year' runs from 1st July, and every spring the controllers of the Main Directorates meet the Chairman to prepare a work plan for the coming twelve months. This meeting, known as the Collegium, is a formal showpiece. All the real work is done beforehand and behind the scenes. Stanov had vainly been trying to improve the process for the last eight years.

'Every time it is the same,' he snapped. 'What I need is hard intelligence: not wishful thinking, not obsequious flummery, not lies, but genuine intelligence. Yet you insist on trying to deceive me. Why?'

The six Deputy Chairmen of the KGB stared up the long table, their expressions varying from abashed to annoyed. The first annual planning session was always like this. It ran to a precise pattern. Stanov gave everyone a bollocking for rigging the statistics, then went meekly along to the Politburo and lied with the best of them. Everyone knew the KGB was inefficient. Nobody seriously believed that each year the number of recruits went up by 12.67 per cent, or that each year Counter-Intelligence arrested 14.74 per cent more foreign infiltrators than the year before. But it was necessary to give the Supreme Soviet delegates something to applaud before they dispersed to Georgia, and the Ukraine, and

Byelorussia, and who knows where. It had always gone on like this. Why try to change it?

Michaelov leaned forward and opened his mouth to speak. As First Deputy Chairman he carried more clout than the rest of his colleagues.

'You wish to speak, General?'

Michaelov froze with his mouth open, temporarily distracted by Stanov's acerbic intervention.

'Nothing suggests, comrade Marshal, that the statistics are any less reliable this year than last.'

'I know that,' yapped Stanov. 'That's what I mean!'

Michaelov sat back gloomily. The old man was at his unspeakable worst today. All the Deputy Chairmen had been working for months to try to get Stanov to sign Chairman's Order Number 0078, an instrument which, if promulgated, would alter the delicate balance of power which subsisted between the KGB and the Administrative Organs Department of the Politburo. It was now or never, the ramifications of the affair ran deep, and Stanov, who knew perfectly well how important this Order was, still refused to sign it. The last thing anybody wanted was a row.

Stanov had other things on his mind. The fake defection on which so much depended was entering its final phase. Kyril was due to show his face on the streets of London this afternoon. It was hard to concentrate, knowing that if things went wrong the next meeting of the Collegium, for which the men round this table were supposed to be planning, would be his last.

The morning wore on. Stanov turned his attention from false statistics to the increasing number of 'exceptional incidents' which had occurred in the past year: drunkenness, unruly public behaviour, even rape.

Concentration wavered. The Deputy Chairmen knew of these matters, just as they knew the complaints were important and reprehensible. They did not need to be reminded.

Coffee was served at 11.30, and with its arrival flasks were pulled from deep pockets. The meeting resumed in better humour after a 20-minute break, some progress was made. When the adjournment was announced at half-past one there was a general consensus that time had not been altogether wasted, although Chairman's Order No. 0078 still remained unsigned.

Stanov returned to his office on the third floor to find Major Krubykov of the Kremlin Kommandant awaiting him. Stanov tensed. The Kremlin he could do without at present.

'The First Secretary of the Communist Party of the Soviet Union presents his compliments to comrade Marshal Voldemar Stanov, and asks him to attend the meeting of the Politburo which is now in progress.'

Stanov mechanically signalled Yevchenko to bring his overcoat. However courteously couched the language might be, it was unmistakably an order. Normally Stanov had a month's warning of Politburo meetings which he would be expected to attend. This meant trouble.

'Look after things, Yevchenko,' he said, nodding his head to emphasise his true meaning. Yevchenko's job this afternoon was to monitor Kyril, nothing else. But Major Krubykov had another, greater surprise for him.

'Colonel Yevchenko is also requested to attend.'

For a second Stanov could not grasp the enormity of what was happening. Someone was at the back of it, an enemy. Someone who knew the importance of this afternoon to the Chairman of the KGB, a man with a motive for keeping his superiors out of the way while he dealt with a message from London.

Someone who could command the Kremlin? No, it was impossible. However high the traitor, he could not simply snap his fingers at the Politburo, say 'Get rid of Stanov for the afternoon, will you?' Stanov struggled to keep a foothold while the ice cracked and creaked around him. There had to be another explanation, something he had missed...

'Major, it is necessary to make certain arrangements. Perhaps we could join you in the car?'

As the door closed behind Krubykov Stanov swung round to face Yevchenko. 'Quick,' he hissed, 'ring up Sulitsky in the Seventh Directorate. Tell him I want an urgent "time and motion" on cipher traffic between Moscow and London. Don't tell him what it's for, just get him to fix it up by this afternoon.'

'Hopeless. Everyone will know at once, you can't keep that sort of check secret.'

'I know, but it's the best we can do. If they detain us – and oh, my friend, but they will detain us – we must have someone here to watch. What else can we do?'

Yevchenko discreetly watched his chief's face from under thick eyebrows, reading distress and indecision. He was right. What else could they do at such short notice? He lifted the receiver and spoke into it urgently.

A black Zil was waiting in the courtyard to take them on the short journey to the Kremlin. Ensconced in its soft, luxurious interior Stanov spent the drive looking blankly out of the tinted window at the crowded streets. He was at a loss. Yevchenko never went with him to the Politburo. Who was interfering? They would have to try to cut the visit short, make some excuse and leave before three, when, allowing for the time difference, Kyril should be on the streets.

Krubykov rode in front with the driver. Yevchenko leaned across to Stanov and whispered in his ear.

'Does anyone in the Politburo know it's today Kyril is due in London?'

'I've told nobody. *Nobody!*'

'Nor I. Hold on to that. However much the traitor knows, he can't know when and where Kyril is next going to surface. This has to be a coincidence, nothing more.'

Stanov pounded a gloved fist into the palm of his other hand.

'It's a conspiracy,' he hissed. 'You know what this is about as well as I do. They're going to try and separate us. It's come at last, Nikolai, the day we've always dreaded. Look out for yourself, that's my advice.'

'Well… here we go.'

'Good luck!'

The car drew up in another courtyard and the two old men climbed out between saluting sentries. Inside the Kremlin it was warm. Officers came forward to relieve them of their overcoats and gloves. Stanov followed the well-trodden route, knowing that as they rounded the last corner the huge double-doors at the end of the corridor would be opened to permit them to enter without so much as breaking step.

But this did not happen. The doors remained firmly closed. Major Krubykov, who had never left their sides, was apologetic.

'I was warned there might be a short delay. Forgive me for not mentioning it before, comrade Marshal. Please be seated.'

Yevchenko was looking around him curiously. He had never set foot in the Kremlin before. They were in a wide, parquet-floored corridor down the centre of which ran a strip of dark blue carpet. The colour scheme was easy on the eye: pale blue walls picked out in white rising to rococo ceilings embossed in gold leaf. Opposite the double doors leading to the Politburo's chamber stood a bust of Lenin perched on top of a column which tapered downwards to the floor. It looked precarious. For the first time in his life Yevchenko felt he had something in common with the founder of modern Communism.

Time passed. Stanov paced up and down the corridor, muttering to himself and looking at his watch. Yevchenko shared his chief's anxiety. If they did not get their business over with soon they would inevitably miss Kyril's appearance in London.

Something else was troubling Stanov. With every minute that passed, the personal snub to him grew greater. Not even the Politburo had the right to keep the Chairman of the KGB and a Marshal of the Soviet Union waiting indefinitely. His thoughts became positively murderous. Didn't they know what dirt he had on them, back at Dzerzhinsky Square? Didn't they realise?

The double-doors opened. Stanov stopped in mid-stride and rounded furiously – only to find himself face to face with Kazin.

For a few seconds the two men looked each other up and down, neutral smiles on their faces. Whatever their personal history may have been, it was necessary to preserve a dignified public record. Behind Kazin the other members of the Politburo were dispersing in opposite directions down the long corridor, some of them darting curious glances at the two men, standing face to face, about whom so many strange stories were told.

'Voldemar.'

'Oleg.'

They held each other by the elbows, briefly, before separating. Stanov thought: no, you have not changed. A little balder, perhaps, the thick spectacles stronger than ever, but it is you, Oleg Kazin, still you. Still the same.

'We must get together, sometime. Sometime soon.'

Deep in Stanov's guts a rising spasm of anger caught him off guard, nearly gave the game away: I'll see you in the last circle of Hell first…

Kazin stood back, fitting a cigarette into a little cane holder, a genial smile on his face. 'He wants to talk to you, Voldemar. Alone.' A slight twist of the shoulders and an eyebrow raised in the direction of the double-doors indicated that Kazin was referring to the First Secretary. 'He doesn't trust us, you see. For your ears only, eh?' He laughed good-humouredly. 'But I asked if I might borrow Colonel Yevchenko. Well, as I knew you were coming I thought it wouldn't do any harm if I killed two birds with the same stone. There's a sub-committee being formed…'

'Comrade Marshal!'

Major Krubykov stood in the doorway, one hand raised in summons.

'The First Secretary asks if you will take lunch with him.'

Stanov had time for one last furious glance at Yevchenko over his shoulder before Krubykov had ushered him through the double-doors and he saw no more.

Kazin turned back to Yevchenko to find the old colonel's curious eyes full on his face. He smiled. Yevchenko's expression did not change.

'Colonel, I have been asked to chair a sub-committee of the Politburo. If we are to do our job properly we shall need a lot of very high-quality technical expertise, people close to the top in the KGB who know what really goes on there. Naturally, you were our first choice. I'm sure Marshal Stanov can spare you an afternoon each week, eh? Come, we'll meet the other members of the committee, have some lunch maybe. And we can discuss this Chairman's Order No. 0078 – the whole question of the KGB's involvement with the Administrative Organs Department interests us tremendously.' He put his arm round Yevchenko's shoulders and began to walk down the corridor. 'Those two will yak all day. I believe the First Secretary has a number of questions to raise in connection with Bucharensky's famous diary.' He paused in his stride, so that he could look Yevchenko in the face. 'We have lots of time. In fact, we have all the time in the world.'

So it's come, Yevchenko was thinking as he walked down the corridor, conscious of the deadweight of Kazin's hand on his shoulder. It's come at last. Decision time for me, old man.

But why, oh why, he was thinking as they turned the corner together, did it have to happen today?

Chapter 20

The morning passed too quickly for Kyril's liking. Every time he looked at his watch the hands seemed to have jumped an hour or so. He tried to make himself slow down, take things easily, but it was no good. He was going to visit a woman he hadn't seen for six years but who was as fresh in his mind, his body, as the solicitor's secretary he had spoken to yesterday.

He went shopping, then spent the morning constructing a chair, the sole piece of furniture he reckoned he would need during his stay in Battersea. He used oak, dear and hard to come by, but indispensible. When he had finished the basic structure he set about fixing it to the floor, using cast-iron clamps with holes sufficiently large to admit steel bolts. Then he nailed thick leather belts to the arms and legs and made holes in the leather in such a way that the belts could be used to restrain whoever was sitting in the chair from making the slightest movement, however small.

He cut a round hole in the seat part, so that it looked like a crude lavatory. Behind the chair he embedded a large, closed-eye screw in the window-sill, and to this he attached a length of wire which he had unwound from the clay rod of an electric fire, purchased in a junk shop. In the same junk shop Kyril had picked up the last component he needed in order to complete his remarkable chair. Now everything was ready.

At last he stood up, well satisfied. The house would fall down before anyone escaped from that chair.

The chair was for Loshkevoi. Kyril had made up his mind.

Next Kyril turned his attention to the gas. The result of an hour's work was that he could flood the lower floor with mains gas, making it uninhabitable, or divert the stream to its proper use upstairs. His preparations were complete.

He needed a break. For a few minutes he stood back from the window, smoking, while he inspected the street. No one was watching the house, he was sure of it. Apart from the evidence of his own eyes he did not feel watched, and that was the acid test. The nerves of his body did not register surveillance. The house opposite his own was occupied by the same family each day and there were few visitors anywhere along the road. The same cars stood on the street but their positions were different each day, and that was normal. No one made a pretext to come to the door.

Kyril likened the street to a busy river which threw up no sediment, formed no visible sandbanks, but continued to flow uninterruptedly past his door. If one day there was a sandbank, he would notice it.

Kyril ate some more of the insipid loaf and threw the rest away. 'You need a meal,' he said aloud. 'Something to keep you alive. Do you realise you haven't eaten properly for…'

He shut up, suddenly conscious of the folly of talking to himself. But the idea was good: he did not want to faint when she opened the door and he saw her for the first time, did not want to betray anything which might bc construed as weakness.

At last he was ready. He went down the stairs to the front door, put his hand on the night-latch and turned it. A shaft of sunlight flooded into the dingy hall, causing Kyril to blink. The street was empty. He looked to right and left. Nobody came. No curtain moved.

He stepped into the small area of concrete which separated the house from the pavement and pulled the door to behind him. A car cruised slowly up the street. The black youth behind the wheel took no notice of Kyril. Somewhere close by he heard the noise of milk bottles smashing, followed by the miaow of a cat.

Now he was on the pavement.

Before he had gone more than a few paces he heard a door open and slam. The noise came from behind him, on the same side of the road. The door must belong to the house next to his own. Kyril's breathing quickened. That's where they'd be, the enemy... no, of course not, it was too soon. Surely it was too soon.

Footsteps behind him now, quick and young-sounding. A woman.

'Hal-*lo*. Lovely day, innit?'

Kyril reluctantly stopped and turned. His next door neighbour was young and blonde, her hair trailing down to tiny breasts. On her hand hung the same silent child, thumb stuck firmly into mouth, as he had seen earlier. The child stared up at Kyril with unblinking curiosity.

He smiled and nodded. The girl's eyes never quite fastened on his, as is the way of those who talk to strangers. Nothing about his appearance seemed to strike her as odd or worthy of comment. He began to breathe more easily.

'Is that you making all the noise next door?'

Kyril wrestled with indecision. For a second he had thought she meant to move on but now she seemed rooted to the spot, ready to chat all day. He looked at the fourth finger of her left hand and found no ring. His first reaction had been the right one. A single mother; bored, lonely, slave to the voracious little monster by her side.

He pretended to be afflicted with a violent bout of coughing and banged his chest.

'You all right?'

The girl's eyes widened in concern. *Why didn't she go?*

'Me chest,' he croaked. 'Very bad lately.'

'You ought to see someone about that. My movver died of it. Yeah. Bronchal, it was. 'Aven't seen you since you come in. 'Ow you getting on then, all right?'

Kyril nodded again. The muscles of his lower abdomen were tight with nerves. He could stand only so much more of this.

'You don't half make a row. I dunno 'ow I put up wivit. An' you don't look at all well, honest.'

'Feelin' all right. Sorry about the noise. All done now.'

Kyril smiled and turned his back on her. He could feel the girl's eyes boring into him. She did not move. He took a step. And another.

She was by his side.

'Look, why don't you come in for a cuppa tea or somefink. One day soon.'

Kyril nodded and coughed again.

'Yeah, well, look after yourself. I gotta be going now. Playgroup.'

As if to emphasise this last point she gave the child a good shake. It – Kyril couldn't tell the sex – extracted its thumb from its mouth and gave the girl a long, hard look that might have meant pain or just simple hate. Then they were going down the hill away from him, the child half-walking, half being dragged along by its mother, who said nothing but marched straight ahead, not turning back, until they reached the corner and disappeared.

Kyril was certain that the girl did not come from any of the major intelligence services. She was not, in any sense of the term, a 'watcher'. Children were sometimes used as cover, but not children as young as that, and certainly not one-parent children who might suddenly require attention at an inconvenient moment.

Stanov? No. He would not as yet be aware even that Kyril had made it to London unscathed. But there was something of Stanov in the set-up, nonetheless: a babysitter next door, just in case.

Kyril shook his head. He was imagining things in his search for reassurance. She was just a girl, a girl with a bastard child, someone so tied up in her own affairs that she would be unlikely to remember even that she had invited him for tea.

He spent the next half-hour checking for tails. There were none. Once he was sure of that he ceased wandering aimlessly and began to walk with a purpose. He took a snack in a sandwich-bar, scanning the pavement as he munched his roll and drank his milk. When he left the traffic had grown busier, the streets more crowded. At last he was negotiating the busy junction at the end of St Johns Road.

A little shop on the corner caught his eye, and he realised he was getting low on cigarettes. He went in, and for the umpteenth time marvelled at the glittering array of packages and jars which confronted him. Every kind of chocolate, sweet, cigarette, even cigars were on prominent display here, in this tiny south London corner shop. Yet the people he passed on his way to the counter looked dour and dissatisfied, as if all this meant nothing. Kyril dithered for a moment between several brands of expensive king-size filters, enjoying the embarrassment of choice. The shopman took his money without a smile. 'We will bury you', that is what Kruschev had said, and he was right. That is what you did to dead people, people who were long ago rendered incapable of appreciating that they were alive at all.

He looked at his watch. The timing was perfect. A few more steps and he was in Vera's road. Immediately it was like Athens all over again. The criss-cross rays of surveillance meshed to entrap him in their web. Now, however, Kyril did not falter in his stride. He was expecting watchers here; their absence would have spelled danger. He had orders to be seen at this time, in this place.

A car... no, two cars, on opposite sides of the road. Very obvious – the arm on the door, that was poor craft. If it had been up to Kyril he would have had the windows tightly closed and used a mirror from a concealed position on the floor. They must feel very confident.

If they were taking the game seriously, as Stanov predicted, SIS would have requisitioned the houses on either side of Vera's and the one directly across the street from it. As he approached, Kyril vainly strove to see behind the net curtains. Nothing differentiated these houses from all the rest.

He turned into the gateway of Number 48 and walked up the path.

'They sacked her, of course,' Stanov had said, peering closely at him to see how he took it. 'Even the British Foreign Office retains some pragmatism. But she's still living in the old house. She works at home, typing mostly. So she'll be in when you call.'

As his finger hovered over the bell Kyril hoped desperately that she was away, on holiday, in hospital, anything. Like his own house, No. 48 Turpin Road was divided into two flats, only in this part of Clapham they were called maisonettes. Kyril didn't have to look for the right bell. His finger found it as if by instinct.

Behind him in the street a car engine fired. Kyril did not turn his head. He became aware that within the house there was suddenly silence, and he realised that a typewriter had been clacking away in his subconscious ever since he reached the door.

The car drove slowly up the street. As Kyril resisted the nagging voice in his head which told him to look back, the door opened.

She had changed, of course she had changed, but Kyril knew her instantly. The eyes could not alter. The same shy, diffident eyes with the same light in them, the look of surprise he remembered from years ago.

She stood with one hand on the doorframe, her lips slightly parted in the first shock of surprise at seeing a stranger and realising that he was not quite a stranger, after all. Then knowledge came; her mouth fell open, the hand dropped away from the frame, and she was retreating into the hall, her head moving from side to side in slow, disbelieving sweeps.

Kyril came over the threshold very quickly and shut the door.

'Hello, Vera.'

She said nothing at first. Kyril wondered whether she had heard.

'If you don't mind,' she said weakly, 'I'm going to sit down.'

He followed her into the sitting-room. That had changed. The bare walls were now covered with a pretty paper, full of light and space, with neat watercolours carefully chosen to complement the pattern. In place of the old trestle, much stained with the rings left by hot dishes and mugs, was a fine piece of solid pine with carver chairs to match. The carpet looked new, as did the wing-chair in the window and the sofa, both covered with a loose version of the wallpaper.

In the window, beside the chair, stood a Chinese vase containing a spider-plant. That or a similar plant had stood in the same vase six years ago. It was as if someone had dismantled the room Kyril remembered and very carefully constructed a new one round the plant and its vase, so as not to disturb them.

Kyril looked again at Vera, for the first time noticing things other than her eyes. She looked tired but well. Her face was tanned, as if from lying in the sun, but the skin showed few signs of ageing. Only the neck, where the first indications come, was slightly mottled. Her hair was different; she used to wear it long but now it was cut short, curling inwards round her neck. It suited her. She was neither fatter nor taller than he remembered. The features were the same. Why was it, then, that she was no longer pretty?

He struggled for something to say, anything to break the silence. 'This is… wonderful. You've done well.'

She looked around in response to his gesture, a look of puzzlement on her face.

'The flat?'

'Yes.'

She studied him, as if unsure whether he was playing a joke on her.

'It's all very cheap. It's all I can afford.'

He stared at her. 'But… in Moscow there is nothing like this. Only for wealthy people.'

She shook her head, the beginnings of a smile on her lips.

'You never learn, do you? In England you have to be very poor now not to have a room like this. You and your Moscow. Oh Ivan.'

Her voice was a mixture of tired amusement and hopelessness. There was a new, inner calm about her which Kyril found unsettling, he couldn't fathom why.

Her clothes were different, too. She was wearing a pair of faded denim jeans, the sort of thing which fetched a good price on the black market at home, and a thick, chunky sweater. With a little start of surprise he realised that almost everyone in London seemed able to afford clothes like that.

'Oh Ivan, why did you go?'

She was sitting on one of the carver chairs, hands folded in her lap. He stood up abruptly and went to the window, taking care not to disturb the net curtains. One of the two cars was still there, the other had disappeared. The house opposite showed no sign of life.

'Still the same Ivan. Who's following you this time?'

Keeping his back to her he said, 'Do you have a radio?' For an answer she got up and went to a cabinet by the far wall. A second later loud pop music spilled into the room. 'Nothing changes, does it Ivan?'

He moved about restlessly. Her probing annoyed him. 'Some things do. For instance, I'm not sure, but I think they have a laser beam directed at this window. Whatever we say gets ferried along the beam to their receiver in the house over the way. Have you had any unusual visitors lately?' She thought. 'No.'

'Telephone repairmen, gas inspectors, that sort of thing?' Vera shook her head. 'Nobody. Unless…'

'Yes?'

'Well, unless you count the solicitor.'

Kyril moved close to her. 'Where did he stand? Did he sit?'

She showed him by acting out Sculby's movements as far as she could remember them. Kyril watched her intently. 'Wait… what was he doing over there?'

'His case wouldn't shut properly… he rested it on the table.'

There were a number of possibilities, but the first guess turned out to be correct. His fingers slid along the edge of the table and almost as once found a tiny plastic box on a spike, the size of a drawing pin's. He held it up between his fingertips for her to see before throwing it on the floor and jumping on it.

'Come.'

He beckoned her over to the sofa. She followed slowly, her wide eyes darting this way and that, the first signs of fear apparent on her face. As she sat down beside him he pulled her close and left his arm around her shoulder. She stiffened but did not pull away. After a while she relaxed a little and unconsciously nestled into the crook of his arm.

'Whisper. Who was this solicitor? Tell me about him.'

'He made an appointment to see me. He thought I might be able to help one of his clients by being a witness, I think…'

'Name?'

'Sculby. I've got his letter somewhere.'

She went across to the mantelpiece and felt behind the clock. 'Here.'

Kyril read it quickly. Vera saw him crumple the paper at one point, as if something in the message had moved him. Then he held it up against the light. The letter seemed innocent enough. He handed it back to her with a frown on his face.

'You can keep it if you like.'

He shook his head. 'I'll remember. What else did he say to you about this… Loshkevoi?'

Vera told him the morning's events. Kyril sat with his head in his hands and his eyes closed, as if recording every word. When she had finished he said nothing. After a while she subdued the nervousness which his silence inspired in her enough to ask a question.

'What are you doing?'

Kyril opened his eyes and licked his lips.

'Defecting.'

Her eyes widened still further and for a moment she did not speak.

'Who's out there?'

'Everyone. The KGB. They have to stop me, you see. And the British.'

'Can't they protect you? The British, I mean. If you're going over to them…'

He shook his head sadly. 'It's not as simple as that. I have to choose my own time, Vera. They think I'm a plant, in any case. They're just as likely to shoot me as the KGB.'

At the word 'shoot' her hand tightened on his arm, and immediately relaxed.

'Then why have you come here. You must know they'd be watching me if they're waiting for you…'

'I had to see you. Don't worry, Vera, I want nothing from you, not shelter, not money, nothing. But… can you understand this? I'm in the middle of making a decision, the biggest decision of my whole life. And if I get it wrong…'

He pulled her closer, and she gave without resistance. 'But how can I help?'

'By talking. About the past. About… us. You never married after I left.'

'No, I never married.' Her voice was suddenly cold. She allowed her head to loll back on the sofa so that she could stare at the ceiling without meeting Kyril's eyes. 'I told myself to forget you. I *did* forget you, in a way.'

'In a way…?'

'Yes. There never was a day went by without my thinking of you, seeing your face. The memories are blurred now.'

She slowly raised her head and turned to face him.

'Not like they'll be tomorrow. When you're gone. Because you are going, aren't you?'

He hesitated for a second before nodding.

She shook her head sadly. 'Then why did you have to come back, Ivan? I could live without you. I have done for six years. Why come back and spoil it all. Wasn't it enough, what you did to me?'

For several minutes the music from the radio was the only sound to be heard in the sunlit room. Vera pulled herself up abruptly and went to stand by the window, her arms folded, hands caressing forearms in a remote, despondent gesture.

'Stay away from the window,' warned Kyril. Vera shook her head violently.

'I said...' Kyril jumped up and reached out to jerk her back. Vera pulled away from him, keeping her head turned, and he realised that she was crying.

Inside Kyril something snapped. All his roughness died away. When he reached out it was to take her in his arms and hold her tightly, clutching her body to him while his hands began to stroke her hair, the glorious raven-black hair. It was as if his hands were reliving a memory. They had done this before, so many times. Vera's body was shaking, the sobs communicating her distress straight into him, while they stood, locked together, uncaring, before the bright white window.

When he picked her up Vera did not protest. She lay quiescent in his arms, looking at him like a trusting child. As he laid her on the bed she raised her hands to help him remove the sweater, and when his own hands fumbled with the strap of her bra she showed him how it went. Only when he lay down beside her did she hold him away for a moment while looking up and down his body, as if in wonder. Her hand went to hold his erect penis, stroking it gently upwards in a way he remembered; Kyril lay there, passive, striving to keep his body under control while she renewed her acquaintance with his body. At last she raised her hand to his lips and he kissed the fingers one by one, tasting the faint musk of his own genitals, before folding her in his arms. The second before penetration, just as he was gently lowering his weight on to her, she pushed at his chest with her hands, in a moment of rebellion; then the same hands slipped round to his back and as her flesh closed round his he felt the sudden reflexive rending of her nails.

For Kyril everything was old and familiar and new and exciting. They made love twice, very quickly, and then, after an interval, a third time, more slowly. It was as though they were trying to compare the memory with the reality, unable to decide which was best. When they were tired and the room was growing darker he made her put on the sweater, nothing else, and lie in his arms with her head on his chest. For the first time, they began to talk: talk as old friends, old lovers.

'What did they do to Stefanie?'

For a moment Vera wanted to pretend that the name meant nothing to her, but only for a moment. Poor, dear Stefanie, whose negative vetting did not disclose that she worked for the KGB, relaying information to the embassy through Ivan Bucharensky. First my boss, then my flat-mate, thought Vera. Friends. Until the day when, through a mixture of appallingly bad luck and Stefanie's negligence, Vera had met Ivan.

'Nothing, in the end. There wasn't quite enough evidence for a trial. She went abroad, wrote for a while.'

'And you?'

'Oh come on, you know what happened to me.'

It was not hostile. They continued to lie in the gathering gloom, still content.

'And you're really poor?'

She smiled. 'Not really. Not in the way you mean. It's just… oh, I don't know. We always lived in different worlds, you and I. The stuff in this flat, the furniture, the clothes, the food even, they're *ordinary*, Ivan. Can't you understand that? They're the sort of thing we have in this country, that we're used to. It's funny, do you remember the famous weekend in Paris?'

His face crinkled in a frown. 'Paris. I can't…'

'I'd been saving for months, long before I met you, a little bit put by every week, for two days in Paris.

Stefanie and I, just us. And when we told you, you were so angry. Don't you remember? You went on and on about extravagance, and decadence. When I learned the truth, later, about you and her... well, I thought perhaps Paris interfered with one of your plans, or something. But then I thought: no. It's because where Ivan comes from people don't go away at all. Because they can't. And even if they could, even if the authorities would let them, they don't have that kind of money. They don't have the freedom to blow everything on one glorious spree of pink champagne and smoked salmon. The Soviet state will save them from their folly.'

She wriggled out of his arms and went to the dressing-table. Kyril heard the scrape of a match and smelled smoke.

'Cigarettes? You?'

'Oh yes, me. People do change, you know. England's changing.'

'How do you mean?'

'We're getting like you.' She inhaled deeply and lay back in his arms, letting the smoke escape with her next words. 'The state is determined to save us all from ourselves. Look. Have you seen this. Oh damn, it's dark in here...'

She reached out to the bedside light, but he restrained her gently. 'Just tell me.'

'It says on the packet: Her Majesty's Government Health Warning. Smoking can be dangerous to your health.'

'Yes. I've seen it. But we don't have that in Russia.'

'No, but it's all the same thing. It's the low road, and we've started to tread it. Bit by bit, year by year. So slowly that we don't even notice it's happening any more.'

Kyril lay back, cradling his head in his arms, and looked at the ceiling. He didn't understand. What had a packet of cigarettes to do with travelling abroad? In Russia every citizen had to carry an internal passport containing the all-important *propiska*, which entitled the bearer to reside in a particular locality. In England it was different. In England everyone was free. The greenest new *schpick* enduring his first day's training in the KGB knew that.

'Ivan.'

'Yes.'

But Vera did not respond at once. Instead she drew hard on her cigarette; Kyril watched the little point of red fire glow in the darkness of the bedroom before dying away.

'Ivan, have you come back to me? Have you? You said you were defecting...'

For a moment Kyril did nothing. Then he swung his legs off the bed and began to dress.

'Ivan, no, listen to me, please listen to me. I didn't want to interfere, it's just that you said...'

'I know what I said.' His voice was low and sad and somehow humble. 'Vera, I... I think I made a mistake to come here. I'm sorry.'

This time she managed to switch on the light without him sensing in advance what she was going to do. They blinked in the sudden flash. In a split second Kyril was by the window, drawing the curtains with a violence that surprised even him. As the anger drained away he let his head fall forward on to his hands where they met, holding the curtains tightly together.

'I see.'

Vera stood up and mechanically began to smooth down the crumpled bedclothes. When she had done that she started to dress, keeping her back to Kyril.

'Vera, listen.' Kyril swung her round to face him. Vera's eyes were cold, her expression closed against him. 'Everything's a mess at the moment. But if I manage to sort things out, if I can get through safely, then… then yes, I've come back to you. I promise.'

His hands dropped from her shoulders; she swayed a little, as if missing their support, but her eyes never left his face.

'I love you, Vanya,' she said evenly. 'I've always loved you, right from the first. I'll always love you.'

For an answer he held out his hands, and she came to him. 'Tell me what to do,' she said after a while.

'Let's get dressed first.'

When they were sitting in the front room again she brought him gin and supper. It was the first decent food Kyril had tasted since he arrived in England.

'No vodka I'm afraid. Too painful. Silly, isn't it?'

Kyril shook his head gently. 'Not silly.'

She tilted her glass at him, and they drank.

'The first thing is this. People are going to come and talk to you, lots of people. Tell them the truth and they won't hurt you. I came. I stayed a while. I didn't tell you anything except I'm defecting but I have problems. They know all that anyway. But most important, you don't know where I am.'

'Vanya, I…'

Kyril held up his hand. 'No, Vera. It has to be this way. When I leave you, you don't know where I'm going, and you can't tell them what you don't know. They'll see the sense of that. They don't seriously expect you to know.'

Her face seemed to have shrunk. He could see fear in her eyes, fear and the realisation, at last, of what it all meant.

'No one'll want to hurt you,' he said reassuringly. 'But they'll ask you things and they'll be very insistent. Don't give in. And don't – Vera, this is so important – don't have anything to do with this solicitor who came to see you. Or his client. If Loshkevoi turns up here, don't let him in, just call the police at once, you hear?'

She nodded numbly. For the second time her Vanya was turning the world upside down. She didn't want to face the future, not yet.

Kyril stroked the hair off her forehead.

'Be patient,' he said. 'Don't believe anything you hear on the radio or television or read in the papers. Promise.'

She nodded again.

'And now you have to help me get out of here.'

She looked up sharply, tears glistening in her eyes. 'Now?'

'Yes, Vera. I'm sorry. Now.'

He put down the tray and helped her to her feet. She clung to him and they kissed, long and hard. Then she pushed him away to show that she was ready, and he pointed to the telephone.

'I want you to call a taxi. Choose a firm you haven't used before. If they ask where you want to go, give an address somewhere quite close, but Vera… make sure it's a real address. Ask them to say how long they'll be in coming.'

Vera started to flip through the Yellow Pages. Kyril stood by the window, pushing aside the curtain a fraction, enough to give him a restricted view of the road. Everything was quiet.

It took a while for Vera to find a company prepared to answer the phone, let alone undertake the journey, but at last she had discharged Kyril's instructions to the full.

‘Get your coat. You’re coming with me to the station.’

‘The station…’

‘I have a plan, Vera. But I need your help. Outside there are at least two men waiting for me, maybe more. One of them is British and he doesn’t matter. MI6 are waiting for me to make the first move. So long as they can see me they won’t worry. But the KGB are out there too, and they’re a different proposition. I’m wanted in Moscow – alive. Not even the KGB are stupid enough to kidnap me here, especially with a MI6 agent watching what goes on. But it’s doubly important for them not to lose me. Their only chance is to tail me from here back to my home-base.’

‘But can you be sure? Mightn’t they risk anything if they want you enough?’

‘They need to know where I’m staying. I’m supposed to have stolen one of their project-plans and it’s extremely unlikely that I’d have it on me.’ He smiled bleakly. ‘Don’t worry, Vera. I’m only followed if I want to be followed. And this time, I don’t. But you’ve got to help me. Now listen…’

About a quarter of an hour later a minicab drew up outside the house, and as the driver opened his door to get out he found the fares already slipping quietly into the back seat.

‘Clapham Junction,’ said Kyril, adding, as the driver was on the point of complaining, ‘We’ve changed our minds. Will ten pounds cover it?’

The driver said nothing, but started the engine.

Kyril looked back through the rear window. The darkened street was full of cars parked down both sides. Even as he looked, one of them pulled out and started to follow.

The minicab reached the junction of Turpin Road with St Johns Road, and stopped. The side-lights of the car behind approached very slowly, halting perhaps ten yards behind the cab. Beyond that Kyril could just make out a third car, its indicator winking.

The cab-driver turned right and began to accelerate. Through the rear windscreen Kyril saw both cars copy the manoeuvre, and smiled. The convoy travelled at a steady 40 mph, 20 or 30 yards between each car.

'Your money's on the seat.'

The driver looked askance at the notes which fluttered on to the Draylon beside him.

'Ten for the firm. Ten for you. And you've never seen either of us.'

'Blind,' said the driver. 'That's me.'

'It must make driving very difficult. Left here and stop *hard*.'

The driver obeyed, instinctively snapping to the command in Kyril's voice. He gave no previous warning and Kyril had a sudden view of the car behind sailing on through the traffic-lights, which obligingly changed to red.

'Out.'

Vera leapt out of the car and ran across the road to the footpath which led up to Clapham Junction station, Kyril at her heels. As he rounded the corner he caught a glimpse of the second car narrowly avoiding a collision with the stationary cab.

They were through the barrier and racing for the platform before the sleepy ticket-collector could do anything about it.

'Just pray we don't have to wait long.'

'Platform Twelve,' panted Vera. 'I can hear it coming.'

They reached the top of the steps just as a Victoria-bound train was squealing and grinding its way to a halt. Kyril hustled Vera into a compartment of a carriage with no connecting corridor and stood at the window, like a lover who wants to discourage company on the ride.

'Stan' 'way!' yelled a porter.

The whistle blew. Kyril's fists clenched. What was the hold up? Why didn't they *go*?

He heard the hiss of the vacuum brake and relaxed. The train started to move. A man flung himself up the last two steps to the platform and dived for the nearest carriage-door, wrenching it open and scrabbling with his feet for the running-board. He made it, just, and Kyril swore.

'One,' he said as he slammed up the window. 'Too bad. But… only one.'

He and Vera had the compartment to themselves. They sat holding hands for most of the short journey to Victoria. When the train halted for a signal outside the terminus they each stood at a window, staring out.

'D'you see anything?'

'It's dark this side… no, nothing.'

Again the hiss of the brake. The train began to roil forward. Kyril raised his window and turned to Vera.

'He stayed put, then. No movement my side. I half-expected him to crawl along the footway. He's biding his time. Maybe…'

He fell silent.

'Maybe what?'

'Nothing.'

He did not want to tell Vera the thought which had crossed his mind, that in the few seconds it had taken them to board the train the tail might have had time to radio his base and arrange for them to be met at Victoria.

Suddenly lights were everywhere; they were coming into the station. Kyril hurriedly took Vera in his arms and kissed her.

'Now look.'

She broke away from him and lowered the window on the platform side.

'About a dozen people scattered along the platform… I can see a door opening, I think it's him, he's only a couple of compartments down. There's a porter…'

The driver applied the brakes and the train shuddered.

'Only another twenty yards…'

They were going at little more than walking pace.

'Ten yards… oh Vanya, *Vanya*.'

The train halted. Doors opened. Vera got out and turned to face the compartment, smiling up as if to snatch a last kiss before saying goodbye. Out of the corner of her eye she could see a man. Unlike the other passengers he was not walking away from her, down the platform to the barrier. She had an impression of jeans and a wind-cheater but kept her face upturned to the window, reaching for that final kiss. Her lips moved, as if talking to the unseen man inside. In fact, she was praying for the simple subterfuge to work.

A number of things happened very quickly.

The stranger reached across Vera to see that the compartment was empty, its far door open and a dark void on the other side. In the same instant he hurled himself forward into the compartment, thrusting Vera aside, only to fall flat on his face. Through bewilderment and pain he realised that Kyril had been concealed under the seat all along, and had reached out to grab his ankle.

Strong hands collared the stranger, he felt a knee in the small of his back and heard a voice cry, 'Get in!'

It took a moment for Vera to realise that Kyril meant her. She scrambled back into the train and slammed the door, shutting off the melee from any curious passengers who might come along the platform, and stood looking out as Kyril had done earlier.

Behind her she could hear the muffled grunts and thumps of a fight. She clenched her fists to the glass and stared out as if her life depended on it. She was talking to herself: please finish it, finish it...

Through the open door on the other side of the compartment came another sound, that of a train drawing into the station along the adjacent track. It grew rapidly louder and was suddenly punctuated by the howl of the wind-horn: its driver must have seen the open door and sounded a warning. The approaching train was almost level with Vera's compartment, its horn moaning continuously. Suddenly she could bear it no longer, and swung round crying 'Vanya!'

But Kyril had gone. The compartment was empty.

With a piercing squeal of brakes the oncoming train ground to a halt outside the door opposite Vera, its horn still sounding a single note.

Her mouth fell open. For a second the carriage went round and round, somebody seemed to be twisting a band of steel into her forehead...

Vera Bradfield clutched her stomach and was violently sick.

-

Kyril lay between the rails, fighting to get his breath back. His brain had temporarily seized up. All he could think of was stories of men who suffered terrible amputations and could feel nothing, numbed by shock into the belief that they had miraculously come through unscathed.

He moved his right leg, then his left. He was alive. He could feel all his limbs.

And he could hear. A horn, the sound of many voices. It was time to go.

Carefully avoiding the live rails he flipped from under the train across to the track nearest the platform where he had arrived with Vera a few moments ago. He wanted to look back to see what had happened to his attacker but his brain, active once more, forbade it. Better not. You've got enough to cope with. So has Vera…

Using the monkey crawl he edged his way along the tracks beneath the first train, making for the end farthest from the barrier. There, all was peaceful. He poked his head out cautiously. Anyone who had been standing at this point a moment before would understandably have been attracted back along the platform where all the commotion was. He climbed from under the train and stood upright between the rails. There was nobody about. No one looked in his direction.

Kyril vaulted up on to the platform. A few metres away he could see an iron stairway leading to a gantry which spanned the platform. He ran up it three steps at a time, coming to rest in the shadow of the overhead air-terminal which the gantry was designed to serve. He peered round the corner to find that he had a bird's eye view of the scene for which he was responsible.

Vera stood in the middle of a crowd of people, her face white. She was crying. A policeman was standing next to her, notebook in hand. An ambulance advanced slowly down the platform towards them.

On the other side he could see where the incoming train had stopped well short of the buffers, and there the crowd was smaller, more professional. A second ambulance was already parked close up to the train, its open doors flanked by policemen who every so often waved back a curious passerby. But for the most part the casual watchers had gone, repelled by their glimpse of what lay under the wheels of the train.

A necessity of the mission, Kyril told himself as he walked casually along the gantry, making for the platform farthest from the scene of the 'accident'. For Vera he had no worries, once the initial shock had worn off: before leaving the house he had primed her with things to say if it went wrong, and he never doubted her ability to stay cool in a crisis.

For a moment he allowed his heart to go to her in a spasm of sympathy and remorse; then he was himself again. He had to go on. No matter what, he must succeed.

He took his seat in a 'local' which was going to Battersea Park. From there it would be a short walk to the house in Queenstown Road. Then a long, long sleep.

As the train accelerated out of the station Kyril allowed himself the brief luxury of visualising a scene in Moscow Centre. Against all the odds the moving, highly charged magnet conjured up by Stanov had reached London. Stanov was talking, perhaps even now...

'There was a telex this afternoon... it came in at 1548 Greenwich Mean Time... it came to you... why did it come to you, comrade...?' Comrade what, Kyril wondered. Colonel, probably, but a general was not out of the question.

Anyway. 'Why did you not report this?' Stanov would go on. 'Why did you hold back?' Or perhaps... 'Why did you at once order an executioner from the A2 Institute to go to England?'

Kyril blanked out his thoughts. Hour by hour, minute by minute. That was how he had to live. Let the next minute come, that was all.

Above the clatter of the Battersea train crossing the points outside the terminus, Kyril's sensitive ears detected the first high screech of a siren.

Chapter 21

The news of Kyril's sighting came through to Centre shortly after three. The head of the First Main Directorate consulted with Col. Gen. Povin and gave certain orders. Since then General Michaelov, rather unusually for him, had been reading a dossier. When he had finished it he remained lost in thought for a moment before lifting the telephone.

'Is he here?'

'Yes, comrade General. Shall I show him in?'

Michaelov hesitated. 'Very well.'

Two sentries delivered Sikarov to the door of the First Deputy Chairman's office. Michaelov impatiently signed the chit which acknowledged his receipt of Employee No. ZPQ 09458, Dept. V, A2 Institute, and dismissed the escort.

His visitor remained standing rigidly to attention. As Michaelov turned back from the door he caught a glimpse of Sikarov's upturned chin and was reminded irresistibly of a human skull; the skin was stretched so tightly over the jaw that the line of his cheekbones seemed to dominate the whole face, making of it a death's head.

'Sit down, Sikarov.'

As he resumed his chair behind the desk Michaelov was aware of an acrid, unpleasant smell radiating from Sikarov's clothes. His nose wrinkled in distaste. Michaelov did not hold with all this pansy deodorant nonsense, which seemed to be gaining a suspiciously firm hold in Dzerzhinsky Square, but he liked his men to wash and he preferred them not to wear clothes which stank of death.

'I have a job for you. In England. You are ready to move at once?'

'Certainly, comrade General.'

Sikarov continued to stare ahead of him, his gaze just missing Michaelov's eyes.

'It will be very quick; you go in, you come out, in less than forty-eight hours. Absolute secrecy is essential. If at all possible you must make the job look like an accident, but the important thing is to secure a quick death. Understand?'

Sikarov nodded abruptly. 'Who is the target?'

'Colonel Ivan Yevseevich Bucharensky. Casename "Kyril".'

For the first time Sikarov looked directly at Michaelov and his eyes came into focus. Michaelov regarded him curiously, trying to assess the effect of his former colleague's name on this crude assassin. What memories did he have of that single occasion when they had worked in tandem?

'Excuse me, comrade General, but according to the Chairman's personal order Colonel Bucharensky is to be brought back alive.'

Michaelov smiled. 'Don't trouble your head about that, Sikarov. It's not your concern. But to reassure you, let me say this. Some orders are to be obeyed. Some are to be lost in the pipe. You follow?'

Sikarov's tense face relaxed into a grin. 'Yes.'

'Some orders get back to the enemy in the West. They are meant to get back, no? And when they do, the information contained in those orders serves its purpose.'

Sikarov nodded. 'I quite understand, comrade General.' Then he frowned. 'You are, with respect, sure that the target is in England. There was some doubt...'

'He was observed on the street in south London less than one hour ago. We do not know where he is based, not yet. That is for you to find out.'

Sikarov waited to be dismissed. His body had begun to tingle with suppressed excitement, his eyes burned with nervous tension. He had been desk-bound for too long. But Michaelov seemed dissatisfied about something.

'The reason why I am briefing you myself, Sikarov, is that you are not to talk to anyone about this. Not to anyone at all. Do you understand?'

Sikarov nodded again.

'If you get into trouble in London you are to call on *me* – you will report your presence in the UK to the London Resident but after that you will leave the embassy right out of it. You may even get a little opposition from that quarter. You're not the only one going around parroting Chairman's Orders, let me tell you. Ignore it. Ignore everything except what I tell you. This is a matter of high policy. If it later emerged that you had disregarded my instructions, Sikarov...'

Michaelov allowed his sentence to taper off in a smile.

'I shall say nothing, comrade General. Believe me, the embassies are nothing but trouble. I am honoured to have been selected for this mission. Traitors... well, traitors are special, no?'

Now it was Michaelov's turn to nod curtly.

'And I want no funny business, Sikarov; no police involvement. Understand *that* also.'

Two points of colour burned in Sikarov's gaunt cheeks. 'That is in the past.' There was a trace of sulkiness in his tone. 'A regrettable lapse.'

'Lapses, Sikarov. Plural. First Berlin, then Paris. Innocent people dead, and women in each case. I quote from the report of Colonel – then Captain – Ivan Yevseevich Bucharensky: "It brings too much attention." What an understatement!'

Sikarov scowled at Michaelov, who saw his fists suddenly clench. He banged the desk-top. 'You come highly recommended to me, Sikarov. They tell me you're cured of all that. I've read your file very carefully. I'm going to trust you. But if you fail…' Michaelov lolled back in his chair, his lower lip jutting. 'You won't be coming back to Moscow. Now listen. There's not much to go on. London is arranging to have Kyril followed but I shouldn't place too much reliance on that if I were you. Kyril is good. Better than we thought, in fact.'

Michaelov grunted, stung by the memory of Athens.

'But we have two other leads. Kyril is reported to be hunting a man called Loshkevoi, Victor Gregory Loshkevoi, don't ask me why. Also, he used to have a girl in London. It's all in the case-file, but find those two and Kyril won't be far away. Understand?'

'Yes, comrade General.'

'Good. One other thing. If you get a chance to interrogate Bucharensky, do so. See what he's carrying in the way of papers. But don't expect miracles. You'll be on your own in a foreign country. The death's the main thing. That's all. On your way.'

A faint smell hung in the room long after Sikarov had been delivered back into the care of the sentries. Michaelov stood up and went to throw open the window, braving the cold March air for the sake of a clear head. He remained there for a long time, looking down into the Square, wondering if he had done the right thing. It was a gamble, he knew that. After a while he decided to take advice and comfort.

Povin's office was but a step down the corridor. As he entered Povin himself was sitting beside the coal fire, one leg draped over the arm of his chair, a book in his hands. On seeing Michaelov he stood up with a smile, straightening his uniform. Michaelov laid a hand on his shoulder and pushed him gently down, conscious of a sudden feeling of warmth for Povin, who after all these years still rose automatically when his chief entered the room. That mattered to Michaelov.

'Has Sikarov been to see you?' Povin asked.

'Yes, a moment ago.'

Michaelov was not surprised to hear his deputy speak these unguarded words, in other times an unforgivable breach of security. Ever since the night of Povin's party, when he had gone back to Dzerzhinsky Square and found 'Sociable Plover' in the blue safe, Michaelov had had their offices electronically 'swept' twice a day. So far he had not uncovered any evidence of surveillance. But since that night he had suffered from an irrepressible need to talk to Povin at regular intervals, almost careless of the possible consequences.

Michaelov sat down, his face gloomy. 'If we're wrong about Stanov...'

'Now Valery, we've been through all that. It's a policy decision. Either we can afford to lose Royston or we can't.

We both know that we can't. By the way, remember I told you I'd heard a rumour that the Second Main Directorate were trying to foul things up? It's true.' He leaned forward, offering his cigarette-case to Michaelov as he did so. 'You know old Yatsyna in counter-intelligence? We were at training-school together, we still go drinking now and then. He's told me, in confidence of course, that Veber is trying to use A2, but the Institute won't play.'

'Veber!' exploded Michaelov. 'The deputy head of the Second Main Directorate! Why, I'll kill him. A2 is ours!'

'I know, Valery, I know, but that's how things are right now. Everyone's angling for position. We all know the old man can't last...' Povin shrugged a dismissive shoulder in the direction of Stanov's office. 'Who's going to come out on top, that's what everyone wants to know. Veber thought he'd steal a march by sending an A2 raiding party to Brussels, but they turned him down flat, or so Yatsyna told me. Asked to see an order signed by the First Deputy Chairman personally, and threatened to report to Yevchenko when Veber couldn't produce it. They all know about the diary now, that's the trouble. But do me a favour, Valery, don't mention this to anyone. Yatsyna's a good man, even if he is with Second.'

Michaelov chewed his lips, and for a while there was silence.

'All right,' he said eventually. 'The last thing I want to do is cut out your contact in Second. But I'm telling you, Stepan, A2's ours.'

'Of course, Valery, but you see the point. If they're trying to muscle in on the Institute, the word's gone out. The old man's finished.'

Michaelov nodded. 'And if anyone's going to terminate that poisonous little rat Kyril...'

'It's going to be us. Quite.' Povin smiled and extinguished his cigarette, as if to end the meeting, but Michaelov remained deep in thought.

'Stepan… why did you recommend Sikarov?'

Povin frowned. 'Did I?'

'Well, you said you thought he was fully rehabilitated.' Povin's frown relaxed. 'Oh yes, I did say that.'

'We were talking about Bucharensky, you remember…' Povin nodded slowly. 'It was about the same time, yes, you're quite right, Valery. He was very good, in the old days. Before the trouble. When I was under Golunov we always used him, there were never any complaints. And of course, as you know, he once worked with Bucharensky. Perhaps I thought he might recall some of Kyril's style, that it would give him a head start over the rest. Why do you mention it?'

'He's a funny bastard. Even Bucharensky said so after that time in Paris.'

'They all are. Do you realise, Valery, we are now one of the only three major intelligence services in the world that still has an execution squad? I mean, a squad on day and night call, year in and year out? All the full-time Institute boys are odd.'

Michaelov still wasn't satisfied. 'He's not worked for a long time, you know. In fact, he's worked very little since… Moiseyev.'

Michaelov seemed to have trouble over pronouncing that name. For a while neither man spoke. Moiseyev could still silence his murderers.

'Ah yes,' said Povin at last. 'I had forgotten that.' He gave a sudden laugh, humourless and short. 'It always stuck in my mind,' he said. 'That report. "He was forcibly drowned in the Black Sea at a depth of 156 cm…" Why

156 cm, Valery? Why not 160 or even 150 cm, for the sake of a round number?'

Michaelov grunted but did not reply.

'"Mechanical asphyxiation as a result of drowning", that's what the death certificate said. Of course it was Sikarov, yes, I had forgotten that.'

'Did you ever see Malsin?' Michaelov interrupted gruffly.

'Malsin?'

'Moiseyev's commanding officer. A lieutenant-colonel. He really hated all those Christians, and as for the Reform Baptists… well, they were the worst. When Moiseyev started to have visions and disrupt the unit he threw a fit. He had high connections in the old man's office, no wonder the Institute were called in. I saw him a few months after it all happened. He'd just lost his only child and his wife was having a nervous breakdown…'

'It's coming back to me.' Povin sounded doubtful. 'I recall something of the kind. Didn't he get invalided out? Delusions, something about delusions…'

'He thought he was being pursued by the judgement of God,' said Michaelov sombrely. 'And it finished him.'

Povin nodded slowly. 'Well,' he said at last. 'Sikarov's done some good work since then, Valery. I don't think you need have any worries.'

'But he's never done anything big, not since 1972 when Moiseyev died. He smells.' He stopped, suddenly conscious that he had said something funny, and both men laughed.

'Cleanliness is not his strong point, that I grant you. But he's a good man, I'm sure of it. I don't actually remember recommending him, Valery, but he should do all right. He's a natural-born killer, through and through. If anyone can liquidate Bucharensky it'll be that little swine, right enough.'

Michaelov stayed sunk in thought for several moments, still only half-convinced.

'They hate each other, you know.'

'Mm?'

'After that time in Paris. Bucharensky and Sikarov. They hate each other.'

Povin frowned. 'I'm not sure that's such a bad thing, Valery.'

Michaelov stood up, his fears somewhat allayed by Povin's unshakeable calm. 'I'm sorry to have taken up your time, old friend.'

Povin smiled. 'I was glad to be interrupted.' He held up the book which had lain in his hands since his chief's arrival. 'I'm trying to see why the Dublin *referentura* is so excited about this rubbish.'

Michaelov peered closer, and saw that the book was entitled *A History of Christian Philosophy*.

'The author's one of ours,' explained Povin. 'In Dublin University – what's it called, Trinity? The Resident is worried he's turning subversive.'

Michaelov shook his head, laughing. 'The things we have to do for the Motherland. I'll let you get on.'

But at the door he turned.

'Loshkevoi.'

Povin looked up, surprised. 'What about him?'

'Had you ever heard the name before this?'

'No.'

'Nothing on file?'

'No, I've looked and checked with London.'

Michaelov shook his head. 'Then where the hell did the old man get the name from?'

Povin's face set in a guarded look. 'He's playing a very deep game. I'm scared out of my wits, I don't mind telling you. Always plotting away and never telling anyone. Take Sociable Plover, a good example. I've been thinking about that...'

Povin stood up and threw the book on to his chair. 'Look, what have we got? You went to find out what was in the blue safe and you found Sociable Plover. We know that Kyril hasn't got it. For some reason Stanov's using Kyril as disinformation. I've been thinking what I'd do in his place. I'd have told Kyril that Sociable Plover doesn't really exist. I'd lie to him, in fact. Then if he's caught, SIS are going to be confused: does it exist or doesn't it? In other words, I think we can forget about Sociable Plover. It's a blind.'

'But why go to so much trouble?' Michaelov shook his head in exasperation. 'He seems to be hell-bent on stirring us up, not the British. If anyone's being fed disinformation, it's us here in Dzerzhinsky Square. What *is* the point of it all?'

Povin lowered his eyes. 'I told you what Kazin thinks.'

'Aah, that's a load of shit. I'll believe a lot of things, Stepan, but not that the Chairman of the KGB is on the point of defecting to the West. Not *this* Chairman.'

'Then... what?'

'I don't know. But I'm damn well going to find out. One thing at a time. First we liquidate Bucharensky and protect Royston. *Then* we go to work at this end. And no sleep for us until we know all the answers.'

Michaelov banged the door-jamb with his fist.

'You've never been followed, Stepan. You don't know what it's like. It's getting so I can't sleep nights. I'll never forgive him. Never!'

On leaving Povin's office Michaelov looked at his watch. Five o'clock. As he walked back to his own room he became aware of a commotion at the end of the corridor. Stanov swept past the sentries, closely followed by Yevchenko, their faces black as thunder. The Chairman of the KGB seemed excited about something; his voice was raised and despite the distance which separated them Michaelov could distinctly hear the sound of a fist pounding wood. He ducked quickly into his own suite of offices and closed the door firmly behind him.

'No calls,' he growled to the young lieutenant who guarded the inner sanctum. 'If the Chairman asks for me, I've gone for the night.'

Once inside his own room he relaxed a little. Sikarov was already forgotten. Most of the afternoon had been wasted and waste put General Michaelov out of sorts. There was a lot to do. He reached for the phone.

'Get my wife… Hello? Nadia? Look, I'll be working late tonight. Don't wait up.'

-

For several minutes after his boss had left the office Povin remained motionless before the fire, the book forgotten. He stared into the middle distance, a half-smile on his lips. Then, like a man who has done with a daydream, he put down the book and walked over to the cupboard under the window. Inside was a bottle of petrovka. He uncorked it and poured himself a generous measure, which he downed in one before pouring another and drinking it more slowly. After he had put away the bottle and the glass he swept a strand of hair from his forehead. His hand was shaking so badly that he had to do it twice.

Chapter 22

'We always thought Kyril was only a moderate performer. But he's good. He's very good indeed.'

C stood at the window looking out over the Thames, his spectacles dangling loosely in his hands. He seemed distracted. Royston bit his tongue and refrained from snapping at his chief. 'I know that,' he wanted to shriek. 'I don't need an old fool like you to tell me that we've lost him, perhaps for ever...'

Royston had not been sleeping well. His doctor prescribed a course of Tuinal, and at first the tablets helped. Now Royston was almost back to where he started: a period of sleep between midnight and two, followed by a long drift into wakefulness and uneasy dreams. Jenny was concerned. So was Royston.

'You could step up surveillance on the Bradfield woman,' said the Head of the Inquisition. 'She'll be out of hospital tomorrow.'

Royston turned smouldering eyes on him, but remained silent. In the good old days, if the London Station-Chief had a good idea he'd go along for a chat with Maurice Oldfield, who'd be as likely to talk about cricket as anything else and make him feel in ten minutes that it was worth £2700 a year. Christ, thought Royston savagely, to think we used to live on that. No London weighting then... and no bloody kitchen cabinets, either;

no interminable discussions, always ending with a reference back to Accounts and Audit...

'And this other man, Loshkevoi,' put in the Senior Planner. 'If Nidus is right in supposing that Kyril wants to see him, for whatever reason, I was wondering whether it might not be a good idea to propose a joint venture to someone with superior capacity... the CIA, now...' Royston twisted sharply in his chair and the Head of the Inquisition tut-tutted. Only Sir Richard Bryant did not move or say anything, but continued to stare out of the window.

'I think that Edward's well-known preference for liaising at every level with the Cousins should not be allowed to cloud the fact that this is, ah, essentially a domestic matter.'

'I agree,' said Royston, mildly surprised to find himself supporting the Head of the Inquisition for once.

'And so do I.'

C's voice was very gentle.

'There's been far too much noise as it is. Soviet agents under trains... Once we invoke the Cousins we'll find them wanting participation rights. It's happened before.'

He turned to face the room and Royston saw that his face was dark with trouble.

'You probably do not know – there is no reason why you should – the terms on which Nidus is reimbursed. He is a man of some principle. At his own request, his monthly stipend is paid directly into a numbered UNICEF bank account in Geneva. For reasons into which I have never inquired, dollars, in any shape or form...'

C's voice was at its most austerely chill.

'...are not acceptable. No, gentlemen: leave the Americans out of this.'

C resumed his seat behind the desk.

'Bradfield and Loshkevoi: they are your immediate targets. Watch them and eventually Kyril will cross your line of sight.' He smiled briefly. 'Damn the expense; take what you need.'

He nodded to indicate that the meeting was over, and two of the other men present at once stood up. Royston remained stubbornly rooted to his chair. C raised an inquiring eyebrow and tilted his head slightly.

'I need a few moments with you alone, please.'

Royston felt that in his present exhausted state he would have had to submit to anything C said or did. The relief he experienced when Bryant waved the other two out found tangible expression through all the taut muscles of his aching body.

'If we're going to get him... I mean, get him properly, nail him down... I need a nugget.'

'Yes. I thought it might be that.'

'Nugget' was a Service euphemism for a lure. It could take many forms: a woman, money, political asylum.

'Kyril was very high,' Royston continued, keeping his eyes fixed on C's face. 'Stanov's man. I need something he can identify with – a piece of information only the Chairman or his assistant would be likely to know. Something... rare.'

'Rare in the sense of precious. Quite so. A shibboleth.'

Royston's eyes widened. He had not expected such a sympathetic hearing. 'Yes, that's it. Something to show we're two of a kind.'

C said nothing. That look of trouble had returned to his normally placid face. Royston became conscious of a hollow, faintly nauseous feeling in the pit of his stomach. He couldn't face breakfast these days, not since it first crossed his mind that during his recent spell in Dzerzhinsky Square Kyril might have learned a lot more about a man called Royston than C ever knew.

'Did you have anything specific in mind?'

'I did, as a matter of fact. There used to be an executive arm of the Kremlin on which we could never get any hard information. Maybe things have changed since my Moscow-watching days, I don't know. Some kind of inspectorate. The members had to swear a special oath of allegiance to a plenary session of the Politburo. Strictly for officers only. It went under several names. The one I remember was Kremlin Kommandant.'

'Used to be...?'

This response puzzled Royston. Why was C prevaricating?

'Still is, I'm sure. If my contact-man could persuade Kyril that he's a member of the Kommandant...'

C stood up and turned his back on Royston. The air of restless trouble had now overlaid his entire manner. Royston's puzzlement grew. What was wrong? *For Christ's sake, what did they know? What did Kyril know?*

'The Kremlin Kommandant still exists, yes; nothing has changed. Brezhnev's personal inspectorate: the spies who watch the spies. Their powers are almost unfettered. But you're asking a lot. There is only one source for a secret of that magnitude. If it became known that a western intelligence agency had penetrated it, well...'

Royston leaned forward.

'But if that source you mention was himself in danger... if the Chairman of the KGB was on the point of capturing a man who could unmask him...'

C wheeled round.

'You underestimate Nidus,' he said curtly. 'We cannot dictate to him. He helps me in fits and starts, at his own pleasure, and usually only in the gravest of emergencies. I doubt very much whether personal considerations would play any part in his decision to give or withhold the information you seek.'

'You seem very sure of that...'

Royston made no attempt to keep the cynicism out of his voice. The two hard points of C's gaze dissolved, went hazy and out of focus.

'Yes,' he said. Then, after a long pause – 'I am very sure.'

Royston stood up too quickly and suffered a momentary penalty of giddiness. For a scintilla of time he wanted to say, 'By the way, just who is Nidus?'; then sanity returned. If he ever chose to ruin everything he could do it in much finer style than that.

'I will do my very best for you,' said C. 'I understand your point of view. I regard it as having validity.'

He nodded dismissively. On his way out Royston heard him say, 'This is not a time for illness. I need fit men. Try to take a day's leave.'

A holiday, thought Royston as he rode down in the lift.

That's what I need. Twenty years in which to think things over...

Chapter 23

Sikarov timed his arrival to coincide with the middle of the trans-Atlantic rush-hour. Four Jumbos had disgorged their human cargos in the last 30 minutes and the Russian had no difficulty in finding a package-party to join. Passengers and immigration officers all looked equally haggard.

As he approached the high, sloping desk a man in a dark grey suit materialised beside the immigration clerk for no apparent reason. While Sikarov's passport was checked this man stood behind the clerk's shoulder, his impassive stare never leaving Sikarov's face. The Russian gazed stonily back at him. As the clerk stretched out to give him back his passport the man in the grey suit took it and examined the open page. Sikarov felt no qualms. It had been made in East Germany and was of the first quality. It proclaimed him to be Pietr Gablenz, an Austrian businessman on his way from Paris to London, and the visas were authentic.

The man in the dark grey suit handed Sikarov back his passport with a smile.

Once in the taxi Sikarov used its darkened rear window to observe the traffic without himself being seen. Before they reached the end of the motorway spur he knew that he was being followed and had identified the vehicle.

He frowned. He had crossed enough frontiers in his time to know the power of coincidence, but this looked suspiciously like a prearranged tail. The MI5 officer at the immigration desk had a reason for being there at the precise moment when Sikarov presented his passport. But it was unlikely that Five were having him followed on mere suspicion.

Someone had talked, then. In Moscow or, more probably, here in the London *referentura*. Sikarov's lips curled back from his prominent teeth in the snarl that passed, with him, for a smile. Well, he would have a bit of fun. A short holiday before getting down to business.

He directed the cab driver to Piccadilly, and Fortnum & Masons. A large tip secured a promise to wait while the fare picked up some parcels. As he went inside Sikarov glanced to right and left. The tail vehicle, a brown Capri, was stuck behind a bus in the slow lane. Sikarov had a fleeting impression of an irate driver straining over his shoulder to find a gap in the impenetrable traffic. Excellent.

For the next five minutes the staff of Fortnums were kept very busy. Box after box was handed out to the street, there to be piled into the back of the cab by an obliging doorman. After a while there were so many parcels in the taxi that the driver had to get out and start rearranging them, putting some in the front compartment, and some in the boot. Just as everyone was starting to wonder where the fare was going to sit a number of things happened simultaneously. A policeman came up and demanded to know where the hell the cabbie thought he was, in the garage at home? The driver realised that he had not yet been paid for the trip from the airport. The shop-girl who had been kept busy taking Sikarov's order woke up to the fact that he had not, as promised, left his American Express card with her while he went out to supervise the loading. The driver of the brown Capri collected a ticket. But Sikarov went clean into London – and disappeared.

After his initial and unexpected brush with MI5 Sikarov was forced to rethink his strategy. He felt isolated. It was time to invest in a little insurance.

When he reached the embassy later in the day it was to find everything at sixes and sevens. He learned that Kyril had been seen at the house of Vera Bradfield, but then there had been a balls-up which resulted in the death of a *schpick* and the target escaping surveillance. A full-scale cover-up was in progress. Sikarov grunted. He was too used to this kind of error for it to worry him. As long as he had the girl's address he would manage somehow.

On the pretext that his gun was jamming he visited the armoury on the third floor and handed it in for a quick service. While the armourer was working on it Sikarov leaned over the counter and with a gloved hand picked up the Luger that was lying on the shelf.

'What's wrong with this?'

'Faulty trigger-setting. It's mended now.'

Sikarov weighed it thoughtfully. The armourer was coming over.

'Should be all right. There was some dirt caked round the pin.'

Sikarov nodded. He had put it there.

'Want to try?'

'Sure.'

'We'll have to go down to the cellars, then. That's where the range is.'

Sikarov pretended to hesitate. 'All right. But it'll have to be quick. Can I try the Luger?'

'Sure, why not.'

A few minutes on the range revealed that Sikarov's gun was now in perfect working order. Then he loosed off six shots from the Luger. It felt fine.

'Thank you. I still prefer my own though.'

The armourer shrugged. 'We don't use them much now. That belongs to someone in Department V. He won't part with it.'

Sikarov's body was between the armourer and the table on which the guns lay. It was the easiest thing in the world for him to switch holsters.

'I left my bag upstairs. I'll carry these up for you.'

While the armourer turned off the lights Sikarov buttoned down both holsters firmly. Now it was impossible to tell which was which, unless you knew.

On his way out Sikarov wondered whose fingerprints would be on the Luger with which he killed Colonel Ivan Yevseevich Bucharensky. Not that it mattered. Nothing was going to mar his enjoyment of this mission, not while Kyril still owed him for what happened in Paris. And anyway, the boys in A2 enjoyed a joke.

Chapter 24

Povin nearly always woke up early, even at weekends. This Sunday he opened his eyes to find a bar of sunlight lying across his face and he blinked, surprised; did that mean spring would be early this year?

He slid out of bed and went to stand at the window whence he could look out over his neighbours' roof-tops. Povin had long ago become entitled to occupy a larger flat on the second floor but he preferred the tiny suite of rooms tucked under the eaves for what in any case he regarded merely as a pied-à-terre. The sky was a bright, cloudless blue. He opened the window and took a deep breath of fresh air, cold as ether.

Somewhere, far away, a church bell was ringing.

He closed the windows reluctantly. That was an illegal, if frequent occurrence, and the outcome was always the same. Soon the bell would stop, the arrests and interrogations begin. Povin didn't want to think about that.

He was used to this flat. 'My penthouse' he called it, with a rueful smile, but the accommodation, which was cramped and tiny, belied such a grand description. A bedroom just large enough to hold the single bed, a living-room too small to do his Grundig stereo justice, kitchen fitted out with a microwave oven and precious little else; bathroom with no bath, only a shower. It was enough for the nights during the week. When he entertained he used the dacha in Zhukovka, which he regarded as 'home', and it was on the dacha that he spent his money.

He went across to the record-player and put on the Bruch No 1 violin concerto, played by Perlman, one of Povin's few HMV recordings. A rare exception to his normal collecting policy, he preferred it to the Deutsche Grammophon version by Oistrakh.

In the kitchen he made himself tea and examined the interior of the small, old fashioned refrigerator. He ate only a biscuit smothered with *tvorog*, the stodgy cottage cheese of the peasants. Povin was due to lunch at the Armed Forces Officers Club with a colleague and he found that nowadays he couldn't manage too much food early if he was going to eat a big meal later. The Club was worth saving up your appetite for: it served the best *zakuski* in Moscow. Povin loved hors d'oeuvres, and rarely bothered with a second course if they were good, especially when the milk-mushrooms were in season.

He went back to the living-room with a second glass of tea, still wearing only his dressing-gown and slippers, and sat down to listen to the music. He missed being in the country at weekends. Yesterday, however, he had been lucky enough to obtain a ticket for the ballet, and today there was an offer of a free lunch, a commodity as difficult to come by in the East as in the West, so Povin had decided to break his routine. He was not altogether sorry. In Zhukovka someone was always giving a party or dropping by for a chat, and what he wanted most of all was time to be alone and think.

For reasons which he could not explain to himself he felt strangely relaxed. Perhaps it was the false calm at the eye of the hurricane, but that did not matter; for the moment at least he was sure he was safe.

It was a feeling hard to justify in rational terms, he reflected as he stirred his tea. The picture was fairly straightforward now. Stanov knew there was a traitor and, broadly, where to look for him. Bucharensky might or might not figure in Stanov's scheme of things, Povin wasn't certain. He was probably just a pawn, used by Stanov in an attempt to provoke his suspects into panic. Povin long ago decided to discount the diary. If Kyril was really in a position to unmask a traitor he would have stayed and earned his promotion accordingly, not run halfway across Europe to the very people who were supposed to control their agent in Dherzhinsky Square. Unless... Povin frowned. Unless, of course, he was looking for final proof. But in any case, as long as he could be sure of neutralising Kyril there was no particular need to worry; all he had to do was lie low and demonstrate his continuing loyalty to the Politburo with every passing day. And whatever Bucharensky's function, he would shortly cease to be a factor in the equation. Povin had great faith in Sikarov. If anyone asked questions later, well, it was Michaelov's decision to send Sikarov to England, not Povin's.

From his comfortable armchair high above the Moscow roof-tops, things were looking, if not good, at least not so bad. What could he do to make them even better? The question gave Povin a momentary sense of frustration. All that power at his fingertips, power over life and death, and yet so little effect...

Loshkevoi.

Povin put down his empty glass and went to turn the record over.

It would be better if Bucharensky and Loshkevoi did not meet. Loshkevoi could not identify Povin directly, he certainly did not realise that the general was a double-agent, but still he represented a risk. He must be put out of circulation for a while... yes, maybe that was the answer. Somewhere in Dzerzhinsky Square there was a legal department – of sorts. Povin made a mental note for action on Monday morning. 'English legal system.'

The word 'English' spoken quietly in his own mind sent Povin off at a tangent. Suddenly the day seemed less sunny, less relaxed. New problems all the time...

He went to the bathroom, leaving the door ajar for the sake of the music, and began to shave. What was he going to do about Bryant's request?

When Povin first read the message he almost laughed aloud, would have done if he were not so astonished at being presented with a request for aid which had not been volunteered. But then he had thought – well, and why not?

It was that 'why not' which troubled him as he lathered his face. To respond to Bryant's request would be dangerous folly at the best of times. But now, with Kyril on the loose and Stanov perhaps watching his generals' every move, it would be nothing short of suicidal.

Why, then, did the memory of his talk with Stolyinovich on the night of the party haunt him so? 'Do you ever feel that we could do more?' – those had been his own words. 'No,' said the pianist, flatly rejecting the philosophical tangle behind the apparently simple question. And yet... and yet...

There was so much that Povin might do if he had a mind. Royston, for example: strategically by far and away the most important 'gain' the KGB had ever made within the United Kingdom. Povin had not underestimated his importance when he told Michaelov that the destruction of Royston would devastate their British operation for at least ten years. All it needed was one word from Povin to Bryant... No, these were foolish, wayward thoughts. Why should he jeopardise himself by making such a revelation? The same applied to Bryant's request for information about the Kommandant.

Povin patted his face dry with a towel and considered his reflection in the mirror. Not bad for 55, he decided: the skin had kept most of its tension and his complexion was clear. But that melancholy gaze... where had it come from, and when? Povin shrugged and smiled a faint smile, knowing that it had been there since his early days in the Komsomol, when he first became conscious of a sense of loss, of not quite having found the answer. But at least the pale grey eyes were fearless; they stared back at him without flinching from their knowledge of what lay behind the facade.

Povin went back to the bedroom and stood for a few moments with his head bent in prayer. He never felt quite able to kneel down, here in Moscow, the hub of the KGB's massive wheel of power. With the passing of the years he paid less and less attention to the outward flummeries. Throughout the centuries soldiers had always stood to pray, and Povin was a soldier. He wore a uniform. And he stood on guard. Always.

He dressed quickly, keeping an anxious eye on the weather. The sky was still blue, and when he looked out of the window again the air actually felt warmer. He craned down to survey the little corner of Kutuzovsky Prospekt which was visible from 'the penthouse'. It was only eight o'clock and there were few pedestrians on the street at that hour. Good. He fancied a walk, a long walk. He decided to strike out in the direction of Izmailovo Park and see how far he could get before 10.30, when he would turn back in order to keep his lunch appointment.

There were no watchers, as far as he could see. He wasn't sure whether Stanov had actually got as far as to have the KGB generals followed; in the past year he had sometimes thought one thing, sometimes another, and on balance had written off his fears as groundless. But if there had been surveillance in the past, he was almost sure that it prevailed no longer. Now the only danger was Stanov himself and his beastly dog.

As Povin rode down in the lift he was making contingency plans for evasive action. When Stanov's wife died two years ago the old man bought himself a dog for company, a mongrel of scruffy appearance and uncertain temper. Sometimes when Povin went out early he ran into Stanov exercising the brute along Kutuzovsky Prospekt, and this invariably resulted in an invitation to breakfast with the lonely marshal. Povin disliked pets. They interfered with his fastidious standards of personal hygiene and comfort. To sit in Stanov's overheated first-floor apartment sniffing old man and stale dog through the rich flavour of freshly ground coffee was almost more than he could stomach, but he knew it would be impolitic to refuse.

Povin stepped cautiously into the street and looked to right and left. All clear. He strode away from the discreet entrance of the block of flats, pulling on his gloves. He would think about Sir Richard Bryant's request on his walk. Eight-thirty. Allowing for the time difference, the Englishman would soon be getting up, ready for early mass. As a devotee of the Tridentine rite he was finding it harder and harder to satisfy the spiritual yearnings which were his major point of contact with Povin. So much for religious freedom. In Dzerzhinsky Square they knew of this difficulty, just as they knew most other things about the private and public lives of the head of the British Secret Intelligence Service. Povin smiled to himself. Poor Sir Richard. Yes, he would definitely give his request for information about the Kommandant the most serious attention.

Povin had reached the end of the Prospekt, and there was still no sign of either Stanov or his wretched cur. It was going to be all right, thought Povin as he strode off across the road. If by the grace of God he could only manage to keep his head, everything was going to be just fine.

Chapter 25

As Vera awoke for a second she thought herself back in the hospital; it was the middle of the night, her room was in darkness, and the events of the past few days had so confused her that even during the day she sometimes suffered a sense of disorientation, of loss of Self. Then she sat up in bed and remembered. She was in her own bed in Clapham, home and safe.

She put on the light.

Sitting in her bedside chair was a squat young man dressed in black from head to foot. Every muscle, every nerve in Vera's body instinctively combined to force her back against the headboard, knees drawn up to her chin, arms folded across her breasts, mouth open to scream... But suddenly there was an impediment, a ghastly, suffocating gag which took the pent-up fear and smothered it unborn.

Seeing the terror on the woman's face Sikarov grinned. Everything was going well. Lazily he bent down to untie his shoes, which had begun to pinch. A sour, sweaty smell rose to Vera Bradfield's nostrils, making her stomach churn. This was her nightmare. A burglar. A raid on an empty house while she was safely away, that she could just about contemplate. But this was different. This was a man, and he was here, in front of her. A man who stank and had an evil look about him. Oh God, oh God, oh God...

'Get back into the bed. It's cold. I don't want you to be cold.'

A foreigner. One of the semi-vagrants she saw so many of these days. Christ, just let him not want *her.* Vera snuggled back under the bedclothes, pulling the blanket up to her chin. She was shivering and he noticed it; she felt him notice.

'You cannot make a noise, I am going to give you paper and pencil. Here.' Sikarov rolled up his sleeve to reveal a roll of paper around his forearm, together with a pencil. 'Now you are going to write on it the address of the man you call Vanya or Bucharensky.'

A tiny part of Vera relaxed. So it wasn't rape, not even theft. Then the fear closed down again, numbing and total. They were on the track of Vanya at last. And from the look of the intruder it was obvious that they meant to kill him. The man in the bedroom reeked of death.

Vera shook her head and turned to face the wall.

Sikarov's eyes gleamed with lascivious anticipation of pleasure. They had warned him that she would not be easy.

'You will tell me,' he said. 'I give you one more chance to do it with dignity. Where is Bucharensky?'

Again the shake of the head, but Sikarov could see the trembling bedclothes which told their own story.

'What nonsense has he told you? That he is in danger? That we want to hurt him? What rubbish. You are old enough to see through that kind of tale. We want to help him. He is sick. He needs medical help. Surely you realised that when he came here? Wasn't it obvious?'

The bedclothes had stopped shaking.

'But he doesn't understand that. Won't you help him by telling me where he is?'

Vera turned away from the wall and violently shook her head. Sikarov sighed, and reached out for her. She fought him off until, in a fit of rage, he stunned her with his fist. When she came to her hands and feet were bound to the four corners of the bed.

'For you,' murmured Sikarov, 'the night is only just beginning. Nod your head when you are tired.'

She proved tougher than anticipated. Several times she fainted and he had to revive her with douches of cold water. He became steadily more impatient, his methods cruder. Still she would not break. Sikarov wiped the sweat from his forehead. There were limits to what he could do in a London bedroom, it was not as if the resources of the Lubianka cellars were at his disposal. Blood began to mingle with water and urine on the sodden sheets. Somewhere deep inside Sikarov a tide of sexual desire was beginning to draw inwards, concentrating all his energies. Again and again he fought it down, only to feel it rise again within him.

'*Don't come back to Moscow.*' Michaelov's words echoed in his brain. *Concentrate!*

It was all right, she had nodded. Sikarov ripped away the gag. For several minutes all she could do was pant and gasp. Saliva was running down her chin, and for one terrible second Sikarov wondered if he had driven her over the edge.

'I don't know where he is. If I did… I would tell you. But I don't.'

Sikarov breathed deeply, trying to instill a degree of control. 'Tell me.' His voice sounded murderous. '*Tell me.*'

'I don't *know*.'

Sikarov watched with interest as a figure detached itself from his body. This figure carried a pistol by the barrel.

It walked across to the bed where the naked woman lay, legs apart, and with slow, leisurely swings of its arm began to club her about the head until eventually she stopped groaning, her head no longer tried to evade the pistol, her legs twitched once in a muscular convulsion, and she lay still. Sikarov saw it all as if in a dream, until the figure climbed back into his body and made it whole again. Then he awoke. The room, the gun, the soaking bed, they had all disappeared. There was only the woman. She filled the whole of his consciousness, he could see nothing else. But he could feel. There's no point in hanging on, a voice was saying, no point because it's too late, isn't it. It's too late.

Sikarov climbed on to the bed and knelt between the woman's bloodsoaked thighs. His hand went to the zip and when the gun got in the way he dropped it on the floor. Then his trousers were round his knees, the erection sprang free, and Sikarov's lips curled back into the familiar snarl as his hand set to work.

-

The two-seater van was indistinguishable from many others parked on the south London streets that night, except perhaps in the care which the driver had taken to ensure that he did not breach any of the numerous regulations and byelaws concerning stationary vehicles. The interior of this particular van, however, was unusual. Down one side was arranged a truncated mattress on which a man was uncomfortably dozing, his legs pulled up almost to the low roof. On the other side a second man wearing a pair of headphones crouched with his back to the first. Every so often he reached out to twiddle knobs on the radio-receiver in front of him. For the past half-hour he had been showing signs of increasing restlessness.

'Better wake up, Ted.'

'Wha'? Wassup? Oh fuck.'

The man on the mattress struggled upright, only to bang his head on the van's metal ceiling.

'I can't figure it out. There's been some weird noises in there for about half an hour now. Like… struggling. You know what I mean?'

Ted was unscrewing the top of a vacuum flask.

'No.'

'As if she was having a fight with someone.'

'Lover, maybe.'

'Well he didn't go in the front door, did he? We'd have seen.'

Ted took a sip from the plastic cup while he thought about that.

'Dream. Could be having a nightmare.'

'What? For all that time and never waking up? Do us a favour, will you. I shouldn't…'

The radio-operator's hand moved to the set, his face suddenly tense.

'Listen, Ted, where did they put that transmitter when she was in hospital? In which room?'

'Lounge.'

'The telephone's ringing. If she doesn't come out of the bedroom to answer it, she's in trouble.'

Ted swallowed the last of his cup of tea and, pulling aside a piece of sacking, looked out of the tiny rear window.

'Raining, sod it. I'd better get my coat on.'

'Right. Hallo. The phone's stopped. Seven rings. No answer.'

Ted came to kneel by his colleague, shouldering his mac as he did so.

'Better ring up LS, Phil. We need a car.'

'You do it. I'm listening for a while.'

Ted picked up the radiophone and spoke urgently to London Station. Phil was vaguely aware of what he was saying while he strained to interpret the silence which had once again fallen in Vera's flat.

'Can't do a tail… yeah… two exits, he might go either way… twenty minutes, Christ, can't you do better than that…?'

Ted replaced the handset.

'They're on their way. Twenty bloody minutes, Christ…'

'The phone's ringing again.'

–

Sikarov was dressed and ready to leave. The Bradfield woman had been a bad mistake. He shook his head glumly, mindful of the old Russian proverb which said: 'A woman isn't a jug; she won't break if you hit her'. Well, Vera Bradfield had broken all right.

The important thing now was to do a first-class job on Bucharensky. That way Michaelov's wrath could perhaps be bought off.

Then the phone rang. Seven times.

Sikarov looked at his watch. Nobody rang at that time of night. Wrong number. Unless…

He paused. He ought to leave. But suppose that nocturnal caller was someone who had to be very careful how he contacted Vera Bradfield. Someone who phoned in the small hours and let the phone ring only seven times before cancelling the call, and moving to another phone-box in another area, as he, Sikarov, had done many times before.

Seven rings. The old code. Sikarov sat down on Vera's bedside chair. There was an easy way to test his theory. Sometime in the next 20 minutes Bucharensky – if it was Bucharensky – would call again. This time the phone would ring five times. And then, when nobody answered, he would know that his contact had been blown and fade away into the night...

Sikarov shook his head. Not Bucharensky. Not with this contact. When there was no answer to the second call he would come to see what was wrong. Sikarov knew how Bucharensky's mind worked. He always disobeyed the rules in one vital respect... he telephoned from a box which was too close to the contact. That was what had gone wrong in Paris. Sikarov grinned. He wouldn't make that mistake again. This time he knew that if Bucharensky rang a second time, he would be at the house within minutes after replacing the receiver.

Time passed very slowly while Sikarov waited for that second call. Something told him that it was bound to come, almost as if the five rings were already programmed into the wires which separated Bucharensky from the house. He withdrew the Luger from the waistband of his trousers and checked the mechanism. All was well. There would be no chance for a second shot.

When the phone rang again Sikarov took a sharp intake of breath and held it. Ring-ring. One. Ring-ring. Two. Ringring... Ring-ring... Ring-ring... *Five*... and no more.

Sikarov stood up and moved quickly into the hall, leaving the bedside light on to guide him. The living-room? No, too obvious. The kitchen? Bucharensky would come that way.

The cellar.

The door at the back of the hall gave directly on to a steep flight of steps. Sikarov went down a little way and pulled the door to, leaving a small gap through which he could hear whatever went on above.

The minutes dragged by. Every so often Sikarov hummed gently to himself, to keep his hearing alert. He knew that unless you did that you began to hear imaginary noises and the last thing he wanted was to emerge from his hiding-place too soon.

When nothing had happened after 20 minutes Sikarov began to worry. This wasn't the Bucharensky he remembered. Perhaps he had been wrong about the phone call. But then, who else would use the Leningrad Response in the middle of the night, in order to make contact with a woman called Vera Bradfield? Sikarov forced himself to remain silent and tried to shore up his rapidly slipping patience.

Occasionally his thoughts strayed to what Bucharensky would find upstairs and his lips parted in a wet smile. Traitors were special, that was what he had told Michaelov. They were singled out for special treatment.

Then at last he heard the click of the latch on the kitchen door, and he knew the waiting was over.

In his mind Sikarov began to follow Bucharensky's cautious movements. First he would discover the circle which Sikarov had cut into the glass-panelled door, and use it to insert a hand and make his own entry. Then he would stand for a while in the kitchen, taking the flat's pulse, as the instructors called it. Next… ah yes! Sikarov's ears had not deceived him. Bucharensky was moving out of the kitchen, passing within inches of the cellar-door, to the threshold of the bedroom. Any minute now…

The quiet footsteps overhead, audible only to someone with Sikarov's superfine hearing, stopped. There was a moment of silence during which he stared up at the ceiling of the tiny cellar, lips faintly parted. Then the man upstairs turned and broke into a run. Sikarov heard him pound through the kitchen and out the way he had come, reckless as to whether he made a noise. Sikarov waited a few seconds, then vaulted up the stairs and out of the back door, into the yard.

Ahead of him he could hear Bucharensky noisily clearing a succession of garden walls in his progress towards the end of the terrace, and the road. Sikarov smiled. Good. That should be easy enough to follow. He set off in pursuit.

He had no intention of putting a quick end to the affair.

Bucharenksy's nerve had broken, so much was obvious. He would run back to his 'secure' base and bolt the door behind him, seeking the illusory warmth and comfort of that unnatural womb in which to rest and recover. Sikarov would follow. It would be a simple matter to destroy the wretched Bucharensky in his present unmanned state, before ransacking his lair at leisure. The death was what mattered: those were Michaelov's express orders. But before leaving Moscow Sikarov had heard rumours, some of them very interesting. There was talk of a sensitive project-plan, and Michaelov himself had spoken of papers. If Sikarov could find the project-plan which Bucharensky was supposed to have stolen, that would be an added bonus – quite sufficient to neutralise any unpleasantness which might otherwise have resulted from the woman's death.

Bucharensky had reached the last garden wall which bounded the house at the end of the terrace from the street. For a second his crouched figure was outlined against the orange glow of the street-lamp; then he was gone. Sikarov raced after him. As he cleared the final hurdle and landed on the pavement, a shadow unmoulded itself from the darkness 50 yards away, and joined the hunt. Ted was cold and tired and still half-asleep, but from his position on the pavement between the end of the terrace opposite Vera's and the monitoring van he had seen Kyril jump the wall. When Sikarov followed and set off in pursuit, Ted took a deep breath and broke into a trot.

-

Kyril was running as if to win the 100-metre sprint. The sound of his own heart's blood throbbing in his ears kept him from remembering. As he ran his footsteps rat-tatted the same grim tune.

Sik-a-rov, Sik-a-rov, Sik-a-rov...

They were in Paris, working the old tandem game. The girl was pretty, rich and damn near nymphomaniac; the prize, a minister, was rare, almost unobtainable. Sikarov had been sent along to add weight, do the heavy stuff at the end. He was regarded as an expert, then, a top professional, and Gaczyna had yet to produce a better marksman. Only later did Kyril discover that there had been other occasions, other corpses...

Sik-a-rov, Sik-a-rov. Now there was grass beneath his feet. The common.

A Leningrad Response had brought up nothing. Something about the empty, hollow dialling-tone spelled danger. Kyril had taken a taxi instead of following the rules and proceeding on foot. He had opened the door of the 'nest' with his passkey. And there was Sikarov, his trousers round his ankles, masturbating over the bloody thing which lay on the bed, its head unrecognisable as belonging to a human being.

Ve-ra, Ve-ra, Ve-ra.

The strange sound in Kyril's ears was the heartbroken moan of a man at the end of his tether, a child who cries to ease the pain, its rhythmic ululation keeping time with the throbbing hurt.

His last view of Sikarov had been from the glass-walled corridor of the terminal at Orly, three men walking out to the Aeroflot Ilyushin after all the other passengers had boarded, two of them a pace behind the third, hands in pockets, collars upturned. Goodbye, Sikarov, he had thought then. For you, this is the end of the line...

He had reached the foot of Queenstown Road. If he did not stop soon he felt his heart would burst. Perhaps it was better that way.

Sik-a-rov, Ve-ra, Sik-a-rov, Ve-ra...

The traitor had never meant much to Kyril, until now. Suddenly he was face to face with an enemy, and the deadly game had become personal. No longer was Kyril merely trying to do his duty to the Homeland. His enemy had chosen Sikarov deliberately, ordered him to destroy Vera as a warning, as the first instalment of punishment. Now at last his way forward was clear. He would butcher Sikarov, that was the first thing. And then he would seek out this traitor, as Stanov had commanded. He would exact vengeance.

Kyril opened his front door, slammed it behind him and fell on his knees, hands clasped to his forehead. He was sobbing.

The crisis quickly came and passed. He allowed himself the luxury of release for a moment, no more, before dragging himself upright and dusting off his clothes. His body was exhausted but his brain was functioning. Revenge. Never before had he contemplated such dangerous luxury, the poison asp concealed beneath the figs' sweetness. He must plan carefully if he were to combine it with Stanov's plan. Escape. That was the first thing. He must break away from the house, go underground...

Kyril lifted his head, straining to listen. Was that a noise he had heard in the street? Surely it was his overheated imagination? He breathed deeply. His heart was almost back to normal, the throbbing in his ears had reduced to a low murmur. He must think. *Think!*

Suddenly he was back in Athens, in the hotel room again, listening so hard and for so long that his hearing had begun to fail. Kyril shook himself angrily.

Suppose Sikarov had been in Vera's flat all the time, and had followed him; suppose that it was Sikarov out there...

Kyril held himself perfectly still. The thought struck him cold. For the past half-hour he had been in the grip of an emotion so terrible that he had ceased to take even the most elementary of precautions. If Sikarov was in the flat, or even nearby, it would have been a simple thing to follow the raging maniac who raced across the common to Queenstown Road, never once looking back.

But then... why was he still alive? Why had Sikarov not finished him with a single shot? Kyril leaned against the wall and closed his eyes.

Of course. The project-plan. Sociable Plover. Sikarov had orders to retrieve it. That was only logical. If Sikarov was indeed outside... if, if, *if*!

Kyril went slowly up the stairs, feeling his way to the door of the living-room and round the crude trapdoor which he had cut in the floorboards, now supported by only a few millimetres of sawn-through wood.

After a moment's hesitation he decided to put on the fight. That could not make matters any worse. As he fit a cigarette his eye fingered on the half-empty bottle of vodka which lay by his mattress. Yes. It was wrong, but he so desperately craved something to fill the void which Sikarov had created inside him.

A man kneeling… blood everywhere… *Vera.* Kyril upturned the bottle and swallowed greedily. The neat spirit had no immediate effect other than to kindle a weak, warm feeling in his guts. He took another swig and replaced the stopper. The red haze which separated him from the outside world was beginning to dissolve.

It was necessary to make plans. Sikarov had to be flushed out.

Kyril went over to the window and listened. Suddenly he was sure.

The killer was out there. He had come to the house like a moth drawn to a flame, and like a moth he would come closer and closer until at last the flame killed him. But Kyril had to sit and wait. He could not escape. He could not even go out. All he could do was sit here, in this upstairs room, alone, in the dark… and wait.

You will be utterly alone, that was what Stanov had told him at their last meeting. Until this moment Kyril had never understood the full depth of those words. Mention of Stanov reminded him that the Chairman of the KGB could not escape responsibility for Vera's death. Everything done by his agents was done in his name. Had Stanov foreseen this night, wondered Kyril? Did he realise the part which Vera was destined to play in unmasking the traitor? Was that one reason – perhaps the main reason – for choosing Ivan Yevseevich Bucharensky?

The time passed slowly. Kyril chain-smoked until he felt sick. Every so often he would go to stand by the window to listen and wonder if the tiny noise outside was real or a figment of his imagination. To keep himself awake he played mental games, always pushing to one side the dark thoughts which insisted on forcing their way into his tired brain, thoughts of a half-naked man kneeling over a dead woman…

At last he could stand it no longer. He stubbed out the cigarette which he had lighted only seconds before, and stood up. Sikarov's life was worth a few risks. He was going out.

-

As soon as Sikarov rounded the corner and saw the house sheltering under its high embankment he had a sudden premonition of danger. It was a loaded gun, that house. Someone had primed it and oiled it, spun the chambers, inserted the bullets, cocked it. Now it was pointing at Sikarov, ready to go off.

The first glance was enough to tell him to avoid a frontal approach. But the wall at the side was too high and too smooth for a man to scale without assistance, and Sikarov was alone. The embankment, perhaps? He returned to the other side of the bridge, where only a fence separated the road from the earth wall. That was better. It did not take him long to clamber over the fence and struggle up the embankment. Eight pairs of tracks lay between him and the far side of the permanent way, each with its sinister, gleaming third rail to carry the current.

If he could only cross those tracks he would be on top of the embankment on the other side, overlooking the house which he had seen Kyril enter.

Sikarov hesitated. It was very late; the current was probably off. He would be bound to hear a train long before it came close enough to harm him. But for some reason he could not make himself embark on the short journey which led to his target.

Kyril had been inside the house for some time now. He would have had a chance to recover his self-control, perhaps even to put two and two together. Kyril would remember the incident in Paris; was it not his report which had so nearly finished Sikarov's career? He would realise the danger he was in, and he most certainly was not the kind of man to underestimate an adversary.

With every step that Sikarov took across those tracks, he would be advancing into danger. He was already regretting his decision not to finish off Kyril in Vera Bradfield's flat. But the longer he left it, the better prepared Kyril would be.

That decided him. He began his cautious journey, lifting his feet carefully over the third rail of the first set of tracks so that not so much as a trouser-leg would brush the dull grey steel.

He was about halfway across when he saw the figure silhouetted against the sky, and dropped to a crouch.

About twenty metres away someone was standing on the lip of the embankment, motionless. While Sikarov was trying to identify this apparition he heard a goods train start up somewhere close by. Clank-clank-clank... so the current wasn't off. Sikarov stared uneasily at the rail by his feet, only to look up sharply as the figure on the embankment moved. It was coming slowly towards him.

Sikarov drew his gun. At the feel of the metal on his skin he underwent a subtle change: his mind and body slotted together in the first stage of an instinctive technique. It was like pulling on an old, comfortable glove.

With half his mind he registered that the approaching train was diesel-powered, after all: he could hear the harsh idling of its engine. From the left, nearby...

The figure opposite had crossed the first set of rails and now stood motionless again. Sikarov fancied that the man – by now he knew it was a man – was peering into the darkness, across the tracks, in his direction.

The train approached with a squeal of brakes. As Sikarov raised his gun the diesel crossed his aim and he swore out loud. The goods train had slowed almost to walking-pace for a signal.

He could no longer see the figure opposite. He lay down between a pair of rails and strove to see underneath the train, but the low-slung trucks effectively impeded his vision.

The train was picking up speed again, its badly connected couplings giving out a cacophony of metallic grunts. Sikarov raised his gun to the level of the third, live, rail and prepared to fire.

But the last truck passed across his sightline to reveal only empty space where the other man had been standing a moment ago. Sikarov lifted his head cautiously and looked to right and left. Nothing. The mysterious figure had completely vanished.

He raised himself on one knee, taking his time about it. Nothing moved. By now the goods train, travelling fast, was disappearing into the distance, its red tail-light no bigger than the glow from a cigarette-end. Sikarov waited until the sound of the trucks had died away to silence while he considered his next move.

There were several possibilities. The man on the embankment might have boarded the train and been wafted away on one of the trucks, but that seemed unlikely. Assuming the man to be Bucharensky, it meant he had left his base unguarded. Or, he might have used the train as a shield while he slipped down the embankment into the back garden of one of the houses adjoining his own. Sikarov didn't think so. The man had seen him, he was sure of that. The most likely thing for him to do was retreat down the embankment the way he had come… and wait.

Sikarov licked his lips. He had to make a move. Once the news of Bradfield's death filtered back to Dzerzhinsky Square his own future would hang by a thread. Everything depended on his finishing Bucharensky, and quickly. There was only one answer. He had to go forward.

Sikarov stood up very slowly. Everything was quiet. Quelling the first signs of noticeable panic he forced himself to cross the next pair of tracks.

It took him five minutes to reach the far edge of the embankment, every move a slow, painful mixture of doubts and fears.

Safely across at last, he dropped to one knee and took a long look at the back of No. 703. He was almost level with its roof, and from his vantage point he could see a number of possible entrances. A light showed in an upstairs room. That must be where Bucharensky was holed up. Sikarov had noted the separate front doors: obviously there were two flats, one up and one down. His lips jerked back in their customary snarl. That was another problem. Somebody underneath might hear. Perhaps Bucharensky wasn't such a fool, after all, burying himself in the middle of London, surrounded by people.

There was no sign of Bucharensky anywhere. Where *was* he?

The downstairs flat gave Sikarov another idea. There would be no special defences there. It would be easy to force a door, gain access to the building, and then… yes, that was the plan. Get in downstairs, silence the occupants. Gain.

Sikarov lay down alongside the set of rails nearest to the house and thought about his plan for a long time. It wasn't perfect, but for the moment he couldn't think of anything better. He looked at the face of his luminous watch. Almost four, too much time wasted already.

He tested the Luger's mechanism and left the safety-catch off. Then he crawled along the tracks until he was almost at the bridge over the road, in the shadow of the high wall which bounded Kyril's back yard.

A long, last look revealed no movement, and he could hear nothing. Sikarov swallowed. His lips were dry and his heart had begun to beat much faster than usual. But there could be no going back now.

Using the wall for cover he slid down the embankment. At the bottom he forced himself to remain still while he counted up to a hundred, faintly marvelling at the discovery that he was still alive. Nothing moved, no one gave the alarm. His progress down the bank had been noiseless and by good luck he had landed in a flowerbed instead of on the concrete slab which began just a few inches away.

On the other side of the wall a car cruised slowly along Queenstown Road. Sikarov waited until it had passed and silence had descended once more. That car could have represented a golden opportunity for him to move up to the back of the house, but even so he wasn't going to hurry. In London there was always a covering noise, even at this time of night, if you only waited long enough. Sikarov lurked in the shadows at the foot of the earth-bank, surveying the house inch by inch. Apart from the lighted window on the first floor its huge, black mass was indistinguishable from the night which surrounded it.

A quarter of an hour went by. Time to make a move. For several minutes Sikarov had been aware of a distant plane, beginning its long circle of the capital before the descent to glideslope. As it passed overhead Sikarov slipped into the shadows of the house itself.

Another ten minutes went by while the sound of the plane droned into the west. Nothing changed. Sikarov craned up, trying to see where he stood in relation to the lighted window on the first floor. But the light no longer burned. Someone had extinguished it. His hand touched the drainpipe; it came away wet. He frowned, and reached out to grasp the pipe more firmly. This time his fingers found a barb and he jerked his hand away. Something slimy coated his hand. Paint. Sikarov nodded slowly in grudging appreciation. So much for that idea. It would have to be the back door, then.

It was unlocked. Every nerve in Sikarov's body screamed danger. He pushed at the door and stood quickly aside, half expecting a trap. The kitchen was dark and silent. Sikarov reached inside and gingerly felt his way round the frame. There was nothing unusual. He hesitated. Was this the way Kyril had come? Perhaps the owners were merely forgetful, after all it took a brave burglar to cross the railway tracks or scale the high wall.

He stepped over the threshold, sniffing as he did so. The house seemed safe, down here at least. He felt his way round the room to the internal door and through it, into the scullery. A smell of old tobacco, that was all.

Sikarov weighed his next move. Without light he was in continual danger of tripping over furniture, but he dare not risk the wall-switch. He pulled out a tiny torch and sent the thin beam dancing round the room. Empty. Ah, a door... where did that lead to?

Sikarov advanced slowly towards the hall, his head cocked to listen for the slightest noise. In the hall he paused. A sound, from the next room. Or was it above? He looked up sharply, directing the beam to the ceiling. No. In the next room.

The door was ajar. Sikarov pushed it open very gently. It made no noise. He was in the front room; he could tell without the light because the windows were a slightly paler shade of charcoal than the surrounding darkness. The noise was coming from here.

Sikarov froze. Breathing. Somewhere, close by, another person was breathing. He tensed his muscles, ready to fling himself in any direction, out of danger.

The breathing continued at the same, even rate. Sikarov moistened his lips. Then it came to him. He was in a bedroom. The breather was asleep.

Very gently, so as not to disturb the sleeper, Sikarov fitted the silencer on to the barrel of his gun. It would take only a second. A flash from the torch, to direct his fire, and the bullets would follow instantaneously. Sikarov turned until he sensed himself to be facing the unseen sleeper, and raised the gun in his right hand. In his left he carried the torch. He extended his arms in front of him and gently brought his hands together. Any second now...

In the room above, someone moved. Sikarov held his position. Even the slightest movement could give him away. The muscular strain began to tell. He could not hold out his arms for much longer. His hands had begun to shake.

Upstairs, all went quiet again. Sikarov lowered his arms, feeling the sudden ache as the blood flowed back to the wrists. He took a dozen slow, deep breaths, and raised his hands together for the second time. Now they were level. Inhale.

The beam of light lanced out to illuminate Trumper's sleeping form on the bed and in the same second Sikarov fired twice, the shots coming so close together that they sounded like one. Instinctively Sikarov raised his eyes to the ceiling. Nothing happened. No one moved.

Sikarov lowered his arms. There must be another room somewhere, surely? He padded back into the hall, only to wheel round at the sound of other breathing. No, not breathing. Hissing. A low, even sound, not unlike the very distant sough of the sea. Ignore it, he told himself. Move.

He found the other room. It contained a bed but no one was in it. His nose twitched. There was a funny smell in here. He backed away, into the hall. The smell seemed to follow him.

Keeping his back to the wall, Sikarov retreated silently to the scullery. The smell did not diminish; rather it seemed to be growing stronger. The hissing, what was that?

Gas.

Involuntarily Sikarov shuddered. Somebody had turned on the gas-tap. All the while he had been in the house, someone else was there too, noiselessly following him. And he had turned on the gas…

What kind of gas? Domestic gas? Coal... natural...? Was the gas they used in England poisonous? Was it volatile? But wait a minute, who said it was mains gas? Suppose it came from a cylinder...

Sikarov, unwisely, opened his mouth, and at once started to cough. Stuffing a handkerchief into his mouth he headed blindly towards the kitchen, and safety. There was the door leading to the back yard. Another couple of paces and he would be out of this hellhole, another step...

He heard nothing until the last moment. Then someone took a blunt instrument and with neat, surgical precision applied it to the length of his skull; for a fleeting second Sikarov thought he could feel the skin unpeeling itself from his head; then he fell forward into the darkness and disconnected.

-

When he awoke and his eyes came into focus the first thing he saw was the gaping hole in the floor, and he understood. The man he had seen on the embankment was Bucharensky. He waited until he was sure Sikarov would follow before retreating back to the house and sealing off the upper flat, whence he could direct a stream of gas into the downstairs room. When Sikarov turned to run he dropped through the hole to follow him. That was clever.

Sikarov turned his head to one side and retched phlegm on to the bare floor.

The light was on. Bucharensky stood leaning against the far wall by the window, smoking. When he saw Sikarov vomit he picked up a basin from by his feet and came over. The douche of cold water hit Sikarov in the face. A lot of it went down inside his collar.

He began to register details. He was sitting in an uncomfortable chair constructed of solid wood. When he tried to move, straps restrained his arms and legs. They were very tight: bands of white flesh showed on either side of the leather.

He looked down. He was naked from below the waist. His genitals hung through a hole in the seat. Something was twisted round them, something that stung when he struggled…

'When I last saw you…'

Kyril spoke dreamily, like a man under the influence of drugs. To Sikarov it seemed as if he had passed on to an altogether different plane of existence, bloodless and remote.

'…you were walking out to a plane. In Paris. Do you remember Paris?'

Kyril took a long drag on the cigarette and held the smoke in his lungs. His eyes were closed. Sikarov said nothing.

'I remember Paris, Sikarov. Every detail.'

There was a long silence. Kyril's eyes remained closed, as if concentrating on some scene being played out behind his eyelids. Sikarov's tongue had gummed itself to the roof of his mouth.

'I thought to myself then: that's it. The finish. Siberia or the Lubianka cellars. We are not animals, I told myself. Within the ranks of the KGB there is no place for excrement like that.'

Kyril's eyes opened and Sikarov saw that the pupils were unnaturally dilated.

'But oh Sikarov…'

Kyril's head tilted so that at last his burning eyes rested on Sikarov's body.

'...how I underestimated our masters then.'

He moved away from the wall, arms folded across his chest, and slowly advanced towards the chair. Sikarov tried to shrink away, found he couldn't move, and knew a second of black horror which almost threatened to shut down his conscious mind.

'...I had forgotten that for the true killer, for the psychopath... there is always a role. Nemesis. Sikarov. Someone has sent you to be my Nemesis.'

Kyril sat down on his mattress in front of the chair and brought his legs up like a Buddha. Now he was staring directly into Sikarov's eyes and the prisoner found he could not turn his face away: it was as though invisible steel bars ran between the two men, forcing them to endure each other's souls.

'You have this choice. You can die quickly, and painlessly, from a bullet. Or you can die from...'

Kyril lifted a hand, the movement slow and clumsy like a deep-sea diver's, and gestured vaguely at the chair.

'...that.'

There was another long silence. Sikarov knew that very soon now the contents of his bowels were going to flood all over the floor.

'Who sent you, Sikarov? That's all you have to do to buy yourself an easy death. Tell me the answer to just one question. Who... sent... you?'

Sikarov said nothing. A slow smile spread across Kyril's lips.

'Let me tell you about that... thing... you are sitting in...'

Kyril unfolded his legs and stretched them out in front of him, like a man who wants to make sure he is comfortable before embarking on a long story.

'It's oak. Fastened to the floor. As you realise, you can't move. Wrapped round your… equipment… is what we used to call "the adulterer's knot". You've heard of that, have you? I hadn't heard of it. When I was a boy…'

Kyril stood up to light another cigarette and moved away from Sikarov.

'…We lived in a village just west of the Urals. The oldest man in the village was a cossack… he must have been ninety if he was a day.'

Kyril halted and looked at the wall, his face set once more in its smooth, dreamy expression.

'Do you know anything about the cossacks? They're a strange crew. This old man, one day my friends and I were discussing the local harlot. Married, she was. I suppose we got a bit high-spirited, you know how boys do…'

Kyril was in no particular hurry now. The memory of his childhood was very close, very real.

'The old cossack, he said… "where I come from, they'd put you louts in an adulterer's knot". "Where do you come from, grandad?" we answered, although we knew. He'd come from western Siberia… Surgut. Do you know Surgut?'

As if mesmerised Sikarov very slowly shook his head. 'But then we got curious… and one of us, I forget who, asked him about this knot. And he showed us. It's for when one cossack finds that another has stolen his woman. You take thin wire… not so thin that it breaks when fire touches it…' Sikarov flinched. Kyril saw, and allowed another long silence to develop.

'…And you tie it, so… if you look down you'll see… in such a way that, as it heats, the knot contracts upon itself, eating through anything that gets in its way…'

Sikarov's face had turned perfectly white, even to the lips. 'I've had to improvise a little. Do you know what this is? It's called a bunsen burner. You fix it to a gas pipe, so…' Kyril plugged the rubber tube over a gas-tap let into the skirting-board.

'Then you turn on the gas and… you see?'

Kyril flicked his lighter, and watched the flame reflected in Sikarov's dull eyes as it moved towards the burner. A wing of yellow leapt into the air; Kyril adjusted the stem until all the yellow had drained away, leaving in its place a thin, purple column of naked heat.

'Behind you, the wire is attached to a hook in the wall, like the one you see holding it in front of you. As the wire turns red it cuts first through the upper edge of the penis, while underneath it severs the little neck of skin which connects the scrotum… you understand the principle?'

Kyril put down the bunsen burner in front of Sikarov, where he could see it, and sat back on his haunches. For a moment there was silence. Then Sikarov moaned, and his bowels opened. The stench which filled the room was indescribable, but Kyril betrayed no emotion.

'I ask you again. Who sent you?'

The pause seemed to go on for a very long time. Sikarov's fists clenched and unclenched, his eyes fluttered open and shut. Kyril tried to imagine what was going on in his brain, what loyalties were asserting themselves, or finally being put to rest. How would I react, he asked himself, what would I do?

Sikarov's eyes opened wide. 'No.'

Kyril reached for the burner, and applied it to the wire. Both men watched, fascinated, as it began to glow. Then the red started to travel along the wire towards the chair. Kyril placed the burner directly under the wire, and waited.

He had not known what to expect. But the reality was frightful.

If an impressionist artist wanted to illustrate the meaning, the concept, of 'Scream', he would have painted Sikarov. The man's body slammed forward against the straps, his spine arched, his head went back until the horrible, glazed eyes were staring at the ceiling. All ten fingers stuck out rigidly. The lips curled back in a terrible rictus, laying bare the gums.

The stench began, a new smell to add to the old. Burning flesh. Seared meat.

And the scream. Explosively loud, expelled from Sikarov's body as if by an overpowering force, a high-pitched wail that spoke of death and things beyond death, a scream that suddenly rippled with syllables...

'Meee-ay, Meee-ay...'

Kyril snatched away the burner. '*Michaelov?*'

Sikarov's scream faded to a low, background moan. His head lolled on his chest. Kyril dared not look down his body to see what the fire had done.

Was there a name buried in that awful scream? Mee...? It could have been Michaelov, it had to be Michaelov...

Kyril went to kneel by Sikarov's body. The man was slipping into unconsciousness. Kyril took him by the chin and hauled him upright in the chair.

'*Who sent you?*'

Sikarov's head rolled backwards, the eyes staring and blank.

Somewhere, as from a great distance, Kyril heard Stanov's own words to him, weeks before. *You will be alone.* When the lessons stopped, in the place where there were no more lectures and trade-craft failed, every agent was alone. In a sense. But not like this. Officers of the KGB, even the professional killers of the A2 Institute, went with the support of their fellows, in the knowledge that they could call on them in need.

Only Kyril, only he had been truly alone.

He picked up the Luger which had fallen out of the assassin's pocket when Kyril stripped him and used it to blow away the side of Sikarov's ugly head.

Chapter 26

The car stank of smoke. Ted Jacques sat in the front with the driver, wondering what the hell was going on, while the man in the back seat alternately chewed on a nail and smoked his cigarette. Ted wanted to turn round and look at him but didn't like to. He had no idea what was happening but he realised that for the London Station Chief to come and sit in the back of a car under a bridge in Battersea at seven o'clock in the morning it must be something pretty big. Especially when the London Station Chief in question was a quivering wreck.

'Let's have it once again.'

Ted screwed up his mouth but did not protest.

'I followed two men from the house in Turpin Road. The leader was in a great hurry and the other one was following him. Neither of them looked back. The car got here about forty minutes later. Everything was quiet. Then we saw a movement…'

'What time was this?'

'About ten to four.'

'Go on.'

'We saw something move on the embankment. A man. He stood on the top with his back to the house, we could see him outlined against the skyline…'

'Yes, yes, go on.'

'He came down in a rush and a while after that this second man followed over the edge. He must have come over the tracks.'

'And then?'

'Nothing until about half-past five. Then we heard a scream, very long and very loud. Even for round here. Nothing since then.'

'The scream came from No. 703?'

'Yes, we think so.'

'Any reactions? Lights on along the street, doors opening, that sort of thing?'

The driver of the car laughed. 'Here? You've heard of the wrong side of the tracks? Well…' He jerked his thumb upwards, to the bridge. 'Those are the tracks.'

'And you haven't made a move yet, you've done nothing to alarm the occupants?'

'No sir. You said to wait and we waited.'

Royston lit another cigarette from the butt of the old one. Ted continued to face the front, maintaining a watch on the street. The night was thinning out, it was possible to distinguish the houses one from another. Suddenly he leaned forward.

'Movement,' he said softly.

Royston's head materialised beside him.

'Where?'

Ted pointed. 'See that flash of white… some kind of… stick, I think. Yes, that's it. A blind chap. Coming out of the downstairs flat.'

Royston was puzzled. 'How do you know it's the downstairs flat?'

'Well, there are two front doors, you see. Next to each other. I didn't see the first man enter the house, but the second man did, because he was there ahead of me, and he spent a lot of time just nosing round the door on the left. There've been lights on upstairs, so I reckon the door on the left leads to the upper flat…'

'And the blind man came out of the door on the right… yes, I understand now.'

Royston lowered himself back into his seat.

'He's reached the gate. Shall I go and take a look?'

'No, don't do that…'

But Royston was too late. The tense, polluted atmosphere inside the car had become too much for Ted. He stood on the pavement, drawing in gulps of fresh air, then strode off towards the house under the embankment. Royston's hands tightened on the seat in front of him, but he said nothing.

As Ted approached the house another door opened further along the terrace and a shaft of light illuminated the pavement. A young woman emerged, holding in her arms a child who seemed to be asleep. She reached her front gate just as the blind man with the stick stepped on to the pavement.

''Allo, there, Mr Trumper,' said the girl. ''Ow are you, then?'

As Ted sauntered past in the grey half-light he was vaguely aware of a shabby mac and dark glasses obscuring the upper part of an elderly face. The old man muttered something that Ted couldn't catch.

'Oh dear, your chest bad again, is it?'

The man nodded and coughed bronchially. Ted was almost past now.

''Ere, what was all that racket upstairs, then? Screamin' and that.'

'Din' 'ear nuffin'.'

‘Coo, wish I could sleep like that. Well, look after y’self. Cheers, then.’

Ted walked on a few paces, crossed the road and began to retrace his steps. The girl hurried off down the hill, still carrying the child, while the old man shuffled slowly in the opposite direction. Ted walked back to the car and reported. At first Royston said nothing, his face creased in thought.

‘This man’, he said suddenly. ‘The one with the stick. You’re sure the girl knew him?’

‘Oh yes, no question. She spoke to him like an old friend.’

‘He wasn’t one of the men you followed?’

Ted suppressed a desire to laugh. ‘No sir.’

‘Even in disguise?’

‘Different build, different… everything.’

Royston remained in thought a few moments longer.

‘Right,’ he said at last. ‘Check with the second car on the other side of the embankment. See if anybody’s gone out that way, over the railway lines.’

The driver’s hand moved to the radiophone.

‘Then we’ll go and get a warrant. Or rather, the Special Branch will. It sounds from what the girl said as if you’re right about the upstairs flat, then. I want to take a look in there.’

The driver turned to Royston. ‘No one’s been out that way.’

Royston nodded. ‘Get going, then.’

Chapter 27

Sculby drifted into sleep to catch the first gleam of the silver blade in the crook of the officer's swinging arm as he stormed across Red Square in search of him. Throughout the night the dream intermittently returned, and this was typical. The most he could achieve was a light doze, interspersed with periods of wakefulness whenever the officer with his flashing sword came too close for comfort. All the details in the dream were clear by now. Only the face was still missing. Every time Sculby dropped off the sword gleamed brighter in the piercing sunlight, until it almost blinded him. An inner reserve of fatigue was building up inside him much as other men acquire reserves of courage or moral strength.

He woke to find Judy's letter still beneath his hand where it lay on the quilt. He had come home the night before to find it pushed through the letterbox, unstamped. The long scrawl was rambling and difficult to read but its general message was clear enough. We are not suited. Goodbye.

Sculby screwed up the letter and tossed it down the loo. He had to flush it three times before the heavy, waterlogged paper disappeared round the bend, taking Judy out of his life.

That morning he was too tired to be conscious of any particular emotion, other than a mild annoyance at one of the phrases she had used in her letter. 'I don't mind trendy lefties,' she had written. 'God knows, I've had enough of them, and they're okay as long as you don't take baby seriously. But pseudo-trendies, playing at playing at it, no darling...'

Playing at playing at it; that's what got up Sculby's nose. He wanted to believe that Judy would someday find out about the work of national importance he'd been doing for Royston over the last six years, would come grovelling to him in abject, humiliated apology, 'Laurie, I never realised...'

He saw where his thoughts were leading and angrily brushed them aside. Fantasies could be damaging. Pathos crippled. What he needed was breakfast.

While he made the toast Sculby forced himself to concentrate on Loshkevoi.

Today the magistrates would finally decide whether to commit him for trial by jury at Inner London Crown Court. Sculby had consulted Spencer Gyddon and together they had decided to allow the case to go through on the nod, without challenging the written statements provided by the police. This was called a 'Section One' committal.

'They've got just enough there to open the case to the jury,' said Gyddon. 'Don't worry, Laurie, I'll get it knocked out at half time.'

On the whole Sculby agreed with that assessment, but in the taxi to Lavender Hill he couldn't help wondering whether they oughtn't to have been submitting today that there was no case to answer. Spencer Gyddon was unavailable, however, and Sculby neither wanted to take in another barrister at this late stage nor to risk doing the case himself, so a Section One committal it was.

He met Loshkevoi in the foyer and took him to an interview room. The first thing his client said was: 'I tried to call you last night, Laurie. I didn't want you to come. It's all off.'

Sculby sat down and said nothing for a moment. He took out a cigarette, lit it and enjoyed a long drag while he thought about his next move.

Royston had never so much as hinted that this might be in the pipeline. Sculby had no instructions to drop the case.

'What's up, Victor?' he asked gently.

'I don't need you any more, Laurie. I've decided to go it alone. I'm pleading guilty.'

'What?'

'I did it, you see.'

Loshkevoi darted a sharp look at Sculby as he spoke these words, and the solicitor had a sudden hunch that his client knew perfectly well what the effect would be. No lawyer who was advised of his client's guilt in that way could thereafter put forward a positive case of innocence to the court.

'But why, Victor? Why save it up for now?'

Sculby was genuinely astonished. He had known clients do all kinds of crazy things, but nothing as outlandish as this.

'Have they threatened you? Have they promised you a deal?'

Loshkevoi merely shrugged and looked away.

'I can't just take this lying down, you know. In your own interests, I've got to try to talk you out of it.'

'You'll be wasting your breath. Leave it out, please Laurie. You can't do any more to help me now.'

Sculby considered his client. Loshkevoi seemed preoccupied, distraught; something far outside this courtroom was preying on his mind. The lawyer was conscious of a barrier between them, a wilful refusal on Loshkevoi's part to meet his situation face to face. Yet underneath it all he was scared out of his wits. Somewhere very near the surface was the jerky madman who had screamed from the dock on the day of the first hearing. If only Sculby could get through to him…

'You could go inside, you realise that, don't you?' Sculby's voice was suddenly hard. 'Doing bird is no fun, Victor. You don't want to get involved with that. Remand in Brixton, that was nothing, that's a doddle. Have you ever *really* been in prison before? Three men to a cell, and they all shit?'

'Laurie, I…'

'The smell at night, have you thought about that?'

Loshkevoi stood up and banged his clenched fists on the table in front of him.

'Get out!'

'Now look…'

'You're sacked, you hear me? Sacked!'

Sculby gave him a long, cool look, then packed up his briefcase and made for the door.

'I'll be in court,' he said just before he went out. 'If you change your mind, all you've got to do is say.'

Once outside Sculby thought about phoning Royston, actually went as far as the phone-booth, before deciding he couldn't go through with it. He had a 'life or death' contact number but somehow he couldn't bring himself to use it. Three months was the most Loshkevoi could expect, even if the worse came to the worst, and besides it was P.4's function to watch, not manipulate. Its members were 'spies' rather than 'agents', their powers limited.

Sculby reluctantly put the change back into his trouser-pocket and entered the court.

Today there were a number of matters to be dealt with before Loshkevoi's case was called on. Sculby sat in the solicitor's row and doodled in the margin of his notebook. At last he heard his ex-client's name and turned to see him in the dock, hands resting on the bar in front of him. The clerk to the justices ran through the formalities like an announcer reeling off stations. Loshkevoi declined to apply for Legal Aid, opted for summary trial, waived any claim to trial by jury. At a sign from the chairman of the magistrates Loshkevoi sat down.

'Sergeant?'

Detective-Sergeant Fitzgerald rose to his feet.

'Sir, normally there would be no objection from the police to summary trial on these charges. But there has been a slight complication...'

Sculby looked up from his notebook to see that Fitzgerald was suffering from an advanced case of policeman's smirk.

'Owing to information very helpfully supplied by the accused himself, and I want to say now that the police have received the very fullest co-operation, certain other offences have come to light.'

Sculby turned to the dock, willing Loshkevoi to look him in the eye, without success. His former client was alert but relaxed, and again Sculby was conscious of a feeling that he knew what he was up to, almost as if acting under advice.

Fitzgerald handed a typewritten list to the bench. The chairman looked up from reading it and said sharply,

'Two of these offences were allegedly committed while the accused was on bail pending these present charges, the ones with which we are concerned today.'

'Yes, sir.'

The chairman's lips puckered. To Sculby he seemed mildly embarrassed at finding himself in such low company for the discharge of a public duty. 'Well-meaning' was the phrase the Divisional Court would use when quashing his decisions.

'Er... Mr Loshkevoi, perhaps you'd like to reconsider your position. You're not legally represented...'

'It's okay.' Loshkevoi was standing again. Sculby, who had long ago ceased to write, sat with his mouth open.

'...I just want to get it over with. Finish. You understand?'

The bench went into a huddle. Sculby knew what would happen and it did.

'Put these further charges,' said the chairman. The clerk ran through the same rigmarole all over again and Loshkevoi renewed his guilty plea.

'Anything known?'

Fitzgerald stood up.

'No sir. The accused is a person of hitherto good character. There are no antecedents.'

Again the chairman's lips puckered.

'Mr Loshkevoi, do you wish to call character evidence or say anything on your own behalf?'

Sculby half rose to his feet, thought better of it, and subsided.

'Not really. It's the temptation, you see. I mentioned this to the sergeant there and he agrees. Very easy in the used car trade.'

The chairman looked incredulous. 'Is that all you want to say?'

Loshkevoi shrugged. 'Sure. Why not?'

'Do you regret having committed these offences?'

'Oh sure. Pity I got found out, eh?'

And Loshkevoi laughed, a hearty, booming sound which caused everyone in court to stop whatever he was doing and look at the prisoner in the dock, amazed.

Sculby put away his notebook and reached for his coat. The proceedings were now drawing to a close which he regarded as inevitable. The bench went into its usual huddle; then the chairman was speaking again.

'We do not think we have adequate powers to deal with you. We therefore propose to commit you to the Crown Court for sentence, in accordance with the warning which the clerk read to you earlier.'

As Sculby left the courtroom the last thing he heard was the magistrate refusing Loshkevoi bail for which he had not actually applied.

Chapter 28

The crypt was exactly as Kyril remembered it. Plain, whitewashed walls, tatty strips of carpet, red lights glowing outside closed doors. The central room, what was it called? 'Grocer's Gift.' Kyril had never understood that name. Nursing a cup of sweet tea he looked around with a tinge of nostalgia. The people here were so nice, so kind. The lady in reception had asked him if he minded waiting until someone was free. No, said Kyril, he didn't mind. He had all the time in the world.

The Samaritans were a unique find. Every agent has his personal trade secrets, things which he never reports back to Centre or shares with others. The Wallbrook headquarters of the Samaritans was one of Kyril's little personal treasures. He had used it only once before but he had great faith in it. You went down the steps and immediately became anonymous. You didn't have to give a name or an address, although one usually did in order not to be conspicuous; Kyril had told them his name was Ian, just that. Then after a decent interval one disappeared through the man-sized ventilator at the back of the centre corridor, the only fire escape on the premises… and that was that.

But not today. Today was different.

Kyril pulled Trumper's macintosh a little more snugly over his shoulders. Getting the right build had been the most difficult thing; that and trying to emulate a stooping walk which he had never actually seen in life. The first problem he had solved by wrapping himself in several of the old man's woollies. The walk he had left to chance.

After disposing of Sikarov he had dropped down into the flat below through his trapdoor. The old man lived in conditions of extreme poverty; it was not much of a life to leave, thought Kyril. He concentrated on clothing. When he had removed all that was wearable from the bedroom he began to rummage through drawers, jackdaw-like, in search of anything useful. There was a pair of dark glasses in a newish case, perhaps prescribed by that bugger of a doctor, but not worn, out of pride. Kyril pocketed them. The white stick was also useful. In height he and the old man were not dissimilar; cotton wool and hair dye would go a long way towards perfecting the substitution. He knew the power of 'type': a watcher would see only a white stick and dark glasses, say the word 'blind' to himself, and look elsewhere for the elusive Russian agent he was supposed to be seeking.

From the depths of his rucksack Kyril extracted a small, lightweight box containing his make-up. He had brought nothing special, just the most basic kit for emergencies, but it was enough. By inserting pads of cottonwool into his cheeks and moving them around with his fingers he was soon able to fashion a face the same shape as the dead man's. Kyril shared Trumper's weather-beaten complexion so he did nothing with that, trusting the dark glasses, scarf and hat to cut down to a minimum the area of skin that could be used for comparative purposes. Thereafter it was a simple matter of high-lighting and ageing, with particular attention to the corners of the eyes, the neck and, last but most important, the hands.

Next came the difficult bit. He had to assume Trumper's walk, but he had almost no idea what it looked like. The thick cane was the only real indication he had to go on: it was used to support the bearer as well as warn others that he was blind. So it would pay to go slowly, rather than risk going too fast. Kyril had 'played blind' before, he knew all the business with the stick, but the rest he was going to have to chance.

The worst part had been waiting for the noises next door which would indicate that the girl was on her way out. Kyril used the time to ensure that he had forgotten nothing. His rucksack was stripped of its contents and discarded, everything of value now being secreted on Kyril's person. Then he stood in the hall, listening with all his might. At last he heard the tell-tale sounds: a door slammed in the adjoining house and footsteps thudded down the stairs. The girl pulled the front door to behind her and turned to see old Mr Trumper almost on the pavement.

From then on it had been easy. In a different frame of mind Kyril would have enjoyed the casual, dismissive glance which was all the MI6 agent in the street could afford. But today what mattered was escape. He discarded the white stick and the glasses behind some bushes on the Common, then made his way to Bank by tube. Now here he was, safe for a time. They would never think of looking for him here.

He looked around. For some reason things looked different. Kyril couldn't think what it was. Then he remembered.

'Excuse me...' A young woman was passing his chair.

'Yes?'

'The cats, are they still here? You called them Push and Pull, I remember them so well.'

'Oh they died, I'm afraid.'

Kyril's face fell. 'I'm sorry.'

'That was a long time ago.'

'I've been away, you see.'

'Can I help you?'

Kyril looked up to see that a young man had come to stand by his chair. The woman used the opportunity to slip away while Kyril studied the man's face and his badge. 'John 1696', they never told you the surname. The security here was excellent, they would have made good spies.

'I'd like to talk to somebody.'

'Please. Come this way. We'll go into "Godfrey".'

Kyril followed the young man into the cubicle, sat down in an old armchair from which the stuffing had mostly escaped, and folded his hands in his lap. He was conscious of the young man's eyes upon him, and behind those eyes he knew that John 1696 was busily attaching labels. Shabby clothes. Old tramp. Query drunk, or just here for the hand-out.

'I don't really know how to begin.' He tailed off. The young man leaned forward.

'Take your time,' he said. 'There's absolutely no hurry.' Kyril pretended to study his hands. 'You see, the trouble is… it all seems so implausible.'

The young man shook his head and smiled. 'We're used to hearing all kinds of things here. It never goes any further.' After a further period of reflection Kyril began his story. 'I must tell you first that I am a spy. I am a colonel in the KGB, attached to the staff of its Chairman. I have been sent to England on a very delicate mission –

to expose a traitor in our ranks. What I think you call a "mole", no?'

The young man sat back, his smile intact. 'Goodness,' he said. 'I've never met a real spy before.'

'There aren't many of us. Now you see, my problem is this. The mole has sent an executioner after me. He's outside there now, in the street. He's armed, of course. And the question is, what am I to do?'

The young man appeared to be lost in thought. After a while he spoke. 'There's somebody here who I think could help you more than I can. Somebody who's, er, used to this kind of thing.'

'Really? You mean, he's a spy too?'

'Not exactly. He's a… well, a doctor, actually.'

Kyril nodded. 'Perhaps I could talk to him, then.'

The young man stood up.

'Please wait here. I shan't be a moment.'

He went out, closing the door behind him very firmly. Kyril smiled. It would take John 1696 quite a while to brief the resident psychiatrist on the latest nutter and there was a good chance that he would warn everyone else to stay away from 'Godfrey' until 'Ian' had been dealt with. He could spin this out for a while yet. First there would be the long, circuitous questioning designed to establish what the real problem was; then, later in the day, he would persuade them to find him a hostel for the night. Meanwhile there was time to think…

Stanov's moving magnet had come to the very end of the road. Either the traitor stood revealed by now or the plan had failed: Kyril had no means of knowing. Three times he had shown himself on schedule; three times he had evaded capture. '*Lisa's*' executioner… executed. That left only Loshkevoi. The biggest question-mark of all…

Other images crowded into Kyril's tired brain.

An old man locked into a stuffy office overlooking Dzerzhinsky Square, who lied to his own men and spun fine webs from the ruthlessly mangled lives of people he despised…

A younger man on a bed, half-concealing a bloody corpse…

An anonymous traitor who must be destroyed so that his very name was blotted out…

Kyril closed his eyes and sat back in the old, tattered chair. His head had begun to ache. It was going to be a long, long day.

Chapter 29

At first Michaelov paid scant attention to the news of Loshkevoi's imprisonment, marking it down as just another mystery in the Bucharensky saga which would one day find an explanation. Then in the course of the afternoon Yevchenko came along the corridor to give him a tiny insight into what Loshkevoi had been really doing for the last few years and the picture changed. Now Povin and his boss were up before Stanov to learn the worst.

Michaelov noted with grudging approval that the old man looked suitably contrite. As soon as he saw the First Deputy Chairman he spread his hands wide and said ruefully, 'Valery Vasilevich, what can I say? Every rogue gets found out in the end, no?'

With difficulty Michaelov restrained himself from asking whether '*Lisa*' had been found out yet, and said, 'If you had felt able to confide in me just a little, comrade Chairman.' Stanov found it hard to resent the censorious tone of Michaelov's voice. For years he had, in effect, been running the show behind his deputy's back. As Kyril observed weeks before, it was a system which worked only when things went well. Today things were going very badly indeed. 'Have you heard anything?'

'He is in Wandsworth Prison. He was taken there at 1430 local time after a short period in police custody. Since then he has been held incommunicado.'

'Is that usual in England?'

'Very unusual.'

It was Povin who spoke. His voice betrayed no hint of criticism, merely a desire to press on with whatever might be necessary. Stanov had a lot of time for Povin just then.

'Do we have anyone inside Wandsworth Prison?'

'Unfortunately not.' They were on Povin's home ground and he spoke with authority. 'Six months ago, MI5 took over a cell block at Wandsworth and turned it into a top security holding centre. We think not even the governor is allowed to know exactly what goes on in there. It stinks of anti-terrorism. I've been trying desperately to get a pair of eyes in there, but these things take time, and…'

Stanov waved a hand. 'No matter, comrade Colonel-General. You've done well. But… it could not have happened at a worse time. First Bucharensky, now this.' He stood up and walked over to the window. Behind his back he could sense the other three weighing up his reactions. Yevchenko, loyal to the end but allowing personal concern for the chief to get the better of his judgement. Michaelov, unimaginative, concerned only to watch his step while he built bridges towards Stanov's as yet unknown successor. And Povin…

Stanov turned back to face the room. 'He must be brought out, Colonel-General,' he said quietly. 'Brought out or otherwise dealt with.'

Povin nodded curtly. 'I'm working on it, comrade Marshal. My own inclination is to liquidate him fast, and not waste time on trying to spring him.'

Stanov nodded thoughtfully. 'I agree.'

'It should not be difficult.' Michaelov, impatient at being left out of the colloquy developing between his chief and his deputy, was determined to make a contribution. 'I have recently dispatched an A2 to London, comrade Marshal. It's not a problem.'

Stanov nodded. He seemed absentminded, as though his attention was on other things. Through half-closed eyes he watched the two generals. Michaelov wore an expression of pompous self-esteem. Povin's face was impassive. Did Stanov detect a trace of surprise at Michaelov's last words? Had Povin known that an executioner had been ordered to his territory? Stanov fancied not. But Povin was always loyal. If there was one thing Stanov valued in a senior officer it was loyalty. Loyalty was like oxygen. The higher you rose, the scarcer it became.

'Keep me informed, comrades. I want to hear of progress within the next twenty-four hours. Povin, I take it there is no news of Bucharensky, or you would have told me?'

'There is no news, comrade Marshal. I regret...'

Stanov waved him away. The debacle in Victoria Station had been no fault of Povin's. The two generals saluted and withdrew, Povin standing respectfully aside for his superior.

'That Michaelov is a condescending, fat-arsed pig...' Yevchenko began, but Stanov stopped him by raising his hand. For a while there was silence. Yevchenko was about to resume when Stanov said, 'Nikolai, you remember the day we went to the Kremlin?'

Yevchenko felt his cheek-muscles tense. They had spoken little of that day. Despite Stanov's assurances, Yevchenko could never be quite certain that the chief accepted his version of what had occurred over lunch with Kazin. The more Yevchenko protested that he had kept Kazin at bay, the more cynical Stanov's sideways glance became, as if the old man were quietly saying to himself, 'I'll bet'.

Yevchenko found this galling, not least because Stanov's suspicions were eminently justified. It had been a difficult lunch. He was a tough old man who had seen much, but when there was a pause in the conversation and he looked up to find those pebble lenses glinting at him over the table he had known fear. 'Stalin's baby'... such pink, well-preserved skin on one so evil, it was an unfair anachronism. It was as if he had found a way of channelling some of the fresh young blood he had spilled into his own veins. And the voice... that melodious, silken voice with its promises and blandishments still echoed in Yevchenko's ears.

He quelled the thoughts of treachery which rose to the surface whenever that day was mentioned and tried to concentrate on the present crisis.

'Of course. We came back and there was nothing, nothing at all. Every message in its appointed place, no tampering, no delays. Povin dealt with the matter as one of top priority. Surely you don't think...'

Stanov shook his head impatiently. 'No, it's the date that concerns me. It was on that day that Kyril first showed himself in London. You remember how I issued an order for his return to Moscow *alive*?'

'Of course.'

'Nikolai!' His old eyes were bright with excitement. 'It's going to work! He's panicked. Kyril arrives... an A2 is dispatched to London... Loshkevoi is arrested...'

'You're going too fast. What's the connection?'

'Why, don't you see? Loshkevoi's been taken out of circulation. He's been put away. *Somewhere Kyril can't reach him.*'

Yevchenko pursed his lips.

'You're assuming a lot.'

'Am I? It can't be coincidence, it can't be. *First* the executioner, *then* this business with Loshkevoi. And Loshkevoi is in touch with the traitor!' He checked himself. 'But you're right, Nikolai. It has to be gone over very carefully. You must do it yourself. Discreetly. I want to know what Povin has on in London at the moment which would require an operative from A2. And if, as I suspect, the answer is "nothing"...' Stanov shot a glance at Yevchenko and saw the beginnings of a reluctant conversion in his face. '...You can come back here and tell me, Nikolai, precisely when and why General Michaelov took it upon himself to order an executioner to the United Kingdom.'

Chapter 30

Looking back on it afterwards Sculby was never quite sure how it happened. He had gone to the outer office to say goodnight to Betty and watched while she bundled up the last batch of post. As he went back to his own room he heard the outer door close and the night-latch click. He sat down at his desk and was collating the sheets of an affidavit when he heard the voice.

'Don't move.'

Something in the tone compelled obedience. A sheet of paper slipped from Sculby's fingers; he sat rigidly, his head still bent downwards to the desk.

'Place both hands on top of your desk… that's right.'

Sculby noticed that his hands were shaking and pressed them firmly down on to the leather, deliberately tensing all his muscles. He had been wondering for a long time how he would react when this moment came. Now, looking at his hands, he knew.

The Soviet officer did not wear a uniform and the flashing silver-white sword had been replaced by a small gun. The face, so long concealed, had dark circles round the eyes, sunken cheeks, tousled, unkempt hair and at least a day's growth of stubble. Kyril's eyes were hard and flat, two bright shiny buttons sewn into the dark circles. Sculby knew that Royston had told him only the truth: from now on he was fighting for his life. And he was terrified.

Kyril walked across to the window and drew the curtains. To Sculby it was as though his office halved in size. It become very claustrophobic, very hot. The slightest movement by the Russian seemed to come within inches of Sculby's face.

'I've put off visiting you for too long, Sculby. I should have realised a long time ago that you weren't just a meddler.'

The clipped, too-perfect English sounded coldly in the solicitor's ears. Something was at work deep inside Kyril, a hard core of fission which bordered always on the critical. Sculby made himself concentrate on the man's face, keeping his eyes off the gun.

'Last night a woman was killed. A woman who was important to me. Vera Bradfield.'

Seeing Sculby's involuntary start, Kyril raised the gun.

'You didn't know?'

Sculby shook his head.

'I wonder if that's true. You visited her two days ago. You talked about Loshkevoi. I want to know why, Sculby. Who put you up to it? Who are you working for, MI6?'

There was silence. Kyril slowly shook his head.

'Don't make me work for it. I'd enjoy it too much.'

'Yes, I work for MI6. Department P.4.'

Sculby's voice seemed to come from a great distance, perhaps deadened by the thick layer of fur which coated the inside of his mouth.

'What is P.4? Be specific.'

'P stands for professional. Doctors, lawyers, accountants. People who learn secrets about other people's lives. Their finances. Their habits. Their crucial needs.'

Kyril's eyes widened and narrowed again. 'That is clever,' he said softly. 'In Russia that would not work, but here, in England... yes, I think I see the value of that.'

His face hardened once more.

'So you were told to find about Loshkevoi's secrets... and Vera's.'

'Loshkevoi's, yes. I visited Vera Bradfield only because he mentioned her name.'

'Why should he do such a thing?'

'I don't know.'

Kyril strove to assimilate this latest piece of information. He did not doubt that Sculby was telling the truth: the lawyer was obviously scared out of his wits. But why should Loshkevoi ever know about Vera? Only Stanov understood her significance. *Stanov!*

'Tell me his exact words.'

Sculby did his best to remember. Kyril ran a hand over his face. As it brushed his mouth he became aware that his breath smelled terrible.

'Were you followed to the house?'

'I have no idea.'

Kyril bared his teeth in a snarl and restlessly took a few steps towards Sculby, who stayed motionless. The Russian wants information, he told himself, keep hold of that. As long as he thinks you have that information, he will not kill you.

'This P.4...' There was a sneer in Kyril's voice. 'Why do you do it, eh? You English lawyers, with your "ethics" and your "etiquette". You're not an agent, you're a solicitor. What have they promised you, eh? What do they pay you? Is it worth it?'

'I do it...'

Somewhere inside Sculby a great, billowing cloud of hot air was beginning to expand, buoying him up, making him heady with excitement.

'…I do it for love of the Motherland.'

As he said it the balloon inside him collapsed. The absurd phrase made him sound like a brightly coloured figure in the 'Boys' Own Paper'. But the effect on Kyril was remarkable.

He froze in the act of raising the gun in Sculby's direction and his lips parted. After a second of stillness he rubbed his hand across his face, as if trying to remove some tight, invisible mask, then repeated the gesture once, twice. He was sweating.

'You're lying.'

'I'm sorry?'

Sculby raised his eyebrows and subjected Kyril to a long, wooden stare.

'You're not a *schpick*. You're too… too…'

Kyril did not finish the sentence. Sculby was breathing more easily now. The intricate, precarious balance between the two men had shifted marginally in his favour.

'You can always check with Centre. Do you mind if I smoke?'

On the last word he slowly reached out for the box with his right hand. If Kyril noticed he gave no sign. Keeping his movements calm and smooth, Sculby lit a cigarette. The first gulp of smoke tasted bilious, and for a vile second he wanted to be sick, but the sensation passed.

'Tell me what to do,' said Sculby. Kyril's eyes had never left his face, and behind them the lawyer read doubt. The odd sensation of buoyant floating was coming back, aided by the nicotine. The room no longer seemed so hot. Only the gun remained to convince Sculby that this was real, everything Royston predicted had come to pass, his life was no longer guaranteed. From trying to ignore the gun Sculby had now started to concentrate on it as a reminder that this was actually happening, he was no longer dreaming.

'Do…? Oh yes, I'll tell you what to do.'

Kyril's voice had recaptured its former note of resolve. Now he spoke like a man who chooses his words with care.

'You're Loshkevoi's solicitor. You can get me an hour alone with him in prison.'

Sculby bit his lower lip. The initiative had shifted back again.

'Difficult. Loshkevoi's being held in Wandsworth jail. Some months back MI5 took over a cell block and transformed it into a top-security isolation centre. Loshkevoi's in there. I can't get in without a special pass. Besides, I'm no longer acting for Loshkevoi. Anyway, why do you want this?'

Kyril looked up furiously. 'Sculby, it would give me a good deal of pleasure to kill you, right now. You with your lawyer's questions… Just listen. Listen and do as I say.'

Sculby's fingers involuntarily pinched the cigarette, giving it an almost flat waist. Kyril's head was sunk on to his chest; he seemed to be lost in thought. When he spoke again Sculby had to strain to catch the words.

'Then you must get him out of prison, mustn't you?'

Sculby opened his mouth to protest but Kyril forestalled him. 'No, you can do it. Don't underestimate yourself. Tell whoever it is you tell these things that this is my price. I propose… a deal. On your side, one hour alone with Loshkevoi. On mine… I will come over to the

British. Not the Americans… keep them out of my life, you hear!'

During this speech Sculby had been thinking furiously. Make friends, that's what Royston had said. Win his confidence. The prize is worth having: a defector from Moscow. But his use of the coded phrase had done little more than temporarily faze Kyril. What he needed was something concrete and constructive, something real.

'There might be a way,' he began, almost reluctantly, and Kyril's lips creased in a humourless smile.

'What?'

'Loshkevoi was booked on false charges. Five wanted to search his garage while he was out of the way. They found arms, grenades, all kinds of things. They decided to let it run, and turned him loose…'

'Like hell!' Kyril was almost spitting with rage. 'He's in prison, you told me so yourself. When I asked at the garage earlier they told me he could be gone months.'

'It was nothing to do with us. I had firm instructions to look after him and see he got off. He chose different, don't ask me why.'

'What do you mean, he chose different?'

'He sacked me and pleaded guilty. Threw in some other stuff as well, just to make sure he went inside. I told you earlier, I'm not acting for Loshkevoi any more.'

'You mean… he *planned* this?'

'Yes. Or someone planned it for him.'

It was obvious to Sculby that for reasons he didn't understand this last remark stopped Kyril in his tracks. Every muscle in the man's restless body suddenly became still. During the long silence which followed Sculby stubbed out his cigarette and dusted the ash off his suit. Kyril did not object to this succession of unauthorised movements. 'What are you telling me? You said you had an idea...' Sculby took his first tentative step across the abyss, teetering gingerly on a thin, taut wire of improvisation.

'It was going to be part of my job to go to him after a while and say, look, we have the goods on you. The arms, we know about them. Do you want to come clean or do you want to rot in jail for the rest of your life? That was the pitch. It was up to me to say when the time was ripe.' Sculby waited until he was sure that Kyril was looking at him directly before he spoke again. 'I think maybe the time just became ripe.'

There was a long silence, broken by Kyril sitting down in the nearest chair and saying, 'Give me a cigarette'.

Sculby obliged, remembering to keep all his movements nice and slow. Kyril smoked half of the cigarette in total silence, continually running the fingers which held the stub across the line of his lips. Sometimes he looked at Sculby, as if trying to gauge his sincerity; mostly he stared at the floor.

'But would your bosses buy that?' he said at last. 'After he sacked you...?'

'They might. They don't know how he sacked me, remember. Or what was said. Then I throw you into the scale. You and he together add up to something pretty big, I'd say. Especially if they think you're connected in some way. They're bound to be curious, and that's all you'll need to persuade them to give you an hour alone with Loshkevoi.'

This time the silence seemed to go on for ever. Sculby was uncomfortably aware of smoke-induced nausea, coupled with a burning desire to urinate. Something must snap soon. The initial floating feeling had worn off, to be replaced by a grey, dead weight around his heart and stomach.

'All right.'

Kyril had finished the cigarette. He ground it into Sculby's carpet and looked up with a smile.

'This is one total agreement. SIS must assent to all or none, you understand?'

Sculby nodded.

'One. Time alone with Loshkevoi. Two. Immunity for all crimes I may have committed against English laws, ever. Three. A new identity and maximum protection. Four, I'll give everything I know except what would endanger agents working in the field at this moment.' His lips curled. 'That includes you, Sculby. You're part of this agreement. And you come in on a side-deal, too. It goes like this. You fix up the main trade and get SIS to agree to it. I won't betray you. And I won't kill you. But Sculby...'

Again the curl of the lips.

'...If you don't succeed in persuading your bosses to make the main trade, P.4 is going to need another solicitor. I mean it.'

'I know you do.' The words were wrung out of Sculby against his will. He couldn't help it. He knew that Kyril was sincere.

'Now listen. They will ask you many questions, probing to see what is in this agreement for SIS. I understand that. Do you know anything about the art of defecting, Sculby? What you are, you sell. I am carrying with me the plan which the Chairman of the KGB calls "Sociable Plover". It contains details of the KGB's contacts with world terrorism. In the right hands it could blow the KGB apart for years to come. It is my passport... my deposit. It guarantees that I am who I say I am. Have you got that?'

'Yes.'

'Repeat it then.'

Sculby did as he was told. When he had finished the Russian grunted.

'Tell them also that I will be on the main drive at Crowden at three o'clock in two days' time.'

'Crowden?'

'Never mind. The people you report to will understand. They have used this place for similar meetings before and I know it. Tell them that.'

Kyril stood up and Sculby resisted the urge to cry out. The room had shrunk again. The intruder seemed to fill every available square inch, blocking off any chance there might be of escape.

'I'll contact you after noon tomorrow. Stay here, by the phone. I won't have much time, so be quick. When I ring, say "Yes" or "No", that's all. This is strictly take-it-or-leave-it trade. You understand?'

Sculby nodded, and Kyril smiled. It did not extend to his eyes.

'Get them to tell you what happened to Vera Bradfield, Sculby. Read the pathologist's report. Then see what I did to the man who killed her. *Stay still.*'

As he moved round behind Sculby's chair the lawyer involuntarily squirmed away, raising his arms to protect his head in a primeval, instinctive gesture of defence.

'I'm not going to hurt you... not yet. But if you double-cross me... if you're not a genuine sleeper...'

Sculby waited in vain for the rest of the sentence. He did not hear the street door open and close. When he finally looked round, unable any longer to bear the sinister silence which followed Kyril's last words, he was alone.

Sculby held his hands to his eyes. He was shivering, his skin felt clammy. It was several minutes before the worst of the tension wore off. His vision was blurred: a curious medley of wheels and chains ground before his eyes until he shook his head roughly a couple of times and it cleared.

Kyril had come and gone unheard, unseen. That terrified Sculby. If the Russian called for him again there would be no warning, no chance of self-defence. Until this nightmare was over, Sculby would be alone. No matter where he was or what he was doing, irrespective of who was with him, he would be a target. An accessible target…

Running through his brain were the digits of a phone number. He had been warned never to use it except as a last resort, a matter of life and death.

'P.4 is going to need a new solicitor…'

Sculby dialled. There was a long wait while the 'hams' at London Station tracked down their quarry. Then – 'Royston,' said Sculby. 'I want to see you. *Now.*'

Chapter 31

For once the kitchen cabinet was not in attendance; Sir Richard Bryant and Royston were quite alone. C sat with his hands folded on the bare desk, never once removing his steady gaze from Royston's face. The London Station Chief could hardly lift his head from lack of sleep. They were nearly at the end of a long, wearisome conversation.

'Have you any idea of the damage that man can do, has already done?'

In view of what had gone before Royston correctly assumed this to be a rhetorical question.

'The woman Bradfield, dead. Why? Because Kyril, as he persists in calling himself, led an executioner straight to her. Why was there an executioner in the first place? Because Kyril is carrying one of the most dangerous secrets to run loose from the Kremlin since the last World War. The executioner, dead; mutilated to death in a particularly gruesome fashion. The suburbs of south London are being turned into a Mafia's playground and I am under pressure to frame proposals for dealing with the situation.'

If C waited for constructive suggestions from Royston, he waited in vain. Certain aspects of 'the situation' Royston found highly attractive. Sikarov's death, for example. When first he learned of Sikarov's arrival in the UK he nearly panicked, reasoning that A2 had been ordered to liquidate him before Kyril could reveal his treachery to his employers. Even now that the picture was clearer the memory of Sikarov's gruesome mutilations did not appal.

'Also, I want from you a written appreciation of the events of the past two days. In a form fit for presentation...' C jerked his thumb to the north, in the vague direction of Whitehall.

'Appreciation?'

'It should not be difficult. The basics are reasonably clear, are they not? A defector on the run looks to a former mistress for shelter. A KGB killer, sent to destroy the defector before he talks, murders the mistress and is himself killed, doubtless as an act of revenge. That's all you need say. Nothing about who sent the killer, or why. No mention of Nidus. No hint that the killer was sent to stop Kyril falling into *their* hands, rather than ours. But there is one thing you can say. You can make the point that if only Five had been good enough to let us know of Sikarov's arrival a little earlier, none of this need have happened. Use red ink and underline it. As for Kyril...'

C unclasped his hands and spread them wide.

'Get everyone out on the streets looking for him. I want his description circulated to every police station in the land. I want every known A2 operative's description put on the wire. I want you where I can contact you twenty-four hours a day. Above all, I want this matter cleared up and I want it *soon*.'

Royston raised his haggard face and looked across the desk at C.

'Anything else?'

'One thing. The CIA are proving tiresome.'

'What?'

'Somehow they have found out about what they are pleased to call our "temporary local difficulty" over Kyril. Apparently they tried to kidnap him in Brussels and if we're not careful they may try the same thing again over here. Try to find out how much they know about Kyril and why they tried to snatch him in Belgium. Go and see Gulland. Stall him. We need time and I don't want any solicitous offers or American help in finding Bucharensky, thank you.'

Suddenly Royston wanted a drink more than anything in the world. Joe Gulland kept a bottle of Glenlivet in his room at Grosvenor Square. He placed his hands on the lip of C's desk and levered himself out of his seat.

'Right,' he said.

–

Less than an hour later he was sitting comfortably in a deep, leather-covered armchair, savouring the single-malt Scotch his host had just given him. A tiny pulse of life was beginning to beat inside him.

His feelings about Grosvenor Square were mixed, rather like those of poor relatives obliged to visit their better-off kin for a family reunion. It was on the whole pleasant to relish the good things of life while counting up the number of export licences the British government must have refused in order to furnish this room. The centre-piece was a large rosewood table. Royston had seen one very like it in a shop near his house in Sheen. It cost £3500.

His eyes returned to Joe Gulland, mixing himself a Bourbon-and-branch at the drinks tray. Rather a well-stocked tray, thought Royston as he remembered his own, pitifully limited supply of Amontillado sherry.

'There you go.'

He raised his glass politely in response to the informal toast, and drank.

Gulland was his chief liaison with 'the Cousins' at their London office. That made him reasonably senior, though like Royston himself his precise ranking was never disclosed to allies. The two men had known each other for five years, had visited each other's homes and were, in so far as the term has meaning in this context, friends.

Gulland took off his jacket to reveal a couple of Oxford blue stains under the arms of his Cambridge blue shirt, and loosened his tie.

'I sure as hell am glad we were able to meet like this, Mike.' Gulland swung his legs over the arm of his chair and smiled to reveal several gold fillings. 'Tell you the truth, things have been a little difficult right now. This Russky they been burning up the wires over. Cigarette?'

'Please.'

Gulland went through the long process of selecting a Kent from the packet on the occasional table by his side, lighting it, inhaling, flicking some ash into the brass saucer, and sending a compact column of smoke on its way to the ceiling. If he had hoped to provoke Royston into making a hasty response, he was disappointed. He would dearly have liked to know what was going through the Englishman's mind at that moment. Royston was thinking that fat men shouldn't smoke, and they certainly oughtn't to drink as much as Gulland.

'We were kind of wondering whether you'd be interested in going into joint venture over this, Mike. As I see it, we have better facilities for debriefing this man, and that's a fact.'

'This man...?'

Royston held out his glass. He waited until Gulland was busy at the drinks tray before he spoke again.

'I'm sorry, Joe, I'm not quite with you. Which man are we talking about?'

Gulland turned away from the table with Royston's drink in his hand and a glassy smile on his face.

'Bucharensky. You got him, right?'

'No,' said Royston. 'We don't.'

'Aw, come on now...'

'We are expecting a man of that name,' Royston explained politely. 'We would like to interview him.'

'Yeah,' said Gulland. 'And we all know why, don't we.'

Such goodwill as had existed at the start of the meeting was now somewhere up by the ceiling with the dead smoke from their cigarettes.

'Why?'

'Because he knows the name of your precious damn source in Moscow.'

Royston was too tired to feign lack of concern. The shock must have been written all over his face, for Gulland went on, 'Don't act so surprised. It had to get back to us in the end. For years we've known you were sitting on something good but we played along, pretending to swallow it when you fed us some crap about what some guy said to some other guy in a brothel. Well now we know, see? That's what finally convinced us that Bucharensky's genuine. We have our source in Moscow too, and the word has gone out from Dzerzhinzky Square: Kyril left behind a diary which says he carries the name of a traitor. Right?'

Royston gave the matter some thought and decided to come clean. 'An officer in the rank of general,' he said curtly. 'We've had him for years. C is the only person who knows his name.'

Gulland nodded. 'Okay,' he said sourly. 'We can argue about that later when this shit's been cleared from off the front porch. What are you doing about it?'

Royston shrugged and said nothing.

'Why not let us give you a little help, Mike? We can do it.'

'Sure you can. Just like you did in Brussels... oh yes, Joe, we know about that. We wondered what the hell you were up to and now we know. A "covert operation"; everything left nice and clean and sanitised... and the next thing we hear, Bucharensky's living in New Mexico under an assumed name. We'll let you know whatever we get out of Kyril. It's the usual arrangement, Joe. Don't you trust us?'

'Not overly. He's here, in England. You snap your fingers and where does that leave us? An accident, you'll say, how unfortunate. He tripped in the can, broke his prick and bled to death.'

Royston was about to reply when the phone rang. Gulland snatched it up.

'Who? Yeah... put him on.'

He handed the instrument to Royston at arm's length as if wary of contamination. Royston raised his eyebrows and held the receiver to his ear.

'Royston,' he heard a voice say. 'I want to see you. *Now.*'

Chapter 32

Povin lay spreadeagled on the bed in the 'penthouse', his head turned towards the square of darkness, slightly softer than the rest, which was the window. He had been staring at it for some time, to the point where it now seemed to advance and retreat in a silent beat. He made several attempts to close his eyes, and failed.

He had been drinking since late afternoon. He was used to it and his constitution was strong, but he had long ago strayed over his normal outer limit. He wasn't sure whether he wanted to get up and couldn't, or no longer even had any desire to get up at all. Everything was undefined. The slightest movement made him giddy, so it was better to lie still and do nothing, except think about the names.

The bedroom was littered with tiny scraps of paper: on the bed, the dressing-table, the floor; it was as if someone had taken a full wastepaper basket and flung its contents about the place. Several scraps lay on Povin's chest, moving rhythmically up and down in time with his breathing. On each scrap was written a single name. There were hundreds of them. Inside Povin's head were hundreds more which he did not have time to write down before the vodka disabled him.

Each tiny scrap of paper represented a death for which he had been responsible, in one way or another. It had started almost as a joke with himself, a simple exercise in memory. Who was the first, he asked himself as he tossed back the glass of petrovka. Let me write it down...

The first was Stanislav Petrovich Illyin. He could recall all three names quite clearly. Illyin had been a student with Povin at Officers' Training School. One day he had made some offhand remark about Lenin at a time when he and Povin were alone together. Afterwards Povin became frightened that someone else might have overheard, and reported the matter. Next day, Illyin had gone. No one ever saw him again. After the celebration which followed the passing-out parade for his year the commanding officer of Ryazan summoned Povin and told him that because of his zealous and entirely correct conduct in regard to Illyin he had been singled out for special work. Povin asked what had happened to Illyin and the colonel laughed. 'He was shot. What else do you expect? That's why Russia needs people like you, Povin.'

'People like you.' It was the memory of this phrase which made Povin take the first sheet of paper and write on it Illyin, S.P. Who was the second...?

Some of the scraps contained only initials or patronymics, all that Povin could remember of their former owners. Some merely had a bare description, such as 'Redhead', or 'Limp'. He could not remember many of the faces, but hundreds of names were there, ready to be summoned out of his subconscious mind with the vodka to act as solvent.

Some of the scraps contained merely a number, Povin's rough approximation of the extent of a particular group which he had consigned wholesale to extermination.

Some of them bore little crosses in the corner. They were the Christians.

Povin had long ago recognised the futility of penitence. Penitence, properly expressed, meant a martyr's death for which he was not prepared. To pray for absolution was pointless, unless you were willing and able to turn your back on sin. Povin relished the story by Camus of the man who went to the same prostitute every Friday, year in, year out, made confession, was absolved... Povin knew that God was not like that. God did not read Camus...

In the early years particularly, when Povin was still working under Major Oblensky, there had been many Christians to deal with, mostly Orthodox. Their deaths had helped to mould Povin into his present dilemma. If he did not repent he was damned; if he turned his back on it all he was doomed. But for his early association with the Russian Orthodox community he probably would not have come to this pass.

He could not put a name to his first Christian martyr, only a sense of atmosphere, of place. Povin had been detailed to preside over an interrogation during a spell of duty in Minsk. It turned into a kind of macabre game between the prisoner and his torturers, to see if they could make him recant. This was no part of the interrogation; the prisoner was suspected of disseminating illegal literature, but what began as a sideline soon developed into the main event.

The suspect knew something, that was obvious. Equally obvious was that it could not be anything of great importance. Povin remembered him as young, with everything to live for. There was no reason to kill him: in those days it was not uncommon to work someone over for a night and then toss him out with the garbage next day, on the offchance that he might let slip something useful. But this young man made a mistake. He wanted to hide what he knew. When the pain grew unbearable he started to sing a hymn, stifling his agony in a soft, tuneless chant that somehow filled the smoky cellar to its very corners… and so the game began. At first Povin merely watched, detached from the heartless brutality inflicted before his eyes. Don't be silly, he wanted to say, tell us what we want to know; nothing is worth all this. But as the night progressed he gradually became drawn into the grim tableau, no longer a disinterested, slightly bored spectator. The inquisitors were oafs, two lusty peasant lads from the steppes assigned to the task because they were brutish, unimaginative and strong. Like bulls, they took time to work up their full fury. The more they laboured over him, the harder the brave young man in the chair chanted. It was provocation, a direct and inescapable challenge.

Towards dawn the prisoner fell into a coma, exhausted. One of the inquisitors poured cold water over him until he was awake. As his eyes fluttered open his mouth began to writhe, almost unconsciously, or so it seemed to Povin.

'Yes?'

The older lad was leaning close to catch the words, evidently anticipating the breakthrough they had been waiting for: the state secrets which could bring down the Soviet Union overnight, carried in the head of this hapless boy.

'Speak up, cretin!'

The boy shuddered. 'Our Father… Who art in heaven…'

The inquisitor shut him up with a clenched fist, then undid the straps which held the prisoner in his chair. The boy collapsed on the floor. The first lout kicked him hard in the small of the back, then bent down to pick him up by the legs.

'Ay, Volodiya!' squealed his companion excitedly, and Povin realised that he was witnessing the repeat of an earlier incident. He knew he should stop it, but remained in his chair by the wall, mesmerised.

The larger soldier began to swing the boy round the room, leaning backwards to steady himself and preserve momentum. Faster and faster he turned, the boy's body now almost parallel with the floor.

The second inquisitor was dancing about the cell, clapping his hands to a beat which grew faster and faster.

'Ay-oh-la, ay-oh-la, ay-oh-la...'

Povin shrunk back, paralysed by the knowledge of what was about to happen. Sweat was pouring off the first soldier's face, his neck muscles stood out over his tight collar, the physical effort required must have been enormous.

'Ay-oh-la, ayohla, ayohla, ayohlaayohlaayohLA!'

The soldier let go and the body went hurtling head first into space, missing Povin by inches.

The wall of the cellar was solid brick.

Povin rose slowly to his feet and raised his arms above his head in an exaggerated stretch. He was suddenly very tired.

'Sluice this place out,' he said from the doorway. Then he turned to go, and as his feet crossed the threshold he had a sudden vision of himself entering a narrow corridor with no exit: unable to be a Christian, unable not to.

The vision stuck and proved to be frighteningly prophetic. He never did escape from that narrow corridor.

By making a great effort Povin moved his head to brush the scraps of paper off his chest, knowing that among them was one that bore the name of Vera Bradfield.

Illyin was the first name. Bradfield was the last.

Povin accepted full responsibility for her death the moment he learned of it. True, he had not dealt the blows, he had not even been there, but her murder was the natural consequence of his act in sending Sikarov after Bucharensky and so he took the blame. He did not attempt to split fine semantic hairs, or prevaricate. He prayed for her soul and went through the ritual of saying he was sorry in the knowledge that his words were empty: how could he repent of one out of so many? Death, for Povin, had become a habit, like Michaelov's papirosy cigarettes, and his own petrovka. It wasn't that he did not regret the scraps of paper, for he did; but what was the point of whining to God about things you couldn't change?

If it wasn't possible to bring Vera back to life, there was perhaps something he could yet do for her memory, a kind of invisible monument to be erected in her name.

The room had begun to revolve slowly around Povin's bed. His head ached. He thought longingly of cold water, but knew that it was beyond him to get up and go to the bathroom. Sleep. That was the only cure. Sleep and oblivion.

There was a way in which he could discharge the obligation. A kind of sin offering, Old Testament rather than New... Not all at once. Not Royston, not yet. But the Kommandant...

The last thought to cross his mind before temporarily giving up the ceaseless struggle with bootless conscience and remorse was that tomorrow he would send a message to Sir Richard Bryant and so, by betraying the brutal regime which had moulded him, perhaps take the first hesitant step towards redeeming his soul.

Chapter 33

It was very cold in the loft which, as Royston vaguely recognised, meant that laying the Cosywrap last winter had been a worthwhile investment. As he rummaged about in the pile of wood-chippings under the cold water tank he was shivering: from the cold, and also from an uneasy feeling which bordered on panic that what he was looking for might have mysteriously vanished.

His groping hand made contact with an oilskin package and he nearly moaned aloud in relief. He drew it out of the wood-shavings and dusted it off in the feeble light of the torch which he had brought up with him when he climbed into the roofspace, muttering to his wife about leaking water-pipes. The package was intact; God knew why it should not be. Royston's fingers were numb with cold and tension. It took him a long time to unwrap the oilskin, wipe down the gun and test its mechanism.

The gun was a Police .45 Magnum. Royston had 'acquired' it early in his career, when he still occasionally went on the streets. No one else knew of its existence, the original owner now being dead, and Royston had kept it hidden in the roof for years, just in case.

On a visit to FBI headquarters in Washington, the part the public doesn't see, he had once watched a marksman blow down a solid wall, using just such a gun. The squat bludgeon of a weapon was difficult to hold in one hand, both were required to steady it, and even then its accuracy was poor. But if you were lucky enough to score a hit, the party stopped right there. Even the FBI armourer was in awe of what this gun could do.

Royston knew himself to be in mortal danger. Kyril was rumoured to have supplanted Yevchenko as Stanov's right hand man. It was inconceivable that he had not heard Royston's name spoken in the spacious, high-ceilinged office on the third floor in Dzerzhinsky Square. Whatever his motives in coming to England, he had to be silenced once and for all.

Royston looked down at the heavy gun lying in his hands. 'Don't fire it unless you intend to kill', that's what the FBI armourer had said, and Royston proposed to accept his advice.

'Michael…'

He looked up, startled to hear his wife's voice.

'Telephone!'

He stuffed the heavy weapon into his pocket and started to crawl back towards the ladder.

Chapter 34

The car swung on to the gravelled drive through large, ornate wrought-iron gates.

'What is this place?' asked Sculby.

'Crowden House. One of Surrey's finest country estates. Grade One listing, very good gardens, or so they tell me.'

'They?'

'National Trust. We have the use of one wing and share the running expenses.'

'Christ, there's people all over the place.'

The car was nearing the house and coaches were visible, drawn up in a neat line alongside the tennis courts.

'That's the point,' replied Royston. 'Basically we use this place as a convalescent home for "difficult" cases – getting back to normality, and so on. But it's also useful for meetings with people like Kyril, who don't like closed doors. See that lot?'

Sculby followed the direction of Royston's pointing finger. Several people were straggling after a uniformed guide in the direction of some greenhouses.

'Loshkevoi needs reassuring as much as Kyril. What could be more cosy than for the two of them to strike up a conversation on the lawn, in the open air, two tourists free to come and go as they please? With me? Thank

God Easter was early this year. The place looks crowded enough for a bank holiday.'

Royston parked the car outside the main entrance next to a family of four picnicking out of the boot of an Allegro. Sculby looked at his watch. 'Nearly time.'

'Look… there he is.'

Sculby saw Loshkevoi come into view at the end of a grassed avenue winding in front of the house. Two men were with him but they kept their distance. It all looked very natural. Loshkevoi was wearing his own clothes and one of his companions had a camera slung round his neck.

From the front seat of Royston's car he and Sculby had an uninterrupted view of the main drive. Kyril was due to keep his appointment at three o'clock.

'No sign of him yet.'

Loshkevoi stopped as he reached the drive and turned back uneasily. One of his companions spoke to him and Sculby saw a look of panic-stricken protest appear on the face of his former client. The other man raised his hands in a calming, placatory gesture.

Royston picked up the radiophone and Sculby saw the third man raise the camera as if to adjust a setting.

'Tell him we've got marksmen all round the perimeter wall,' said Royston softly. 'Tell him anything, but for Christ's sake ditch him. It's three o'clock.'

'Loshkevoi doesn't know…'

'That Kyril wants to meet him?' Royston snorted. 'Too damn right he doesn't.'

The man with the camera moved across to join the other two. A few seconds later the bodyguards sauntered off towards the main gate, leaving a bewildered and apprehensive Loshkevoi to stand on the drive alone.

Minutes passed. Kyril was late. Several people passed within a few feet of Loshkevoi but none of them made any attempt to speak to him. Royston looked at his watch for the umpteenth time and swore.

'Look!'

Royston watched curiously as a well-dressed woman picked her way across the grass towards Loshkevoi. When she was almost touching him she spoke and Loshkevoi's lips moved in reply. Then the woman's hand moved in a tiny wave and she started to walk away, the encounter plainly at an end. Royston reached for the handset, his face tense. 'Right,' Sculby heard him say. 'Pull them both in and bring them back to the house. Only for God's sake, do it quietly.'

He replaced the receiver and got out. Sculby followed. Royston led the way through the main hall and over a red rope carrying a 'private' sign. At once the decor became less elaborate. After a few minutes' walk they arrived in what Sculby guessed must have been part of the old kitchen, now partitioned off. Most of one wall was taken up with a large, sooty fireplace. The room was bare except for a table and half a dozen chairs, in one of which the woman they had seen on the drive was already seated. Royston lounged over to the fireplace, keeping his back to it, and put his right hand in his pocket.

'Introduce me,' he said quietly.

Sculby now saw that the woman was young, pretty and extremely composed. She was smoking a cigarette, but apart from that slight indication of nervousness showed no sign of surprise at her situation. Sculby wondered why. On hearing Royston speak she crossed her legs and sat back.

'He said it would be just like this,' she observed conversationally. 'How frightfully interesting.'

'He?'

The woman smiled and deposited some ash in the cocoa-tin lid on the table in front of her.

'That rather dishy man with the Slavonic-sounding name. Kyril.'

Her husky, well-bred voice conveyed that when she described Kyril as dishy she was speaking from intimate personal experience. Sculby was becoming more and more mystified.

'What's your name?' said Royston. Hearing the roughness in his voice the woman turned to him and smiled.

'Lucinda Bayliss, my sweet. What's yours?'

Royston said nothing. Sculby sensed that he was every bit as puzzled as the rest of them. The woman smoothed down her dress, drawing every eye in the room to long, attractive thighs.

'Is that all you're going to ask me?' she said lightly. 'How dreadfully disappointing. Kyril assured me there'd be lots of men in jackboots wielding rubber truncheons. It all sounded quite thrilling…'

'What are you?' interrupted Royston aggressively. The woman smiled at him.

'Expensive, my sweet. Very, very expensive indeed.'

Sculby watched comprehension dawn in all the other faces round him, and knew their expressions matched his own.

'So you're on the rent,' said Royston. Lucinda shrugged, apparently quite unruffled by the sneer in his voice.

'You could say that. At my end of the profession we call it an honorarium, darling.' Seeing the look on his face she added, very softly, as if not to embarrass a thick child, 'From the Latin.'

Royston moved away from the fireplace. Like everyone else in the room he seemed partly mesmerised by this outstandingly cool performance.

'And how did you meet this... Kyril?'

'He rang me up, then came round later. At first I couldn't place him at all. He was refreshingly honest, you see.' She rolled her eyes upwards. 'My God, you don't know how refreshing honesty can be until you've done my job. He said some very nice things about my body but he didn't want to sleep with me, only to marry me. Look, isn't it nice?'

She held up her left hand, enjoying the effect which the sight of the gold band produced on the roomful of men.

'You married him?' said Royston incredulously.

'Oh no. Not really. Although he did say he'd rather like to...' She giggled. '...and he wanted me to keep the ring as a momento of the occasion. But no, I didn't actually marry him. He said he was playing a very elaborate joke on an old friend and if I helped him he'd pay me three times my usual hourly rate. He was a very generous man, was Mr Kyril. The kind who settles in advance without being asked...'

Sculby wanted to smile but the look on Royston's face deterred him.

'What exactly did Kyril want from you?'

'Well, he wanted me to go on a coach trip with him. As his wife, you understand. I'd never ridden in a coach before. I know you shouldn't knock anything 'til you've tried it, especially in my line, but it was pretty disgusting, actually. Then, when we arrived...'

Royston sat down heavily in the nearest chair. 'Do you mean to tell me,' he interrupted very quietly, 'that Kyril is here, now? In this house?'

The woman's eyes widened. 'Of course, my sweet. Didn't I just explain it all to you?'

For a moment nobody spoke, and Sculby fancied he could hear the sound of his own heart beating, it was so quiet in the room. Then Royston spread his hands in a gesture of hopeless inquiry and looked at the bodyguards, both of whom shook their heads. Sculby read consternation on every face, Loshkevoi's most of all.

'My God,' said Royston. There was another awed silence. 'My God, and we never saw him. Go on.'

At a sign from Royston one of the bodyguards slipped from the room while Lucinda resumed her story.

'Well, after we got here he pointed him...' (a wave at Loshkevoi) '...out to me and asked me to go over and say a few words to him. First of all he said goodbye and gave me something extra, he really was terribly, terribly sweet about the whole thing...'

Royston drummed his fingers on the table.

'What... *exactly* mind you... did he tell you to say?'

'He told me to say: I'll be late, wait for me.'

'Those were his exact words?'

Lucinda nodded.

'You're sure?'

'Quite sure.'

'And nothing else?'

Lucinda shook her head. Royston turned to Loshkevoi. 'Is that right?'

Loshkevoi roused himself with an effort. He seemed dazed.

'Yes. It's what she said. Then I said something… I can't remember…'

Royston turned back to Lucinda Bayliss. 'What did he say?'

Lucinda's brow puckered in thought. 'He said: okay, thanks. At least, I think that's…'

'What were you supposed to do then?'

'Nothing. I'd earned my money and that was the end of it.'

The jerky, unpredictable silences were starting to get on Sculby's nerves. Loshkevoi's fingers played over his face, the remaining bodyguard frowned, Royston was lost in thought. Sculby wondered just how badly things were off course.

'What was he wearing?'

Royston's question seemed unnaturally loud after the long silence. Lucinda laughed, a soft ripple of sound which sent a tingle up Sculby's spine.

'I never look at what men *wear*, darling.'

Royston nodded, as if accepting a valid point made against him, and for a while nobody spoke. At last he seemed to make up his mind.

'That gentleman will give you tea and take you through this story of yours again.' Royston gestured at the remaining bodyguard. 'Then you're free to go.'

The woman pouted and consulted what was obviously a very expensive gold watch.

'Can't I go now? I've been here simply ages.'

Royston stood up.

'Try thinking of it as helping the police with their inquiries.'

Lucinda unfolded herself slowly from the chair in which she had been sitting, and the men saw that as well as being beautiful she was also very tall. Beside her Royston looked tense and shrunken, and for an instant Sculby was reminded of those countless fairy stories where the lovely princess falls into the hands of an ugly dwarf.

'You look as though you could use a little help,' she said, casting a look of cold appraisal over Royston's unattractive body, and again Sculby wanted to smile but dare not. Royston's face remained impassive, as though he had heard nothing.

Sculby was nearest the door. He opened it for Lucinda Bayliss to pass through, and was rewarded by a delightful, lingering smile. Loshkevoi waited until the door had closed again, then said: 'What the hell is going on around here?'

'Shut up.'

'No. I won't shut up. First of all you give me this headache…'

Royston stirred impatiently in his chair.

'When you refused to get into the laundry basket you left us no choice. The doctor says it'll soon wear off.'

'Would *you* have agreed to get into a basket? Too much like a coffin. Then who the hell is this Kyril?'

'Oh, for Christ's sake, leave it out. You know bloody well who he is.'

'Look, I…'

'We know about the arms in the garage, Loshkevoi. And the radio. And the money. And don't pretend you don't know what we're talking about, because we've got a lovely set of prints of you digging Kalashnikovs out of the rubble.' Sculby had read about people going grey but had never seen it, until now. Loshkevoi looked as though he had gone into a state of suspended animation. Royston, on the other hand, seemed to be warming up.

'You want to know what's going on? All right, I'll fucking tell you. We have made a deal, see? If you say who you're working for, why, for how long and all the other details you know, it is just conceivable that we will not leave you in jail for the rest of your stinking, useless life. But that's for later. Right now, you're bait. Colonel Ivan Yevseevich Bucharensky wants to talk to you, very badly. So this is a trap and you're the lure. We're going to pot both of you.'

Loshkevoi shot Sculby a furious look. 'I should have known you were bent, all along. My *Christ*, but I should!'

Sculby turned his back on him and walked over to the fireplace.

'You're not very smart, are you?' Royston agreed. 'Next time, be a bit more choosy.'

Loshkevoi took no notice. 'You heard what that whore said,' he gibbered. 'He's here! Inside this house...'

'So you *do* know what we're talking about.'

Loshkevoi's face fell and he mumbled something Sculby couldn't catch.

'Better start talking, Loshkevoi, if you want to buy some protection.' Royston's eyes were gleaming. 'It doesn't matter to me whether Kyril gets to you or not. You're not important. All we've got to do is watch your garage and sooner or later we'll have all the answers anyway. So if Kyril means to harm you, that's okay with me. He's another matter. It's true he's slipped through undetected so far, but even if we had spotted him we'd still have let him in. Don't be under any illusions about that.'

Royston stood opposite Loshkevoi, his hands resting on the table. The faces of the two men were very close.

'We'll gamble your life away, Loshkevoi, if we have to. You come cheap. It's Kyril we want, not you, and we want him so badly it's like a disease!'

It really is like a disease with you, thought Sculby wonderingly. Something pervasive and rotten. Syphilis, perhaps.

'Now you'd better start talking if you want us to help you.'

Royston lowered himself into a chair.

'For a start, try explaining why Kyril needs to get to you so desperately. What's the big attraction?'

Loshkevoi opened his mouth and uttered some incoherent noises. He looked sick. For a few seconds of painful suspense Sculby thought that he was on the point of refusal. Then the damn broke and he started to babble.

'You keep Bucharensky away from me! All right, I'll grass, I'll say anything you want, but keep him off my back, you hear!'

He paused, gasping for breath, and loosened his collar. Royston nodded curtly. 'Go on.'

'I'm not part of the regular KGB. They pay my salary but Stanov's my boss.'

'You mean you report direct to Centre?' Royston interrupted him.

'No. I mean I report direct to the Chairman. He has this job for me. Terrorism. It's his pet game. He's been working on it for years. That's where I come in. I liaise for Centre with the Provisional IRA, National Liberation Army, a few others as well. I'm their banker. It's through me Stanov puts together his operations in this country. I'm telling you this as a guarantee of good faith, okay? To show that the source is impeccable. I can finger the men who killed Mountbatten...'

'Go on.' Royston's voice was still tired but now he was having to work to keep the emotion out of it.

'You want to know why Kyril's trying to see me? Because that's his real mission. Everything else is straight cover. This fabulous plan he's supposed to be carrying...' Loshkevoi did not attempt to conceal his scorn. '...It doesn't exist. Or if it does, Kyril hasn't got it, that's for sure.'

Royston had taken out a notebook and was busily writing in it, so that Loshkevoi couldn't see his face.

'That trek of his across Europe... a blind. It's me he wants...'

'How do you know that Kyril hasn't got the project-plan?' said Royston, looking up from his book.

'Because it's in Stanov's blue safe.'

'And how do you know that?'

'Because Nidus has seen it there, he told me.'

Royston held his pen up to the light and squinted at it, as if something was wrong with the nib. 'Nidus?' he said casually.

'Oh come on,' said Loshkevoi wearily. 'You know who Nidus is. And I work for him on the side now. That's the trouble. Stanov suspects. You really don't know who Nidus is?'

Royston shook the pen a couple of times and tested it. 'No,' he said, after a long pause, and Sculby saw a look of cunning suddenly appear on Loshkevoi's face.

'I forgot... of course, only Bryant knows... well, you ask him then. I'm not telling.'

The nib seemed to have cured itself, for Royston was writing again.

'Tell me this... why should Kyril want to see *you*?' Royston did not look up from his book while he waited for a reply. Sculby couldn't detect how important these answers were to him.

'Because I can identify Nidus. Stanov wants to know who he is.'

'And that matters?' Royston seemed befogged by his total ignorance of who or what Nidus might be. Loshkevoi sniggered.

'Ask Bryant. He'll tell you if it's important or not.'

'But you know the name... I mean the real name, of this Nidus?'

'No, I... When I said I knew who Nidus was, I meant I could identify him. I know what he looks like. And there's nothing Bucharensky wouldn't do to get that out of me. It's the whole point of his mission, I tell you. Bucharensky's loyal to Stanov, always was. Stanov suspects I know something. And he's damn right!' The rising note of panic was clearly audible now. 'He knows I couldn't stand the torture. Please! Give me a break, will you? Look, I can help you. I can...'

Royston started to interrupt but at that moment the door opened to admit one of the bodyguards. Royston looked up with annoyance and the man shrugged, spreading his hands to indicate that the search had drawn a blank. Royston appeared to deliberate for a moment.

'We'll go upstairs.' He looked at his watch. 'Five o'clock. There's not much daylight left. My guess is that he'll wait for nightfall before making a move, but I don't want to get caught down here.'

Royston nodded at the bodyguard. 'Take Loshkevoi upstairs to the first floor and wait there. I'm going to see if Franklin's had any more luck with the Bayliss girl, and then we'll all join you. Whatever happens, stay put.'

The man nodded, and beckoned Loshkevoi. Royston was about to follow them through the door when Sculby grasped his arm.

'Do you need me any more?'

'For your own protection, Laurie, don't try to leave now.'

Sculby registered the note of anxiety in Royston's voice and his eyes narrowed. 'So there is a problem?'

Royston expelled some air in what might have been an expression of humour or annoyance.

'I don't know,' he said at last. 'The theory went like this. There was no point in saturating the place because that would only scare Kyril away, right? But with four of us – Barnes, Franklin, you and me – five I suppose if you count Loshkevoi – he shouldn't have been able to give us any trouble. We put a few men on the outer wall, in the hope that they'd spot Kyril as he came in and after that we'd monitor him. Well, it didn't happen. It's obvious that Kyril's not going to keep to the deal he put up through you. But whether that spells danger, I don't know.'

Sculby swallowed. 'You think I'd be at risk if I tried to leave?'

'It's a long drive down to the main gate, Laurie, and I can't afford to send anyone with you. Frankly, I need you here, if you're prepared to stay. One extra body could make all the difference.'

Sculby nodded slowly, touched by Royston's evident concern.

'Okay, Michael. I suppose we've just got to sit it out and hope. Are you armed, by the way?'

Royston nodded reassuringly and patted his jacket pocket.

'Good. That makes me feel a whole lot better.'

Sculby led the way through the door into the hall as he spoke these words, and so unfortunately did not see the expression on Royston's face which they provoked.

Chapter 35

Kyril's appearance had changed since his visit to Sculby's offices. Everything from the colour of his hair to the condition of his Bally casuals was different. No one who had only a photograph or a verbal description to go on could possibly have recognised him.

After he had said goodbye to Lucinda Bayliss he walked away without looking back once, leaving her to get on with the job. He was confident that she would not let him down. Kyril instinctively understood business people. He had chosen well there.

By joining one of the conducted tours he was able to build up in his mind a fairly accurate picture of the house. Upstairs, on the top floor, were the private rooms belonging to the family. Kyril wasn't interested in them. But the west wing was sealed off from the rest of the mansion by solid-looking oak doors, besides which sat a watchful attendant. Kyril subjected him to a long discreet scrutiny and concluded that he was more than a National Trust hack in uniform. So that's where the treasure was.

He wandered out to the terrace which flanked the south of the house, fixing the topography in his mind. At the west end of the terrace, paving stones had been taken up and a rough barrier erected to discourage the inquisitive, and the ground floor windows all had shutters across them. To the south, several acres of parkland rolled down to the road along which they had come earlier. He swung slowly round. To the east were the formal grounds, looking wasted and forlorn in the grey March light; beyond them an overgrown square of grass bordered by trees, a disused cricket pitch perhaps.

Somewhere inside the house a bell was ringing. Kyril looked at his watch. Three o'clock. They would be closing up, public viewing was restricted during the off-season, and about now Loshkevoi would be meeting Lucinda Bayliss on the other side of the house.

Someone was calling all visitors, reminding them that the house was closing. He did not have much time.

Kyril went in from the terrace and quickly made his way to the staircase. There was no one about. He slipped under the red rope and vanished into the upper regions of the house.

On the top floor he paused and looked about him. He was in a long corridor running the length of the north side of the mansion away from the terrace. Here the doors were of less substantial construction, and everything was covered with a heavy layer of dust. He cocked his head to listen. It was very quiet. He tried one of the doors but it was locked. He knelt down to the keyhole, which afforded a glimpse of off-white dust sheets and packing-cases. It was as he surmised: the family was away, for a long time too, by the look of it.

He stood up and began to pad down the corridor towards the west wing. Long before he came to the partition which blocked off the passage he could see that it was made of solid brick, a clumsy job, not like downstairs where the public went. The builder had simply run the masonry into the centre of a large mullion and coated it with paint.

Kyril rested his back to the partition wall and let himself slide down to his haunches. He needed time to plan the next move.

He had never visited Crowden before, although its functions were known to the London KGB, at least in outline. Unfortunately he had not had access to a plan of the interior, and he was having to rely on guesswork, which made for slow progress.

The light was failing and darkness would come quickly. Soon they would organise a search of the house; he must find deep cover before then. He stood up and retraced his steps along the passage, trying the doors. Most of them were locked but at last one gave under his hand; he looked through it to see a narrow staircase twisting away from him to an upper floor. The servants' quarters, under the eaves. And where there were eaves, you usually found access to the roof.

There were three rooms at the top of the narrow stairs, and he found what he was looking for in the last one he searched, just as he was starting to feel alarmed. A trapdoor led up into the roofspace. He took it down and with the help of a chair hauled himself through the tight opening.

He would need light. Fortunately he had had the foresight to bring with him a small torch capable of transmitting a thin beam, powerful enough to illuminate the darkest cavity.

Kyril closed his eyes, orientating the house in his mind. West was... over there. He began to crawl, painfully picking his way across the slats. The roof was filthy and before long he was having to stifle a cough. He rested for a moment, and studied the ceiling. Lathe and plaster, nothing unusual about that. No soundproofing...

although of course, that might be on the other side. Well, he would have to risk it.

Kyril flashed the beam around. Ah! Another trapdoor, like the one he had come through in the east wing. He began to crawl towards it. When he reached it he laid his ear against the wood and listened.

Not a sound penetrated the constricted space beneath the roof. He ground his teeth. When the time came, that would be the risky part.

Kyril slowly lowered himself to a prone position and strove to make himself as comfortable as possible across the slats. For the moment he was safe. Now he would rest awhile. There was no danger of them leaving the house: wait, he had said, and he knew they would. He'd give them time to become drowsy, off their guard.

It was too painful to sleep. After a while he gave up trying to doze and began to review the plan he had made before leaving London.

Kyril was no longer working for Stanov, or anyone else. He was working for himself. If it had been a matter of simple loyalty, of doing the job, he would have gone back to Moscow in the hope that *Lisa* had been detected, and reported inability to complete the mission because Loshkevoi was being held incommunicado. However disappointed Stanov might have been at the outcome, he would not have blamed Kyril for something outside his control, no fault of his.

But it was no longer a matter of simple loyalty. Kyril had been lied to, used, squeezed into a role in a play which he never fully understood, one where the script was constantly being rewritten between and behind the scenes. Now he was looking for one thing only. The truth. If he owed Vera nothing else, he owed her that.

Somebody was trying to prevent him from talking to Loshkevoi. The same somebody who was responsible for Vera's death. But if Sculby could be believed, Loshkevoi was responsible for his own imprisonment, he had pleaded guilty, and that was, it could only have been, on someone's orders.

Who was Loshkevoi *really* working for?

However slight the chances of success, he had to make one last effort to see Loshkevoi. Then, well… even in Moscow he had never given much thought to the end of the ride.

After a while he grew bored with his thoughts. He used his torch to illumine the face of his watch. Late. It must be dark outside, the search would be over by now.

Time to go.

He was reluctant. The roof was cramped and stuffy, but it was cosy too – a haven before the last stage of his journey.

He crawled the final few inches to the trapdoor. This was the hard part. This was where it all mattered. Because if he lifted up the trap, and had guessed wrong about this house, a photo-cell beam would break and bring every guard within a mile racing to the top floor…

Kyril pressed down on the wood for greater purchase, clasped the cross-beam, and lifted.

Chapter 36

One of the many spending cuts ordered by the Politburo involved an across-the-board reduction in staff. The Time and Motion people decreed that a particularly fruitful area for curtailment of overmanning was the nightshift, when little of importance came into Centre but the same number of employees sat around talking or playing cards. (High among the reasons for Michaelov's unpopularity with his subordinates was an irritating habit of coming in unexpectedly late at night and finding the duty officers monitoring Radio Luxembourg.) Now only two men staffed Radio Operations between eight at night and six the following morning, and they had little to do. The telex machine had vastly reduced the amount of cipher-traffic passing between Moscow and its far-flung embassies: a telex could be delivered at any time and unless it was urgent no one need read it until morning. Thus in another small respect did the KGB approximate more closely to the huge, inefficient capitalist conglomerates which it was dedicated to destroy.

Immediately beneath the small Union Jack which designated UK Sector two clocks showed the time in Moscow and London: nine and seven o'clock respectively.

One of the two officers on duty in Rad. Ops, had gone to the canteen for his break, leaving his colleague to concentrate on Playboy. He sat with his feet propped up on the desk in front of him, strategically placed to see if a 'call' sign lit up anywhere along the bank of receivers which lined the far wall of the European Division. When a 'pig' hissed through the pneumatic system and thudded into his In tray he did not hurry to pick it up. Without taking his eyes from the centrefold spread out on his knees he unscrewed the top of the cannister and felt for the message. Something else rolled out, an inch of evil-smelling black ash, and he wrinkled his nose in disgust. Something about the smell was familiar. He took a quick glance at the message, saw the green paper of the First Main Directorate with Michaelov's squiggle under 'Authorisation Code', and sat up abruptly, the magazine forgotten.

It was a long message and the transmission instructions were detailed and precise. It consisted of 49 groups with a specific but different number of seconds being allowed to elapse between each group. The transmission had to begin at exactly 2123 Moscow Time. That meant a computer job. The radio operator looked up at the clocks and swore. This was going to have to be done in a rush. Trust it to happen just when Aleksei had gone for his break, half an hour early, too.

By 2120 the message had been fed into the machine and was ready to go. All the officer had to do was set the automatic key, wait for the computer to send the transmission at the appointed time, and switch itself off. Yet he was troubled. There was scarcely any incoming traffic after six in the evening, and outgoing messages were rare enough to attract attention. That was one thing. But for a general to send a message under his own initials... well, that was extraordinary. The officer's hand hovered over the key. Should he send it? Obey orders and forget it…?

His hand moved across from the console and picked up the telephone instead.

Someone answered, and the officer held the receiver away from his ear. Whoever was on the line had one hell of a cough.

'General Michaelov here.'

The officer, a non-smoker, waited patiently while the speaker got over another furious bout of coughing. Everyone knew that Michaelov was smoking himself into an early grave with those damned 'papirosy' cigarettes of his. Filthy habit.

He took a deep breath. 'Forgive me, comrade General, but I wished to verify this message.'

'Yes, yes. What about it? Have you sent it yet?'

'No, I…'

'Well send it, idiot! What the hell do you mean by it, eh? Can't you read?'

'Yes, comrade General.' The officer was starting to feel wretched.

'Aren't the instructions clear enough?'

'Perfectly clear, comrade General.'

'Well then, don't make me come down there and sort you out. Damned insolence. Why if I…'

The call terminated amidst another bout of chesty coughing. The officer replaced the receiver and wiped the sweat from his forehead, wondering what he could salvage from the wreckage of his career. One thing was certain: he had better send that message before it was too late…

Outside in the corridor someone whistled. That must be Aleksei, returning from his break. Aleksei would know what to do. Every fucking night there was something:

do this, do that, run here, go there, kiss my arse… Why couldn't Michaelov stay at home and poke his old woman like the rest of the brass did?

'What's up?' said Aleksei, catching the look on his colleague's face.

'Wait 'til you hear. It's the damndest thing…' The radio officer explained what had happened in his friend's absence. 'Do you think I should report it in the morning?'

'I shouldn't', said Aleksei knowingly. 'Forget it. Until you're asked. And maybe not even then.'

That sounded like good advice; and if Povin could have heard it as he walked slowly back along the corridor to his own office, his fingers convulsively squeezing the tiny crucifix in his pocket until it was slippery with sweat, he would certainly have endorsed Aleksei's opinion.

Chapter 37

It was very hot in the first-floor room. Sculby and Loshkevoi sat at opposite ends of a long sofa like a couple of colonials who haven't been formally introduced. In front of them was the fireplace, where a modem gas-fire radiated uncomfortable amounts of heat. Sculby had tried to turn it down but the control was jammed. Heavy velour curtains were drawn across hermetically sealed windows; it was difficult to breathe.

The only light was provided by a single bulb encased in a glass bowl above the sofa, quite inadequate for such a large room. Sculby likened the whole experience to being in the ante-chamber of Hell, not yet dead and not quite burning either.

The door opened to admit Royston and Franklin.

'Aren't you hot?' asked Royston.

Sculby explained. Franklin went to kneel by the gas-fire and after a moment the orange glow abated.

'Can't we open a window? It's stifling in here.'

'Sorry. Too risky.'

'You really think he might come in through a first-floor window?'

Loshkevoi turned to look at him with an expression of unmitigated contempt on his face. Royston didn't even bother to answer.

'What about the girl?'

Royston was methodically working his way round the room's outer defences.

'Nothing more… except would you believe she had the best part of a thousand quid in her handbag? Jesus Christ… expensive, I should bloody well think she was.' He paused and looked up, as if struck by a sudden thought. 'I wonder if that's KGB money she had. Ah well…'

'Is she still here?'

'No. We called her a taxi.'

'You might have told me, Michael. I could have gone too.' Royston sniggered. 'You don't think I'd risk you in the same cab with her, do you?'

Sculby was exasperated. 'Seriously, Michael…' Loshkevoi stood up and began to pace around the room, hands clasped behind his back. Everyone turned to look at him.

'Do you have to do that?' asked Royston sourly, after a while. Loshkevoi stopped in mid-stride and flung himself down on the sofa again.

'Can't we have some more light in here?' he asked. 'There's too many shadows in this room. They make me nervous.'

'Shut up and sit quietly. Now listen…' Royston was addressing the room at large. 'You all know the set-up. The outer wall is guarded and floodlit, so Kyril can't get out. He's somewhere in the grounds, or possibly the house. Sooner or later he's going to show. We sit here, patiently, and wait. He *has* to make the first move and together we outnumber him conclusively, I'd say. So just make yourselves at home and relax, 'cos nobody's leaving. Here, you two…' He pointed at Barnes and Franklin. 'Pull up those chairs by the door, facing each other at an angle... that's right. Now you can cover the only entrance and exit.'

He rounded on Sculby.

'You keep to that sofa. You too, Loshkevoi. I'm over here in the corner. If you must talk, keep it low: I want to be able to hear anything that happens in the corridor.'

Royston took a final look round the room, checking that everything was in order. Apparently satisfied, he walked quietly over to the door and opened it, leaving a narrow rectangle through which Sculby, by looking over his shoulder, could see the passage outside.

Royston backed away from the door and retreated to the far corner of the room where he sat down by a low table, half opposite the lawyer. On the table was a phone. Sculby saw him lift the receiver and listen for a few seconds before replacing it on its cradle.

'Just testing,' said Royston as he caught Sculby's eye. 'The line's okay.'

Silence fell. During the next few minutes Sculby discovered that he had three problems. He was nervous. He was hungry. And he was bored.

After twenty minutes of silence these problems seemed to have doubled in size. Instead of being nervous he was scared; his stomach ached with emptiness; his mind was darting from topic to topic in nightmare fashion. He cursed his folly in not bringing paperwork to keep himself occupied. Every few seconds his eye flew to his watch. Only half an hour gone. Christ. Perhaps he could sleep. He sat back and closed his eyes to find all three problems still there, only somehow worse for being in darkness. He opened his eyes again.

The room was hardly luxurious. It reminded Sculby of the dayroom in his house at school: all tat and second hand. The carpet was threadbare and stained; the walls were bare of pictures, in the corner stood an old radio, its aerial bent almost double. None of the chairs matched each other or the sofa. One of the curtains had a jagged tear in it. Pinned to the back of the door was a notice typed on yellow Ministry of Defence paper. 'Warning!' it said. 'Extinguish all power before leaving. Silence rules.' Sculby distracted himself by trying to work out the syntax. Was silence an adjective in this context? Or a noun – in which case should there not be an 'OK?' on the end? And why 'power'? Why not just say 'light' like everyone else, and have done with it?

Loshkevoi was sitting forward with his head in his hands, apparently absorbed by something on the floor. Royston reclined in the corner chair, looking vacantly at the ceiling. Sculby looked over his shoulder to see Barnes and Franklin both sitting upright, their faces tense with concentration. The two men had removed their jackets, revealing full shoulder-holsters.

Sculby closed his eyes again and tried to concentrate on a mantra. After a while he drifted into a light doze, pausing apprehensively to see if the Soviet officer with his swinging sword would invade his troubled brain. Nothing happened. Sculby slept.

He awoke what seemed like hours later and at once looked at his watch. It had stopped at five past seven. Other sensations began to make themselves felt. Somewhere nearby voices were being raised in disagreement.

'I'm telling you, I have to take a crap...'

Loshkevoi was by the door being restrained by Franklin while Barnes looked questioningly at his chief.

'Can't it wait?' snarled Royston.

'No it can't. I'm standing on one fucking leg as it is.'

Royston wiped a strand of hair away from his face, which was white with fatigue. You're not in control, thought Sculby, and then – Oh, God, Michael, don't give up now...

'All right, all right. Barnes, you go with him. Franklin, while they're away you sit in the doorway. And for God's sake, hurry up.'

'Get some sandwiches while you're at it,' put in Sculby, and was rewarded with a furious look from Royston.

'Don't do anything of the kind. Just get on with it as fast as possible and come back here. Now move!'

Sculby swung his legs on to the sofa and rested his head on a cushion. 'Sorry Michael,' he murmured. Royston grunted and was about to reply when suddenly the phone rang.

Everyone froze. Royston let it ring five times. Sculby reckoned he was trying to bring himself back under control after the initial shock had worn off. At last he reached out his hand to take the receiver.

'Yes? Yes, I recognise the voice.'

Royston listened in rapt silence. To Sculby the call seemed to go on for ever. Only once did Royston speak, to say 'Repeat, please'; he terminated the call by hanging up without saying goodbye to whoever was on the other end. Sculby raised an inquiring eyebrow but Royston steadfastly refused to meet his gaze.

The lawyer was about to close his eyes again when Royston did something which made him decide to stay awake after all. From his coat pocket he took a large, ungainly gun and a box of ammunition from which he proceeded to load the weapon. Both gun and bullets looked enormous. Sculby watched with growing apprehension. Royston's lack of familiarity with what he was doing became more obvious by the minute, and in their relative positions he looked far more likely to shoot Sculby than any assailant bursting through the half-open door which led to the passage.

Sculby heard a noise behind him and turned. Franklin was standing in the doorway, gun in hand, facing outwards into the corridor. He was listening with all his attention.

'What is it?'

Sculby stood up and went to stand behind him in the doorway. 'I don't know,' Franklin whispered. 'I thought I heard a noise. They'd been gone such a long time, I thought I'd take a look.'

He laid his hands on the door, as if to open it further, but as he did so Royston spoke.

'Stand still,' was what he said.

Chapter 38

Kyril squeezed a little closer to the wall, palms spread out against the panelled oak, eyes closed. His breathing had slowed, his heartbeat was way below normal and his hands were wet. He was listening. With every scrap of energy in his body concentrated on that one activity, he was listening.

He had been in the west wing, undisturbed, for several hours. It had taken him that long to descend from the topmost floor, testing every step before he took it, examining each door-jamb for the hidden beam that would break at a touch, forcing himself to be slow, slow, slow.

What *was* this place? He wished he had paid more attention to Crowden when he was in England six years ago. It was half-public and half-private, so obviously it did not rate a top-secret security classification. He vaguely remembered it as a retreat for agents who needed to recuperate in circumstances of peace and normality after a particularly gruelling tour of duty, a sort of hotel for washed-out staff. Also, it was useful for meetings which had to be 'open', because the target was feeling edgy. Kyril had known that happen even in Moscow: a defector would ask to roam the streets, looking in shop-windows, rubbing elbows with pedestrians just for the sake of human contact, while KGB agents hovered nearby.

He was aware that round the next corner, ten metres away, a door stood ajar, and through the gap light filtered into the gloomy corridor. Kyril could occasionally catch the sound of voices speaking quietly inside the room beyond the door. How many people were inside? How many guards did SIS maintain at Crowden? Not many, surely? Was Loshkevoi in that room?

Time ticked on. Kyril shuffled plans like cards, all discards. Somehow he had to get inside that room. By a process of exclusion he knew that this was where his target lay, had to be. A frontal attack would be certain suicide. But every second he stayed where he was shortened the odds against his remaining undetected. He had to act, and soon, but… how?

Kyril opened his eyes. Inside the room was a sudden commotion, with voices raised in argument. He flattened himself more closely against the wall and strove to listen. Suddenly the voices grew louder: that must mean the door had opened… people were coming out.

Opposite Kyril was another door. Without once pausing to alert his conscious brain some crucial instinct of self-preservation sent him hurtling towards it. The door was unlocked. It gave on to a short, dark passage at the end of which was another door set with panels of frosted glass. And in that same split second he realised that he had succeeded only in trapping himself, for someone inside that lighted room wanted to use the lavatory where Kyril now was…

Footsteps outside. Kyril flashed his torch at the ceiling, saw the bulb and jumped for it.

'Damn. Light's gone.'

From behind the door which led into the main passage Kyril saw an arm feel along the wall opposite him, its owner guided by the glimmer of light from outside. He heard voices. Two men.

'Can you manage?'

'Yeah. Just.'

Loshkevoi had groped his way down the short, inner passage almost to the door of the lavatory. Now the second man was following him.

Kyril launched himself forward. The door slammed awkwardly against the body of the second man who drew a breath, about to cry out when Kyril's fist landed right in the centre of his adam's apple and he fell, the scream for ever lodged in his throat, unuttered. Kyril did not spare him another thought. His body was already twisting in a 90-degree vector so that by the time his right foot hit Loshkevoi in the stomach he was almost parallel with the floor. The fat man crumpled up double; Kyril bounced off the tiles and in a single co-ordinated movement had him rammed up against the glass-panelled door, forearm across the throat.

The precious moments he fought to control his breathing while his brain frantically re-ran the events of the past few seconds over and over again, trying to calculate how much noise they had made. The passage outside remained dark and empty. So far so good.

'Whaaaah...'

Kyril levered his arm a little more snugly into the folds of Loshkevoi's neck and whipped out the Stechkin, holding the cold metal to the prisoner's cheek.

'You know what this is.'

The rasping whisper seemed to reach Loshkevoi as from a great distance, so quiet it was.

'One squeal out of you and you're *dead*.'

If Kyril had shouted those words Loshkevoi would probably have screamed for help. But that whisper... something about it spoke directly to Loshkevoi's central nervous system, by-passing all rational thought. As long as Kyril continued to use that harsh, far-off whisper, little more than a breath in his ear, Loshkevoi was like a doll in the hands of a puppet-master.

'We're going out.'

Kyril removed his arm and swiftly used his free hand to wheel Loshkevoi round. His prisoner's foot collided with Barnes' body and he stumbled heavily.

'Careful!'

The two men, locked together in a tight embrace, picked their way over the corpse. Now they were in the main corridor.

'Left.'

Kyril guided Loshkevoi away from the room whence he had emerged a few minutes earlier.

'Wait.'

Kyril knew that a door at the far end of the corridor, by the stairs, was unlocked: he had checked it earlier as part of his cautious progress through the house. He hustled Loshkevoi into the room beyond and closed the door behind them, his fingers groping for the key.

Here there were no curtains. Through the windows opposite, Kyril could see the glow from the floodlights along the perimeter wall.

'No lights. Stay where you are. I can see you silhouetted against the window. Make a move I don't like and I'll shoot.'

Kyril spoke quietly, but without using that terrible whisper, and Loshkevoi relaxed a fraction.

'I have no quarrel with you. I have no orders to kill you, either.' Kyril spoke rapidly. 'The quicker you tell me all I need to know, the sooner you'll be out of here.'

'I've been...' Loshkevoi's voice cracked with fear; he cleared his throat and began again. 'I've been expecting you. You must help me.' The pleading in his voice was unmistakable but there was cunning also. 'You have got to help me. Please. Please...'

'*Stand still!*' Loshkevoi had taken a step towards Kyril. 'What was that?'

Kyril pressed his ear against the wooden panel of the door. Was there a noise outside? Long seconds passed. Nothing. He turned back to see Loshkevoi's huge form high-lighted against the windows. His shoulders were heaving. Kyril could not see the man's face but with a stab of excitement he realised that Loshkevoi was in the grip of an emotion powerful enough to transcend even his fear.

'Yes, yes, I will help you. That is part of my message. We are going back to Moscow, you and I. Together. Tonight. Stanov knows that you have been troubled in your mind. That is why he sent me. But you'd better talk fast. Who is Nidus? Who sent Sikarov to England? Believe me, it's your only chance: to talk, tell everything.'

'Who?... Sikarov... I...'

'The A2 *gaybist*. Executioner.'

'I can guess who sent Sikarov,' said Loshkevoi dully. 'There's only one candidate. It has to be...'

'Quiet!'

Had there been something, out there in the passage? Kyril flattened himself against the door, listening. The corridor was silent. He backed away from the door and felt his way towards Loshkevoi.

'You were saying,' he hissed. 'It has to be...'

'The man in the suit. He came from Moscow. Not through the embassy, not the first time. He came from Stanov, he said. I believed him. He knew things that only someone next to the Chairman could know, details about my operations which Stanov was never supposed to confide in anyone. But this man knew them. I couldn't figure him out at all. He never wore a uniform, just a suit, the same suit every time we met. He asked me... if I was happy. Can you imagine that, eh? An officer of the KGB asking if you were happy?'

Kyril forced himself to be patient and swallow his anger. Loshkevoi was on the point of talking. Beyond all hope or expectation, he really did know something. The slightest interruption, the merest hint of irritation, and the delicate skein of understanding between them would be lost.

'I told him... no. Not the first time, but afterwards, when he came again. I said, the terrorism, it's getting so that I can't stand it. They're all mad, all insane. I was starting to drink a bottle a day, it scared me so. But... he understood. The man in the suit, he knew everything. He talked to me so... so kindly. And he kept coming, and every time he came he seemed to know more about me, what I did, how I felt. Until one day...'

'Yes?' Kyril could not keep the urgency out of his voice. Loshkevoi seemed not to hear.

'One day he just said.... would you like to work for me, as well as Stanov, and I said... yes. I would.'

'You mean he was CIA, he was an agent?'

'No. You don't understand. He was one of us. Only he did things, he saw things differently from the rest. He understood, you see, he realised there were limits. *Human* limits.'

'So he was a traitor…'

'No!' Loshkevoi seemed genuinely surprised: Kyril detected shock as well as doubt in his voice. 'At least, I…'

Kyril had a sudden, sharp vision of Sikarov kneeling over Vera's body.

'It was he who mentioned Vera Bradfield?'

'Yes. That's right. How did you know that? He wanted me to go and see her, find out if you were coming… and he told me what to do when you finally arrived, so that I'd be sure to be sent to prison, and be safe. It was then I realised he meant to kill you. He wanted me out of the way, clear. I knew then there had to be a killer, somewhere.'

'His name. What was his name?'

In the second of silence that followed Kyril heard two shots, quite loud and close and then two more. He whirled round, mouth agape. Loshkevoi seemed not to notice.

'I don't know. He never told me. He wore this suit…'

Kyril moved quickly back to the door. The silence outside was unbroken. For five, ten, fifteen seconds he stood in exactly the same position, listening. Those *were* shots. He was sure of it, as sure as he was that Loshkevoi stood behind him, his hands held up to shield his face. Out there, along the passage, someone had fired.

Kyril crept back to his former position beside Loshkevoi. Why had nobody come to rescue Loshkevoi? Had they found the body in the lavatory yet? What was the shooting? *What was happening?*

Kyril shook his head angrily. *Think*.

'We haven't got much time.' His voice grated with tension. 'This man in the suit. The man from Moscow. Did you tell them anything about him next door?'

'No.'

'You're sure?'

'Sure.'

'Then describe him to me. Quickly.'

'Oh... cleanshaven. Blue eyes. Not much of a chin.'

'Blue eyes... did he have two deep clefts, here...?' Kyril traced them on Loshkevoi's own face with a finger.

'Yes. Where it shows if a man smiles a lot.'

'And the eyes...'

'Blue eyes.'

'Yes, yes I know, but how were they set?'

'Deep. The brows overshadowed them.'

Kyril slapped Loshkevoi's shoulders. He was almost sure. One more question and he would have it. He wanted to bounce up and down he was so excited.

'Think, Loshkevoi. Think harder than you've ever thought before in your life. His ears... *Tell me about his ears!*'

For a moment there was silence. Loshkevoi was swaying from side to side, as if the effort of concentration was too much for him. Kyril was suddenly glad he couldn't see through the darkness; the desire to smash out at the fleshy, petrified face would have been irresistible.

'Ah! You know him then... of course, you must do, to mention his ears.' Loshkevoi sounded awed. 'You know this man in the suit, too? Who was he, eh? What was his name?'

Kyril forced himself to count to ten, very slowly. Then – 'Tell me,' he said, 'about his ears. You were going to say something about his ears.'

'Pointed. Like goblin's ears.'

Kyril leapt into the air, throwing his arms above his head as high as they could reach. He had the name. For a second he almost wanted to shriek it aloud. He wanted to kick off his shoes and dance, he wanted to laugh and cry, he wanted… he didn't even know any longer what he wanted. He had the name.

Povin.

Loshkevoi was speaking again, the note of pleading back in his voice. 'You will tell them in Moscow… I helped you, didn't I? And, and… you will be careful.'

Kyril was only half-listening. 'Careful?'

'He… he knew things only the Chairman is supposed to know.'

Kyril froze. 'What?'

'This man. In the suit. He knew things only Stanov knew. They were friends. He told me so. They… *liked* each other.'

An icy miasma distilled out of the four corners of the room, wreathing its slow way round Kyril's heart. Friends. They were friends. He wanted to think about that. But not yet. Later.

No, not later. Now.

Suppose Stanov was the traitor?

Kyril found himself staring at this thought, lacking the will to send it away. It had been waiting on the fringes of his subconscious for weeks.

What was the purpose of this… charade? Had Stanov been using him, and if so, why? What deep game was being played, what devious dealings at the heart of the Politburo had driven him here, to London, to be somebody's pawn? The more he struggled to keep a clear head, think his way through the maze, the less he understood.

'You will be flying very near the sun…', that was what Stanov told him at their first meeting. Did those words conceal some dark, ironic secret?

It was possible. Some little part of Kyril had always acknowledged it was possible. Now, however, it seemed more than just possible, it seemed likely. Kyril knew who the traitor was. Povin. It ranked among the world's more dangerous secrets. Suppose it really was Povin, just suppose for a moment… didn't the very name waft from person to person like a virus, fatally contaminating everyone it touched? Could Stanov afford to let him live?

Kyril took a fold of flesh between his teeth and bit it until tears sprang to his eyes.

Chapter 39

The dimly lit room was hazy with smoke and the throaty reek of cordite when Kyril stepped gingerly over the threshold. Royston had not moved. He still sat in the corner chair, the gun lying loosely in his lap.

As the two men saw each other they half-heartedly lifted their weapons, only to let them fall again.

'We have not much time,' said Royston, putting the gun back in his coat-pocket. 'You saved me the trouble of coming to find you. My men have orders to stay on the outer wall come what may, but the shots are going to bring them to the house before long. Where are Loshkevoi and Barnes?'

Kyril looked up wonderingly from the scene of carnage at his feet. One man lay across the doorway, his back split open by some incredible force. Another, younger, man lay half over the arm of the sofa, most of his ribcage and neck smashed to pulp. Blood was everywhere, on the floor, the walls, the ceiling...

'Why...?'

Royston hesitated. 'There was noise outside in the corridor. When I warned them not to go out they became suspicious, they wouldn't listen. Besides, we don't want any witnesses. It was necessary to get rid of them. Especially the younger one,' he added bitterly. 'I ask you again... Loshkevoi and Barnes?'

'Loshkevoi is on his way out,' Kyril said quietly. 'The other man is…' He gestured at the nearest body, and Royston nodded.

'A pity about Loshkevoi, then. My marksmen have orders to shoot anyone who doesn't have the password. If he tries to run for it he doesn't stand…'

Voices and the sudden crackle of gunfire outside brought very different expressions to the faces of the two men. The smoke had almost cleared now. Royston spoke rapidly. 'You know who I am?'

'Loshkevoi said they called you Michael. I guessed who it was. You're Royston.'

'You've heard of me?'

'Oh yes. I've heard of you.'

'Good. That saves us a lot of time. I guessed what was happening. These two wanted to go after you. I hope the sight of them will help you decide what is to happen next. You don't trust me, Bucharensky, and that's tough, because now you have to make up your mind about me faster than you've ever done anything before in your life. You heard the shots outside. In ten minutes, maybe less, this house will be overrun. In your mission, you have succeeded. Oh yes, I understand your mission very well. You were supposed to panic the traitor into making a mistake, weren't you. That and Loshkevoi… Stanov knew he'd lost control of Loshkevoi a long time ago. It was obvious you'd make for him. And it worked. The traitor sent Sikarov, to kill you before the regular KGB could catch up and twist the name out of you. But you won, all along the line. If you leave now, you can still make it back to Moscow as well. Here's a passport.' Royston reached into his coat pocket, looking to see if the gun jerked in Kyril's hand. It did not move. He read doubt in the man's face, doubt and exhaustion. 'Money. A credit card. You can be out of the country before daybreak. The password is "Icepex", though I doubt if you'll need it…'

Kyril looked up sharply. 'What?'

'Icepex. As in Icepex G. 17, Bucharensky. Oh yes, it's true. The Kremlin Kommandant, formerly the Palindrome Directive, before that Line "H". I've been attached to it for years. Seventeen because today is 30th March, work it out Bucharensky…'

'You're lying!'

Kyril was rocketed into a whirling, insane vortex of uncertainty. The Kommandant… no, it could not be true. But Icepex… *no one* knew about that, not even the Deputy Chairmen… or maybe the Deputy Chairmen did know, but…

'You have to be lying.'

Still the gun in Bucharensky's hand did not move.

'My casename is Pisa. Italy, Bucharensky. What does that tell you, eh? How many people know about the Kommandant and its casenames? You do, for one. You stood by Stanov's chair for months. You couldn't fail to know.'

Kyril held his hands to his eyes, trying to shut out the insidious voice. Royston knew all the details of his mission. Perhaps he could have deduced those, it wasn't so difficult, but… Pisa. G. 17. *Icepex*. They couldn't be faked. No one outside the Kremlin knew those things. Except perhaps a handful of the most senior Deputy Chairmen. Except *Stanov*!

'The name, Bucharensky, the name. I must have it. I know you wouldn't tell any mere defector in place, no one would, but you're looking at a member of the

Kommandant, and I am ordering you to give me the name.'

There was a long silence. Kyril's head was going round and round. Could he afford to trust Royston? Could he afford not to? Three men only were in a position to identify the traitor: Povin, Bryant and himself. Why make a fourth? Besides, he had no proof. Povin, Michaelov, Stanov... He was at the centre of a maze, they were all using him.

'Think, Bucharensky. *Rodina*...'

Kyril looked up, his eyes widening. 'You... say that... to me?'

Rodina. Motherland... the very name had an aura about it; spoken aloud it made Kyril want to weep. For a second he saw the rolling green hills of his childhood, heard the river frothing down to the plain, could feel the sun on his back. Russia...

'What... what do you want me to do?'

Royston released his pent-up breath. 'This is the plan. I will turn my back on you. You use the gun to stun me: not so hard that I am killed but hard enough to make it convincing. They will come to find me. You overpowered me and got away, that is what they will think. But in case you do not make it, I must have the name. You must have a fall-back. I am all you have. The name, Bucharensky, *the name*...'

The room was going up and down. Kyril struggled to clear his head. He was so tired, all he could think of was sleep. Perhaps Royston was right. He *had* to be genuine; to offer to turn your back on a man and invite him to knock you out... But which name?

Povin.

Yes. Povin was the traitor. Loshkevoi said so, as Stanov had told him he would, right at the start. Stanov had not lied about Loshkevoi, after all.

And yet… what had Sikarov been trying to say in his last moments? Was it really Michaelov? If so, Michaelov was the traitor, for he had sent Sikarov to London. The First Deputy Chairman of the KGB, second only to…

Stanov.

Why had Stanov left him all alone in the field, defenceless, a running target? Why had he chosen Kyril out of so many others? Was it because of Vera? Did he foresee how Kyril would react, what Stanov would do? A cunning fox, Stanov…

Fox… *Lisa*…

Why did Vera have to die? *Why?*

Rodina. For the Motherland. For Russia…

Kyril looked into Royston's eyes. It was all true. He really was a member of the dreaded Kommandant. Either that, or Stanov had told him its innermost secrets…

Stanov… Stanov… *Lisa*…

Kyril was surrounded, trapped. Royston might represent his last, his only chance of sending home the vital name.

Kyril swallowed, licked his lips and opened his mouth to emit the little puff of breath that would herald 'P…'

No.

He had not reached the end of his mission. This was only the beginning! Inspiration filled him, seemed to raise him a few inches off the floor. The truth lay elsewhere, in Moscow. And that was where he must go to find it.

Kyril's eyes narrowed to fine slits. The light hurt them, they were suddenly sore. *Think*. One thing at a time. Royston. It was necessary to get rid of Royston. Nothing dramatic, now. Nothing obvious. Reassure him. That's right, make him think you believe him. Win him over. Give him a name… any old name, except the prime, the number one suspect…

Somewhere inside Kyril's head Sikarov's dying scream reverberated.

'It was Michaelov,' he said casually.

Royston nodded and turned his back. Kyril did not reverse his gun, as he would have to do if he were to stun the other man. Instead he stepped forward, his finger tightening on the trigger.

But as his brain commanded the final pressure that would trip the trigger mechanism his tired eyes saw the strange thing that was about to happen. A black, smoky hole exploding outwards from Royston's pocket as the gun, concealed there since shortly after Kyril first came in, was fired. A sudden pain, very sharp, very severe, in his chest. Kyril's eyes widened, then narrowed. Royston was rising up… no, that was wrong, he, Bucharensky, was sliding to the floor. It was very dark in the room, although he knew that the light was still burning. His brain transmitted its last message. Royston had stood with his hands in his pockets, and reversed the gun…

Bucharensky died.

Royston leaned against the wall and stayed like that for several minutes. From every angle it looked good.

Above all, Royston knew relief. Now Kyril could never betray him. The agony was over.

He knelt to the Russian's body and took the gun from his hand, exchanging it for his own. The coat with the black-fringed hole in the pocket he folded up carefully and placed by the door, ready to go with him when he left.

Kyril had committed suicide, that is what they would all think. The price of failure. Such a pity that before he took his own life he had to kill the foolhardy Sculby, whose overwhelming bravery got the better of him at last. That would go down well. The trendy lefty lawyer had nearly redeemed himself after all, no doubt in remorse for his duplicity in visiting the Bradfield woman (presumably on Stanov's orders) and his treachery in proposing a deal to Kyril. A good thing he had had the forethought to bug Sculby's offices. The tape of the lawyer's nocturnal conversation with Kyril played over very nicely. The phrase 'For love of the Motherland' sounded particularly well.

Royston raised his arms above his head and stretched. Noises from below indicated that the rescue-party had reached the front door. Time to find a hiding-place from which to emerge, pale and trembling…

After the debriefings, the inquests, when things were quiet again, Royston would write a postcard. Michaelov, that is what the apparently innocent, coded message would say. Bucharensky got the name, and then he died before he could be interrogated. But he got the name. Michaelov.

Stanov had been right about so many things. Loshkevoi, himself turned traitor; Sikarov, sent by Michaelov. The Bradfield woman. Stanov had been right about that also.

Royston was looking at the future. And it worked.

Chapter 40

It had been a false spring, after all. April came but in Moscow the nights were freezing once more, and brown slush coated the streets by day. The office on the third floor, however, was warm and fuggy. The Chairman had given orders for the central heating to be switched on again – and to hell with the Politburo, he thought privately to himself as he signed the chit. Let them save roubles some other year, after I've gone.

He had spent the past hour proofreading a report, now ready for his signature. Its subject was the identity of 'Source *Lisa*', and the steps which Stanov had taken to uncover the traitor.

When he had finished reading the report he removed his spectacles and went to stand by the window in his favourite spot overlooking the square. He was smiling. Nowadays it was fashionable to decry the role of intuition in espionage. Take Kazin, for example; he would never have understood the subtle mental processes which had led Stanov to the traitor.

So many straws in the wind, so many hints over the years. A non-drinker. Daughter on the verge of becoming a dissident. No sense of humour, no gift of relaxation, no flair. Perfect material for the West. A Georgian. Stanov frowned. How the hell had they ever appointed a Georgian to be head of the First Main Directorate?

And the evidence! He was almost sure at the beginning when he briefed Bucharensky, but look at what had happened since then. Who sent an executioner to the UK? Michaelov. Who left traces all over Radio Operations, with those filthy papirosy cigarettes? Michaelov. Stanov shook his head sorrowfully. To betray the Inspectorate, the Kommandant itself: a bitter blow. But they had caught him, at least there was that consolation.

Intuition. That's what you needed. That's why he was going to remain head of the KGB for ten more years at least, while Kazin was going to the Ministry of Agriculture, there to rot with his own collective farm manure. Stanov shook his head again. Kazin would never have appreciated the value of men like Loshkevoi. Or Royston.

Royston stood particularly high in Stanov's good books that day. With advancing age the Chairman was growing tired of elderly Cambridge dons with their peculiar sexual habits. He found them faintly obscene. A meritocrat like Royston came as a refreshing change.

Yevchenko knocked and came in. Stanov turned away from the window.

'Strange,' he said. 'Strange to think that Loshkevoi actually knew the name. I suspected many things of him, but never that.'

'A pity he did not live to confirm the identification, then.'

Stanov shrugged. 'What more could he have said? And this way it saves us the cost of a bullet. They are ready downstairs?'

Yevchenko nodded. In his hand he held a bunch of heavy keys. While Stanov watched with satisfaction he walked across to 'The Door' and unfastened the twin padlocks. It swung open to reveal a short, gloomy corridor, and a single light-bulb suspended from the ceiling by bare flex. Stanov rubbed his hands together.

'Come, Nikolai. It's been a while since I looked at the Lubianka cellars, and I'm sure the general doesn't want to be kept waiting. By the way, you remember what we were talking about yesterday? I've decided on Michaelov's successor and now we've finally got double-oh-seven-eight through, those bastards over the way can't stop me, eh? Normally I don't believe in promoting deputies at that level, but I'm going to make an exception. Povin it is. Excellent officer. Loyal. I like that, Nikolai. Remind me to tell Michaelov before they start…'

'A popular appointment, old man. I approve.'

Stanov paused on the threshold, struck by a sudden thought. He rested a hand on Yevchenko's shoulder and when he spoke there was genuine doubt in his voice.

'Nikolai… should I have told Kyril more, like you said? Would it have been better for him to die knowing all along that he was expendable, nothing more than a target? D'you still think I was wrong?'

Yevchenko smiled ruefully.

'If you'd told him the truth he would never have got to Loshkevoi. You were right not to trust him completely. I admit it. As it is, he was a good officer to the end. He died in the knowledge that he had not failed, that the name would get through.'

Stanov smiled, and removed his hand from Yevchenko's shoulder. They went through 'The Door' together. As Stanov turned to close it behind him he caught sight of 'The Chair' and it occurred to him that in say another ten years there would be a vacancy in the office of Chairman. Just time enough for Povin to show what he could really do. And then, perhaps… Who knows?

The Door closed behind him. In Dzerzhinsky Square the street lamps fizzled into life, illuminating the first snow of the night as it fell, untouched, through their incandescent blue circles. The room was silent and empty. As the natural light drained away, so one by one the features of the office dissolved into the surrounding darkness and became part of it. Andropov's vacant face was the first to disappear; then the quartz clocks, the telephones, the gigantic desk and, last to go, as if reluctant to surrender to the night, the ornate wooden chair…

The Chair… which, in the eyes of Soviet law, is never empty.

Afterwords

We are all spies. One reason is that we seek power, particularly the kind of power that is wielded in secret, beyond the ken of moralists, committees, juries and judges, because what is not known cannot be condemned – it's said that knowledge is power, but its absence may also be our protection. We particularly want to find out the stuff that will help us to put one over on our neighbours, or conquer our rivals on the stock market, or beat the other candidates for that job we covet. Then again, some of us spy for the more mundane reason that we simply like to *know*, and we feel respect for those who know more than we do. Perhaps we are even a little jealous of the miasma of mystery cloaking certain privileged individuals who ooze an aura of knowing things denied to lesser mortals. Sometimes, of course, we sense that they're faking it. We see through those pretentious dweebs and recognise them for what they are: writers of spy thrillers. Authors who've made a living from smoke and mirrors, fooling some of the people some of the time. People like me.

The main character in the novel you've just read (or, if you're peeking ahead, are about to read) is Stepan Ilyich Povin, a colonel-general in the Russian secret service formerly known as the KGB. 'My Stepan', as I've come to think of him. Where did he come from? Why is he here?

To those questions there is a short answer and a longer one. Let's start with the short one, keep things simple for now, because later on they'll be getting fraught.

Stepan first became a twinkle in his father's eye on a cold March day in the flat of my agent, Julian Friedmann, who believed that I had demonstrated enough talent to be worth spending a brainstorming afternoon with. Everything we discussed always circled back to the late John le Carré. He was my role model, and how could it be otherwise? In the spring of 1979, George Smiley was still a few months away from showing his face on television, but even then he dominated the spy-thriller genre in a way few characters have before or since. So one of us, I forget who, asked 'What's the opposite of le Carré?' And the answer turned out to be an intensely private, able spy who worked for the other side, for Russia, but also for us, here in the West, not just a spy but a traitor, too. A double agent who felt betrayed by the behemoth that the Russian state had become, an *apparatchik* turned idealist in whose tortured, closet-Christian soul the saints had supplanted Stalin.

'The opposite of that' chimed well with my seething ambition. It was an oddly unsatisfying time in my life. I had striven to become a barrister and succeeded, only to find that it was far from being all that my imagination had cracked it up to be. My speciality, I used to tell people, was 'death': wills, probate, trusts. Death both in truth and in terms of my sense of dissatisfaction. I was ready to embark on a major life change. However, I had a wife and two young children, so I needed money. Whatever I wrote had to be better than good, which also meant that it had to be dramatically different.

Stepan quickly found a place in my routine. On the morning train to London I would coax him into existence in a blue Counsel's notebook, using a ballpoint pen. My Russian colonel-general gestated over a series of forty-five-minute journeys on the Southern Region. I may have been the only passenger who never minded if the trains ran late. My children did mind. They only saw me at weekends.

The book was finished. Julian sold it to Sphere and publication was set for October 1981. Then came a stroke of luck. Martin Cruz Smith published *Gorky Park*, which became an international bestseller. Like *Kyril*, my own novel, it was set in Russia and peopled almost exclusively by Russians. Suddenly there was this New Wave, and I rode it.

Success followed. Stepan had evolved into a complex character. He was a Christian, a spy, a traitor and a civilised human being, beset by doubt. He was also gay, not that I chose to dwell on that. For twelve years, homosexuality between consenting adults in private had been legal in England, but just because something is legal that does not necessarily make it sit comfortably in the public psyche. Back in 1981, the only way you could combine 'gay' and 'hero' in a sentence was by discussing the swashbuckling roles of Errol Flynn. So Stepan stayed firmly in the closet, with sly nods and winks.

I dwell on this because when a publisher wants to bring an old trilogy to new readers the first question everyone asks is, 'How are these books relevant to life today? What light do they throw on where we are now?' Indeed, one of the things aspiring writers are taught is always to put themselves into the mind of an imaginary reader who wants to know, 'Why am I reading this?' So when a reboot of the Stepan trilogy was mooted I went back and read the novels with that question in mind. As a result, I reached certain conclusions, though your mileage may differ.

Consider what was really going on during the period covered by the Stepan trilogy and in the years that followed. First there was the Cold War. Then we got Brezhnev and a thaw and everybody said Russia would develop, its people would throw off the shackles, democracy and prosperity would herald a brave new world. Then we got Putin. The message Stepan sends *me* across the years is this: Russia can modernise, but it can't change. It just reboots the cycle. The message is a sombre warning and I'm glad of a chance to refurbish it, because it's never out of date. Perhaps, in a not-too-distant future fashioned by the Alt-Right, we too shall once again succumb to the thrill of banging people up because we don't like the people they're banging.

If Russia didn't change, I certainly did. For one thing I bought a word-processor. It cost north of £2000 (in 1982 money) and offered two options: green letters on a black screen or black letters on a white screen. It couldn't perform any of the other functions we now associate with even the humblest computer, phone or tablet. For the first time in my life, I became a trailblazer. At first the other members of my chambers in Lincoln's Inn regarded me with sub-Luddite suspicion. My clerk in particular was most upset but he knew his place – he was the grandee who wore an expensive suit that fitted whereas I was the brash young man who wore a cheap one that didn't – and kept his thoughts to himself. Then another, more senior colleague bought a proper desktop computer, one that could actually do sums, tempering my pride with the uneasy sense that I'd have done better to wait and do more research into technology trends, particularly pricing.

Ah, research. If you have already read *Kyril* you will have encountered confidently presented descriptions of what life in Russia was like, back in the day. Kind people ask me, 'How many times did you visit Russia, to glean all that information, that sense of place?' I have never visited Russia. The information was hard won. In those days, Google was a typo for a kind of cricket delivery, nothing more. I went to libraries, many libraries. I sent off money orders to obscure American publishers and received in exchange shoddily printed studies of the Russian Orthodox church, or the inner workings of a Soviet frigate, or recipes for borscht, all enclosed in the kind of padded envelopes that were used to mail us our condoms at uni. ('You know nothing, Jon Snow, *nothing.*')

What I couldn't research, I cheerfully, shamelessly made up. I put my imagination to work. To paraphrase Laurence Olivier, 'It's called acting, dear boy.' The only real advantage I had was unlimited confidence in the proposition that few of my readers would have visited Russia either. MI6 and the KGB must have faced similar limitations in the eighties when it came to gathering and analysing information (although I hope they resisted the urge to sex up the dossiers more than their successors – and I – liked to do). The spies I wrote about would have recognised their counterparts in the times of Peter the Great and Elizabeth I under Sir Francis Walsingham, the founder of England's secret intelligence service. Pausing only to buckle on a dagger and swirl a cloak around their shoulders, they'd have slithered into the darkness to get the work done properly, face to face and often *mano a mano*. Technology? Using lemon juice to write invisible messages that revealed their secrets in the warmth of a candle flame. *The* latest thing. Nowadays, MI5 and MI6 have websites on which they recruit openly, cloaks and daggers no longer a requirement. No, what you need to bring to the party today is an ability to code coupled with a moral vacuum where hacking is concerned; still the Great Game but played with different tools. If my Stepan asked a promising candidate how good he was at 'double-tap', he'd have been expecting to hear about the applicant's skill with the SAS's legendary quick-fire killing shot to the head. Now, perhaps not.

The difference in approach has found its way into fiction. Here's a sentence from a 2020 review of a recently published spy thriller: '...a cat and mouse game played by well-matched enemies ... a brainy FBI rookie with skills in data crunching, verbal analysis and profiling...' And now here's a line from the dismissive, three-line first review I ever received, from *The Times* no less: 'One of the most unpleasant torture scenes ever set down in a work of fiction.' I can no longer hope to stay in lock-step with an ever-changing world, but even if my Stepan could magic away the intervening forty years since he came to life I'd still put his finger on a taser, not a smartphone. I never had the pleasure of meeting John le Carré, although I used to buy all his work on publication, but from his recent novels I imagine he felt something along the same nostalgic lines. I deliberately set out to waft a faint but withering miasma of comedy through the airless corridors of KGB headquarters in Dzerzhinsky Square, something akin to what Ricky Gervais was later to achieve with *The Office*, and the trope of le Carré's later work resonates with me. An old-school protagonist is brought into sudden and bewildering contact with The New Normal at MI6, where half the characters at his interrogation are one-third his age and three quarters of them are – gasp! – women, the latter brighter, tougher and often nastier than the boys. And why not? John le Carré and me, too.

For the second novel in the trilogy, *A View from the Square*, I needed to gather data about a state-of-the-art surveillance aircraft, and extra bookshelves were built in the study to accommodate the inflow of materials on military hardware. In later years, my son would recall learning an '*obscene*' amount about guns from Dad's filing cabinet, which earned him the soubriquet, in those days much prized by schoolboys, of 'pretty cool'. (My daughter went through a teenage Goth phase, when she wrote poetry about piercings that benefitted from the 'Torture Methods' folder in the filing cabinet, so more help there then. Education… so priceless…)

At around that time I met my first real Russian spy. The only one, actually, and I keep his card in my wallet even now. No, I don't pass myself off as him; it's a reminder that we yield to preconceptions at our peril. The two things I vividly remember about this bloody Bolshevik revolutionary are his charm and the elegance of his clothes: he was clad in a small Savile Row fortune and all the charisma that went with it. The card proffered by Colonel… actually no, I may be mad but I am not stupid… by this attaché at the Embassy of the USSR, 16 Kensington Palace Gardens, W8, was all of a piece with its owner, expensive and engraved in exquisite Gothic script. He and I were at the same cocktail party on account of Julian Friedmann, by then a well-known literary agent. Comrade Attaché had wangled an invitation because he was 'fascinated' by Western ideas about life in the Soviet Union and made a point of cultivating writers of discernment (meaning, for all of five minutes, me) who could share his delight in quality fiction and serious journalism, reading groups, literary societies…

God, the man was good. If that's who 'my Stepan' sent to London, one quails to think who was doing the dirty work in Washington DC.

Then came the third novel, and a parting. *Nocturne for the General* was the first book where I was allowed by my paymasters to run a little wild. It is essentially a two-hander, a series of interrogations between Stepan and a very bright young woman indeed. I cried out loud when I typed the last sentence (still IMHO one of my best), but I knew that we were done. I'd discovered China, and at that time no other writer in English of spy thrillers had. I was fretting to be off on the latest adventure, but there has never come a time when I don't look back over my shoulder now and then to see how Stepan is doing. How life has treated him and his ilk. And I raise a hand to the man who put my children through expensive schools while launching my literary career. It gives me much pleasure now to acknowledge the debt owed to my first true fictional friend.

What happened after that?

I left the Bar and became a full-time novelist. They made a two-parter TV play of *Kyril* and at the invitation of producer Beryl Vertue, my wife and I visited a lovely stately home in Hampshire to watch Richard E. Grant studying his lines over a sandwich and Edward Woodward take notes from the armourer responsible for his handgun. At one heady moment the owner of the stately pile rushed around yelling, 'Where's the bloody shotgun?' and we thought that life was about to overtake art in a big way, but it turned out to be only an adder on the lawn.

That was a brief but golden age. For a few years, publishing was rife with larger-than-life characters vying for the award of Big Swinging Cheque Book Commissioning Editor; then it all ground to a halt and I had to find something else to do. I mentioned earlier that there were two explanations for the genesis of 'My Stepan', and although I did not know it at the time, this 'crisis' was the first step on my journey to discovering who Stepan really was and why he had insisted on being born.

My travels around the world resulted in me being able to make myself misunderstood in three languages other than my native tongue, in each case ending up better able to read the words that have always paid my bills than say them out loud. For six years I worked in Taiwan, or a province of China according to your politics, and there two things happened. First, I learned to be afraid of China in a way that apprehension about Russian ambitions had never affected me. In my capacity as editor of the *Taipei Review*, the government's flagship English-language publication, I got to know a lot about China. That country can modernise far more effectively than Russia, but the end is different and that won't be changed or even diluted. The name says it all: *Zhong Guo*, the Middle Kingdom, the centre of the world to which all roads must inexorably be made to lead. The Kingdom's (anyone who follows the rise of Xi Jinping will recognise a royal dynasty in the making) world view was forged centuries ago and has consistently nurtured a governmental mindset inspired by adamantine malevolence towards anything considered contrary to Chinese interests. That, at least, is something which China has never, throughout millennia, seen the slightest *need* to change.

The second thing was my initial brush with Buddhism. More of that later.

At one point I was holding down four well-paid jobs in Taipei. After my daytime stint at the government coalface I used to sub the next day's *China News* for four hours, six days a week. I had a weekly column in one of the Sundays. Then there was the consulting editorship of Taipei City Hall's English-language magazine. To stave off the possibility of boredom I taught English privately, and at all hours and in every kind of venue enjoyed contemplating the tale of two cities that was Taipei in the nineties: a brew of workaholic native Taiwanese and expatriates who had alcohol, if little else, in common. Taipei was a hard-drinking town, not one for cissies. I became what I now think of as a borderline functioning alcoholic. The funny thing was that the more I drank the better I wrote. In terms of character development, not so much.

I quit one month ahead of being fired, by my estimate; not because of the drink but on account of a change of government, resulting in a regime with high-falutin' ideas about taking the party line if you chose to take the party's dollar. I was fifty-two years old and have never had a job since, thanks in part to my Stepan. For a decade I commuted between a condo in Kota Kinabalu and the family's permanent base in Lewes. My flat overlooked the South China Sea; I'd sit in my rattan rocking-chair and watch the sunrise segue into sunset while reading Proust. I must have read *À la Recherche…* more than twenty times, often turning back to the first page as soon as I'd finished the last. Please don't let your eyes glaze over, for this section is brief and there is a point. It is thanks to Proust that I am now, finally, able to offer you the long answer to the question: 'Where did Stepan spring from?'

For Proust had been there before me. He had been everywhere before everyone. What's his secret? First, in his own words: 'The function and the task of a writer are those of a translator.' And now a comment by E. M. Forster that expands and illuminates the concept: 'How amazingly does Proust describe … the personal equipment of the reader, so that one keeps stopping with a gasp to say "Oh! How did he find that out about me? I didn't even know it myself until he informed me, but it is so!"'

Despite all the personal stuff that Proust helped me to translate, I still could not quite figure myself out. Fortunately, karma was at hand. It dispatched me to spend long periods in north-east Thailand surrounded by rice, nothing but rice, in a little wooden house on poles, where the shower was a plastic dustbin full of rainwater and the toilet was something you don't want to hear about. There, thousands of miles from Sussex and uncountable aeons from the hedonistic lifestyle to which my former life had accustomed me, I became a Buddhist. That taught me about the interconnectivity of all things and the unreality of everything we think we know. It was as if I had spent much of my adult life in a darkened room, watching a sheet of photographic paper bathing in developer. Suddenly the picture was there. All of it. Warts and all. And it was a picture of my Stepan.

In Proustian terms, when I wrote *Kyril* and all the books that followed, I was in effect but unwittingly translating something for myself and at the same time seeking to make readers relate to it in themselves. What is that something? I had been adopted six weeks after my birth, and I only learned about that while at my first school, in distressing circumstances. Someone I'd thought of as a good friend told everyone I was a bastard, a term which had to be explained to me by my loving and very distressed adoptive parents. In those days and in my mind, a bastard, however they might dress it up, was someone whose mother could not abide the sight of him. Someone fit only to be discarded by the person who is supposed to love them the most. A freak. A misfit. A monster.

For a long time the resulting catastrophe lay buried so deep inside me that a few years after I'd become a published writer and left the Bar, on the verge of lusted-for triumph, I had a mental breakdown. I tried to kill myself, but used what my GP described as 'the wrong kind of tablets'. (Since then I have comforted many people staring into the abyss with the reflection that the best things in my life, almost without exception, occurred after that botched suicide attempt, so think what I would have missed.) At the time, a wonderful therapist fixed me up but warned that in the absence of a lengthy period of analysis the cure was unlikely to be permanent. So it proved. As the years passed, every so often something would spark off a memory of his final words to me: 'I'm sure this is somehow all to do with your mother.'

After becoming a Buddhist in 2012 I applied myself to meditation with considerable success. As a result, at six minutes to four in the morning of 11th February 2018, I had my first electrocutive *vipassana* insight. I saw, with crystalline clarity, that my mother had not given me away because she hated me, as deep down I'd always supposed, but because she loved me enough to make the most agonising of choices and do what was right. She was not a traitor. She had not set out to wreck the being she loved. She had done her best to save him.

All my books are essentially about the same thing: what we do when the person who loves us most yanks the rug from under us. That's where my Stepan comes from. That's the secret that he and his successors as my protagonists were seeking to uncover.

I hope you will like him as much as I do. A few words of caution, however: please do not stare into his eyes for too long. Eyes like his have a habit of turning into mirrors. And what has once been seen cannot be unseen afterwards.

l: Racism, Identity and Multiculture in the
es Back and Tim Crabbe)
ed with Les Back)

with Martin Bulmer)

s Back)
ith John Wrench)

nd Policy

with

Also b

A Comp
Goldb
The Ch Footba
Engli author with L
Theories Racism (co-edi
Racism (th Martin Bulmer)
Ethnic tudies Today (co-edited
Racism a (co-author with Les Back)
Race, Pol Social Change (co-author with L
Racism ation i Western Europe (co-edited w
Race and olitics (co-edited with Wendy Ball)
Black You ism a the State: The Politics of Ideology a
The Roots ban Uest (co-edited with John Benyon)
Racism an qual ortunity Policies in the 1980s (co-edited
Richard kins)

Race and Racism in Britain

Third Edition

John Solomos

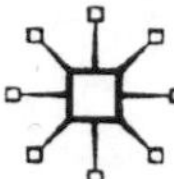

First edition 1989
Second edition 1993
Third edition 2003

Published by
PALGRAVE MACMILLAN
Houndmills, Basingstoke, Hampshire RG21 6XS and
175 Fifth Avenue, New York, N.Y. 10010
Companies and representatives throughout the world

PALGRAVE MACMILLAN is the global academic imprint of the Palgrave Macmillan division of St. Martin's Press, LLC and of Palgrave Macmillan Ltd. Macmillan® is a registered trademark in the United States, United Kingdom and other countries. Palgrave is a registered trademark in the European Union and other countries.

ISBN 0–333–76408–0 hardback
ISBN 0–333–76409–9 paperback

This book is printed on paper suitable for recycling and made from fully managed and sustained forest sources.

A catalogue record for this book is available from the British Library.

A catalog record for this book is available from the Library of Congress.

10 9 8 7 6 5 4 3 2 1
12 11 10 09 08 07 06 05 04 03

Printed and bound in Great Britain by
Creative Print & Design (Wales) Ebbw Vale

To the memory of ***Cleopatra, Solomos, Styliani****, and* ***Yiannis****, who missed out on the opportunities I have enjoyed, but whose experiences remain with me*

In loving memory of ***Nikolas Solomou****, who showed me at an early age the value of internationalism in the face of hatred and evil*

Contents

Preface to the Third Edition

When the first edition of *Race and Racism in Britain* came out in 1989 there were few books of its kind and race and racism in British society was still a relatively neglected field of study. In writing that edition I was seeking to fill a gap in the literature by providing an accessible overview of the main features of the changing dynamics of racial relations in Britain since 1945. This overarching concern determined both the style of the book and the organisation of the core chapters around key areas of political debate and processes of social and cultural change.

When producing this third edition I tried to remain close to my original objective and eschewed the tendency in much recent writing to play with neologisms and to become engrossed in theoretical analysis for its own sake. Rather, I sought to produce an analysis of race and racism in Britain that would be theoretically informed but focused on the need to understand the processes of political and social change that have been at the heart of developments in the past fifty years or so. I also decided to keep broadly to the style and content of the second edition, with the exception of a few changes, most notably the inclusion of a new chapter (Chapter 11). All the key chapters have been updated by adding material on recent trends and developments, as well as on new areas of scholarship and research.

Much has changed in the past decade, both in academic debates on race and racism and in the social and political environment of Britain. With regard to academic and scholarly debate, there has been a rapid growth in the number of studies that seek to analyse various facets of race and racism. Aspects of this body of work are discussed in the conceptual and empirically based chapters of this volume. More importantly, perhaps, I have sought to engage critically with some of the most influential studies produced in the past few years.

The growth of interest in this field – as reflected in the outpouring of theoretical writings and research and the recent expansion of specialist journals – has made the production of this edition both more interesting and challenging. It has been more interesting because recent research and scholarship has filled in major gaps in our knowledge of contemporary forms of racism. It has been more challenging because the literature on the subject is much more diverse than it was in the late 1980s when I was writing the first edition. Hence I have had to engage with new literatures as well as to reflect on the trends and debates that helped to shape the first two editions of this book. I leave it to the reader to judge how successful I have been in my endeavours.

In terms of changes in the wider social and political environment, perhaps the most important of these was the election of the Labour government in May 1997, which ended the long period of Conservative domination of political life. The demise of Thatcherism and the emergence of New Labour as the dominant political force have added a new dynamic to debates on immigration and race relations that is discussed in a number of chapters in this book. New initiatives by the 1997–2001 and post-2001 Labour governments include new legislation on immigration and refugees, the publication of the Macpherson Report on the murder of Stephen Lawrence and the 2000 Race Relations (Amendment) Act. While it is too early to provide a rounded account of New Labour's interventions in this field, in the relevant chapters I have included a critical analysis of its key policy initiatives and changing priorities. I have also added some discussion of the current debates on issues that have come to the fore in the past decade, namely multiculturalism, ethnic segregation and cultural difference in urban localities.

In addition to these political transformations there have been notable changes in the nature of race and ethnic relations in Britain. Perhaps the most notable of these is the emergence of ethnic identity politics, including growing awareness of the relevance of the intersection between class and racial divisions, the role of religion, and forms of ethnocultural identity. This has involved a questioning of the appropriateness of using categories such as black and Asian to describe the diverse range of minority communities in British society, the proliferation of new forms of racial and ethnic conflict, and the growth of consciously racist and neofascist groupings and ideologies. All of these concerns came to the fore during public debates in 2001 and after the outbreak of racial conflict and violence in Bradford, Oldham and Burnley.

More importantly, a wide range of new policy agendas have emerged in Britain and other European societies, partly in response to questions about the civic and social rights of minority communities and the position of new groups of migrants and refugees and asylum seekers. All of these issues have become important topics of public discourse and have encouraged new forms of racist and anti-immigrant mobilisation across much of Europe. These trends are discussed at some length in this new edition.

When I was writing the first edition of this book I had little idea that it would become a standard course text for over a decade. It is interesting to note in this context that although there has been a proliferation of theoretical texts in this field, particularly in the United States and Britain, there is still a relative dearth of accessible texts that explore the changing forms of racism and racial relations in specific societies. A few attempts have been made to cover some aspects of the range of issues covered in this volume, and some of these have helped to push forward the debate on key issues (see for example Goulbourne, 1998; Mason, 2000; Favell, 2001). There is, however, no single text that provides an overview of both the conceptual debates and the empirical trends and developments in this field. It is largely for this reason that I decided to produce a third edition of this volume.

When thinking about what to do with this edition I was helped by the suggestions of a wonderful group of friends and colleagues: Alice Bloch, Les Back, Martin Bulmer, David Theo Goldberg, Clive Harris, Michael Keith, Tony Kushner and Karim Murji. I have worked closely with Les Back over the past decade and have learned much from him. A marvellous group of former research students, including Chetan Bhatt, Sarah Neal, Liza Schuster and Brett St Louis, have taught me much through their own scholarly work and discussion. Liza Schuster, with whom I am working on another project, kindly made some important suggestions about the types of issues to include in this edition. I have also benefited from feedback by my students on various courses at Birkbeck College, the University of Southampton, South Bank University and City University. During the penultimate stage of producing this edition the Faculty of Humanities and Social Science at South Bank University provided an ideal environment in which to work. At South Bank I particularly benefited from the support of Claire Alexander, Harry Goulbourne, Azra Khan, Stina Lyon and Jeffrey Weeks. Finally, the Department of Sociology at City University gave me the time and intellectual environment needed to push the project to completion. Thank you to Tony Woodiwiss and Rosemary Crompton for welcoming me and helping me to settle.

Steven Kennedy at Palgrave Macmillan has been an ideal and patient editor. He has not only put up with many delays with a sense of humour, but cajoled and encouraged me along the way in his own inimitable style. A big thank you for believing in me even when I let you down. Keith Povey copy-edited the typescript in a very impressive manner, and I am very grateful to him for making the book more readable.

The greatest joy of my life since the second edition has been the arrival of Nikolas Stephen Solomos and Daniel Theo Solomos. There are no words that can adequately express my love for Nikolas and Daniel, and their constant affection and smiling faces have kept me smiling, even though they do not see the value of my spending so much time in the study. To them and Christine I can only say 'One Love'. The years since 1993 have, however, been hard for the Baggies, whose struggle to reach the Premier League has kept me busy on so many Saturdays and Sundays. The members of the London supporters' branch have provided good company on many trips to watch our beloved Baggies at away games and tolerated an eccentric 'Prof' in their midst. In the last months of finishing the book we had the excitement of gaining promotion to the Premier League. The final game on 21 April against Crystal Palace and the celebrations in the Black Eagle afterwards will live on in my memory for a long time.

I dedicate this book to the memory of my beloved grandparents and my late father. Without them, of course, none of this would have been possible.

City University, London JOHN SOLOMOS

Introduction

The study of racial categorisation in British society can be traced back to the 1940s and 1950s, when the work of scholars such as Michael Banton and Anthony Richmond established the foundations of the academic study of the social and cultural impact of migrant incorporation and exclusion. Later, in the 1960s, John Rex and others produced valuable insights into the political sociology of race and ethnicity in British society. Yet by the late 1980s, when the first edition of this book was published, the study of race and racism was still very much on the margins of key social science disciplines such as sociology and politics. There were relatively few specialised courses at the undergraduate and postgraduate levels, and scholarly debate and research was concentrated in a few major research centres in the United States and Britain. The situation is now markedly different. At the beginning of the twenty-first century it is clear that there has been a major transformation in this field and a noticeable flowering of theorising and research on race and racism. It is also evident that the study of race and racism is now of some importance in a wide range of academic disciplines, including sociology, politics, cultural studies, history, anthropology, geography and literary theory (Solomos and Back, 1996; Bulmer and Solomos, 1999a; Back and Solomos, 2000). In this context it was inevitable that both the theoretical underpinnings of this book and the chapters that deal with political and policy transformations had to be rethought and revised.

More importantly, perhaps, the public debates on race and racism are rather different at the beginning of the twenty-first century than they were even a decade ago. Perhaps nothing better reflects the current phase of public debate on this whole area than the twin preoccupations we see all over Europe with the policy dilemmas raised by multiculturalism and the growing numbers of asylum seekers and refugees. We have seen intense debate on both these questions, as well as related issues such as racism and right-wing political mobilisation, in a variety of societies in Eastern and Western Europe as well as in the Americas, Australasia and parts of Africa. Taken together with the growth of academic research and debate on topics linked to these issues, these developments suggest that we are at the beginning of a new phase in the study of race and racism in Britain and elsewhere (Bulmer and Solomos, 1999b).

This has helped to stimulate the development of a number of research paradigms and has been reflected in work emanating from a variety of national contexts and disciplinary backgrounds. From being a relatively neglected field of research the study of race and racism is now closer to the heart of contemporary scholarly debates. The proliferation of scholarly texts and journals on various facets of race and ethnicity is symbolic of this broader trend. In general this development has been positive and is to be welcomed, given the importance of racial ideologies in shaping social relations in a number of societies. It is worth noting, however, that much of the recent literature in this field is rather abstracted from the analysis of political, policy or everyday trends in specific societies or contexts. A good example of this is the proliferation of theorising that focuses on issues of race and culture or postcolonialism. There may be much of value in this growing body of work, but it is disappointing that few attempts have been made to link theory to the analysis of social and political trends in specific societies or parts of the globe (for attempts to make such links see Goldberg, 1993, 2002; Cohen, 1999). Rather there has been a noticeable retreat from the analysis of societies and processes of social change into the analysis of texts and images in ways that are abstracted from the everyday realities of the societies in which we live.

Given the changes and developments noted above, I have chosen to remain close to the concerns I had in mind when writing the first edition of *Race and Racism in Britain*. My first objective is to provide an analysis of race and racism in contemporary Britain by focusing on trends and developments since 1945. The analysis includes a discussion of theories and conceptual debates on race and racism, and draws particularly on debates over the past two decades. The main focus, however, is on the historical context of race and racism in British society and political responses to black immigration and the growth of multiculturalism. This includes an analysis of the pressure for legislative controls and restrictions on immigration, national and local policy developments, policing and urban unrest, and the shifts in racial ideology that have taken place over the past fifty years or so.

The second objective is to explore and analyse key facets of the racialisation of political life and social relations in Britain. This is done through an analysis of ideologies that focus on race as an important political symbol and on the part played by racist, antiracist and ethnic minority political mobilisation, and through an exploration both of the impact of social and economic restructuring on racial and national identities in British society and of alternative visions of multiculturalism. The discussion includes a detailed consideration of the possibilities for social reform and of antidiscrimination policies as a tool for tackling racial inequality, as well as a review of current debates on the role of public policy in this field.

Fulfilling these objectives requires detailed analysis of both historical and contemporary issues. This is reflected in the balance of the volume as a whole and in the fact that each chapter includes evidence from a range of historical sources as well as current scholarship and research. This inevitably means crossing disciplinary boundaries as the study of race and ethnicity is by no means limited to one discipline. For example there has been an intense growth of interest in these issues by feminists working in a variety of fields (Ramazanoglu, 1989; Collins, 1990; hooks, 1992; Ware, 1992; Brah, 1992, 1996; Mirza, 1997). Consideration of their work and that of others allows us to move beyond the narrow disciplinary and conceptual frames of analysis that dominated the study of race and racism until the 1980s and to suggest a more dialogical analytical framework.

The concerns of *Race and Racism in Britain* are therefore partly historical and partly conceptual. Its main focus is the complex set of historical and contemporary processes that have shaped the development of racialised politics in British society since 1945. The chapters that follow provide an overview of key trends and processes during this period, reflect on the part played by specific issues in shaping racial politics, and explore the changing priorities of public policy, as reflected in central and local government interventions. By studying the role of race and racism in contemporary British society it is hoped that this volume will help to shed light on the reasons why we have arrived at our current state of affairs and the prospects for the future.

Before moving on to this account, we shall consider some of the key theoretical perspectives and concepts that have influenced the analysis of race and racism.

Contemporary trends and developments

The past two decades have witnessed rapid change in the politics of race and immigration in Britain, the US and many European countries. There has been a resurgence of racist social and political movements in both Western and Eastern Europe, at least partly because of the mobilisation of anti-immigrant sentiments (Wrench and Solomos, 1993; Castles and Miller, 1998). Alongside this trend we have seen the development of new patterns of migration and heated political debate on the best ways to respond to the challenge posed by asylum seekers and refugees in a large number of West European countries. Widespread reportage in the media has highlighted the emergence of new forms of racism and the impact they are having in a variety of national contexts (Glasgow Media Studies Group, 1997; Philo and Beattie, 1999). Indeed in many countries immigration, the position of minorities and the growing numbers of refugees have become key issues on the political agenda, shaping the ideologies of both left-wing and right-wing political parties.

At the same time the debate on immigration has become inextricably tied up with wider preoccupations about the social and political position of established ethnic and racial minority communities, many of whose members cannot be viewed as 'immigrants' in any meaningful sense (Castles and Miller, 1998). Nonetheless the social and political status of second- and third-generation descendants of settled migrants is the subject of intense and in many cases hostile public debate.

Events in Britain, France, Germany, Austria, Belgium and elsewhere in Europe over the past decade have highlighted the volatility of this issue and the ease with which it can lead to conflict and disorder. On the one hand there has been growing racism and hostility towards migrants, with neofascist and right-wing political parties using the issue of immigration to attract support (Husbands, 1991; Balibar, 1991; Wrench and Solomos, 1993; Eatwell, 1998; Kushner and Knox, 1999). On the other hand, numerous policies have been introduced to deal with the social and economic problems of minority communities (European Parliament, 1998). Both of these phenomena are part of the uneasy compromises on the question of immigration and ethnic minorities that have shaped public policy on immigration and race across Europe over the past few decades. Such trends emphasise the need for us to be aware of the complex set of policies that are part of the public culture of Britain and other European countries. Moreover recent trends in both Europe and the US can be seen as important watersheds in terms of the racialisation of politics and the resurgence of avowedly racist political movements (Appiah and Gutmann, 1996).

Such trends have led to widespread concern in Britain and the rest of Europe about the prospects that lie ahead in this area. A number of key questions have been hotly debated. Are we witnessing the emergence of a new racism? What is the prospect of developing an adequate response to this phenomenon? Is there evidence that minority communities are developing their own political responses and strategies for the future? What can be done to tackle the root causes of racism and racial inequality in contemporary Europe? To what extent have we seen the emergence of a vibrant multiculturalism across Europe?

These are just some of the questions that need to be addressed if we are to make sense of recent events. It should be clear, however, from what has been said already that the present situation is best characterised as inherently unstable and contradictory. It is therefore important to go beyond the obvious and reflect on key aspects of the current situation, the historical background to current issues and alternative models to shape political opinion in the future. Before we can make a reasoned assessment of likely trends and the possibilities for action we need to situate present events against the processes and political debates that have shaped them. *Race and Racism in Britain* can therefore be read as a map of the trends in Britain over the past six decades that have been at the heart of the development of what is popularly called 'race relations'.

Race and racism in Britain

A number of questions arise when one looks at the changing face of the politics of immigration and race in Britain. First, is there something unique about the debates on race and immigration in British society? Is there something about Britain's colonial past that holds the key to everyday notions about race and colour in contemporary British culture? Second, why have we not seen the emergence in Britain of mass racist movements and parties that are able to mobilise popular support? A point of comparison in this regard is the support for Front Nationale in France over the past two decades, and for similar organisations in countries such as Germany, Austria and Belgium.

These questions highlight issues that are addressed at various points in this book. It is important, however, to provide an initial response to the questions in order to situate our approach in relation to others. With regard to the specificity of the British situation, for example, there have been a number of interesting attempts in recent years to compare the situation in Britain with trends in other European countries (see for example Joppke, 1999; Favell, 2001). Although it is clear that there are substantial differences between the situation of immigrants and minorities in, say, Germany, France and Holland and the position of minority communities in Britain, there are also areas of comparison. A similar point could be made about the comparability of the British situation with trends in the US. Without wishing to deny the importance of different national political traditions and historical legacies it is essential to avoid collapsing the analysis of recent trends and contemporary transformations into readings of the past. This is a recurrent theme in much of the analysis in this volume, and particularly in the analysis of the changes and transformations that took place around the question of race and racism from the 1950s onwards.

Let us take the impact of the legacy of colonialism on contemporary British race relations as an example. This is a common theme in much of the literature and it has led to some interesting research by historians as well as sociologists (Harris, 1988; Goulbourne, 1998; Bush, 1999). There is clearly much we can learn from a rigorous engagement with historical evidence on the part played by colonialism in shaping popular ideas and cultural values in Britain and colonial societies alike. However it is important to remember that there is danger in reducing complex contemporary processes to essentialist notions about the role of colonialism in shaping the present.

To return to the second question raised above, namely the absence of a mass racist movement or political party in Britain, it is argued in this book that this phenomenon should be situated in a wider context, particularly in respect of the place held by race and immigration in the ideologies of the mainstream political parties and in wider social and political trends. During the 1992, 1997 and 2001 general elections, for example, although questions about race and immigration were on the political agenda they were by no means key issues. Despite warnings that the 'race card' was likely to be played during the election campaigns there was relatively little public debate on this issue until the 2001 general election. Even then, broader social and economic preoccupations took precedence during the election campaign. Certainly race was an important issue in some localities, such as East London, Oldham and Burnley, but a plethora of other social and economic issues attracted more public attention. Yet it is also clear that race and immigration are by no means static items on the political agenda. The shifting tides of public opinion on such issues as religious differences, refugee and asylum policy, immigration and more recently illegal immigrants have highlighted the changing dynamics of the politics of race and racism. The events leading up to the 2001 general election helped to highlight the extent to which race and immigration remain live issues in British political culture, even when mainstream political parties attempt to create a consensus politics around them. This is a theme to which we shall return in the detailed discussion of political ideologies in Chapters 8 and 9.

Public debates on race and immigration during the 1990s and the early 2000s indicate that we are in a period of rapid change and transformation. In this context it seems clear that race and immigration issues need to be seen as part of the wider social and political environment, though they are by no means reducible to broader sociopolitical processes.

Racism in contemporary Europe

If we broaden our focus from Britain to the rest of Europe the relevance of the above arguments becomes clearer. Trends and developments during the 1990s across a number of European countries highlighted the fact that debates on immigration or racism do not make sense outside particular social, political and economic contexts. It is not possible to draw a direct comparison, for example, between the situations in France and Britain. Discussions on race and race relations have taken complex forms in contemporary Europe and it would be a mistake to use the experiences of Britain to draw conclusions about other societies. This is evident when we look at the changing terms of public debates on immigration and citizenship across a wide range of European countries (Bovenkerk *et al.*, 1990; Lloyd, 1991; Soysal, 1994; Joppke, 1998, 1999; Favell, 2001). It is quite clear from these debates that there is by no means a consensus on how the boundaries of citizenship and social inclusion should be drawn. There is a need, therefore, to be aware of the complex processes of migration and settlement that have shaped the politics of various nations.

What is also clear, however, is that recent political debates on race and immigration have been fundamentally transformed by trends that have had an impact on European societies as a whole. Two factors are often singled out as having helped to shape recent developments. First, it is argued that events in Eastern Europe and the former Soviet Union since 1989 have created fears about the likelihood of mass emigration from the former communist states to countries as diverse as Germany, Italy and Austria. Indeed this issue has been widely debated since 1989, though it is not easy to predict future patterns of migration or the nature of political responses to them (Cohen, 1991; Castles and Miller, 1998; Kushner and Knox, 1999). The second factor is the likely pattern of migration movements in the future. A key concern here is that immigration and the movement of refugees will in all likelihood increase in the coming decades and thus remain a key political issue in Europe as well as other parts of the globe. For example it is argued that political instability and demographic changes will lead to pressure to migrate or seek refuge from persecution. Events in former Yugoslavia and parts of Africa have highlighted the global nature of such pressure and suggest that migratory and refugee movements will grow in the coming years (Papastergiadis, 2000).

This is a time of uncertainty and confusion about the economic and political orientation of the 'new Europe', the new 'European identity' and the dissolving of established national and ethnic boundaries. It is therefore, perhaps not surprising, that the position of ethnic and racial minorities already living in Europe has become intimately bound up with the politics of immigration. What is even more disturbing is that the rapid transformations experienced by a number of societies over the past two decades, particularly in relation to their economic and social infrastructure, has provided fertile ground for extreme right-wing parties and movements to depict ethnic and racial minorities as 'outsiders', 'foreigners' and 'enemies within'. In Britain this has led to the racialisation of issues such as employment, housing, education and law and order. Although it has not led to the emergence of a mass racist social movement it has given rise to a resurgence of racial attacks and violence in some areas of the country. The experience of areas of London during the 1990s, and more recently in parts of Bradford, Oldham and Burnley, has shown that such processes of racialisation have prompted everyday patterns of racial conflict and exclusion. This indicates that the potential for ethnoracial divisions to become established in urban localities needs to be explored in relation to transformations in both the economic and the social environment.

This process has moved public and political debate beyond the question of immigration and race relations *per se* and towards the identification and resolution of specific social problems that are perceived as linked to ethnicity and race. The link to the immigration question is maintained at another level because it is the size of the minority populations, whether in schools or the unemployment queue, that is identified as the source of the problem. Such developments have fuelled the growth of political movements that hold racist and anti-immigrant views. In this environment it seems quite clear that the issue of immigration policy cannot be seen separately from a broader set of policy agendas on the social, economic and political position of migrant communities. This is evident from recent debates on immigration in a number of West European societies, and as will be argued in this book it has long been evident in public policies on the position of ethnic minority communities in British society.

Perhaps the main issue of concern at the moment is that extreme right-wing parties and anti-immigrant groups are beginning to have an impact on political life in a number of European countries. The relative success of extreme-right politicians in countries as diverse as France, Austria, Belgium and the Netherlands has influenced political debates on a wide range of social and cultural issues across Europe. The support for the Front National under Le Pen during the 2002 French presidential election and for the late Pim Fortuyn's populist anti-immigration movement in the Netherlands are the latest examples of the political impact of far right politics in this area. They are also symbolic of wider trends that have become part of the political life of Europe and have influenced the political ideologies of both left and right. Indeed over the past decade it has become evident that questions on immigration and asylum and religious and cultural difference are likely to provide fertile ground for the political ideologies of the far right and nationalists.

Rethinking the study of race and racism

Until recently the study of race and racism in British society has concentrated on a narrow range of issues. To be sure, there is a long history of research in this field, much of it going back to the 1950s and 1960s, but its contribution to our understanding of both the history and the contemporary forms of racism and racial categorisation in British society remains at best limited. For example a wide range of sociological studies have focused on particular communities or on discrimination in specific employment, housing and service delivery situations. Yet there is only a limited body of research on the relationship between racial categorisation and social and political relations in contemporary Britain. This neglect is hard to understand, given the relatively high position that racial questions have occupied on political and public policy agendas since the 1950s.

It has become clear since the early 1980s that any rounded analysis of contemporary British politics and society must include the study of political mobilisations based on race and immigration (CCCS Race and Politics Group, 1982; Gilroy, 1987; Solomos and Back, 1996). The outbreak of violence in many inner city areas during 1981, 1985 and beyond provided the stimulus for increased attention to be paid to the political arena as a field of research. At the same time the growing presence of minority politicians at both the local and the national level has led to greater awareness of the role of political parties and institutions in shaping debates on race relations in Britain. The experience of the Labour Party, and to a lesser extent the Conservative Party, since the mid 1980s provides an insight into the politicisation of questions about representation and minority communities. It has also become clear over the years that questions about employment policy, welfare provision, local government, policing, housing and youth provision have a strong racial element that needs to be taken more fully into account.

All these issues help to explain why, particularly from the late 1960s onwards, race has come to play an increasingly important part in public political debates and official policy analysis. For many on the right, immigration and race are important issues because of their supposed impact on Britain's cultural and political values. Statements by politicians, press commentators, the police and government agencies have helped to build up the view that without drastic steps to control immigration and deal with the internal impact of race at the local and national levels the whole fabric of British society could come under threat. For the left, too, the emergence of race as a theme in political debate has challenged many received wisdoms about working-class politics and class formation. While rejecting many of the most extreme images of the impact of immigration and race on British society, for example, during the 1960s and 1970s the Labour Party adopted positions that were influenced by its desire to protect itself from accusations of being soft on immigration. Similarly since its return to power in 1997 it has adopted policies on asylum seekers and refugees that are premised very much on the need to appease anti-immigrant sentiments in Britain.

In the present context it is clear that the changing forms of racial discourse are an important component of social and political relations in Britain. Political debates on immigration and multiculturalism since the 1990s have done little to challenge the confusion and political uncertainty that have shaped policy changes in this area since 1945. They have also highlighted the need to situate the position of ethnic and racial minorities against the background of wider changes in the political economy of postwar Britain and the social and cultural transformations that are taking place at present. This book seeks to outline a framework of analysis for the study of race and racism in contemporary Britain, and suggests some avenues for further research and analysis. The prime focus is on developing a critical analysis of the major processes that can help us to understand the use of race as a political symbol and the growing importance of debates on racism and antiracism (Bonnett, 2000).

In the course of this account it will be necessary to address some of the recent conceptual and theoretical debates that have surrounded the study of race and racism. This is partly because, although this study is not concerned with theoretical debates as such, it is necessary to address some of the conceptual problems raised by key notions such as race and racism. It is also because contemporary social theorists are not in agreement about the meaning of the concepts of race and racism, and often use them in a wide variety of analytical frameworks (Miles, 1989; Goldberg, 1990a, 1993; Solomos and Back, 1995, 1996; Malik, 1996). Indeed in recent years a lively debate has developed on the terminology used by social scientists to discuss these issues. It is therefore necessary to clarify how these concepts will be used in the course of this book.

Taking the concept of race first, notwithstanding the long history of debates on this term it has long been recognised that races do not exist in any scientifically meaningful sense. Yet it is clear that in many societies people continue to act as if race exists as a fixed objective category, and this belief is reflected in political discourses and at the level of popular ideas. Commonplace classifications of race have relied on a variety of variables – such as skin colour, country of origin, religion, nationality and language – to define groups of people. What are the consequences of racial categorisation for politics, ideology and social action? How does the meaning attached to race as a social category generate political debate and discourses? These are some of the questions that this book addresses in the context of contemporary British society, and its central focus is the construction of and changing meanings attached to the category of race and how in specific contexts race has become a signifier for a range of social problems and conflicts.

Moving on to the concept of racism, in this study racism is broadly defined in that it is used to cover ideologies and social processes that discriminate against others on the basis of their putatively different racial membership. There is little to be gained from seeing racism merely as a signifier of claims to biological superiority, since it has become clear in recent years that the focus on attributed biological inferiority is being replaced in racist discourse by a concern with culture and ethnicity as historically fixed categories. This is why a central argument in this book is that racism is not a static phenomenon. In countries such as Britain racism is produced and reproduced through political discourse, the media, the education system and other institutions. In this wider social context racism has become an integral element of diverse social issues, such as law and order, crime, the inner cities and urban unrest. In this sense the notion of racism that we are working with in this study shares much with George Mosse's understanding of it as an ideology that has to be situated in specific historical and social contexts in order to make sense of it (Mosse, 1985).

These are complex issues and we shall address them in more detail in the course of the review of theoretical perspectives in Chapter 1. In the context of the substantive concerns of this book they are also questions that we shall inevitably come across when we explore the changing usage of race and racism in political discourse and public policy.

Overview of the book

The general rationale of this book has already been outlined, as well as some of the key themes it addresses. This section briefly describes the content of each of the chapters in order to make explicit the concerns that guide the volume as a whole and the choice of specific themes and issues in individual chapters.

Chapter 1 provides an overview of key aspects of contemporary theoretical debates on race and racism. When discussing these debates I shall also outline some of the basic theoretical concerns that guided the writing of this volume. Given that the book as a whole focuses on the identification and analysis of the historical context of race and racism in British society, I have chosen to concentrate on issues that relate to this specific topic rather than on broader conceptual debates. (There are already numerous works that explore the changing contours of theoretical debates from a variety of perspectives and historical examples. For two recent collections see Back and Solomos, 2000; Goldberg and Solomos, 2002.) In particular the chapter looks at the development of the main theoretical approaches in this field: attempts to theorise the role of the state and political institutions, and explorations of the interplay between racist political action, antiracism and social movements. We shall return to some of these points in subsequent chapters.

From this starting point, the book develops a critical assessment of theoretical and empirical approaches to the study of race and racism in Britain. It does this through an analysis of some of the most important facets of political debates on race and immigration since 1945, and of the role of political ideologies and practices in framing the racialisation of British politics and society. A volume of this size cannot hope to address all the conceptual questions raised in Chapter 1. Taken together the chapters are intended as a critical and historically grounded exploration of the changing morphology of race and racism in British society. Each chapter explores this broad area from a specific angle, but they are all linked by an argument that resonates throughout the volume, namely that the analysis of racism in its various forms requires us to move beyond abstract generalisations and assertions that are not based on empirical research. First and foremost it is important to recognise that racialisation is a historical political process.

It is precisely for this reason that Chapters 2 and 3 reconstruct the history of debates on immigration and race in Britain. Chapter 2 examines the historical background of more recent trends by looking at key aspects of debates on race and immigration during the late nineteenth and early twentieth centuries. Part of the concern of this chapter is to explore the links between developments since 1945 and processes with a longer history. The account is continued in Chapter 3 with an analysis of the main trends in the decades after 1945, including pressure to introduce controls on immigration through legislative measures and the introduction of state agencies to regulate the entry of black labour from the colonies. This chapter pays particular attention to debates within political parties on immigration and the reasons why a political consensus in favour of regulation was established in the 1960s. It continues this analysis by examining how, from the 1960s to the present, policy agendas on race and immigration have been shaped by a concern to combine strong controls on immigration with a public commitment to tackling issues such as racial discrimination and inequality through legislation and government intervention. The concluding section looks at how questions about refugees and asylum seekers have come more to the fore in debates on immigration and race relations over the past decade or so.

The account in Chapters 1 to 3 is complemented by four interlinked chapters that focus on key areas of policy change and conflict in this field. Chapters 4, 5, 6 and 7 explore the history, mechanisms and outcomes of state intervention aimed at regulating and managing key areas of race relations in

Britain. Chapter 4 considers the role of race relations legislation in dealing with discrimination in such key areas as employment and housing. Legislation against discrimination has been a major plank of state policy in this area from the 1960s and it has played an important part in recent political debates. After a period of little legislative change the Labour government introduced new legislation in 2000. In so doing it demonstrated its commitment to the promotion of racial equality and justice, but the extent to which legislation can deal with the root causes of racial inequality remains unclear. A key concern of this chapter, therefore, is how effective race relations policies have been in tackling racial inequality. This is followed in Chapter 5 by a review of the urban politics of race. The local dimension of racial politics has been an important aspect of policy debate since the 1980s, so this chapter explores the dynamics of policy change and conflict in shaping racial politics in urban environments.

Chapters 6 and 7 focus on the dynamics of policy change in relation to policing and urban unrest. The relationship between the police and minority communities has long been a matter of concern in many urban localities. The history of this relationship is explored in Chapter 6, which looks particularly at the wider social and political context in which the activities of the police in multiracial localities have come to be viewed. It also includes a review of debates on racism within the police force as an institution and touches on the Stephen Lawrence case to highlight the subject of institutional racism. Chapter 7 looks specifically at the issue of violence and urban unrest. Since the 1980s urban unrest and violent confrontations between the police and members of black communities has led to widespread debate on the part played by racial inequality and racism in producing the conditions for public disorder. Chapter 7 presents a critical analysis of both the background and the wider social and political impact of this unrest.

The focus shifts somewhat in Chapters 8, 9 and 10 to political mobilisation and social action. Chapter 8 begins by looking at the impact of ideologies of race and nation on political mobilisation. By analysing the continuities and discontinuities between various forms of racist ideology and mobilisation it reveals the material foundations of the reproduction of racism in contemporary Britain and the implications this has for the struggle against racism. Chapter 9 then takes up the question of political mobilisation by black and ethnic minority communities, and the impact of antiracist politics and oppositional social movements on the political agenda. As well as dealing with current examples of such mobilisation the chapter also explores its historical antecedents and the reasons for the limited success of antiracist strategies in removing entrenched racist practices. This is followed in Chapter 10 by a more detailed discussion of the interplay between race, culture and identity politics in British society, and the role of wider social and economic relations in shaping the course of change. Questions about culture, religion and ethnic identity have become increasingly important in recent debates and this chapter seeks to draw out some of the broader implications of this for the future of race relations in Britain.

This links up with the issues covered in Chapter 11, which considers how social changes have helped to shape race relations in British society. The chapter reflects the growing importance of this topic in public discussions on the societal position of racial and ethnic minorities. The substantive part of the chapter explores the interaction between race, class and gender in structuring contemporary racial relations in Britain. This issue has become a key concern in many of the research endeavours in this field, and this chapter provides an overview of important facets of recent research and policy debate in order to determine the likely impact of social change on patterns of racial conflict and on political mobilisation by minority communities.

Chapter 12 reflects on the key themes addressed in the book as a whole and outlines key processes that are likely to transform the question of race and racism in Britain and other societies in the near future. Given the growing importance of developments in Europe as a whole for British society, these processes are presented in a broad comparative framework that reflects the need to move the focus beyond the boundaries of the nation state.

Taken together the twelve chapters provide an overview of the most important issues in the study of race and racism in contemporary Britain. In places the limits of a single volume mean that some issues cannot be explored in detail, but the *Guide to Further Reading* lists key works in which such issues can be followed up.

This book will have achieved its objective if it convinces the reader of the need for a critical approach to the analysis of race and racism in British society. Given the developments that have take place over the past decade or so there is an urgent need for more research, reflection and reasoned political debate on what is likely to remain one of the most controversial social issues in the early decades of the twenty-first century.

1 Theorising Race and Racism

The study of race as a field of social scientific inquiry and research originated in the earlier part of the twentieth century with the work of a number of American sociologists and anthropologists, most notably during the 1920s and 1930s. These scholars were influenced by the work of Robert Park, one of the key early sociological writers in this field. Between the 1920s and the 1950s they helped to establish what later came to be called the study of race relations, particularly in respect of segregation, immigration and race consciousness in the US, and during the interwar period they developed a body of sociological concepts that were later refined into the sociology of race relations. Their studies of the specific contexts in which ideas about race became socially meaningful remain among the classics of the field (Goldberg and Solomos, 2002).

Up to the 1960s many of the American studies of race were influenced by the ideas of this group of writers and concentrated on the analysis of the social and economic inequalities suffered by blacks, and of their cultural and psychological make-up, family relations and political isolation. Following Park, the dominant assumption seemed to be that race relations were types of social relations between people of different racial characteristics, particularly morphological characteristics. In his classic definition of the notion of race relations Park argued that the main feature of such relations was consciousness of racial differences:

> Race relations, as that term is defined in use and wont in the United States, are the relations existing between peoples distinguished by marks of racial descent, particularly when these racial differences enter into the consciousness of the individuals and groups so distinguished, and by so doing determine in each case the individual's conception of himself as well as his status in the community (Park, 1950: 81).

Although in some of his and his students' work there is acknowledgement of the economic and social conditions that help produce race consciousness, the focus is on the nature of relationships between races. Thus Park and his followers tended to see the development and perpetuation of racial conflicts in terms of the ways in which phenotypical differences came to be understood as the product of racial definitions and identities. The emphasis was on a 'cycle of race relations', leading to the assimilation of different racial groupings into a common culture. This cycle consisted of four stages: contact, conflict, accommodation and assimilation (ibid.: 82–4).

While Park's work was by and large descriptive and untheorised, it was instrumental in the development of a distinct subfield of sociological studies of race relations in the US. This trend was helped by the publication of Gunnar Myrdal's *An American Dilemma* in 1944, which documented the history of black inequality and racial prejudice in the US. Arguing forcefully for the integration of blacks into mainstream American life, Myrdal predicted that integration and assimilation would eventually replace conflict and segregation (Myrdal, 1969a, 1969b).

From the late 1940s to the 1960s this model of assimilation exerted a dominant influence on research in this field in the US. Pierre L. van den Berghe, for example, characterised the American studies of race in the following way: 'The field has been dominated by a functionalist view of society and a definition of the race problem as one of integration and assimilation of minorities into the mainstream of a consensus based society' (van den Berghe, 1967: 7). Sociological theorising on race and racism in the US thus developed around the notion that race relations and the race problem were an outcome of group contact and social interaction. Race was considered a relevant empirical referent only with regard to the extent to which cultural and social meanings were attached to the physical traits of a particular social group. This in turn helped to popularise notions about the origins of racial conflicts and prejudice that concentrated on situations of cultural contact. During these decades the emphasis in sociological studies of the race problem was on the origins of racial prejudice, the interplay between prejudice and conflict, the impact of assimilation on the life of black Americans and the processes through which racial conflicts could be mediated or overcome.

Sociological studies of race relations in a number of other societies were influenced from the beginning by various aspects of the American literature, as well as by the experience of racial differentiation in South Africa. This was certainly the case in Britain, where the study of race was established during the 1940s and 1950s. At that time British studies were dominated by two main themes: the issue of 'coloured immigrants' and the reaction to them by white Britons; and the part played by colonialism in determining popular conceptions of colour and race in British society. Most studies of this period concentrated on the interaction between specific groups of coloured immigrants and whites in local situations. Little theorising was attempted, and writers such as Sheila Patterson and Ruth Glass were in fact critical of attempts to subsume the situation of the black immigrants into generalised categories of race relations (Glass, 1960; Patterson, 1963).

These early studies of race did not actually talk about racism as such. The concept and its usage are linked to the rise of Nazism in Germany. When the Nazis came to power and articulated and put into practice their ideas about racial superiority the term racism was used to refer to the defining of some racial or ethnic groups as superior and others as inferior. This usage of the term was first suggested by Ruth Benedict in her book *Race and Racism*, which defined racism as 'the dogma that one ethnic group is condemned by nature to congenital inferiority and another group is destined to congenital superiority' (Benedict, 1943: 97). In this context racism referred to those sets of ideas that defined ethnic and racial groups on the basis of claims about biological nature and inherent superiority or ability (Jones, 1996).

Since the 1960s heated political and theoretical debates on what we mean by racism have led to what Miles (1989: 41) refers to as a process of 'conceptual inflation', resulting in the term being used to cover disparate sets of ideas and sociopolitical relations. Radical and neo-Marxist researchers have argued that the focus of research needs to be on the dynamics of racism and not on race relations. We shall return to these points later, but first let us look more specifically at the sociological study of race in Britain.

The sociology of race in Britain

Since 1945 a number of developments outside the US have encouraged interest in the study of race and racism in other societies. Perhaps the most important of these developments was the emergence of migrant labourers as an important social group in many West European societies. Migration from the ex-colonies and Southern Europe led to the establishment of racial and ethnic minority communities in countries such as Britain, France, Germany and Holland. Another important development was the entrenchment of the apartheid system in South Africa, a process that aroused the interest of both social scientists and political activists, particularly in relation to the role of the political and legal system in enforcing racial segregation and the 'separate development' of different racial groups.

In Britain and other European societies growing interest in the theorisation of race and racism ran parallel to these developments, resulting in a number of important and sophisticated analyses of the politics and ideology of racism. There were two central concerns in these early European attempts to theorise racial and ethnic relations: the patterns of immigration and labour market incorporation of black and ethnic minorities; and the part played by colonialism in determining popular conceptions of colour, race and ethnicity in European societies.

A number of early studies of what in Britain came to be called 'race relations' were carried out in the 1950s and 1960s by scholars such as Michael Banton, Ruth Glass, John Rex and Sheila Patterson. Most studies of this period concentrated on the interaction between minority and majority communities in employment, housing and other social contexts. What is interesting in hindsight, given the virulence of some of the theoretical debates since the 1980s, is the relative absence of a clear theoretical perspective on (a) what constituted the object of analysis of these specific studies, and (b) the absence of a wider sociopolitical perspective on the interplay between race relations and other kinds of social relations.

By the 1960s, however, there was a noticeable growth of interest in the theoretical study of the new forms of migration and settlement being experienced in Britain and elsewhere and in other types of race relations. Michael Banton's book *Race Relations* is a good example of the texts of this period. It looks at race relations from a global and historical perspective, concentrating particularly on situations of cultural contact, beliefs about the nature of race, and social relations constructed on the basis of racial categories. By looking at the changing patterns of interaction over time, Banton identified six basic orders of race relations: institutionalised contact, acculturation, domination, paternalism, integration and pluralism (Banton, 1967).

During the 1960s what Banton and others called the 'race relations problematic' became the dominant approach in this field (Banton, 1991). Banton quite rightly pointed out that the preoccupation with race relations was reflected both in the research agenda and in public policy. In other words, both social scientists and policy makers were increasingly talking about the need to understand the nature of race relations and deal with racial discrimination in British society. It was perhaps not surprising, therefore, that the 1969 conference of the British Sociological Association took as its theme 'The Sociology of Race and Racialism', with the explicit aim of encouraging the sociological study of race relations (Zubaida, 1970).

It was at that time that John Rex's influential text *Race Relations in Sociological Theory* first appeared; it remains one of the most ambitious attempts to provide a theoretical grounding for research in this field. According to Rex's analytic model the definition of social relations between persons as race relations is encouraged by the existence of certain structural conditions: frontier situations of conflict over scarce resources, the existence of unfree, indentured or slave labour, unusually harsh class exploitation, strict legal intergroup distinctions and occupational segregation, differential access to power and prestige, cultural diversity and limited group interaction, and migrant labour as an underclass playing stigmatised roles in a metropolitan setting. He defines the field of race relations in the following terms:

> Race relations situations and problems have the following characteristics: they refer to situations in which two or more groups with distinct identities and recognisable characteristics are forced by economic and political circumstances to live together in a society. Within this they refer to situations in which there is a high degree of conflict between the groups and in which ascriptive criteria are used to mark out the members of each group in order that one group may pursue one of a number of hostile policies against the other. Finally, within this group of situations true race relations may be said to exist when the practices of ascriptive allocation of roles and rights referred to are justified in terms of some kind of deterministic theory, whether that theory be of a scientific, religious, cultural, historical, ideological or sociological kind (Rex, 1983: 159–60).

From this perspective the study of race relations is concerned with situations in which structured conditions interact with actors' definitions in such a way as to produce a racially structured social reality.

When developing his empirical work Rex was particularly interested in two fundamental questions: the extent to which black immigrants were incorporated into welfare state institutions and enjoyed equal access to housing, education and employment; and the consequences of racial inequality for the development of a 'racialised' consciousness among both the white and the black working class. These questions formed the basis of his studies of Sparkbrook and Handsworth, and of his work on general aspects of race relations policies (Rex and Moore, 1967; Rex and Tomlinson, 1979).

Other attempts were made during the late 1960s and 1970s to develop a generalised sociological framework for the analysis of race and racism. Spurred on by the increasing politicisation of racial issues in the US, Britain and elsewhere, a mass of sociological theorising, monographs and case studies was produced during this period and British sociologists began to show serious interest in the subject, both as it concerned Britain and as a global phenomenon.

These concerns were articulated clearly by Rex in two studies of race relations in Birmingham during the 1960s and the 1970s. In the study conducted by Rex and his associates in Handsworth during the mid 1970s (Rex and Tomlinson, 1979) the aim was to explore the degree to which immigrant populations shared the class position of their white neighbours and white workers in general. Their analysis outlines a class structure in which white workers had been granted certain rights won by the working class movement via trade unions and the Labour Party. The result was the establishment, in the 1970s, of a state of class truce between white workers and dominant social groups. Immigrant workers and their children were excluded from this truce and experienced discrimination in all the areas where the white workers had made significant gains, that is, employment, education and housing. It follows from this that immigrant workers were placed outside the working class as an 'underclass':

> The concept of underclass was intended to suggest… that the minorities were systematically at a disadvantage compared with their white peers and that, instead of identifying with working class culture, community and politics, they formed their own organisations and became effectively a separate underprivileged class (Rex and Tomlinson, ibid.: 275).

From this point Rex and Tomlinson developed a model of political action and even a political agenda for black populations as they had become a 'class for themselves'. Immigrant minorities were forced into a series of reactive/defensive political strategies. This process took different forms in the Asian and the West Indian communities. In Asian communities it resulted in concentration on capital accumulation and social mobility. In the West Indian community it took the form of complete withdrawal from competition and the construction of a black identity. This led to what Rex has referred to elsewhere as the 'politics of defensive confrontation' (Rex, 1979).

The work of both Banton and Rex therefore helped, though from rather different starting points, to establish the study of race relations in the social sciences during the 1960s and 1970s. They also helped to institutionalise research on race relations by running, at different stages, the major British research centre in this field.

Politics, power and racism

With a few notable exceptions most studies of race relations in Britain during the 1950s and 1960s did not analyse questions of power and politics in any detail. Zubaida wrote in 1972 of the atheoretical and ahistorical nature of many sociological studies of race relations, which led authors to ignore the political context of political parties, trade unions, local and central government in their analyses:

> In spite of the great importance of this issue, this political area of race relations appears to be little researched at any significant level. There is a plethora of studies… which are concerned with 'attitudes', 'prejudice'

> and 'discrimination'. They are remarkably uninformative; for the most part, they tell us about the relative readiness of sections of the population to subscribe to one set of verbal formula rather than another. What we need are studies of the way the race relations issues enter into the structures, strategies and ideologies of political parties and trade unions and governmental bodies (Zubaida, 1972: 141).

Authors such as Rex did raise the issue of politics and power, but it remained a secondary consideration in mainstream sociological studies of race relations. Moreover few of the influential authors of this period analysed the political context that helped structure the meanings attached to race and racism. At a descriptive level some of the issues that Zubaida raised were considered, but they were not integrated into the wider conceptual debates on the theory of racism or into the analysis of processes of racialisation in contemporary Britain.

This relative neglect of the political dimension of racial issues continued well into the 1970s and 1980s, and was heightened by the relative absence of racial questions from the agenda of both radical and mainstream political science during this period. Dominant approaches within political science concentrated almost entirely on the class and status determinants of political ideology and behaviour in the belief that the logic of politics in advanced capitalist societies sprang from the nature of the social structure. Issues such as gender, race, environmental policy and novel forms of political organisation received relatively little attention, and even then they were generally added on to existing analytic models. This neglect is even more noticeable when compared with the voluminous literature on the sociology of race relations and the social anthropology of immigrant communities, fields of study that have expanded greatly since the early 1970s.

What is also clear is that the focus of those texts which have looked at the politics of race has been limited to just a few aspects of the integration of black minorities into established political institutions. Since the 1970s these issues have received some attention, although not always from a political science perspective, and have led to a small but growing body of literature on each subject. Many of the questions asked in these studies have related narrowly to the role of political parties, parliament and interest groups. The preoccupation of much of the literature on British politics with what John Dearlove and Peter Saunders (1991: 3–4) call a 'narrow view of politics and power' has thus been reproduced in the literature on the politics of racism.

In works produced since the early 1960s surprisingly little attention has been paid to the substance of state interventions in this area and who has benefited from them; the causes of changes in ideology and policy; the interrelationship between policy changes in the racial sphere and other areas of economic, social and welfare policy; and, perhaps more importantly, mediations between state and society that have brought about changes in political and ideological relations.

The relative absence of race from the agenda of mainstream political analysis needs to be set against a number of factors. As a number of writers have pointed out (Coates, 1984; Moran, 1985; Leys, 1989), in Britain political science has developed along conventional lines and often has not linked up directly with the changing realities of political life. Dearlove has pointed out that, unlike most other social science disciplines, British political science was left largely untouched by the intellectual unrest of the 1960s. It was only in the acute economic, social and ideological crisis of the 1970s, which resulted in a period of soul searching and critical self-evaluation among political scientists, that the discipline experienced the intellectual turmoil and strife that other disciplines had experienced during the 1960s. It was this turmoil that led to a strong feeling among many political scientists that 'the established discourse is no longer an adequate basis for understanding contemporary British politics' (Dearlove, 1982: 437), and to a lively debate on the theoretical and empirical basis for the study of the political context of economic, social and political inequalities.

From this account of the development of postwar political science it is possible to begin to make sense of how the encounter with race was dealt with, an encounter that broadly covered the two terms of Dearlove's periodisation. During the 1960s and early 1970s the political study of racism remained underdeveloped, particularly when compared with the massive growth of the sociology of race relations over the same period. Having produced little in the way of textbooks and monographic studies during the previous two decades, the political science approach to race issues was boosted by the growing political impact of the National Front during the late 1970s and the series of violent protests that took place during 1980–1 and 1985. With the break-up of what Dearlove has called the established understandings of British political life, issues such as gender and race began to receive more serious attention from mainstream political scientists, even if only at the margins of established political issues such as inner city policy and unemployment.

A number of sociological and neo-Marxist writings on racism provide a useful starting point for rethinking the relationship between race, power relations and political structures (Gilroy, 1987; Omi and Winant, 1994), although there are few analytically clear studies of this aspect of racism. During the 1960s and 1970s some studies of voting behaviour, immigration and race relations legislation were carried out within the framework of political science, but few of them became part of the teaching syllabus in politics departments or attracted the attention of non-race specialists, whether in the mainstream or in the radical sections of the discipline. This gap has been bridged in recent years by the attention given to questions of race and ethnicity in debates on political theory.

Since the early 1990s new avenues of research have been opened up by a number of scholars whose work focuses on forms of political mobilisation and participation. Some of this research has been conducted at a comparative analytical level and looks at the role of racial politics in different nation states (Goldberg, 1993, 2002). Such research situates race and racism within a specifically political analysis of power and considers how the latter reproduces ethnoracial domination in particular societies. Other studies have focused on the working out of racial ideologies and everyday ideas on race within political parties (Solomos and Back, 1995), the role of race in electoral politics (Saggar, 1998b, 2000) and the growth of racist movements and political parties (Cheles *et al.*, 1995).

Studies such as these have made important contributions to the political analysis of racism in contemporary Britain, but there remain many gaps and these can only be filled by integrating the findings of the studies referred to above into a theoretically rigorous and empirically grounded political analysis of racism. However a theoretical and empirical clarification of the roots of racism has not been forthcoming. Indeed racism remains a sadly neglected issue in most discussions of British politics, even in those which are influenced by radical and feminist ideas. This is despite the attention given to this issue in other disciplines.

Analysis of the politics of racism is far more developed in the US, where social scientists from a number of disciplinary backgrounds have provided detailed historical accounts of race-related political issues. The race riots of the 1960s, the civil rights movement, the black power movement and the emergence of a black political elite have all been issues of concern not only for political scientists but also for sociologists and economists. In addition, numerous historical and contemporary case studies of the political context of racism and racial ideologies have done much to illuminate the political dilemmas faced by American blacks.

Manning Marable (1981) attributes this emphasis on the politics of racism to a number of factors, but he draws particular attention to the stress that both black and radical white intellectuals put on the part played by politics in determining the social and economic position of blacks in American society. He also cites the riots of the 1960s as an important source of research on political power and powerlessness in relation to racism. A number of other American studies have highlighted similar processes, albeit from divergent analytical perspectives (Preston *et al.*, 1982; McAdam, 1982).

It is also worth mentioning that a number of writers on race issues in Britain have been American, most notably Ira Katznelson (1976), Donley Studlar (1978, 1980), David Kirp (1979) and Anthony Messina (1985, 1987, 1989), who have used their knowledge of events in the US to analyse the British experience, and sometimes to theorise about the similarities and differences between the two situations. Katznelson provides examples of the comparisons that can be made between the British and the American situation, as well as a powerful analysis of the interplay between politics and social change in the formation of racialised politics (Katznelson, 1976: xxii–xxiv).

Critiques of the race relations problematic

Since the 1980s a number of radical critiques of research on race and ethnicity have emerged, influenced in the main by neo-Marxist, feminist and post-Marxist thought. Indeed for some commentators these approaches have now become the dominant approach to the study of race and racism in Britain (Hansen, 2000b). Although it is by no means clear that this is the case in practice, there can be little doubt that much of the most lively and challenging scholarship in this field in the past two decades has been inspired in one way or another by a concern to produce a radical alternative to existing models of racial and ethnic conflict.

Marxist discussion of the relationship between class relations and social differentiation based on racial and ethnic categories has been intense since the 1970s. This certainly contradicts the oft-cited argument that the preferred response of Marxists to non-class forms of social division is either silence or an attempt to force a complex reality into narrow and deterministic models. But what advances have been made through these debates? To what extent have the problems encountered been due to a failure to move beyond economistic interpretations of class?

The early 1980s saw the emergence of a number of substantial criticisms of research on race relations, written largely from a Marxist perspective. Such criticisms were influenced by both theoretical and political considerations, and they helped to stimulate new areas of debate that to some extent continue to this day. A number of key questions dominated these debates. First, there was the question of Marx's and Engels' views on the subject, or rather their supposed failure to analyse it systematically. Second, there was the problem of how Marxist concepts of class could help us to understand the dynamics of societies structured by racial and ethnic categorisation. Third, there was the question of how Marxist debates on ideology, hegemony and overdetermination could help us to understand the development of racism as an ideological force in contemporary societies. Fourth, there was the question of how debates on the class position of women and on sexism interlinked with the analysis of race. Finally, a lively discussion took place on the allegedly Eurocentric bias of Marxist theory.

The starting point of the majority of Marxist studies of the dynamics of race and class is that classical Marxism provides no systematic treatment of this question. It has been pointed out, for example, that although the works of Marx and Engels contain a number of scattered references to the pertinence of racial and ethnic relations in certain social formations, for example there is a reference to race as an economic factor in slavery in the US, they contain little historical or theoretical reflection on the role of such relations in the capitalist mode of production as a whole. Perhaps even more damaging, a number of critics have argued that several statements on race by Marx and Engels reveal traces of the dominant racial stereotypes of their time and an uncritical usage of racist imagery (Robinson, 1983). In addition a number of critics have argued that Marxists' reliance on the concept of class has precluded them from analysing racial and ethnic phenomena in their own right, short of subsuming them into wider social relations or treating them as a kind of superstructural phenomenon (Parkin, 1979; Banton, 1983).

In the writings of Marx and Engels the references to racial and ethnic divisions, along with the related issues of religious differences, regional identity and nationality, are organised around two central themes. The first is the question of internal divisions within the working class. A good example of this is the division caused by the Irish workers who migrated to England and Scotland in search of employment. Both Marx and Engels commented at various points in their work on the impact of this division upon the consciousness of the English working class and the manner in which it was perpetuated. The second theme is the question of nationalism and national identity. Marx and Engels drew frequent attention to the significance of national identity and its interrelationship with class relations. For example they highlighted the effect that the development of Irish nationalism had on the consciousness of the English proletariat, and later they came to perceive the development of a nationalist movement in Ireland as essential to the emergence of a strong labour movement in England. Their historical works are suffused with references to the emergence, development or demise of nationalities. The analysis provided is by no means as detailed as it might have been, but it does allow us to address the fact that Marx and Engels were silent on extra-class differentiation, and it provided the basis for later Marxists to analyse nationalism and racism within the working class.

Early Marxist work on racial and ethnic divisions concentrated particularly on race and class as modes of exploitation. Oliver Cox's *Caste, Class and Race* (1948) is an early example of this. Cox was primarily interested in the historical economic interests that produced racist exploitation and ideologies, and he explained racial inequality as an outcome of the interest of the capitalist class in heavily exploiting sections of the working class. Since he saw class divisions as the fundamental source of exploitation in society, the main thrust of his work was to conceptualise racial exploitation as a special form of class exploitation. This model was subsequently to have a deep influence on the work of Marxist writers on race in the US, and to a more limited extent in European and other countries.

New life was breathed into this question during the 1960s, mainly as a result of the regeneration of Marxist debates on class and historical materialism that sought to transcend economic reductionism, and partly because of increasing political awareness that contemporary racial inequalities were being reproduced in a complex manner that could not be reduced to economistic notions of class. This rethinking of class theory and the historical context of race–class relations is evident in new research on slavery in the US, studies of racism and labour market segmentation, the analysis of state racism in South Africa and the large body of work on the economics of migrant labour.

A number of major themes have emerged from this large body of research and historical writing since the 1960s. These include: (a) the autonomy of racism from class relations; (b) the role of the state and political institutions in respect of racial and ethnic issues; (c) the impact of racism on the structure of the working class and the dynamics of class struggle and political organisation; and (d) the processes through which racist ideologies are produced and reproduced.

The question of the autonomy of race from class brought in theoretical questions that had been posed in the analysis of class formation and the capitalist state by radical and neo-Marxist writers. The particular focus of these writers was the interplay between class forces and political strategies (Jessop, 1982; Evans *et al.*, 1985; Alford and Friedland, 1985; Dunleavy and O'Leary, 1987), but in recent years some attempt has been made to utilise the insights of these studies to analyse the politics of racism in Britain and elsewhere.

One of the first attempts to provide a theoretical critique of the approaches of both Banton and Rex was made by Robert Miles during the 1980s. The starting point for Miles's critique was his opposition to the existence of a sociology of race, and his view that the object of analysis should be racism, which he saw as integral to the process of capital accumulation (Miles, 1982, 1986). His analysis was first articulated in *Racism and*

Migrant Labour (1982) and it was perhaps the most sustained attempt to bring the study of racism into the mainstream of Marxist social theory. His empirical research focused on the situation in Britain and the rest of Europe, and looked at the part played by political, class and ideological relationships in shaping our understanding of racial conflict and change in these societies.

For Miles, 'race' is a human construct, an ideology with regulatory power in society. Analytically race constitutes a paper tiger (Miles, 1988), in that it may be a common term of reference in everyday discourse but it presents a serious theoretical problem. It is here that Miles diverges from what he sees as the race relations problematic. While Rex was concerned with models of social action (that is, for Rex it was enough that race was utilised in everyday discourse as a basis for social action) Miles is concerned with the analytical and objective status of race as a basis for action (Miles, 1982: 42). Race is thus an ideological effect, a mask that hides real economic relationships (Miles, 1984). Hence the forms of class consciousness that are legitimate for Miles must ultimately be reduced to economic relations that are hidden within the regulatory process of racialisation.

For Miles the process of racialisation is connected to migrant labour in that it is the result of the contradiction between 'on the one hand the need of the capitalist world economy for the mobility of human beings, and on the other, the drawing of territorial boundaries and the construction of citizenship as a legal category which sets boundaries for human mobility' (Miles, 1988: 438). In the British setting this ideological work, conducted primarily by the state, acts as a means of crisis management and results in the racialisation of fragments of the working class. Race politics are thus confined to the forces of regulation. For Miles the construction of political identities that utilise racial consciousness plays no part in the development of progressive politics.

While Miles' work does have limitations, he raises some important questions about the nature of political action within communities of migrant labourers. The most important of these is the degree to which black and minority politics are really distillations of class conflict. If this is true, any movement away from class-based political action (that is, movement towards black community politics) are doomed to failure (Miles, 1988, 1989). If one takes this argument further, class-based political action is ultimately in opposition to any sort of sustained political organisation around a notion of race. For Miles the politics of race is narrowly confined to the struggle against racism. This is neatly captured in the way he uses Hall's (1980: 341) statement on the relationship between class and race. He concludes that it is not race but racism that is the modality in which class is lived and fought through (Miles, 1988: 447).

Another influential critique of the sociology of race in the early 1980s came from the Centre for Contemporary Cultural Studies (CCCS) in Birmingham. The CCCS Race and Politics Group was particularly concerned with the changing nature of the politics of race during the 1970s and the development of new forms of racial ideology. The theoretical approach of the group was strongly influenced by the work of Stuart Hall (1980) and they were critical of the arguments put forward by the sociologists of race and by Miles.

The work conducted by the group led to the publication of *The Empire Strikes Back* (CCCS, 1982), which attracted widespread attention at the time and still remains a point of reference in current debates. Two of the contributors to this volume subsequently attempted to develop substantive studies from it (Gilroy, 1987, 1993; Solomos, 1988). A major concern of the group was the need to analyse the complex processes by which race is constructed as a social and political relation. They emphasised that the concept of race is not simply confined to a process of regulation operated by the state but that the meaning of race as a social construction is contested and fought over. In this sense they viewed race as an open political construction where the meaning of terms such as black are struggled over. Collective identities spoken through race, community and locality are, for all their spontaneity, powerful means to coordinate action and create solidarity.

Within this model of political action a multiplicity of political identities can be contained. An inclusive notion of black identity can prevail while at the same time allowing heterogeneity of national and cultural origins within minority communities (Gilroy, 1987: 236). For Gilroy the crucial question here is the extent to which notions of race can be reforged into a political movement of opposition. He holds little hope that this process can be developed within the arena of representative democracy. Instead the way forward is by means of pressure group strategies that have evolved out of community struggles and that utilise a specifically black political vernacular.

A number of studies emanating from the US during the early 1980s also took as their starting point the interrelationship between relations of politics, power and racism. The most influential of these was Michael Omi and Howard Winant's study of the processes of 'race formation' in the US. They placed particular emphasis on the part played by political and legal relations in defining the existence of racial categories and defining the social meanings of notions such as racial inequality, racism and ethnicity (Omi and Winant, 1994).

This theme has been taken up in studies of the situation of ethnic minorities in Europe in the past two decades. These studies have looked particularly at the processes by which minority communities and migrant workers are often excluded from access to political institutions and are denied basic social and economic rights. It is interesting to note in this context that in countries such as Germany and France a key question in current political conflicts is whether migrant workers should be given greater political rights.

In Britain, where the position of black and ethnic minority people is somewhat different from in the rest of Europe, a key concern of a number of studies of the politics of race is the need to conceive of racialisation as a process that has specific effects on politics and ideology. Aspects of this process include the impact of racist ideologies and nationalist discourses antiracist discourses and minority political action on political institutions and political mobilisation.

It is in this context that the concepts of racial categorisation and racialisation have been used to refer to what Robert Miles (1989) calls 'those instances where social relations between people have been structured by the signification of human biological characteristics in such a way as to define and construct differentiated social collectivities'. A number of writers have used these concepts to analyse the processes by which race has been socially and politically constructed in specific historical, political and institutional contexts.

Good examples of such studies include critical analyses of the role of race relations legislation, the emergence of minority representation in political institutions and the development of public policies dealing with specific aspects of racial inequality in areas such as employment and housing. The premise of such studies is that the processes by which race is given particular meanings vary across and within national boundaries and are shaped by political, legal and socioeconomic environments. Comparative studies of immigration policies in Europe have, for example, shown that the drafting of legislation to control the arrival of specific groups of migrants has often been the subject of intense political and ideological controversy.

Culture, community and identity

The debates that developed during the 1980s are still going on and they continue to influence research agendas (Back and Solomos, 1993; Rattansi and Westwood, 1994; Back and Solomos, 2000). But in the past few years we have seen the emergence of new perspectives that go beyond the terms of these debates. The new contributions engage in one way or another, for example, with the arguments of poststructuralism and postmodernism and the need to avoid uniform and homogeneous conceptualisations of racism.

Although not yet part of the agenda of mainstream research on race relations, a range of studies of racialised discourses in the mass media, literature, art and other forms of culture have begun to be produced. There is a growing body of work on the use of race as a symbol in various areas of cultural expression and experience. In response to the perceived lack of an account of cultural forms of racial discourse, a number of writers have sought to develop a more rounded picture of contemporary racial imagery by looking at the different ways in which literature, the popular media and other forms of cultural expression represent race and ethnicity.

As David Goldberg has pointed out, 'the presumption of a single monolithic racism is being displaced by a mapping of the multifarious historical formulations of *racisms*' (Goldberg, 1990b). In this context it is perhaps not surprising that the aim of many texts in this field is to explore the interconnections between race and nationhood, patriotism and nationalism rather than to analyse the idea of biological inferiority. Clear examples of this trend are the growing number of studies that have looked at the role of political interventions in shaping race relations in specific national settings. This has led to growing interest in the development of racist ideologies and the various forms that such ideologies have taken at different stages of their development. Although this issue received little attention from scholars in the past, the recent interest in the analysis of culture and discourse has helped to overcome this neglect and questions have begun to be asked about the historical, cultural, literary and philosophical roots of ideologies of race. Specifically, questions are being asked about how ideological relations can provide a basis for the articulation of racist discourses and practices.

The part played by the press and other popular media in shaping public images of racial and ethnic minorities has been a particular focus. For example a number of detailed studies have looked at how press coverage of racial questions can help to construct an image of racial minorities as outsiders and as a threat to social cohesion. One interesting example of this process was the furore over Salman Rushdie's *The Satanic Verses* and the response of some Muslim political leaders and community organisations to its publication. The attempt by a number of Muslim community leaders to use the affair as a means of political mobilisation received wide coverage in the media and led to a wide-ranging debate on the future of race relations in Britain. Sections of the press used the events surrounding the affair to question the possibility of a peaceful transition towards a multiracial society. Hostile media coverage thus served to reinforce the view that minorities who did not share the dominant political values of British society posed a threat to social stability and cohesion. The affair also gave added impetus to debates on the numerous cultural and political identities that had been included in the broad categorisation of 'black and ethnic minority communities'. This is an issue to which we shall return in Chapters 10 and 12.

Another focus has been the use of race and ethnicity as symbols in a variety of cultural forms, including literature and the cinema. The past neglect of this area of research has been remedied in recent years by the publication of a number of important studies of race, culture and identity. Originating largely in the US, such studies have looked at literature, the cinema and other forms of popular culture in order to show that in contemporary societies the understanding of race, and the articulation of racist ideologies, cannot be reduced to economic, political or class relations (Essed and Goldberg, 2002; Goldberg and Solomos, 2002).

This type of approach is in fact more evident outside sociology. Literary and cultural theorists in the US and Britain have begun seriously to explore the question of race and racism, leading to a flowering of studies that use debates on post-structuralism and postmodernism as a way of approaching the complex forms of racialised identities in colonial and postcolonial societies (Gates, 1986, 1988; Goldberg, 1990a, 1992; Bhavnani and Phoenix, 1994).

Perhaps as a result of broader transformations in social theory this area of research has developed rapidly in recent years. Apart from studies of contemporary trends there has also been a growth of historical research on ideas about race and the dynamics of race, class and gender during the colonial period. This has resulted in important and valuable accounts of the changing use of racial symbols during the past few centuries, and in accounts of the experiences of colonialism and their impact on our understanding of race and culture. For example Gayatri Spivak (1987) has highlighted the complex processes of racial and gender identification experienced by the colonised during the colonial and postcolonial periods (see also, Bhavnani and Phoenix, 1994; Bhavnani, 2001). Other studies have shown that the oppressed produced their own discourses on race and identity in the context of their own experiences of domination and exclusion (Bhabha, 1990a; Young, 1990; Goldberg, 1993; Appiah and Gutmann, 1996).

New ethnicities and the politics of difference

Given the critical tone of the above discussion of the existing approaches to the study of race and racism in contemporary Britain, the question arises as to what kind of alternative analysis will be offered in this book. There are in fact two basic elements that make up the distinctive contribution offered here to the study of the politics of racism. The first is an insistence on the need to look at the impact of racism on politics and ideology in contemporary Britain beyond the bounds of conventional social science. The second is a detailed analysis of the impact of racist ideologies and nationalist discourses, antiracist discourses, and minority political action on political institutions and political mobilisation. Since the 1950s political discourses on race and nation have become a central component of British political culture, a phenomenon that will only be partially understood if one looks merely at the role of extreme right-wing groups or the ideologies of the new right. Much more central, and of vital importance to future political change, are the complex interrelationships of power that are represented in the political language of race.

It is not the aim of this book to provide a detailed analysis of all the issues raised, since the main channel for a historical and multidimensional conception of the politics of racism must be critical and reflective debate among scholars, researchers and practitioners. There are areas of the political analysis of racism that still have to be analysed and yet others that need to be understood more fully. But such work must be part of a larger project that aims to comprehend the 'concrete historical work which racism accomplishes under specific historical conditions – as a set of economic, political and ideological practices' (Hall, 1980: 338–42).

Although much of the work on the analysis of contemporary forms of race and racism can be seen as contributing to such an understanding, there are a number of areas that need to be analysed more fully, including (a) the politicisation of racism from the postwar conjuncture to the growth of Powellism and the institutionalisation of racist discourse; (b) the growth of popular racism and its relationship to the broader economic and legitimation crisis of the British state; (c) the part played by black and ethnic minority politics in redefining the terms of political discourse on race; and (d) the politics of policing and disorderly protest in relation to minority communities and their environment.

A number of studies have addressed these issues in some form or other. For example some scholars have analysed the racialisation of British political culture since 1945 as an outcome of the complex intermingling of economic, political and ideological relations (Miles and Phizacklea, 1984; Tabili, 1994; Paul, 1997). From a more conventional angle, others have provided a detailed historical narrative of the politics of race, particularly in relation to party politics and electoral strategies (Layton-Henry, 1984; Saggar, 1992, 2000). More recently a number of studies have explored the differences and similarities between the responses of various West European societies to immigration and the development of racial and ethnic minority communities (Freeman, 1979; Soysal, 1994; Castles and Miller, 1998; Joppke, 1999). Other studies have analysed black and ethnic minority political mobilisation through mainstream political parties and in relation to specific policy issues (FitzGerald, 1984; Anwar, 1986; Jacobs, 1986; Sewell,

1993; Adolino, 1998; Shukra, 1998). More provocatively, and perhaps too abstractly, some authors have talked of the emergence of a new racism, which is defined by the way it mobilises notions of culture and nation to construct a definition of the British nation that excludes those of a different cultural, ethnic or racial background from the national collectivity (Barker, 1981; CCCS Race and Politics Group, 1982; Reeves, 1983; Miles and Phizacklea, 1984; Gilroy, 1987, 1998).

By and large, however, few of these studies have addressed two core questions in any detail. The first of these questions focuses on the general characteristics of racism in British society and asks: how do political structures and institutions in Britain function in relation to race and in what ways do they produce/reproduce or help overcome racism? The second points to a related but more concrete set of concerns about how racism is formed and transformed historically, asking: how does racism shape the ways in which class, gender and other social relations are actually experienced and how do they structure political action? These key questions will be addressed in the chapters that follow, providing a starting point from which to explore the ways in which political and social processes have helped to shape our understandings of race and racism in contemporary British society. This will be followed by a critical analysis of the racialisation of political life and public debate at specific points in British history, and of state interventions to manage both immigration and race relations.

Summary and conclusion

The past six decades have seen important developments in the study of racial and ethnic issues in Britain. Over this period the politics of race and racism have undergone numerous transformations, some of which have hardly begun to be discussed. No one theoretical perspective is dominant at present. Indeed little of the mainstream research in this field is theoretically informed in any substantial way. Hence there is a need for greater theoretical clarity on key concepts and a broadening of the research agenda to cover issues that have been neglected, such as the politics of culture and identity. In this sense Banton (1991) may well be right to contend that different theoretical paradigms can contribute their own distinctive understandings of how specific meanings are attributed to racial situations.

It is clear that we are a long way from resolving many of the theoretical problems that have preoccupied writers. It also has to be admitted that there are real problems in trying to make sense of the constructions of race that are to be found in particular discursive fields. This is something I have discussed elsewhere in relation to my research on the changing dynamics of race and politics in Birmingham (Back and Solomos, 1992b; Solomos and Back, 1995). These conceptual dilemmas will not be resolved if we retreat into ever more complex forms of theorising and concept formation. There is a need to combine theoretical debate with detailed historical and empirical research, particularly at a time when many of the assumptions about race and racism in contemporary societies have been challenged.

What is interesting is that although many writers argue against the use of race as an analytic category in social analysis, their own accounts are bedevilled by the paradox that ideas on race continue to pervade social, political and cultural relations. The problem that has preoccupied many writers is how to establish the epistemological validity and causal power of racialisation and race formation without endorsing everyday ideological discourses. A number of writers have attempted to use these concepts to analyse the processes by which race has been socially and politically constructed in specific historical, political and institutional contexts. A key concern of these studies is the need to develop a dialectical view of racialisation as a process that has specific effects on politics and ideology. Aspects of this process include the impact of racist ideologies and nationalist discourses, antiracist discourses, and black political action on political institutions and political mobilisation.

Against this background of intense theoretical debate it should be evident that the study of race and racism has clear political consequences, whether intended or not. Any analysis of this issue must therefore have a clear theoretical understanding of the questions to be asked, the methods to be used and the political climate in which the research is to be carried out. This is precisely what this chapter has attempted to do. Many of the conceptual dilemmas it has raised will be revisited in subsequent chapters when analysing specific processes and issues.

2 Historical Background and Context

This chapter covers a feature of race and racism that is inadequately addressed in many texts about contemporary British society, namely the role that earlier processes of migration and settlement played in shaping our understanding of this issue. The focus is specifically on debates on race and immigration in the late nineteenth century and into the early part of the twentieth century. This is necessary because it is impossible to comprehend fully the politicisation of racial questions in Britain since 1945 without a historical perspective, despite the tendency of many recent studies to ignore this dimension.

We shall examine three particular aspects of this historical background: (a) the history of and political response to Irish immigration; (b) the politics of Jewish immigration; and (c) the history of the migration of black and other colonial peoples to Britain, particularly in the early twentieth century. These three aspects can be linked directly to the politics of race and immigration since 1945. All three are deserving of detailed analysis, and indeed some important work on the history of these issues has already been carried out. A number of interesting overviews of the major migratory processes since the nineteenth century can be found in the work of a number of historians who have begun to uncover the hidden history of immigration from the late nineteenth century to the Second World War (Holmes, 1988; Panayi, 1999; Walvin, 1999). The history of black settlement in Britain is analysed in some detail in Peter Fryer's *Staying Power* (1984), which contains a wealth of original sources (see also Gerzina, 1995).

Other aspects are being addressed in the growing and rich body of literature on the history of immigration and on the social and political processes that have shaped the construction of 'Britishness' over the past two centuries (Holmes, 1988; Samuel, 1989a; Colley, 1992; Lindeborg, 1994; Schwarz, 1996; Matar, 1999). Much of the research on these and related questions has highlighted the historically contingent and contradictory forces that have shaped popular notions of Britishness and Englishness, and their interactions with the notions of race and empire in British political life (Rich, 1986).

The historical context of racism in Britain

In line with the arguments developed in the previous chapter, an understanding of the processes that produce and reproduce social distinctions based on racial and ethnic divisions requires an analysis of both the historical context and contemporary social relations. Only by analysing the way in which historical experience overlaps the present is it possible to understand the continuities and discontinuities between current racial ideologies and previous forms.

There is a rich body of comparative literature on the complex forms that racial ideologies and structures have taken in different societies over time and space (Greenberg, 1980; Fredrickson, 1981; Wolf, 1982). These works include studies of the development of racial ideologies and institutions in the US and South Africa, the two situations that have attracted the most attention over the years. But attention is increasingly turning to the history of racial categorisation in other societies, and comparative research is being broadened to include the situation in countries such as Britain.

It is clear that much of the analysis of race relations in Britain since 1945 has been dominated by perspectives that lack both a historical and a comparative dimension. There are, of course, some notable exceptions to this trend, and a number of useful monographs have analysed the complex history of racial thought, of immigration and of anti-Semitic and other racist political trends in Britain (Holmes, 1978, 1979; Lunn, 1980; Fryer, 1984). Such studies have highlighted two interrelated issues: the complex variety of migratory processes that have occurred at various times in British history; and the continuities and discontinuities between the political and social responses to these waves of immigration. Other studies have focused on the part played by colonialism in shaping popular ideas about race, class and national identity in British society (Coombes, 1994; McClintock, 1995; Parry, 1998; Parsons, 1998).

As argued in Chapter 1, however, the relative neglect of racial and ethnic issues in the study of British politics has hindered the development of a detailed political analysis of migration and racial categorisation. Thus while in the past decade there has been a growth of interest in analysing contemporary political conflicts over race, particularly in the aftermath of the urban unrest of the 1980s, this has not resulted in rigorous attempts to analyse the main trends in the historical development of racism in Britain.

Anglo-Saxons and Celts

Irish migration to Britain and the political responses to it are important but often ignored aspects of the historical background to current debates on race and immigration. The issue of Irish immigration is usually considered separately from other migrations since, in the words of James Walvin (1984: 48–60), it is seen as a special case. More specifically, the theoretical work by Bob Miles (1982: 121–50) on migrants has served to emphasise the historical importance of Irish immigration and its relevance to any rounded political analysis of this issue. A number of detailed historical studies of migration from Ireland to Britain and the responses to it have helped to focus more attention on this question (Gilley, 1978, 1980; Curtis, 1984; Swift and Gilley, 1985).

The history of Irish migration to Britain can be traced back to the late eighteenth and early nineteenth centuries (Hechter, 1975; MacRaild, 1999), a period of important economic and social change in both Ireland and Britain. During that time the migration of Irish labourers to Britain seems to have been largely determined by the interdependence of the two societies and the pace of economic and social transformation within them. The genesis of Irish immigration was therefore connected to economic change, urbanisation and class formation in British society. According to Miles (1982: 121–50) it was precisely this process of rapid social change that led to a demand in Britain for labour and a search for new sources of labour.

Meanwhile in Ireland, land consolidation was being carried out in the north and east as part of the process of developing capitalist agriculture (Hechter, 1975; Redford, 1976). The objective was to produce grain, meat and dairy products as commodities for exchange in Britain, but the consequence for many of the people of these regions was dispossession and ejection from the land. In the south and west, which were predominantly populated by small peasant landowners and small tenant producers, the extensive subdivision of plots was underway at a time when the population was increasing and the potato had been introduced as the main crop and means of subsistence. The consequent freeing of sections of the population from the land coincided with attempts to establish capitalist industrial production in Ireland, especially around Belfast, where the demand for labour was growing. Following the Act of Union and the subsequent abolition of protective tariffs in Ireland, the development of capitalist agriculture was intensified while the flow of cheap manufactured goods from Britain stemmed the rise of industrial production in Ireland (Miles, 1982; Swift and Gilley, 1985).

During this early period Irish migration to Britain tended to be seasonal, especially on the part of small peasant producers who sought a cash income to meet increasing rent demands. The potato was planted early in the year and then the men of the family travelled to Britain to sell their labour to British farmers, especially during harvesting (Jackson, 1963; Lees, 1979). In 1841 approximately 60 000 seasonal migrants came to Britain from Ireland, but the numbers declined from the 1850s even though the demand for their labour remained high in certain areas. However seasonal migration was only a serious option for those with permanent access to land in Ireland, and the growing demand for semi- and unskilled labourers in British urban areas resulted in landless Irish migrants settling in Britain.

The outbreak of potato blight in 1845 and the resulting starvation intensified a migration that was already well-established (Jackson, 1963: 7–9). The 1841 census indicated that there were more than 289 404 Irish people living in England and Wales and 126 321 in Scotland. By the time of the 1851 census, largely as a consequence of the famine, the Irish population had increased to 519 959 in England and Wales and 207 367 in Scotland. The peak was evident in the 1861 census, which put the Irish-born population resident in England and Wales at 601 634, although in Scotland it had declined somewhat to 204 083. Thereafter there was a slow decline. In 1901 the Irish-born population was 426 565 in England and Wales, and 205 064 in Scotland (Holmes, 1988: 20–1). As a proportion of the total population, in 1851 Irish people comprised 2.9 per cent of the population of England and Wales and 7.2 per cent of that of Scotland (Jackson, 1963: 11).

In England the main areas of Irish settlement were London and Lancashire, with smaller concentrations in the West Midlands and Yorkshire (Jackson, 1963; Lees, 1979; Gilley, 1980; Waller, 1981; Miles, 1982; Swift and Gilley, 1985). In Scotland the main areas of settlement were in the west, particularly around Glasgow. This migration and settlement led to the formation of distinct communities, identifiable by cultural differences, notably religion (O Tuathaigh, 1985).

In numerical terms Irish migration to Britain over the past two centuries has been far greater than immigration by other groups. Yet there has been little direct state intervention to regulate Irish immigration and settlement, particularly compared with the state's response to Jewish and black migrations to Britain. Part of the explanation for this lies in the fact that in 1800 the Act of Union incorporated Ireland into the United Kingdom. Therefore in practice, and then in law, the people of Ireland were incorporated into a larger political unit where they enjoyed citizenship status and could move from place to place in response to economic and political circumstances, within certain constraints imposed by the British state (Hechter, 1975; Miles, 1982).

This situation was maintained even after the establishment of the Republic of Ireland in 1922 because citizens of the Irish Republic retained the right to enter freely and settle in Britain. Even after the Irish Republic left the Commonwealth in 1947 the British Nationality Act accorded citizens of the Republic the unique status of being free to enter, settle, work and vote in Britain (Evans, 1983: 61). Although there seems to have been some cabinet opposition to the continuation of this status during the 1950s

(DO, 35/5219, 1957), there was no change in the policy of non-intervention in Irish immigration.

This laissez-faire approach to Irish immigration did not mean there was no hostile response to Irish immigrants. There is in fact a long history of anti-Irish stereotypes and images in British culture (Curtis, 1968, 1971; Lebow, 1976; Dangerfield, 1976). At various times during the nineteenth century there was hostility towards Irish migrants and this was helped by popular stereotyping of them in terms of their Catholicism and their supposed biological inferiority (Gilley, 1978; Miles, 1982: 135–45; O Tuathaigh, 1985: 20–3). There were also widespread acts of violence against Irish migrants (Waller, 1981; Millward, 1985; Gallagher, 1985).

The widespread use of anti-Irish images in popular culture during the late nineteenth and twentieth centuries has been illustrated in studies of working-class and elite cultures. For example Holmes (1988: 60) argues that in towns such as Liverpool 'a particularly fierce anti-Irish sentiment existed which was capable of combining various complementary strands of antipathy and susceptible to political exploitation'. Drawing on a study of popular images of the Irish in Victorian England, Curtis (1968: 121) argues that not only were such images commonly held among the working class but that 'many educated Victorians actually believed in the existence of a wide racial and cultural gap between themselves and Irish Celts'. Some of these images were to persist well into the twentieth century.

It is important to note one final point about such beliefs: images of the racial or cultural inferiority of the Irish were based not only on particular ideological constructions of the Irish but also on the definition of Englishness or Anglo-Saxon culture in terms of particular racial and cultural attributes. In later years such images of the uniqueness and purity of Englishness were to prove equally important in political debates on black migration and settlement (Reeves, 1983; Rich, 1986; Brody, 1998).

It is also important to emphasise that Irish migration to Britain in more recent times has been the subject of intense debate (Hickman, 1995; Hickman and Walter, 1997; Mac an Ghaill, 1999, 2001). A number of scholars have argued forcefully that any rounded overview of minorities in British society not only has to account for historical anti-Irish sentiment but also has to explore the ways in which contemporary racial discourses and practices portray the Irish in British society. Mac an Ghaill (2001) argues that in contemporary accounts of race and racism there is relative silence about discrimination against and exclusion of the Irish compared with the abundant accounts of the position of African-Caribbean and other ethnic groups. There is certainly something in this, although the same point could be made about other migrant communities upon whom relatively little research has been conducted. With the emergence of more scholarship and research on Irish and other white migrants the value of such a comparative analysis will no doubt become more evident. This will be particularly the case if new generations of scholars seek to explore the diverse experiences of the various migrant communities that have become part of the social fabric of British society.

Political and ideological responses to Jewish immigration

From the late nineteenth century a significant factor in the politics of immigration was the arrival of large numbers of largely Jewish migrants from Eastern Europe. The political and ideological responses to this wave of immigration have often been compared to the post-1945 politics of black immigration. This interest in comparing the two periods is partly due to the relative importance of political debates on immigration during these two periods. It is also because the Aliens Order of 1905 was a radical departure from previous policies on immigration and laid the foundation for subsequent legislation on this issue until after the Second World War (Garrard, 1971; Gainer, 1972; Gartner, 1973; Holmes, 1979).

The politicisation of Jewish immigration during the late Victorian and Edwardian periods stemmed from the arrival of a new group of Jewish settlers from Eastern Europe. As Lebzelter has pointed out, it was the response of a number of British political organisations to these new arrivals that provides the key to understanding this process. She argues that:

> In the 1880s and 1890s as well as in the post-war period, anti-Semitism in England served as an explanatory model to account for objective problems – unemployment and poverty in the first instance, opposition against British authority in the Empire in the second – by attributing them to the outsider, the Jew (Lebzelter, 1981: 102).

As an illustration of how this process worked she gives the example of how, in the context of economic crisis and high unemployment, the slogan 'England for the English' became popular with both Conservatives and trade union leaders (ibid.: 90).

What is interesting here is that the degree of political opposition to Jewish immigration was not simply related to the number of migrants. The pressure to restrict Jewish immigration contrasted sharply with the continuing and unrestricted entry of Irish migrants into Britain, who numerically were a much larger group. In the late nineteenth century there were approximately

60 000 Jewish people living in Britain, more than half of whom had been born there. The majority of this population were shopkeepers and merchants, a smaller proportion were part of the capitalist class and others were artisans of various kinds (Lipman, 1954: 27–9, 79–81). Between 1870 and 1914 some 120 000 Jewish people migrated to and settled in Britain (Gartner, 1973: 30) and by 1914 the Jewish population had grown to about 300 000 (Pollins, 1982: 130). This was relatively few compared with the Irish population, but from the 1880s to the First World War and afterwards Jewish immigration remained a bitterly controversial issue (Lee, 1980; Kennedy and Nicholls, 1981).

The political debates on and state actions taken in response to this immigration were partly influenced by social and economic changes in the localities of Jewish settlement. For example in the East End of London the debates on Jewish immigration were structured by the competition for jobs, housing and amenities. According to Gainer:

> 'Immigrant' and 'Jew' became synonymous terms because of the extraordinary concern for the social problems of the East End of London which emerged roughly at the time of the first great wave of immigration (Gainer, 1972: 3).

Holmes (1979) has shown that this social situation was an important element in trade union agitation for immigration control, which was the subject of resolutions passed at Trade Union Congresses in 1892, 1894 and 1895, although the section that was strongly in favour of restrictions on entry was small and weak (Garrard, 1971: 71, 174) because the economic consequences of Jewish immigration were only experienced by certain sections of the working class. Similar sentiments were voiced in parliament, where a small number of Conservative MPs took up the issue in order to attract working-class votes. Their support for restrictions on entry was logically and politically consistent with the Conservative demand for state intervention to protect domestic industry (Gainer, 1972: 144; Pollins, 1982: 140). The Liberal Party, on the other hand, was opposed to restrictive legislation because it supported free trade and therefore the free movement of human beings as well as commodities (Garrard, 1971: 90).

Parliamentary support for immigration control was accompanied by extra-parliamentary action. In 1901 a Conservative MP for an East London constituency formed the British Brothers League to agitate against Jewish immigration and settlement. It organised mass protest rallies and attained a membership of around 45 000 (Gainer 1972: 60–73; Holmes, 1979: 89–97). The activities of the league gave public prominence to the demand for immigration control, and agitation within parliament made Jewish immigration a national political issue. The ideological form in which the political issue was expressed, and the motivation for some of the agitation, was explicitly racist (Gainer, 1972: 113) and nationalistic (Garrard, 1971: 56; see also MacDougall, 1982; Newman, 1987).

The progress of the demand for restrictive legislation by parliament is well documented (Garrard, 1971; Gainer, 1972; Alderman, 1983: 66–85). The demand was first made in 1887 but had no hope of being realised until a Conservative government was elected. This eventually happened in 1895, but political circumstances obstructed progress until 1905, when the Aliens Order was passed. This was the first of a series of restrictive measures in the early part of the twentieth century as illustrated by Table 2.1. The legislation applied to the entry into Britain of all non-United Kingdom subjects, or those otherwise defined as 'aliens'. The most important provisions of the legislation were (a) that aliens could be refused permission to enter Britain if they did not have, or did not have the means to obtain, the means to subsist in adequate sanitary conditions; and (b) that an alien could be expelled from Britain without trial or appeal if he or she was found to be receiving poor relief within a year of entering Britain, was found guilty of vagrancy or was found to be living in insanitary conditions due to overcrowding. Other provisions of the order were that the home secretary would have the power to expel 'undesirable' immigrants, and that migrants who were refused permission to enter Britain could appeal to an immigration board. But the order also embodied in law the provision that an immigrant could not be refused permission to enter Britain if it could be proved that he or she was the subject of political or religious persecution (Gainer, 1972: 190; Macdonald, 1983: 8; Bevan, 1986: 71–2).

Soon after the Aliens Order became law the Conservative government was replaced by a Liberal government, which did not repeal the legislation, but implemented it in a non-restrictive manner. Until 1914 approximately 4–5000 Jews entered Britain annually (Lebzelter, 1978: 9), but after the outbreak of the First World War further legislation on immigration was initiated. The Aliens Restriction Act of 1914 passed through parliament in a single

Table 2.1 *Immigration legislation before 1945*

1905	Aliens Order
1914	Aliens Restriction Act
1919	Aliens Restriction (Amendment) Act
1920	Aliens Order
1925	Special Restrictions (Coloured Alien Seamen) Act

day and gave the government considerable power to control immigration through Orders in Council, the justification for such powers being couched in terms of national security in circumstances of war. The legislation empowered the government to decide who could be prohibited from entering Britain, who could be deported and who could be made subject to restrictions on where they lived and travelled.

In the past decade or so various authors have conducted detailed analyses of the social and cultural impact of Jewish immigration on racial imagery and literary discourses in British society (Cesarani 1990, 1992; Cheyette, 1993; Feldman, 1994; Cheyette and Marcus, 1998). These detailed considerations of the ways in which Jewishness has been understood and utilised in political discourses and popular culture have highlighted the complex ways in which racial imagery has been framed in British society. It has also shown that there is much to be gained from a comparison of the responses to the early waves of Irish and Jewish migration and the post-1945 black and Asian migration from the new Commonwealth.

After the end of the First World War the Aliens Restriction (Amendment) Act of 1919 repealed the 1905 legislation and extended the 1914 Act for one year, despite the fact that the original justification for the Act no longer applied. In the following year a new Aliens Order was passed and thereafter the Acts of 1914 were renewed annually under the Expiring Laws Continuance Acts. Under the Aliens Order of 1920 immigration officers could refuse entry to an alien who was considered unable to provide for his or her own support, and they were also given increased powers to deal with aliens who had evaded immigration control. Aliens had to register their address and any change thereof. The home secretary gained the power to deport any alien whose presence was not considered to be 'conducive to the public good'. Finally, if an alien wished to work in Britain he or she could only do so following the issuing to a prospective employer of a permit by the Ministry of Labour, the permit being issued only when it could be shown that no British worker was available to take up the job in question (Evans, 1983: 10–12; Macdonald, 1983: 8–9; Gordon, 1985: 9–11; Bevan, 1986: 72–4).

It is important to note that it was partly within the terms of this legislation that the British state responded to the growing numbers of Jewish and other refugees who fled from Germany following the installation of a fascist government (Hirschfeld, 1984; Berghahn, 1984; Holmes, 1988; London, 2000). It is also important to recall that the substance of that legislation was that aliens considered to be without the means to support themselves could be refused permission to enter Britain, although poverty was not a sufficient ground to refuse entry to those claiming to be fleeing religious or political persecution.

In the event, other circumstances were cited as reasons for denying entry to Britain to political refugees. Throughout the period 1933–9 the British government asserted that Britain was not suitable for immigration because of its large population and high unemployment, and therefore the admission of Jewish (and other) refugees from Germany could only be on a limited scale (Sherman, 1973: 259). During this time about 55 000 refugees from Germany, Austria and Czechoslovakia were admitted to Britain (ibid.: 271). Despite evidence of the plight of Jews in Germany there was political reluctance to act decisively to help Jewish refugees because of widespread anti-Semitism in British society (Kushner, 1994a; Kushner and Knox, 1999).

Race and labour in the early twentieth century

Black people were present in Britain for centuries before the arrival of South Asian and African-Caribbean immigrants from 1945. Indeed by the end of the nineteenth century small black communities had become established in the port towns of Liverpool, London, Cardiff and Bristol.

This is not the place to go into the details of this history, which has been the subject of a number of important and insightful studies (Walvin, 1973, 1992; Shyllon, 1974; Fryer, 1984; Ramdin, 1987, 1999). We should, however, look at some aspects of the politics of black migration and settlement in Britain in the early twentieth century, since it was during this period that the terms of political debate and domestic ideologies and policies towards 'coloured workers' and their communities began to be formed.

Indeed it was during this period that the question of racial difference began to play a central part in the politics of immigration. This was the case despite the relatively small size of the black population and the fact that they possessed the formal right to citizenship. According to Harris a central theme of the debates on black communities during the interwar period was the supposed social problems to which their presence gave rise:

> Social decay was supposed to be connected with the presence of a 'Negro' population of Somalis, Arabs, West Indians, West Africans and so on who constituted an almost insignificant percentage of the population of the sea-port towns (Harris, 1988: 18).

Such issues were to become a more central feature of political debate from 1945, but their origins can be traced to the interwar years and the commonly held image of black communities in the port towns and beyond.

Some of the events of the interwar years have been uncovered by the research of scholars such as Fryer, Rich and Harris, and as a consequence of increased interest in the history of the black presence in British society (Walvin, 1984, 1999; Ramdin, 1987; Tabili, 1994; Bush, 1999). Much more research needs to be done as its importance to any rounded analysis of the politics of race and racism in British political life is clear. Yet the preoccupation of the bulk of studies in this field is with the period since 1945 and is stubbornly ahistorical, even when written from a radical perspective. This means that many important connections and continuities in the history of race and racism in Britain are hardly discussed (Cohen, 1988; James and Harris, 1993).

As discussed in the preceding section, early immigration legislation was concerned with the entry into Britain of people who by law were aliens, that is, non-British citizens. However this legislation also contained provisions on a certain category of British subject: seamen recruited in various parts of the Empire, particularly India and the Caribbean. Despite being British subjects, Indian seamen (widely known as lascars) had been subject to discriminatory treatment by the British state since the nineteenth century, if not before, partly in order to prevent their settlement in Britain when the passage they had worked terminated in Britain.

An Act passed in 1813 required the East India Company to provide subsistence for Indian sailors in Britain until they returned to India, and an Act passed in 1823 stipulated that Indian seamen were not British subjects and were not entitled to become so. These conditions were consolidated in the Merchant Shipping Act of 1894, which set out articles of agreement (to be signed by Asian seamen and their masters) binding seamen to return to their country of origin and giving the secretary of state the power to repatriate those who attempted to become resident in Britain (Hepple, 1968: 42–4; Joshua and Wallace, 1983: 14–16; Gordon, 1985: 5–6). These measures were only partially successful, as shown by the continuing presence of Asian and Caribbean people in British seaports (Fryer, 1984: 294–5; Visram, 1986: 34–54; Ramdin, 1987; Visram, 2002).

After 1918 these discriminatory practices were reinforced and further efforts were made to prevent British subjects of a different race from settling in Britain. This occurred with the ending of the First World War, during which there had been an increase in the number of overseas subjects employed as seamen. With regard to discriminatory practices, Section 5(2) of the Aliens Restriction (Amendment) Act of 1919 legalised different rates of pay for British seamen according to their race (Hepple, 1968: 44–5; Joshua and Wallace, 1983: 16). Furthermore there was a slump in employment in the shipping industry after 1918 and the relevant trade unions campaigned to restrict employment to white seamen. In the resulting competition for work, Indian, Chinese and Caribbean seamen who had settled in Britain became the victims of racist violence in Cardiff, Liverpool and Glasgow (May and Cohen, 1974; Evans, 1980, 1985; Jenkinson, 1985). In Cardiff the police sought to 'repatriate' these seamen (Evans, 1985: 73–4), but the Home Office pointed out that they were British subjects and were therefore not subject to enforced expulsion from Britain. However arrangements were made for the return of as many seamen as might be 'persuaded' to go. This initiative was largely unsuccessful (Joshua and Wallace, 1983: 31–2).

In 1925, based on Article 11 of the Aliens Order of 1920, the Special Restrictions (Coloured Alien Seamen) Order 1925 was drafted (Hepple, 1968: 45; Joshua and Wallace, 1983: 32–5; Gordon, 1985: 7; Evans, 1985: 80–1; Rich, 1986: 122–30). This formally applied to colonial seamen (who had previously been entitled to sign off from a ship in a British port and to seek residence there) who did not possess satisfactory documentary evidence of being British subjects. These seamen were henceforth required to obtain the permission of an immigration officer to land and were subject to removal from Britain. However in practice the police, the Aliens Department and immigration officers also forced 'coloured' British subjects who did possess the required documents to register under the Order, an action that deprived them of their legal status of British subject and thereby rendered them subject to the Alien Restriction (Amendment) Act of 1919 and the Aliens Order of 1920 (including the requirement that they register with the police, to whom they were required to report any change of address) and to the possibility of deportation. Joshua and Wallace (1983: 32) comment that:

> The Order was specifically designed to restrict the entry and settlement of black colonial British citizens. But, because the Conservative government did not wish to undermine the notion of a British subject which was at the heart of the Empire, the Order could achieve its ends through a series of legalistic contortions and double standards.

The response of the state, at both the local and the national level, was dual-faceted. It was responding to local racist agitation and violence against those defined as 'coloured seamen', actions that were grounded in the inability of the economic system to provide full employment (Lunn, 1985). But it was also responding to a wider concern about the settlement of these seamen in Britain: the likely growth of a 'mixed race' population as a result of sexual relations between the seamen and indigenous women (Rich, 1986: 120–44; Ramdin, 1987, 1999; see also Panayi, 1996, on the subject of racial violence).

The two most common responses to black immigration and settlement in this period were political debates on the need to control their arrival and calls for the repatriation of those who had already settled in Britain. Partly because of the violent conflicts that occurred with some regularity in some of the port towns, but largely because of the mobilisation of an image of black enclaves as seats of social problems, even the relatively small communities that developed in the interwar period were perceived as 'alien' and a possible threat to the British way of life. This signalled the types of political debate on 'coloured immigrants' that were to come to the fore after 1945.

Summary and conclusion

In the light of the story told in this chapter it is difficult to sustain the notion that the politicisation of immigration and racial issues is a unique feature of political life since 1945. By the Second World War there was already a long history of political debate on and mobilisation around issues of ethnicity, race and religion. This has only been lightly touched upon in this chapter, although a growing body of work is helping to tell the story of this important period in Britain's immigration history (Bush, 1999; Ramdin, 1999). In the past decade or so there has also been a growing scholarly debate on the historical construction of 'whiteness', migrant communities and racial categories in the US, and this has done much to shape the debate on immigration and racial ideologies (Ignatiev, 1995; Jacobson, 1998).

In part the response of the state and political institutions to Irish, Jewish and black colonial and other immigrants before 1945 was the product of the specific social, economic and political conditions of the time. Yet the experience of the past five decades or so cannot be completely separated from this longer historical experience of racial and ethnic categorisation. Indeed it can be argued that we can best understand the more recent experience of racism in Britain if we look back at this historical background and compare the processes through which racialised political action developed in the different periods. This is a point to which we shall return when we have analysed the history of race and immigration since 1945.

3 The Politics of Race and Immigration since 1945

The story of the politics of immigration from the nineteenth century onwards told in the previous chapter showed how immigration and race were contested issues long before the arrival of large numbers of black colonial immigrants from 1945. We have seen that the response of political institutions to the arrival of Irish, Jewish and black immigrants was complex and not uniform. The response to Irish migrants, despite a degree of opposition and some violent confrontation, was markedly different from the attempts to exclude and control Jewish and black migrants. There was also more limited political mobilisation in defence of the interests of these groups.

In this chapter we shall look at the history of ideological and political responses to the arrival and settlement of black immigrants from 1945 onwards. Of course migrants from a variety of racial and ethnic backgrounds have continued to arrive and settle in Britain, and it is important in any rounded account of migration to look at their experiences also (Holmes, 1988; Panayi, 1999). For the purposes of this chapter, however, we shall concentrate on the politics of black immigration and settlement since 1945.

This period has attracted the attention of most researchers on racial issues in Britain, and there is now a voluminous body of literature on most aspects of this phenomenon. Looking specifically at the political literature, two main themes have been highlighted above all else. First, a number of studies have sought to analyse how the question of immigration *per se* has become inextricably linked to black immigration, that is, the arrival of migrants from the new Commonwealth and Pakistan (Katznelson, 1976; Freeman, 1979; Layton-Henry, 1984; Cohen, 1994). This body of work has looked particularly at the political debates on black immigration and the part played by changing political ideologies in the construction of racial issues.

Second, other research has shown how successive governments have attempted to regulate and eventually halt the arrival of black immigrants through immigration legislation and other means (Sivanandan, 1982; Miles and Phizacklea, 1984; Macdonald and Blake, 1995). According to these works, arguments about the supposed problems created by the arrival of too many black immigrants have been used to legitimise legislative measures that have had the effect of institutionalising controls on black immigrants, thereby excluding potential immigrants on the basis of skin colour.

Both these interpretations have been the subject of much controversy and debate, to which we shall refer in the course of this chapter. The main task, however, is to analyse and explain the political and ideological responses to the arrival of immigrants from the West Indies, India, Pakistan and other Commonwealth countries. The first section provides a critical review of political opinions and policy responses immediately after the war. The discussion then moves on to the impact of state intervention on the patterns of black immigration and how immigration became a focus of political discourse and conflict between the 1940s and the 1990s (Panayi, 1999).

The tensions evident in the political debates on immigration will be considered in Chapters 8, 9 and 10, where we shall explore the various ways in which political mobilisation around racial symbols took place, including racist political actions and the political mobilisation of the black and ethnic minority communities themselves. For the moment we shall concentrate on the processes of political debate and decision making, particularly in relation to immigration and community relations.

Post-1945 European migration

During the Second World War the question of black settlement in Britain came to the fore as a result of (a) the recruitment of the black workers and soldiers from the colonies to fight in the British army or to help with the war effort (Richmond, 1954; Sherwood, 1984) and (b) the arrival of black American soldiers (Smith, 1987). At the time there were two main concerns: the social effect that the arrival of these workers and soldiers would have on the older black seaport settlements; and that the arrival of new black immigrants might lead to conflict and the institutionalisation of a 'colour bar' in a number of towns.

However after the war less attention was paid to black migration because despite arrival of the SS *Empire Windrush* in 1948 with some 400 British subjects from the Caribbean, most of the migrants arriving in Britain were from other European countries. Between 1945 and 1951 some 70 000–100 000 Irish people entered Britain. Although some concern was later expressed about the scale of Irish immigration, there was surprisingly little debate on this issue at that stage (PREM 11/1409, 1956; Jackson, 1963; Holmes, 1988; Kay and Miles, 1992).

During and after the war the Conservative government and its Labour successor were instrumental in encouraging the settlement of Polish soldiers and their families in Britain (Zubrzycki, 1956: 36; Lunn, 1980). In 1940 the exiled Polish government and armed forces (a total of 30 500 persons) were allowed to enter Britain, and the Polish Second Corps, which joined the British Command in 1942, was brought to Britain in 1946, followed by families and dependants of members of the Polish armed forces. The latter were subsequently absorbed into the Polish Resettlement Corps and those who were unwilling to return to Poland were given the option of settling in Britain. It has been estimated that in 1949 the resident Polish population consisted of 91 400 members of the Polish Resettlement Corps, 31 800 dependants of Polish ex-servicemen, 2400 relatives and 2300 additional ex-members of the Polish armed forces. To this group of 127 900 persons one can add 29 400 European volunteer workers of Polish origin (Zubrzycki, 1956: 62).

The other significant group of migrants was recruited by the state specifically to resolve labour shortages in certain sectors of the economy. On the European mainland there were several camps for displaced persons or political refugees who were unable or did not wish to return to their country of birth following the redrawing of political boundaries after the defeat of Germany, and the Labour government decided to send Ministry of Labour officials to recruit some as workers. The occupants of these camps were or had been nationals of other countries and were therefore aliens as far as the British state was concerned, but the procedures for admission under the Aliens Order of 1920, concerned as they were with the admission of single persons, were not appropriate for what was to become a considerable wave of migration. The result was, for Britain, a unique scheme, with the British state undertaking to meet all the costs of recruitment, travel and repatriation on behalf of capitalists who were short of workers. In a number of respects this action anticipated the contract migrant labour system set up by a number of Western European states in the 1950s and 1960s (Castles *et al.*, 1984; Castles and Kosack, 1985; Miles, 1986). The total cost of the scheme up to October 1948 was £2.75 million (Tannahill, 1958: 56).

Displaced persons who came to Britain were required to sign a contract, under the terms of which they had to accept work selected by the minister of labour and could only change that employment with the permission of the Ministry of Labour. These European Volunteer Workers (EVWs) were initially admitted for one year, an extension being dependent upon the individual complying with the conditions of the contract and behaving 'as a worthy member of the British community' (ibid.: 123–8). At first many of those recruited were not eligible to bring their dependants with them, although most of those who eventually settled in Britain were subsequently joined by their families. The conditions of placement of EVWs in employment varied but usually included the requirements that no British workers were available, that in the event of redundancy EVWs would be the first to be made unemployed, that they should join the appropriate trade union, and that they would receive the same wages and conditions as British workers (ibid.: 57).

During 1947 and 1948 EVWs were recruited under a number of schemes, the most important being the Balt Cygnet and Westward Ho schemes, which absorbed 74 511 persons (17 422 women and 57 089 men). Most of these workers originated from Estonia, Latvia, Lithuania, Poland or Yugoslavia. In addition 8397 Ukrainian prisoners of war were brought to Britain in 1947 for political reasons and it was subsequently decided to treat them as EVWs. Under the North Sea and Blue Danube schemes 12 000 German and Austrian women were recruited on a temporary two-year contract, and most returned to Germany and Austria when their contract expired. Five thousand Italians of both sexes were recruited under a similar arrangement (ibid.: 5–6, 30–3). Although approximately 85 000 refugees were recruited in the late 1940s, this total was lower than that originally envisaged. For example it had been anticipated that 100 000 workers would be recruited in 1948 alone.

The encouragement given to these two groups of migrants to settle in Britain contrasted with the government's concern about the social and political consequences of the relatively small-scale migration from the colonies during this period. Recent research has made clear that even at this early stage black migration and settlement was perceived differently from European migration. Privately the government was considering the most desirable method of discouraging or preventing the arrival of 'coloured' British citizens from the colonies.

Migration, colonial labour and the state: 1945–62

At the end of the Second World War the British state had the legislative power, in the form of the Aliens legislation, to control non-British subjects' entry into Britain and access to the labour market. However the vast majority of British subjects in the colonies and dominions had the legal right to enter and settle in Britain. This right was confirmed by the British Nationality Act of 1948 which, in response to the granting of independence to India, made a formal distinction between British subjects who were citizens of the United Kingdom and its colonies and those who were Commonwealth citizens, although both categories of people had the right to enter, settle and work in Britain (Evans, 1983: 59–62; Bevan, 1986: 112–13). In addition citizens of the Republic of Ireland retained the right of unrestricted entry and settlement.

Despite this the state encouraged the use of immigrants from Europe to meet the demand for labour. Some British subjects from the colonies did arrive during this period, particularly from the West Indies, but almost as soon as they began to arrive they were perceived as a problem.

The relatively liberal attitude towards the arrival of European workers contrasted sharply with the fears expressed about the perceived social and racial problems that would arise with the arrival of 'coloured' colonial workers, even though they were British subjects. Both the Labour governments of 1945–51 and the Conservative governments of the 1950s considered various ways of stopping or reducing the number of black migrants arriving and settling in Britain (Joshi and Carter, 1984; Carter *et al.*, 1987; Dean, 1987, 1993). It was during this time that the terms of political debate on 'coloured' immigration were established, leading to a close association between race and immigration both in policy debates and in popular political and media discourses.

Contrary to the arguments of some scholars it seems quite inappropriate to view this period as an 'age of innocence' and lack of concern about black immigration into Britain (Rose *et al.*, 1969; Patterson, 1969; Deakin, 1970). Throughout the period an increasingly racialised debate on immigration took place, focusing on the supposed social problems of having too many black immigrants and the question of how they could be stopped from entering, given their legal rights under the 1948 British Nationality Act.

Considerable publicity was given to the arrival of 417 Jamaicans on the *Empire Windrush* in May 1948 and the subsequent arrival of large groups of West Indian workers, and this focus on 'coloured' immigration helped to obscure the fact that the majority of immigrants came from the Irish Republic, white Commonwealth countries and other European countries (Patterson, 1969: ch. 1; Miles and Phizacklea, 1984: 45–8). The number of West Indian, Indian and Pakistani immigrants was a matter of concern for the cabinet during 1950–5, when various measures to control black immigration and to dissuade black workers from coming to Britain were considered. On the basis of a careful analysis of cabinet and ministerial debates on immigration from the colonies, an influential study has concluded that from 1948 to 1962 the state was involved in a complex political and ideological racialisation of immigration policy (Carter *et al.*, 1987; see also James and Harris, 1993).

The period between the 1948 Nationality Act and the 1962 Commonwealth Immigrants Act is frequently characterised as one in which the principle of free entry of British subjects into Britain was only relinquished with great reluctance and after considerable official debate. This was not the case. On the contrary the debate was never about this principle. By 1952 Labour and Conservative governments had instituted a number of covert and sometimes illegal administrative measures to discourage black immigration (Carter *et al.*, 1987).

Throughout the 1950s the debate on immigration in parliament and the media focused on the need to control black immigration. Although in public debate and private policy discussions attention was sometimes focused on the behaviour of 'undesirable' black immigrants, such as those involved in crime or prostitution, most of the political debates throughout the 1950s were about the desirability of letting into Britain a sizeable number of West Indian or Asian migrants. The 1958 riots in Notting Hill and Nottingham may have helped to politicise this process further (Miles, 1984; Pilkington, 1988), but it is clear that both before and after the riots the question of control was integrated into the policy agenda.

With the growing emphasis on the control of 'coloured' immigration the ideological and policy debates on the future of black immigration turned on two themes that were later to prove influential. First, a vigorous debate took place in and out of parliament on the possibility of revising the 1948 Nationality Act so as to limit the number of black workers who could enter and settle in Britain. The terms of this debate were by no means fixed purely by political party ideologies, and there was opposition from both Conservative and Labour politicians to the call for controls and abandonment of the free entry principle. Second, a parallel debate developed on the problems caused by 'too many coloured immigrants' in relation to housing, employment and crime. This second theme became particularly important from 1956–8 and in the aftermath of the 1958 riots (*Hansard*, vol. 596, 1958, cols 1552–97).

By linking immigration to the social aspects of the 'colour problem' an argument was established that was later to prove influential in shaping both the immigration control legislation and the Race Relations Acts: that it was necessary to use direct state intervention to halt the 'gathering momentum' of black immigration and to resolve the social problems that were perceived to be linked to it.

Controls on 'coloured' immigration had been discussed as early as the late 1940s, and again in 1954 and 1955. A number of arguments were raised in opposition to such controls, and it was not until 1961 that a bill to control Commonwealth immigration was introduced by the government. The reasons for the reluctance to introduce controls remains to some extent a matter of debate, although the release of government documents for the 1950s and 1960s has shed some light on this non-decision-making process (Joshi and Carter, 1984: 55–63; Rich, 1986: ch. 7; Phillips and Phillips, 1998; Wambu, 1998). But at least part of the reluctance to introduce controls seemed to be due to concern about whether legislation that excluded black people could be implemented without causing embarrassment to Britain's position as head of the Commonwealth and Colonies, fear that it would divide public opinion, and doubt about the legality of controls based on colour in both British and international law (Deakin, 1968: 26–30; Miles and Phizacklea, 1984: ch. 2; Howe, 1993).

What is clear is that the late 1940s to the late 1950s was not a period of *laissez faire* in relation to black immigration. Rather it was one of intense debate in government departments and public circles about the impact of black immigration on housing, the welfare state, crime and other social problems. It is important to note, however, that these debates were not purely about the supposed characteristics of black immigrants. They were also about the effect that black immigration would have on the 'racial character of the British people' and the national identity. Harris (1988) makes this point clear when he argues that the debates on black immigration during the 1950s reinforced a racialised construction of Britishness that excluded or included people on the ground of race, defined by colour:

> When individuals like the Marquis of Salisbury spoke of maintaining the English way of life, they were not simply referring to economic or regional folk patterns, but explicitly to the preservation of 'the racial character of the English people'. We have developing here a process of subjectification grounded in a racialised construction of 'British' Subject which excludes and includes people on the basis of 'race'/skin colour (ibid.: 53).

This process was still in its early stages during this period, but it is impossible to understand the legislation passed to control black immigration during the 1960s and 1970s without referring to the genesis and articulation of political discourse on black immigration during the period 1945–62.

Immigration and racialised politics

The 1958 race riots in Nottingham and Notting Hill are commonly seen as an important watershed in the development of racialised politics in Britain. It is certainly true that the events in these two localities helped to bring to national prominence issues that had previously been discussed only locally or within government departments.

The riots consisted of attacks by whites on blacks but this did not prevent them from being cited as examples of the danger of unrestricted immigration. By the time of the 1958 riots, however, the mobilisation of opinion in and out of parliament in favour of controls was well advanced, and the disturbances in Nottingham and Notting Hill were used by the pro-immigration-control lobby to call for the exclusion or even repatriation of 'undesirable immigrants'. They were also used to support the argument that black immigration posed a threat to the rule of law in the inner cities and endangered the 'English way of life'. Lord Salisbury exploited the opportunity presented by the riots to justify his claim that controls should be imposed on black immigration, and argued that 'he was extremely apprehensive of the economic and social results, for Europeans and Africans alike, that were likely to flow from an unrestricted immigration of men and women of the African race into Britain' (*Guardian*, 3 September 1958).

Between these events and the introduction of the Commonwealth Immigrants Bill in 1961 a number of important debates on immigration control took place in parliament and at party conferences (Patterson, 1969; Freeman, 1979: 49–52; Miles, 1984). In parliament a number of Conservative MPs, including Cyril Osborne, organised a campaign in favour of immigration controls, though they made their case against 'coloured' immigrants largely through coded language. The Labour Party, along with the Liberals, generally argued against controls, though this was by no means the case for all Labour MPs and local councillors (Reeves, 1983: ch. 7; Layton-Henry, 1984: 31–43).

Outside parliament there was widespread coverage in both popular and serious newspapers of race and immigration issues. There was a flowering of debate on housing and social conditions in areas of black settlement and on aspects of employment and competition for jobs, accompanied by a resurgence of extreme right-wing groups that sought to use immigration as a basis for political mobilisation. The interplay between these activities produced a wide variety of stereotypes and popular images of black people. In September 1958 *The Times* reported that in one of the areas affected by the riots:

> There are three main causes of resentment against coloured inhabitants of the district. They are alleged to do no work and to collect a rich sum from the Assistance Board. They are said to find housing when white residents cannot. And they are charged with all kinds of misbehaviour, especially sexual (*The Times*, 3 September 1958).

It was on such concerns that right-wing extremist groups focused much of their propaganda during and after the riots. In this context there was no need for their beliefs to be substantiated by evidence, and it proved difficult to counteract such stereotypes. This weakened attempts to resist the pressure for immigration control.

The ambiguities in the pressure for control became even more pronounced during the early 1960s, the period that saw the passage of the first legislative measure to control the immigration of overseas citizens of the United Kingdom and its colonies: the 1962 Commonwealth Immigrants Act. It is to this period that we now turn.

Immigration controls and state racism

In the previous section it was argued that the racialisation of the immigration issue during the 1950s formed the basis for the move towards the control of black immigration, an objective that was first addressed through the 1962 Commonwealth Immigrants Act. Part of the dilemma faced by the Conservative government of the time was how to legitimise a policy that aimed to control black immigration as a more universal measure. William Deedes, who was a minister without portfolio at the time, recalls that:

> The Bill's real purpose was to restrict the influx of coloured immigrants. We were reluctant to say as much openly. So the restrictions were applied to coloured and white citizens in all Commonwealth countries – though everybody recognised that immigration from Canada, Australia and New Zealand formed no part of the problem (Deedes, 1968: 10).

The racialisation of the immigration issue was, in other words, done through coded language: Commonwealth immigrants were seen as a problem, but race itself was not always mentioned as the central issue. The politicisation of such terms was later to lead to a situation where, despite the continuation of large-scale white immigration, all immigrants were visualised as black and immigration became a coded term for racial questions.

Two competing models have been used to explain the move towards immigration control. At the time some scholars saw this shift as a response by the state to the pressure of popular opinion against black immigration (Foot, 1965; Rose *et al.*, 1969). This was also the main line of argument used by some of the principal political figures involved in the crucial debates on the control of black immigration (Butler, 1971; Macmillan, 1973). Others argued that the state was responding to the economic interests of the capitalist class, which required the adoption of a migrant labour system that undermined the right of black workers to migrate and settle freely in Britain (Sivanandan, 1982: 101–26).

Both explanations have been widely used in the extensive literature on the politics of immigration, but as already indicated it seems inadequate to view the state as being purely responsive to popular opinion or economic interests. Throughout the period 1948–62 the state was actively involved in

Table 3.1 *Legislation on immigration since 1962*

1962	Commonwealth Immigrants Act
1968	Commonwealth Immigrants Act
1969	Immigration Appeals Act
1970	Immigration Act
1971	British Nationality Act
1972	Immigration Act
1993	Asylum and Immigration (Appeals) Act
1996	Asylum and Immigration Act
1999	Asylum and Immigration Act
2002	Nationality, Immigration and Asylum Bill

monitoring and regulating the arrival of black workers, and it articulated a definition of the immigration question that was suffused with racialised categories. In addition, archival research indicates that the Conservative government came close to agreeing on a policy of control on black immigration in 1955–56 (Carter *et al.*, 1987).

The genesis of the demand for the control of black immigration during the early 1950s matured during 1955–62 into a concerted campaign by the cabinet, parliament, the media and political parties for action to be taken to 'curb the dangers of unrestricted immigration'. This led, during the period leading up to the introduction of the 1961 Commonwealth Immigrants Bill, to a policy debate on the formulation of legislation to exclude black workers from entry and settlement. This can hardly be interpreted as a move from *laissez faire* to state intervention, since the state and its institutions were already heavily involved in defining the terms of the debate on the problems caused by black immigration. Nevertheless it was a significant step towards the institutionalisation of immigration control, and it signalled the beginning of a series of legislative measures throughout the 1960s and 1970s that not only put controls on immigration but also shaped public debates on immigration and race relations to this day. The key pieces of legislation are listed in Table 3.1 and we shall discuss their impact in this and subsequent chapters.

The 1962 Commonwealth Immigrants Act

Acceptance of the need to turn administrative controls on black immigration into legislative action was formally acknowledged in October 1961 when the Conservative government announced the introduction of the Commonwealth Immigrants Bill. The controls introduced by the Bill were justified by the argument that there was a need to halt black immigration because of the limited ability of the host country to assimilate 'coloured immigrants'. Some MPs and commentators were reluctant to accept that the Bill was simply a way of dealing with the immigration of black workers, and the Labour Party and sections of the media saw it as a response to crude racist pressures. In parliament Hugh Gaitskell, as leader of the Labour Party, led a particularly strong attack on the Bill and its crude combining of immigration with race (Patterson, 1969: 17–20; *IRR Newsletter*, May 1962). But despite strong criticism from the Labour Party and sections of the press, the collective pressure against the entry of black British succeeded when the Commonwealth Immigrants Act became law in 1962.

Since it was the outcome of a sustained political campaign against black immigration it is not surprising that, despite claims to the contrary, the main clauses of the Act sought to control the entry of black Commonwealth citizens into Britain. The Act introduced a distinction between citizens of Britain and its colonies and citizens of independent Commonwealth countries. All holders of Commonwealth passports were subject to immigration control except those who (a) had been born in Britain, (b) held British passports issued by the British government, or (c) were included in the passport of a person allowed entry under (a) or (b) (Macdonald and Blake, 1995). Other Commonwealth citizens had to obtain a Ministry of Labour employment voucher in order to enter Britain. The Act initially provided for three types of voucher:

- Category A: Commonwealth citizens who had a specific job to go to in Britain.
- Category B: applicants who had a recognised skill or qualification that was in short supply in Britain.
- Category C: all other applicants, priority being given to those who had served in the British forces during the war.

The creation of these different categories was justified in coded terms as offering a way of controlling the number of immigrants entering the country, but it was clear from both the parliamentary and the media debates on the Bill that it was widely seen as specifically aimed at black migrants. In this sense the Act can be viewed as the climax of the campaign within and outside government since the 1950s for the control of black immigration.

Public debate on the Act reflected a variety of views, and by no means were all in favour of it. In fact a number of leading articles in the press during 1961–2, along with sections of the Labour Party, expressed opposition to the racist thinking behind the Act. Concern was also voiced about the possible consequences of the passage of the Act for Britain's standing in the black Commonwealth countries (Deakin, 1968).

The changing terms of political debate

Almost as soon as the Act became law there was widespread debate on its effectiveness. From 1963 to 1972, when the voucher system was abolished, there was pressure to cut back the number of vouchers allocated, and this was reflected in a fall from 30 130 vouchers in 1963 to 2290 in 1972. Significantly, no controls were imposed on the entry into Britain of citizens of the Irish Republic. Nevertheless opponents of immigration were quick to call for even tighter controls, and in the political climate of the mid 1960s their voices had a major influence on the terms of the political debate on race and immigration.

The Labour Party's opposition to the Act was not sustained, and when Harold Wilson took office as Labour prime minister in 1964 he announced that the Commonwealth Immigrants Act would be retained. In 1965 the government issued a white paper on immigration from the Commonwealth, which called for controls to be maintained in an even stricter form, along with measures to promote the integration of immigrants. The white paper represented a shift towards what some called a 'Little England' policy (Rose *et al.*, 1969: 229) and signalled the convergence of the Conservative and Labour Parties in respect of immigration control (Wilson, 1971).

This was well illustrated by the nature of the political debate on race and immigration between 1964 and 1970, when the Labour Party was in power. Three good examples of this were the controversies over the electoral contest in Smethwick in 1964, the immigration of East African Asians during 1968–9 and the political turmoil caused by Enoch Powell's intervention in the debate from 1968 onwards.

Smethwick and immigration

The impact of events in Smethwick during 1964 is sometimes forgotten, but it is no exaggeration to say that the political turmoil over the issue of immigration in Smethwick and the surrounding area had a profound impact on both the local and the national political scene. Popular and media interest was aroused by the contest between the Labour candidate, Patrick Gordon Walker, who was widely seen as being liberal on immigration, and the Conservative Peter Griffiths, whose election manifesto was largely about defending the interests of the local white majority against the 'influx of immigrants' (Foot, 1965; Deakin, 1972). In the volatile political climate of the time a slogan commonly heard during the election campaign was 'If you want a nigger for a neighbour vote Labour'. Griffiths later defended the use of this slogan as 'a manifestation of popular feeling' about immigration in the area, and refused to condemn those who had used it (*The Times*, 1968: 139; Griffiths, 1966).

The debate on the implications of Griffiths' victory in Smethwick continued for some time and exerted an influence on both the Labour Party (*The Economist*, 7 August, 1965; Deakin, 1965; Wilson, 1971; Crossman, 1975) and the Conservative Party (Berkeley, 1977; Layton-Henry, 1980). In the West Midlands in particular the events in Smethwick caused both major parties to emphasise their support for strict control of black immigration (Lenton *et al.*, 1966; Deakin, 1972).

East African Asians

One of the features of the 1962 Act was that British citizens living in independent Commonwealth countries were exempt from control provided they held a British passport. This included a large number of European settlers as well as a sizeable number of Asians in Kenya and Uganda. Between 1965 and 1967 a steady flow of these people arrived in Britain, and when in late 1967 sections of the media and MPs started to call for action to be taken to stop their arrival a heated debate ensued.

This debate reached its climax in February 1968. As noted above, between 1963 and 1965 the Labour Party had moved towards acceptance of the need for firm immigration controls and so it came as no surprise when it responded to this political campaign by introducing the second Commonwealth Immigrants Act in early 1968. This Act sought to control the flow of Asians from East Africa by bringing them under immigration control. Under the new law any citizen of Britain or its colonies who held a passport issued by the British government would be subject to immigration control unless they or at least one parent or grandparent had been born, adopted, naturalised or registered in Britain as a citizen of Britain or its colonies.

The political context in which the Act was passed made it difficult to argue that it was non-racial, as had been claimed to some extent by the Conservative government that had passed the 1962 Act. *The Times* contrasted the behaviour of the Labour government with the attitude of the Labour opposition in 1962, and went as far as to call the Act a 'colour bar' and 'probably the most shameful measure that the Labour members have ever been asked by their whip to support' (*The Times*, 27 February 1968).

The transformation of the political climate between 1962 and 1968 was clear enough for all to see in the parliamentary debates on the 1968 Act. Given the highly politicised nature of these debates and the defensive stance taken by the government, only a few MPs and newspaper commentators saw fit to question the racism that underlay the legislation (Freeman, 1979: 56; Miles and Phizacklea, 1984: 59–67). In the period between the 1968 Act and the 1970 election, which saw the return of a Conservative government, there was further racialisation of the immigration issue. Even though it was difficult to see how immigration controls could be made even tighter than those imposed by the 1962 and 1968 Acts, this topic and race relations became subjects of partisan political debate on an even larger scale.

Powellism and political debate

During this period the Labour government was forced onto the defensive by Enoch Powell's famous 'rivers of blood' speech in Birmingham in April 1968, which helped to popularise the message that even tighter controls on immigration would not be enough to resolve the 'race problem'. In this speech, and in a succession of others over the next few years, Powell warned of what he saw as (a) the danger of immigration leading to a 'total transformation to which there is no parallel in a thousand years of British history', and (b) the longer-term danger of American-style racial tensions manifesting themselves in Britain. In the most infamous section of his speech Powell said:

> As I look ahead, I am filled with foreboding. Like the Roman, I seem to see 'the River Tiber foaming with much blood'. The tragic and intractable phenomenon which we watch with horror on the other side of the Atlantic, but which there is interwoven with the history and existence of the States itself, is coming upon us here by our own volition and our own neglect (*Observer*, 21 April 1968).

According to Powell the long-term solution should go beyond immigration control and include the repatriation of immigrants already settled in Britain, thus putting repatriation on the political agenda. In the same speech Powell used all his rhetorical powers to construct an image of white Britons becoming 'strangers' in their 'own country':

> They found their wives unable to obtain hospital beds in childbirth, their children unable to obtain school places, their homes and neighbourhoods changed beyond recognition, their plans and prospects for the future defeated (ibid.)

Powell argued that it was the failure of successive governments to act decisively to halt immigration that had led to the situation where more drastic measures were required to resolve the problem.

The furore caused by the speech was such that Powell was forced out of the shadow cabinet. Nonetheless there was extensive media coverage of the issues he raised throughout 1968 and 1969 and in the period leading up to the 1970 general election (*IRR Newsletter*, April/May 1968, April 1969). This acted as a focus for those who backed Powell's call for action to be taken to repatriate black immigrants residing in Britain (Brown, 1999).

Institutionalising immigration controls

In the political climate created by Powell's interventions and the ensuing political debates, the continuing arrival of dependants of Commonwealth migrants who had settled in Britain helped to keep the numbers game alive, leading to increased calls in and out of parliament and in the media for action to be taken to halt immigration and deal with the problems that were popularly believed to be associated with it. The combined effect of this pressure and the use of immigration as an electoral issue opened the way to further legislative measures.

In 1969 the Labour government introduced the Immigration Appeals Act, which was officially based on the report of the Committee on Immigration Appeals, headed by Sir Roy Wilson (Macdonald and Blake, 1995). This report accepted the need for restrictions on immigration, but argued that a system of appeal would ensure that the restrictions were applied fairly. Although this Act is sometimes interpreted as a positive measure, it institutionalised deportation for those breaking the conditions of entry. It also legitimised restrictions on the right of entry of those who were legally entitled to settle in Britain by obliging dependants seeking settlement in Britain to be in possession of an entry certificate. Such certificates had to applied for at the British High Commission in the country of residence. Applicants had to prove their relationship to the person legally residing in Britain, and if they were unable to do so they could be denied entry. Many controversial cases arose under this system (Moore and Wallace, 1975; CRE, 1985b).

The marked shift of the Labour Party towards the idea of firm immigration control was part of a wider political process that led to the introduction of the 1971 Immigration Act by the Conservative government. During the 1970 election campaign the Conservative Party had promised there would 'be no further large-scale permanent immigration'. When the Immigration Bill was introduced in February 1971 it was justified on this basis, but as a number of speakers pointed out during the debates on the Bill it was difficult to see how it could actually further reduce the number of primary immigrants. In essence the 1971 Act qualified the notion of citizenship by differentiating between citizens of Britain and its colonies who were patrial and therefore had the right of abode in Britain, and non-patrials who did not. The most important categories of patrial were:

- Citizens of Britain and its colonies who were entitled to citizenship by virtue of birth, adoption, naturalisation or registration in Britain, or who were born of a parent who had British citizenship by birth, or who had grandparents with such citizenship.
- Citizens of Britain and its colonies who at any time had settled in Britain and who had resided in Britain for five years or more.

Under the Act all aliens and Commonwealth citizens who were not patrials needed permission to enter Britain. Previously, Commonwealth citizens entering under the voucher system had been entitled to settle in Britain, but after the 1971 Act came into force their entry and right to remain depended on the possession of an annually renewable work permit. This change of status has been defined by some scholars as a move towards the migrant worker system of other European countries, with Commonwealth workers who were not patrials (and by definition almost certainly black) reduced to the effective status of short-term contract workers rather than settlers (Castles and Kosack, 1985, Sivanandan, 1982: 108–12).

During the parliamentary debates on the 1971 Immigration Act the association of immigration with race became a subject of dispute between the Conservative and Labour Parties. Although during the late 1960s the Labour Party effectively accommodated itself to a 'white Britain policy', in 1971 it felt moved to question the treatment of Commonwealth immigrants along the same lines as aliens and the overtly racial criteria that underlay the notion of patriality. Despite the fact that the new Act was rightly seen as racist because it allowed potentially millions of white Commonwealth citizens to enter and settle in Britain under the patriality clause, a right denied to almost all non-white Commonwealth citizens, successive immigration rules issued by the home secretary to supplement the 1971 Act emphasised the intention of the Act to keep out black Commonwealth citizens as opposed to whites (Macdonald and Blake, 1995). With the exception of the Asians expelled from Uganda by Idi Amin in 1972, some of whom were allowed to settle in Britain during 1972–3, this policy has been consistently applied ever since. Such measures have also emphasised the essentially sexist nature of immigration controls (WING, 1985).

In summary the decade 1961–71 saw the introduction of three major pieces of legislation aimed largely at excluding black immigrants. The 1971 Act eventually took away the right of black Commonwealth immigrants to settle, and thus represented an important step in the institutionalisation of racist immigration controls.

Immigration and race under Thatcher and Major

As we shall see in Chapter 4, strong immigration controls and policies aimed at promoting 'good race relations' were fostered by the Labour administrations from 1974–9. In the lead-up to the 1979 general election, however, sections of the Conservative Party, including its leader Margaret Thatcher, chose to emphasise the supposed dangers posed to British social and cultural values by the black and ethnic minority people already settled in Britain. Thatcher's pronouncements on this issue were part of a wider campaign to use race as a symbol for the neo-Conservative ideology of Thatcher's wing of the party (Barker, 1981; Smith, 1994; Ansell, 1997). While the political language used still referred to immigrants, the main reference points of this campaign were the black people already settled in Britain. Immigration control remained an issue of public and policy debate, particularly in relation to the dependants and marriage partners of those settled legally (Gordon, 1985).

The policies pursued by the Conservative governments during the period 1979–97 marked a further stage in the development of immigration policy. There were three main policy changes. First, a number of changes to the immigration rules issued under the 1971 Immigration Act were introduced with the explicit aim of tightening controls even further. Second, the 1981 British Nationality Act was passed under the first Thatcher administration and came into force in 1983. Third, during the 1990s the main focus of public policy moved on to asylum seekers and refugees, and the need for specific legislation to deal with this issue.

Parliamentary debates on immigration during the 1980s signalled a move by the Thatcher administrations to strengthen the controls on immigration from the Commonwealth. A recurrent theme in these debates was the perceived need to circumvent the rights of those black Commonwealth citizens with the legal right to enter Britain and to construct the question of nationality along racial lines (*Hansard*, vol. 5, 1981, cols 765–1193; vol. 31, 1982, cols 692–761; vol. 34, 1982, cols 355–439; vol. 37, 1983, cols 178–280; vol. 83, 1985, cols 893–989). The 1981 British Nationality Act signalled a further stage in this strategy. The government argued that by introducing the Act it was rationalising the existing nationality and immigration legislation in order to create a British citizenship with automatic right of abode in Britain. It did this by dividing the category of Citizen of the United Kingdom and Commonwealth into three categories: British citizen, British Dependent Territories Citizen and British Overseas Citizen. Although the government argued that the Act would make immigration control less arbitrary, public and parliamentary figures criticised it for reinforcing racial discrimination (Layton-Henry, 1984: 157–9). Indeed the category of British Overseas Citizen effectively deprived British citizens of (mostly) Asian origin of the right to live in Britain. In this sense it seems correct to argue that the 1981 Act 'enshrines the existing racially discriminatory provisions of immigration law under the new clothing of British citizenship and the right of abode' (Macdonald and Blake, 1995).

A government document prepared for an OECD conference on immigration policy stated the broad policy objectives in traditional terms, but linked them closely to other areas of concern:

> In recent decades, the basis of policy in the United Kingdom has been the need to control primary immigration – that is, new heads of households who are most likely to enter the job market. The United Kingdom is one of the most densely populated countries in Europe. In terms of housing, education, social services and, of course, jobs, the country could not support all those who would like to come here. Firm immigration control is therefore essential, in order to provide the conditions necessary for developing and maintaining good community relations (OECD, 1986: 1).

In practice, therefore, the strategy pursued from 1979 to 1997 continued to legitimate the supposed link between firm control and good community relations. At the same time the various Conservative administrations steadfastly refused to strengthen the 1976 Race Relations Act or to adopt a more positive approach to discrimination and racism. Even after the Scarman Report of 1981 called for coordinated, government-led action against racial disadvantage, a call that has been repeated a number of times since by Lord Scarman and others, the response of the various agencies of the state was at best limited.

Rather, both the Thatcher and the Major administrations continued to emphasise the need for tight immigration control because 'of the strain that the admission of a substantial number of immigrants can place on existing resources and services' (Leon Brittan, *Hansard*, vol. 83, 1985, col. 893). The logic of this approach was to blame conflicts and strains in race relations on the black and ethnic minority communities as a whole, or at least specific sections of them. This allowed the idea of blacks being the 'enemy within' and a threat to social stability to become more deeply rooted.

If the main rationale of the immigration laws and race relations Acts was to produce an atmosphere conducive to the development of 'good race relations' and integration, it needs to be said that they failed to depoliticise the question of black immigration. The racialisation of British politics proceeded apace during the 1970s and 1980s, and took on new forms in relation to specific issues or groups, for example education, the police, young blacks and urban policy (CCCS, 1982; Miles and Phizacklea, 1984; Jacobs, 1986). The restrictions imposed by the 1971 Immigration Act, and the successive immigration rules issued under this Act, seemingly fulfilled the ostensible objective of post-1962 policies – to control primary immigration and restrict secondary immigration – but the politicisation of race continued to grow during that period (Crowley, 1993).

What importance can be given to the racialisation of political discourses in the context of firm immigration controls? A number of issues are involved, and while not all of these can be analysed in this chapter at least two are worth noting. First, the debates on immigration and race took place and developed the context of widespread social, political and economic change. The rapid transformation of many inner city localities, particularly in relation to economic and social infrastructure, provided fertile ground for the racialisation of issues such as employment, housing, education and law and order (Hall *et al.*, 1978; Phizacklea and Miles, 1980: 42–68; Solomos, 1986). This racialisation process moved public and political debate beyond the question of immigration *per se* and towards the identification and resolution of specific social problems linked to race. But the link with the immigration question was maintained at another level, because it was the size of the black population, whether in schools or the unemployment queue, that was identified as the source of the problem (Castles *et al.*, 1984; Macdonald and Blake, 1995).

Second, the continuing racialisation of British politics in the context of firm immigration highlights the way in which political language was often used to emphasise what people wanted to believe and to avoid something they did not wish to face (Edelman, 1977; Katznelson, 1986). Thus although calls for greater control on immigration were often laced with references to the number of resident immigrants or to the large numbers who might arrive and 'swamp' British culture, such statements were not necessarily based on fact. Rather references to statistics and reports were often highly selective and emphasised fears about the present or future. Good examples of this were the debates that took place during the mid 1970s on the 1976 Hawley Report on immigration from the Indian sub-continent and the report on immigration by Select Committee on Race Relations and

Immigration (1978). In both cases the debates in parliament, the media and elsewhere focused on the danger of 'massive' numbers of immigrants arriving in Britain and the possible social and political consequences of this, despite the fact that firm controls on immigration had been exercised since the 1960s (Freeman and Spencer, 1979). Perhaps a more symbolic phenomenon was the introduction in 1986 of visa controls on visitors from India, Pakistan, Bangladesh, Nigeria and Ghana, ostensibly to control the number of illegal immigrants from these countries. The fact that only 222 out of 452 000 visitors from the five countries illegally remained in Britain in 1985 did not prevent the use of visa controls as another symbolic means of holding back the tide of immigrants (*Guardian*, 2 September 1986).

Another disturbing example of this trend to tighten controls was the way in which the Major government responded to the refugee crisis that followed the collapse of former Yugoslavia. While other European countries took in sizeable numbers of refugees from Bosnia during 1992 the British government placed restrictions on the number of people it would accept as legitimate refugees. It defended this stance by arguing that Britain could absorb only a limited number of refugees. Despite protests from a number of pressure groups and criticism by other countries, the Major administration refused to change its position on this issue.

Agitation by right-wing extremist groups and sections of the Conservative Party for stricter immigration controls and repatriation came to the fore in the late 1970s and 1980s, focusing as much on the supposed dangers of this 'alien wedge' as on the arrival of new immigrants. The words used by Enoch Powell in 1968–9 to warn of the dangers of immigration were reworked in the late 1970s around the issue of the 'enemy within', who in many cases was not an immigrant but had been born and grown up in Brixton, Handsworth, Liverpool and other urban localities. The amplification of the mugging issue in the early 1970s, confrontations between the police and young blacks, and the identification of young blacks as an alienated group within black communities and British society in general, led to the construction of a new racialised discourse on black youth (Solomos, 1988). Increasingly this group was identified as drifting into either criminal activities or radical political activities that brought them into direct contact, and hence conflict, with the police. In the 1950s and 1960s the immigration question had focused on the need to keep black immigrants out. Now the language of political debate shifted towards the view that alienated black youths were a kind of social time-bomb that could undermine the fabric of the immigration and race relations amalgam and possibly society as a whole.

During the early 1990s much of the focus of debates on immigration was on the growing number of asylum seekers and refugees (Immigration Law

Practitioners' Association, 1993, 1996; Spencer, 1994; Macdonald and Blake, 1995; Spencer, 1997). Partly as result of the collapse of the communist bloc in Eastern Europe the question of asylum seekers and refugees became a major concern across Europe during the early 1990s. A consequence of this in Britain was the passage of the 1993 Asylum and Immigration Appeals Act. The main goal of this Act was to reduce the number of asylum seekers and hence the number of refugees who would be able to claim sanctuary. However it also introduced a right of appeal for asylum seekers, and during the period between making a claim for asylum and receiving notice of the secretary of state's final decision on their claim or appeal they could not be forcibly removed from or required to leave Britain. Before 1993 it had been virtually impossible to pursue an appeal from outside the country so this was a very positive development from the perspective of asylum seekers. However the 1996 Asylum and Immigration Act undermined the appeal system by introducing a 'White List' of countries in which there was deemed to be no serious risk of persecution. Applicants from such countries were entitled only to an accelerated appeals procedure. In this environment the political debate on immigration became closely intertwined with the public debate on asylum seekers and refugees.

In summary the Thatcher and Major eras can be seen as a time in which concerns about immigration, asylum seekers and refugees became entangled with wider preoccupations about the social and cultural impact of migrant communities, leading to the institutionalisation of an exclusionary framework that sought to restrict immigration. This was partly due to the growing influence of new right politics in the Conservative Party. The necessity of keeping out 'undesirable immigrants' became an integral element of the Conservatives' strategy during this period.

New Labour, new policies?

The previous section outlined the shift in official thinking from a preoccupation with the immigration numbers game to the question of the 'enemy within' and related concerns about social disorder, although this does not mean that immigration became less important as a political issue. Rather the growing use of political symbols depicting black and ethnic minority communities as the 'enemy within' was inextricably linked to the state responses to immigration analysed in this chapter. Indeed the Conservative administrations from 1979 to 1997 continued to use the immigration question to legitimise the maintenance of racially specific controls in response to the 'fears' of 'ordinary people' about excessive immigration (Spencer, 1997).

During its long period in opposition the Labour Party questioned the basis of this approach (FitzGerald and Layton-Henry, 1986; Shukra, 1998; Saggar, 1998b). During this time the Labour Party, which had after all been responsible for the introduction of the 1968 Commonwealth Immigrants Act, seemingly came to view Britain's immigration laws as racist, and suggested that when it returned to power it would introduce legislation to ensure that all controls were both non-racist and non-sexist. In a parliamentary debate on immigration in July 1985 Gerald Kaufman affirmed that while a future Labour administration would maintain firm controls on immigration, it would ensure that such controls were applied equally to all immigrants regardless of race (*Hansard*, vol. 83, 1985, cols 909–10). He accused the Conservatives of identifying immigration with race, and pointed out that recent immigration patterns contradicted this assumption:

> Viewed objectively, immigration should be neither a problem nor an issue in Britain. Substantial primary immigration ended at least a decade and a half ago, and there is no prospect of it starting again. In most years there is a net emigration from the United Kingdom. In the year only 15.5 per cent of immigrants came from the West Indies, Africa and the Indian subcontinent – the areas from which, according to the government, there is the greatest pressure to migrate to the United Kingdom (ibid., col. 910).

This represented a marked shift from the actions of the Labour governments of 1964–70 and 1974–9, although Kaufman and other Labour politicians remained rather vague about what they meant by 'non-racist' immigration controls, and about how future Labour administrations would break away from the logic of government policies since 1962, which had been to perceive black immigration as a problem. As we shall see later, during the 1980s and 1990s a strong black and antiracist lobby emerged within the Labour Party. This lobby pressed the party for a firm commitment to implement reforms relating to immigration and antidiscrimination (FitzGerald and Layton-Henry, 1986: 110–14; Solomos and Back, 1995; Shukra, 1998).

Since New Labour came to power in 1997 its policy on immigration has been linked to two key issues: the complaints made by pressure groups and minority organisations about the impact of immigration policies on human rights and families (Travers, 1999); and the issues that had so preoccupied the previous Conservative administration, namely asylum seekers and refugees (Home Office, 1999a; Immigration Law Practitioners' Association, 1999; Audit Commission, 2000). The treatment of asylum seekers and refugees had become a major cause of political conflict across

Europe during the 1990s, and by the time Labour returned to power it was perhaps the most controversial item on the agenda of both right-wing and left-wing parties.

The measures taken after Labour's landslide victory in May 1997 were contradictory. On the one hand the 'White List' introduced by the Conservatives was abolished and there was a rise in the percentage of applications that were accepted. The home secretary also granted leave to remain to approximately 70 000 long-standing applicants. The Labour Party had been extremely critical of the White List, which had marked a departure from the principle that every individual had the right to have his or her case examined individually. The Refugee Council and others had argued that use of the White List meant that summary decisions would be taken. The Labour Party had agreed with this criticism so the abolition of the White List was not a surprise. However it seems that a White List continues to operate unofficially, though the absence of persecution is less a criterion for regarding countries as safe than are strategic interests and deterrence. For example when the number of Iraqi Kurds entering Britain rose from 1800 in 1999 to 7080 in 2000 there was a rapid change in the acceptance rate. In July 2000, 14 per cent of Iraqi applicants were refused asylum, rising to 91.4 per cent in October 2000 (*Guardian Online*, 25 April 2001). Finally, while the granting of limited leave to remain has brought relief to many thousands of asylum seekers in Britain, from the government's perspective it has also served to reduce in small measure the pressure arising from the increasingly unmanageable backlog of applications.

On the other hand there are clear signs of continuity with the Conservative administrations' record on immigration. This can be seen most clearly in relation to the new government's response to the arrival of around 800 Roma people from Slovakia and the Czech Republic. In direct response to widespread and hostile media coverage of these arrivals, in October 1997 Home Secretary Jack Straw announced that if officials believed that a claim was manifestly unfounded, an asylum seeker would have only five days to appeal instead of 28 days. This served to confirm the media portrayal of the Roma as 'bogus' asylum seekers.

In November 1996 the European Court of Human Rights had found against the Conservative home secretary in the case of Karamjit Singh Chahal, a Sikh separatist under threat of deportation. The court had declared that because there was no effective domestic remedy to review the home secretary's decision to deport on the ground of national security (Article 13), Mr Chahal's rights had been violated. A consequence of this decision was that the ability governments have to deport people on national security grounds was severely curtailed. In order to address this difficulty, just after its election the Labour government brought the Special Immigration Commission Bill before the House. A commission was set up to hear appeals against the home secretary so that the government could once again proceed to deport. An interesting point here was the amicable tone of the discussions across the floor of parliament and Conservative MPs' approval of the new home secretary's response to the decision of the Court of Human Rights.

Neither of the above cases are likely to have significant impact on the number of people who are allowed to remain in Britain, but they do serve to illustrate New Labour's concern with being tough, and being seen to be tough, on immigration.

The above developments occurred in the first year of New Labour's term of office. In the summer of 1998 the results of the government's migration review were published in a white paper entitled *Fairer, Faster and Firmer: A Modern Approach to Immigration and Asylum* (Home Office, 1998a). Those carrying out the review of the immigration and asylum system had been charged with 'thinking the unthinkable', giving rise to expectations that perhaps policy in this area might move in a new and perhaps more progressive direction. It was accepted that the immigration system, and the asylum procedure in particular, was in a shambles and that something would have to be done. Furthermore the number of people claiming asylum (up from 37 000 in 1996 to 41 500 in 1997 and 68 000 in 1998) and the backlog of cases (peaking at over 100 000) continued to rise under the new administration so a radical rethinking of policy seemed necessary. However the changes introduced were in degree rather than in direction.

The white paper promised a system that would be 'fairer, faster and firmer', with the emphasis on speed and firmness. The assumptions, language and arguments that had been used by previous Conservative governments were all there, coupled with a nod towards the improvement of race relations. The main measures were the introduction of vouchers instead of cash benefits, a system of enforced dispersal outside London on a no-choice basis, and an increase in detentions and deportations. Other innovations included a single, one-stop appeal hearing at which all grounds for appeal (including human rights) would be considered; provision for the posting of bonds on behalf of those whose visa applications immigration officers were minded to reject; and increased usage of airline liaison officers to check documents at the point of embarkation. The only significantly fair measure that was introduced was the right of detainees to an automatic bail hearing. The degree of harshness towards would-be migrants, asylum seekers and ethnic minorities in Britain was extraordinary, though perhaps unsurprising in view of Labour's past record.

The Act that eventually reached the statute books in 1999 was only slightly different from the white paper. The bond scheme had provoked an outcry from minority communities, especially those represented by the South East Asian Support Group, who realised this would have a discriminatory impact on them, so the scheme had been abandoned. Apart from a cash element being added to the voucher system the other measures remained largely intact. The Labour Party's massive majority of 174 meant that the government was able to force through these draconian measures despite a prolonged campaign by many of those who had opposed the previous Conservative legislation.

The voucher scheme, which applied only to destitute asylum seekers with additional difficulties (destitution alone conferred no entitlement), entitled each adult to £37 in vouchers (the equivalent of 70 per cent of income support) that could be redeemed at certain supermarkets and charity shops. Liberal Democrats, Labour backbenchers such as Diane Abbott, Jeremy Corbyn and Neil Gerard, and many of the organisations operating the charity shops accurately predicted that this would lead to the stigmatisation and humiliation of asylum seekers by clearly marking them out as 'different' and 'dependent', and making them targets for hostility. Pressure from a wide range of groups, including those just mentioned, resulted in £10 worth of vouchers being made redeemable at post offices for cash. Continued hostility, most notably from Bill Morris of the TGWU, and reports of the difficulties faced by individuals and families when trying to use the vouchers led to a review of the system and a proposed alteration to (but not the abolition of) the system.

Enforced dispersal was another key element of the 1999 Immigration and Asylum Act. This was designed to relieve the pressure on overstretched local authorities, particularly in London and parts of the South East, especially some localities in Kent. These local authorities were certainly overstretched, but this was a result of the shift in responsibility for asylum seekers from central government to local authorities that occurred after the passage of 1996 Asylum and Immigration Act, and not because of the number of asylum seekers *per se*. Once again, NGOs and concerned others had warned that dispersal was a recipe for racism and racist violence, that it would leave people with limited language skills with little or no support in areas of Britain that were both largely homogeneous and socially deprived. The latter had been clear in the 1998 white paper, which had expressly announced the government's intention to place asylum seekers in areas where accommodation costs were low. Those who had warned that this would mean dumping asylum seekers in sink estates were proved correct. There have been a number of adverse reports from Liverpool about the

Landmark hostel, and the Sighthill estate in Glasgow witnessed the first murder of an asylum seeker. Furthermore the Audit Commission has warned that the conditions in which asylum seekers are being housed are unsafe, often unfit for human habitation, and vulnerable to racist attacks (Audit Commission, 2000).

In some ways the 1999 Immigration and Asylum Act can be seen as a continuation of Conservative policies in the area of pre-entry controls and welfare support for asylum seekers, but it also stepped up the practice of detention, with a consequent increase in the number of places of detention, especially prisons (Bloch, 2000). According to the Home Office, only those believed likely to abscond are detained, and usually at the end of the process. However, many people are detained upon arrival and it seems likely that the purposes of this policy, for New Labour as much as for the Conservatives before them, are deterrence and the facilitation of removal. That this practice is in contravention of Britain's human rights obligations was confirmed by a decision in September 2001, when the judge found there to be no evidence that four Kurds who had been held in custody would abscond, and ordered the government to pay compensation.

The home secretary successfully appealed against this decision but promised that asylum seekers would no longer be held in prisons. As a consequence the construction of purpose-built detention centres grew apace. The first dedicated detention centre for families was opened at Oakington in Cambridge in March 2000, followed by another at Harmondsworth near Heathrow, and one at Yarl's Wood. It is ironic that when the policy of detaining asylum seekers on arrival was originally proposed by Anne Widdicombe (then shadow home secretary) it had been ridiculed by the Labour Party.

The Labour government subsequently introduced a number of other measures to keep asylum seekers at bay. Carriers' liability was extended to trucks travelling to Britain through the Channel tunnel (a common means of gaining entry to Britain), and to the company Eurotunnel, which was forced to invest heavily in security at the French end of the tunnel. Other measures with a direct impact on asylum seekers included the proscription of twenty, predominantly Muslim, organisations under the 2000 Prevention of Terrorism Act, and authorisation by the home secretary for immigration officials to discriminate against certain ethnic groups (including Albanians, Afghans, Chinese, Kurds, Roma, Somalis and Tamils) at the point of entry.

At the beginning of 2001 Home Secretary Jack Straw proposed a significant new direction in asylum policy. He attacked the Geneva Convention, arguing that it was not fitted to today's world. As the general election approached he also spoke with approval of the attempt to find a common definition of 'refugee' at the EU level. This might have been a response to a number of high-profile court cases that had upheld a definition that included non-state persecution. A common EU definition, one that was closer to those used in France and Germany, would probably mean that victims of non-state persecution would no longer be granted asylum in Britain (*Guardian*, 26 April 2001). In defence of this far less liberal policy, Straw argued 'that there is a limit on the number of applicants, *however genuine*, that you can take' (*Observer*, 20 May 2001, emphasis added) and that a cap or quota would have to be introduced. He went on to explain that the limit was dependent on 'the ability of the country to take people and public acceptability' (ibid.) He did not refer to the role that government could play in creating public tolerance and acceptance.

Ironically this tougher line on asylum was taken at the same time as government acknowledgement of the need for migrant labour. In September 2000 Immigration Minister Barbara Roche, conceded that Britain was suffering a skills shortage. Soon afterwards a government-sponsored report emphasised the positive contributions that migrants could make and argued that ultimately immigration was good for the country and the economy (Glover *et al.*, 2001). Inevitably the government commissioned yet more research and produced another white paper, this time explicitly linking race relations with migration. Entitled *Secure Borders, Safe Haven: Integration with Diversity in Modern Britain*, the white paper symbolised the shifting boundaries of government thinking on immigration by linking control with protection of the national interest. It also suggested that those allowed in should be encouraged to develop a 'shared sense of belonging and identity' (Home Office, 2002: 1).

It is worth noting in this context that whatever the merits of the 2000 Race Relations (Amendment) Act, it exempted from its remit immigration and nationality decisions provided for in statutes or expressly required or authorised by ministers. It has therefore had the effect of allowing discrimination on the basis of nationality and ethnic origin to operate lawfully. On paper ministers are not allowed to discriminate on the basis of race or colour, though the government has never answered the question of how a distinction is to be made between race or colour and ethnic or national origins. As the Home Office guidelines on the Act helpfully state: 'This exemption reflects a unique requirement for immigration and entry clearance officers to discriminate on grounds of nationality or national origin as set out in instructions' (Home Office, 2001: 40). It is perhaps a sign of the times that this statement was made in good faith and with no sense of irony.

The shift in government thinking signalled by the white paper led to the introduction in 2002 of the Nationality, Immigration and Asylum Bill, which was based on a clear awareness that both the Conservative legislation of the mid 1990s and the 1999 Immigration and Asylum Act had failed to resolve both governmental and popular concerns. Thus it proposed an immigration hotline on which members of the public could denounce irregular migrants, the introduction of so-called 'smart-cards', a further increase in detention facilities (including those for families) to enable an increase in deportations, and a stepping up of border controls to prevent the arrival of asylum seekers. Though the white paper promised support for the integration of refugees, it is not clear whether this promise has been upheld in practice. As with the Acts introduced by the Conservatives and Labour's own 1999 Immigration and Asylum Act, these proposals were in response to popular expressions of hostility towards asylum seekers and refugees. In this sense they fitted into the longer history of Labour and Conservative policies on immigration and race relations, and it already seems evident that developments in Europe as well as Britain may lead to new legislation, even after the 2002 Bill reaches the statute books.

Summary and conclusion

The central conclusion to emerge from this chapter returns us to the question of the role that political institutions play in regulating the entry and incorporation of migrant labour. The story of post-1945 responses to immigration covered in this chapter shows how popular responses and state policy making have been shaped by specific national and local political situations. The circumstances that bring about particular types of policy response are not predetermined but are the product of policy agendas and ideologies, both within and outside state institutions. During the period covered in this chapter state responses to immigration were by no means uniform, although some trends can be identified.

We need to know more about the dynamics and the limits of state intervention in this field if we are to understand how the interplay between immigration and the state led to racist immigration controls becoming institutionalised.

In this chapter we have concentrated on the broad contours of political debate and policy change since 1945. In Chapters 8, 9 and 10 we shall consider the dynamics of social change and racialised politics in the present. This analysis will inevitably take us into debates on political practice and beyond the confines of a narrow academic focus. In the context of virulent racism and calls for restrictions on immigration it is hardly possible to look at the history of immigration and race since 1945 without reflecting on the impact of immigration controls on the everyday lives of black and ethnic minority citizens. But first we shall look at the other elements of state intervention over the past few decades, namely race relations Acts and national antidiscrimination policies.

4 Race Relations Policies and the Political Process

As we have seen in the two previous chapters, the genesis, implementation and institutionalisation of controls on immigration, particularly black immigration from the Commonwealth, was a complex process. Similarly the development of antidiscrimination legislation and policies aimed at promoting greater equality of opportunity for black British citizens has been a thoroughly contradictory process, based as much on political expediency as on any commitment to justice and equality. The three major race relations Acts passed since 1965, for example, have been highly controversial, with some seeing them as an attempt to favour blacks over whites in the respect of jobs, homes and so on. At times this opposition has boiled over into open calls for the dismantling of the major institutions of what is sometimes called the race relations industry (Flew, 1984; Palmer, 1986).

This and the following chapter will explore the evolution of the politics of race, from the expansion of state policies dealing with racial discrimination and other aspects of racial inequality during the mid 1960s to the contemporary forms of state intervention. This chapter will analyse the national processes involved in this evolution, while Chapter 5 will concentrate on the development of racialised political debates and practices at the local level. This division is not meant to suggest that there is a clearly defined separation of national and local political processes. Indeed it will be made clear throughout both chapters that there are many links between these levels and that to a certain extent it is impossible to understand one without some reference to the other. But for heuristic reasons it seems sensible to present the histories of state intervention at the national and local levels as analytically distinct, albeit with important connections.

This chapter approaches the question of the political management of race by analysing the institutionalisation of the dual interventionist strategy adopted by both major political parties in the mid 1960s, as outlined in Chapter 3: the attempt to achieve a balance between controls on immigration and measures aimed at improving race relations. It will do so by detailing the various legislative measures passed by successive governments since 1965 and the most important political events in this field from the early 1960s onwards. This will inevitably return us to the part played by Enoch Powell in the racialisation of political debate from 1968 onwards, and to the changing ideologies and practices of the Conservative and Labour Parties. The account in this chapter of broad trends in state policies links up with the analysis in Chapters 8, 9 and 10 of the dynamics of racist, antiracist and black political mobilisation by providing the historical background to the development of the movements and groupings discussed in those chapters.

Racism and racial discrimination

It is useful to look at some of the differences between the concepts of racism and racial discrimination. In practice, these two concepts sometimes become merged so that they have little apparent difference. For example Banton (1992) writes that since the International Convention on the Elimination of All Forms of Racial Discrimination was adopted by the General Assembly of the United Nations in 1965, the United Nations has taken racism to mean almost the same thing as racial discrimination. However others establish clear differences between the terms. One difference is that racism is seen as pathological: ‘When referring to racism, speakers and writers often employ medical metaphors, likening it to a virus, a disease, or some sickness that can be spread in the manner of an epidemic’ (ibid.: 70). Racial discrimination, on the other hand, is more normal, ‘in the sense that crime, deplorable as it may be, is a normal feature of all kinds of human society’ (ibid.; see also Banton, 1996).

Some see racism as an ideology and racial discrimination as a practice, with corresponding differences in responses to them. If racism is an ideology, then antiracist movements must emphasise measures to counter this ideology, including the use of mass media and schooling. If racial discrimination is an act, then antiracists must emphasise measures that range from collective action to legislation to prevent such acts. Banton argues that in theory, ‘for every act of racial discrimination someone is responsible and should be brought to account’ (Banton, 1992: 73; see also Banton, 1996). However in practice things are not quite that simple. Research evidence of the treatment of postwar black immigrants and their descendants shows that we should be concerned not only with acts of discrimination but also with processes of discrimination. Processes are established, routine and subtle; only occasionally will an individual act of racial discrimination be visible within these processes, and only intermittently can one individual actor be identified as responsible for the exclusion of another from rightful opportunities. The denial of racial discrimination is common because quite simply it *can* be denied due to its invisibility.

The existence of racial discrimination in employment can be brought to public attention in a number of ways. First, there can be action by antiracists or those discriminated against, such as strikes or other collective action in response to racist practices (for examples see Phizacklea and Miles, 1987: 118–20). Second, there can be discrimination testing by agencies such as the Commission for Racial Equality (CRE) and the Policy Studies Institute (PSI), which have produced a number of notable accounts of the pervasiveness of discrimination (Daniel, 1968; McIntosh and Smith, 1974; Hubbuck and Carter, 1980). Third, there can be research, usually by academic researchers, into discrimination in social institutions.

Race relations legislation in context

The main objective of this chapter is to explain the genesis, development and contradictions of political strategies on race relations, as pursued by Conservative and Labour governments since 1965. But it will also consider the achievements of these strategies, both at a practical and at a symbolic level. Thus as well as analysing the legislation implemented by the state over the decades it will look at the interplay between the stated objectives and the actual outcomes of the most important legislative measures.

From one perspective the various pieces of legislation passed by successive governments since 1965 are largely symbolic or inadequate. Nearly four decades after the first Race Relations Act was passed in 1965 there is little evidence of significant advances against entrenched forms of racial inequality. A recurrent criticism of central government departments in this respect is that they have not shown a clear commitment to or allocated adequate resources to racial equality programmes (McCrudden, 1988; Jenkins and Solomos, 1989; McCrudden *et al.*, 1991).

By comparing the stated objectives with the actual outcomes, this chapter will highlight the problems that past policies have helped to reproduce as well as those they have ameliorated. This will demonstrate the impact of state intervention since the 1960s on the reproduction and persistence of racial inequality, and enable us to explore the possibilities for alternative political strategies to tackle racism and racial inequality more effectively.

The key legislative measures we are concerned with are listed in Table 4.1. This should be looked at in combination with Table 3.1, which lists the various immigration control measures, since in practice the two sets of legislation were inextricably linked.

The main reason for looking closely at these legislative measures is that since the early 1970s the debates and controversies that have surrounded

Table 4.1 *Legislation on race relations since 1965*

1965	Race Relations Act
1966	Local Government Act
1967	Race Relations Act
1968	Race Relations Act
1976	Race Relations Act
1998	Human Rights Act
2000	Race Relations (Amendment) Act

them have served to illustrate the changing terms of political debate on the part played by the government in tackling racial inequality. Aspects of this will be linked to the dynamics of political conflicts and struggles over the politics of race. We shall look at this issue in more detail in Chapters 8 to 10, but it would clearly be impossible to explain the genesis and development of state interventions without looking at the history of racist political mobilisation, black protest and racialised ideologies.

The origins of antidiscrimination legislation

In the 1950s the question of what should be done to counter racial discrimination emerged as a major topic in debates on immigration and race relations. Even in the early stages of black immigration there was an awareness that in the longer term racial discrimination was likely to become a volatile political issue. In the first years of postwar black immigration political debates on race centred on the question of immigration control. However an underlying concern was the question of future race relations. Fear that the arrival of too many black immigrants would lead to problems in respect of housing, employment and social services was already being widely articulated (Patterson, 1969; Freeman, 1979).

In the context of the intense debate on immigration during the late 1950s the Labour Party set up a working party to look at the question of legislation to combat racial discrimination and to make practical legislative proposals (*The Times*, 24 July 1958). Other discussions on this issue were encouraged through the efforts of politicians such as Fenner Brockway and welfare groups with a special interest in the position of black communities, either locally or nationally.

Two problems were seen as in need of urgent attention. The first was the negative response of the majority white population to competition by black workers in the housing and labour markets. In particular localities, such as

London, Birmingham and Wolverhampton, such competition was seen as creating the conditions for future conflict. The second problem was the frustration of black workers who felt excluded from equal participation in British society by virtue of the colour bar that developed in the labour and housing markets, along with related acts of discrimination.

Both these issues were perceived as potential sources of conflict that the government had to control through direct intervention. In the early stages, however, it was not totally clear what the best mechanisms for state intervention actually were.

The genesis of race relations policies

The first measures to deal with potential racial conflict and tackle racial discrimination were taken in the 1960s and took two basic forms. The first involved the setting up of welfare agencies to deal with the problems faced by black immigrants and to help white communities to understand the immigrants. The second involved the passage of the 1965 and 1968 Race Relations Acts, which were premised on the notion that the state should attempt to end discrimination based on race, colour or ethnic origin through legal sanctions and public regulatory agencies charged with promoting greater equality of opportunity (Rose *et al.*, 1969: 511–30).

This dual strategy was clearly articulated in the Labour government's 1965 white paper on *Immigration from the Commonwealth*, which had its origins in the debates of the 1950s and the period leading up to the 1962 Commonwealth Immigrants Act. The notion that immigration was essentially an issue of race was consistent with the views that the growth of black communities was actually or potentially a source of social problems and conflicts, and that it was necessary for the state to introduce measures to promote the integration of immigrants into wider society and its fundamental institutions.

The linking of immigration controls to integrative measures was a significant step forward since it signalled a move towards the management of domestic race relations as well as legitimising the institutionalisation of firm controls at the point of entry. In 1965 the Labour government passed the first Race Relations Act, which enshrined the principle of ending discrimination against black immigrants and their descendants on the grounds of race. Although fairly limited in scope the Act was important in confirming the government's concern about racial discrimination and its broad objective of using legislative action to achieve good race relations (Lester and Bindman, 1972: 107–49).

Much has been written about the inherent contradictions involved in trying to balance racially specific controls on immigration with measures to prevent discriminatory practices. Yet since the 1960s these two facets of state intervention have been inextricably linked. According to Roy Hattersley's famous formula, 'Integration without control is impossible, but control without integration is indefensible' (*Hansard*, vol. 709, cols 378–85). The rationale behind this argument was never articulated clearly, but it was at least partly based on the idea that the fewer immigrants (particularly black ones) there were, the easier it would be to integrate them into the English way of life and its social and cultural values.

During the tenure of Roy Jenkins as home secretary in the mid 1960s, this notion of integration was linked to the idea that unless the political institutions helped to deal with the social problems of immigrants and of the areas in which they lived there was the prospect of US-style racial tension and violence. In this context concern focused particularly on the second generation of young blacks, who were perceived as a potentially volatile group (Solomos, 1988: 53–87).

Given this perspective the Race Relations Acts of 1965 and 1968 concentrated on the twin tasks of (a) setting up special bodies to deal with the problems faced by immigrants in relation to discrimination, social adjustment and welfare, and (b) helping to educate the population as a whole about race relations, and hence minimising the risk of racial conflict developing in Britain in the way it had done in the US.

The basic assumption underlying these measures was, as argued above, the notion that the presence of too many black immigrants might result in racial conflict, but, this numbers game was also tied to the idea that cultural differences between the immigrants and the host population were a potential source of conflict. From 1962 onwards both the Conservative and the Labour Party accepted the need for immigration restrictions to be balanced by measures to bring about integration in housing, education, employment and the social services.

Significantly however, successive governments did not use mainstream government departments to tackle this issue. While the Home Office was directly responsible for the enforcement of strict immigration controls, the responsibility for enforcing the 1965 and 1968 Race Relations Acts was given to regulatory agencies and the judicial system. The 1965 Act set up the Race Relations Board, while the 1968 Act set up the Community Relations Commission and strengthened the powers of the Race Relations Board in dealing with complaints of discrimination (Abbott, 1971: chs 9, 10). Between 1965 and 1975 successive governments left the tackling of racial discrimination to these bodies, and provided little direction or support.

The 1976 Race Relations Act

Critics of the 1965 and 1968 Race Relations Acts pointed out that these attempts to tackle racial discrimination were limited both in intent and in impact, and in the early 1970s they called for a new and more effective strategy to address discrimination, particularly in employment (Abbott, 1971; Lester and Bindman, 1972). At the same time research by a number of bodies showed that a high degree of discrimination persisted, and this was taken as proof that the efforts of successive governments since 1965 had produced little or no change (Smith, 1977). More critical studies took their cue from this evidence to argue that race relations legislation, particularly when linked to discriminatory immigration controls, was no more than a gesture or a symbolic political act to give the impression that something was being done when in practice very little was being achieved (Moore, 1975; Sivanandan, 1982).

The debate on the effectiveness of the 1965 and 1968 Acts raged throughout the early 1970s and began to have an impact on the organisations charged with implementing the legislation. The Race Relations Board, for example, produced a critical analysis of the operation of race relations legislation that argued, among other things, that the effectiveness of the 1968 Act was limited by (a) its concentration on individual forms of discrimination and (b) the lack of resources to implement the law fully. It also argued that racial discrimination was less a matter of active discrimination against individuals than the reproduction of 'situations in which equality of opportunity is consciously or unconsciously denied' (Race Relations Board, 1973). At the same time the Select Committee on Race Relations and Immigration launched a major investigation, culminating in a report entitled *The Organisation of Race Relations Administration* (1975).

Although this report looked at the situation from an administrative angle, it put a number of items onto the political agenda. The most important of these were (a) the need to go beyond the narrow definition of discrimination used in the 1965 and 1968 Acts to include institutionalised or unintended forms of discrimination, (b) the need to strengthen the administrative structures and legal powers of the Race Relations Board to allow for more effective implementation of antidiscrimination policies, including penalties for those found guilty of discrimination, and (c) the need for a more interventionist stance by central government departments, particularly the Home Office, to buttress the role of race relations institutions (Select Committee, 1975: vii).

Taken together, these implied the necessity of stronger government action to promote equal opportunity because 'there is a growing lack of confidence in the effectiveness of government action and, in the case of some groups such as young West Indians, this lack of confidence can turn into hostile resentment' (Select Committee, 1975: xvi–xix). In addition they were seen as highlighting the need for more efficient social policies on race in order to achieve the goal announced by Roy Jenkins during the 1960s: namely a genuinely integrated society where there would be 'equal opportunity, accompanied by cultural diversity in an atmosphere of mutual tolerance'.

More fundamentally perhaps, the evidence that went into these reports had a major influence on a white paper on racial discrimination that was published in September 1975. This accepted the relative failure of past policies to achieve fundamental change, as well as the need for stronger legislation and a 'coherent and coordinated policy over a large field of influence involving many government Departments, local authorities, the existing and future statutory bodies concerned with the subject and, indeed, many individuals in positions of responsibility and influence' (Home Office, 1975: 5). It also accepted the need for broader government involvement in tackling the 'more complex situations of accumulated disadvantages and of the effects of past discrimination'. The rationale for this, according to the white paper, was the government's recognition that the majority of the black immigrants were 'here to stay' and that policies had to be based on recognition of this fact.

In this sense the white paper was a departure from the policies pursued by successive administrations since the 1960s. However, although government participation and a political commitment to racial equality were prioritised there was no detailed analysis of how to link the legal and administrative framework with active political involvement by the Home Office and other government departments in promoting racial equality. More fundamentally, while this strategy was recognised as having major expenditure implications, as well as involving a reassessment of the priorities in existing programmes, no attempt was made to define what these were, or to examine how the government's contribution to the new strategy was going to be implemented.

In the ensuing legislative proposals, therefore, the emphasis was placed on changing the legislative and administrative framework, while the wider changes promised in the select committee's report and the white paper were put to one side. Against this background the 1976 Race Relations Act 'represented a strengthening and extension of existing anti-discrimination policy rather than a new and unfamiliar policy' (Nixon, 1982: 366).

The most important innovations were (a) extending the objectives of the law to cover not only intentional discrimination but also racial disadvantage brought about by systemic racism, (b) amalgamating the Race Relations

Board and the Community Relations Commission into a joint agency, the Commission for Racial Equality (CRE), and (c) introducing a different procedure for the handling of individual complaints on discrimination, with employment cases being handled by industrial tribunals rather than processed through the CRE (Lustgarten, 1980; McCrudden, 1982: 336–48).

The first innovation was intended to overcome the problem of proving the existence of institutional filter processes that were biased against minority workers. 'Direct discrimination' was defined by the 1976 Act quite straightforwardly as the situation in which 'a person treats another person less favourably on racial grounds than he treats, or would treat, someone else'. It also put on the statute book the category of 'indirect discrimination', which was defined as treatment that could be described as equal in a formal sense but discriminatory in its effect on one particular racial group. An example of indirect discrimination was the application of conditions and requirements for jobs in such a way that:

- the proportion of persons of a racial group who can comply with these is considerably smaller than the proportion of persons not of that racial group who can comply with them;
- they are to the detriment of the persons who cannot comply with them;
- that they are not justifiable irrespective of the colour, race, nationality or ethnic or national origins of the person to whom they are applied (Home Office, 1977: 4–5).

The introduction of the concept of indirect discrimination into race relations legislation partly sprang from the US experience of affirmative action against institutionalised forms of racism, which had been widely commented upon during the period leading up to the 1976 Act (Abbott, 1971; Lester and Bindman, 1972). Indeed according to one account, both the American programmes (based on the Civil Rights Act of 1964) and the post-1976 British attention to indirect discrimination were attempts 'to circumvent the problems of proof of intentional discrimination, to go beyond its individualised nature, and to provide a basis for intervening against the present effects of past and other types of institutional discrimination' (McCrudden, 1983: 56).

The second innovation, the setting up of the CRE, resulted from the experience of the organisational management of antidiscrimination policies during the period 1965–75. Combining the activities of the Community Relations Commission and the Race Relations Board was seen as paving the way for a more coherent implementation of the law to promote equality of opportunity and good race relations.

The CRE was to have three main duties: (a) to work towards the elimination of discrimination, (b) to promote equality of opportunity and good race relations, and (c) to keep under review the working of the Act and draw up proposals for amendments to it. For the first two duties the CRE was empowered to carry out formal investigations of organisations in which it believed unlawful discrimination was taking place, to help individual complainants in cases of discrimination, and to issue codes of practice and guidance on (a) the elimination of discrimination in employment and (b) the promotion of equality of opportunity. In addition it was to carry out promotional work aimed at changing the attitudes and behaviour of employers toward minorities.

The third major innovation was to allow individuals direct access to courts or industrial tribunals in order to obtain redress in respect of complaints under the Act. Although the CRE could offer individuals assistance in carrying through their complaint, direct action through industrial tribunals was seen as a stronger strategy against discrimination in the workplace. This view was supported by reference to the desirability of treating cases of racial discrimination in the same manner as cases of sex discrimination and complaints of unfair dismissal.

From policy to practice

Given these stated objectives, and the government's promise of an effective race relations policy, it may at first sight seem surprising that after the 1976 Act came into force much of the discussion focused on the disjuncture between its objectives and its actual impact. Even Lord Scarman's sober report on the urban unrest during 1981 pointed out that policies had failed to make a major impact on the roots of racial disadvantage (Scarman, 1981: para. 2.38).

Offe (1984: 144) pointed out that 'the increasingly visible conflict between the promise and the experience, form and content, of state policies' could result in increased conflict and disenchantment. Broadly speaking this is what seems to have happened. While the Act promised radical changes, the translation of broad objectives into practice was not easy.

Detailed evidence on the workings of the 1976 Act began to emerge in the 1980s, although it was the focus of much critical comment from the early days (House of Commons, Home Affairs Committee, 1981b). It does seem, however, that the translation into practice of the initiatives introduced by the Act was at best limited. Almost all the academic research conducted on the effectiveness of the Act has pointed to three ways in which the policies proved ineffective in tackling racial inequality: the machinery set up to implement the Act did not function effectively; the policies did not produce the intended results; and the policies failed to meet the expectations of the black population (Jenkins and Solomos, 1989; McCrudden *et al.*, 1991).

For example a range of studies indicate that both formal investigations and individual complaints procedures had only a limited impact on discriminatory practices in employment and housing, and that the CRE had a severe problem using its powers effectively to challenge entrenched processes of discrimination (Brown and Gay, 1985; McCrudden, 1987; McCrudden *et al.*, 1991). A Home Affairs Committee investigation of the CRE in 1981 highlighted a number of organisational problems that hampered the latter's formal investigations in the early stages (House of Commons, Home Affairs Committee, 1981b: xxiii–xxxiii). However there is clear evidence that the ambiguous nature of the law also acted as a brake on its ability to carry out investigations successfully and speedily (Applebey and Ellis, 1984). By 1983 the formal investigation procedure was so unworkable that the CRE proposed that its investigative powers be sharpened in order to reduce delays (CRE, 1983, 1985a). It acknowledged that despite the relatively sizeable number of formal investigations, its impact on discrimination had been limited.

The picture in relation to individual complaints is by no means clear due to the lack of critical analysis of the various stages of the complaints process, but research suggests that there was a very low degree of success in proving discrimination. The CRE could claim a certain amount of success in that most of the successful cases had been supported by it, but these only amounted to a small proportion of the reported cases of discrimination, let alone those which went unreported.

Overall it seems clear that during the 1970s and early 1980s black and ethnic minority workers remained in a relatively restricted number of occupational areas, were overrepresented in low-paid and insecure jobs, or were working antisocial hours in unhealthy or dangerous environments. Although black and Asian people were employed in a broader range of occupations than before, these tended to be jobs that were deemed fit for ethnic minority workers rather than white workers (Brown, 1992: 52). In 1984 the Policy Studies Institute published its report on a major survey of the situation of black people in Britain, covering housing, education and employment. It showed that black people were still generally employed below their qualification and skill level, earned less than white workers in comparable job levels and were still concentrated in the same industries as they had been 25 years earlier (Brown, 1984; Jewson and Mason, 1994; Law, 1996).

On top of this black people had a higher unemployment rate, which had increased faster than that of the white population. Particularly badly hit were ethnic minority young people, or the second- and third-generation descendants of immigrants. According to a review of the statistical evidence:

> While employment prospects are discouraging for all young people, the evidence ... shows that black youth unemployment has reached astronomical proportions in some areas. The differential unemployment rates between blacks and whites are in fact generally greater for this age group than for any other. When account is taken of the fact that black people are far more likely to go into further education than whites, we can see that young black people in the 1980s are facing a desperate situation (Newnham, 1986: 17).

However, simple statistics of inequality in employment do not by themselves demonstrate the operation of racial discrimination. Deniers of racism draw on a number of alternative explanations for the persistence of inequality of opportunity among the descendants of black immigrants. In societies such as Britain, where most postwar immigrants have citizenship and civil rights and face no legal barriers to employment, there are still a whole range of forces that can lead to the perpetuation of inequality amongst immigrant groups and ethnic minorities long after the first generation has become settled and consolidated. These include the persistence of language and cultural differences, the existence of identity problems amongst the second generation, the educational achievement of the second generation, the geographical areas in which the immigrants settled, the occupational and industrial sectors in which the immigrants first found work, and their own aspirations, preferences and choices.

By the 1990s the Policy Studies Institute, among others, was highlighting a growing trend towards class and gender differentiation within minority communities in respect of labour market position, as well as in social relations more broadly (Jones, 1993; Modood *et al.*, 1997; Mason, 2000; Cabinet Office, 2001). Such trends pointed to the increasing complexity of the social changes taking place within ethnic minority communities and their different modes of integration into the class structure of British society. This is a theme to which we shall return in Chapter 11.

New agendas and strategies for the twenty-first century

Partly as a result of the developments discussed above, in the past two decades there have been important changes in public policies on racial inequality and exclusion. During the 1980s and early 1990s a number of bodies, including the CRE, lobbied for a major reorganisation of the administration of race relations measures and for a stronger central government lead. Lord Scarman's report on urban unrest and numerous other reports argued for a radical programme of action to tackle the root causes of racial inequality (Benyon and Solomos, 1987).

The CRE joined in the call for a more positive stance by the government. The CRE's proposals for change, which were first made in draft form in 1983, included a number of basic changes to strengthen the implementation process, including (a) clarification of the meaning of direct and indirect discrimination to take account of the complex situation on the ground, (b) the setting up of specialist tribunals to deal with discrimination cases, these tribunals having the power to order changes to prevent a recurrence of discrimination, (c) clarification of the procedures for formal investigation in order to prevent delaying tactics by employers or other bodies, (d) a redefinition of the law to allow for more effective positive actions to redress the effects of past and present discrimination, and (e) a strengthening of the sanctions against those found to be unlawfully discriminating.

Such changes were seen by the CRE and by academic researchers as a way of overcoming some of the most obvious limitations of the 1976 Act, and of reinforcing the government's commitment to racial equality (Edwards, 1995; Favell, 1997, 2001). They were also seen as a way of showing black people that the CRE was able to distance itself from the government and propose changes that were not necessarily popular with ministers and officials. However its calls for change remained unheeded until New Labour came to power in 1997.

Although there was strong evidence that the degree of discrimination in employment, housing and other areas remained alarmingly high, successive Conservative administrations showed little appetite for strengthening the related legislation in order to make it effective. In the absence of a strong lead from the government the CRE attempted to innovate within the terms of its powers. One of the major innovations it introduced during the early 1980s was a code of practice aimed at eliminating discrimination in the workplace, which came into force in April 1984. First published in draft form in early 1982 the code went through a number of changes before the government formally laid it before parliament in April 1983. From April 1984 the code was admissible in evidence at tribunals, and if it was thought that a provision in it was relevant to the proceedings it could be taken into account when determining a question (Home Office, 1977: 39). The CRE considered that the code would 'do much to advance the cause of racial equality at work' (CRE, Annual Report, 1983: 15), particularly when combined with formal investigations and the individual complaints process. Yet a CRE survey of employers' responses to the code revealed that many employers were unaware of its existence (CRE, Annual Report, 1987: 8). The CRE was well aware that the changes made were only touching the tip of the iceberg, and it continued to stress that 'the scale and persistence of discrimination are insupportable in any civilised society' (CRE, Annual Report, 1987: 8).

When New Labour came to power in May 1997 it was expected to uphold its electoral commitment to strengthen the 1976 Race Relations Act, and more generally to respond to demands from within its ranks to develop a more positive policy agenda on racism and multiculturalism (CRE, 1998; Rubenstein, 1998; Home Office, 1999b; Home Office, 2000, 2001; Home Office, Race Equality Unit, 2000). However, the policy debates since 1997 have highlighted the often contradictory and limited nature of New Labour's thinking on the subject. Furthermore, as pointed out in Chapter 3, New Labour's policies on immigration and asylum appear even more draconian than those of the previous Conservative government. In this section we shall explore the evolution of its policies on race relations.

Perhaps the most important developments we have seen in this area have been the publication of the Macpherson Report on the murder of Stephen Lawrence, the reform of the 1976 Race Relations Act and the government's promise to develop new initiatives to tackle racial discrimination in the public sector. More broadly there has been a greater sense of urgency about responding to the challenges posed by the growth of racism and the dilemmas posed by multiculturalism.

When it was in opposition, New Labour worked closely with representatives of minority communities and groups campaigning on a range of issues, from black deaths in custody to asylum and immigration issues. This was not confined to backbenchers such as Harry Cohen, Jeremy Corbyn, Neil Gerard and Max Madden – all of whom had large ethnic minority constituencies. For example shadow cabinet minister Jack Straw was closely associated with the Lawrence campaign and the demand for a public enquiry into the death of the black teenager.

During this period New Labour also formed close links with the National Assembly Against Racism, the Joint Council for the Welfare of Immigrants, the 1990 Trust and a number of other community and campaigning organisations, as well as taking part in public meetings on the 1993 and 1996 Asylum and Immigration Acts. However while the party seemed comfortable with its multicultural, antiracist position a different stance was discernible in relation to migration. During the debates that followed the reading of the 1993 and 1996 bills it was noticeable that senior figures in the party failed to question some of the fundamental tenets of the Conservative government's arguments, preferring instead to focus on the letter of the law and wary of being seen as soft on migration. In the House of Commons Tony Blair spoke of the effect that certain measures were having on genuine asylum seekers, such as the curtailment of leave to appeal for those making an in-country application, the accelerated appeals procedure, which was affecting many more asylum seekers than just those whose claims were 'manifestly unfounded', and the removal of certain rights to appeal (*Hansard*, 2 November 1992). Although critical (at the time) of the use of the term 'bogus', New Labour accepted that the majority of claimants were 'not genuine'.

While Blair argued that 'good race relations cannot be other than harmed when we pass legislation which in the main will adversely affect one part of our community only' (*Hansard*, 2 November 1992, col. 36), it was left to Old Labour backbenchers such as Max Madden, Jeremy Corbyn, Bernie Grant and Robert Maclennan to criticise the racist nature of the proposed legislation (*Hansard*, 2 November 1992, col. 65). In the main New Labour seemed more concerned with addressing its electoral 'vulnerability' on immigration, and avoiding accusations of being soft on the issue.

When New Labour came to power in 1997 and Jack Straw took over the Home Office he was known as someone who was 'good on race relations'. When in opposition he had spoken out not only on the Stephen Lawrence case but also against the 1993 and 1996 Asylum and Immigration Acts. So when his first acts as home secretary were to launch a public enquiry into the murder of Stephen Lawrence and order a review of the entire immigration and asylum system, it was expected that this would be a radically different government in terms of race and immigration.

Turning to policy on racial equality, at least in this area New Labour has attempted to put 'clear blue water' between itself and the Conservative Party. Two major initiatives since 1997 highlight the changing agenda on this issue: the publication of the Macpherson Report and the passage of the Race Relations (Amendment) Act in 2000. We shall explore both of these initiatives in turn.

The Macpherson Report

The publication in February 1999 of the Macpherson Report on the murder of Stephen Lawrence can be seen as a symbolic turning point in New Labour's policy on race and racial inequality. In many ways the report contained little that was new, either conceptually or in terms of policy setting. Rather it was a mixed bag of recommendations on a wide range of issues, based on scholarly research over the previous two decades. Nevertheless the importance of the report can be gauged from the public attention it received upon publication and in the period that followed.

An important element of this is that its recommendations cover a much broader canvas than just the events surrounding the murder of Stephen Lawrence and the police investigation of it. For example it includes recommendations on general policies on race relations, racism, education, social policy and numerous related issues. This is in some ways part of its strength, but it also means that when judging its political effectiveness we have to take account of a wide range of policy arenas and the likely political outcomes.

While the long-term impact of the report in terms of practical policy change cannot yet be assessed, there seems little doubt that it has had a very important impact on New Labour's thinking on institutional racism. The failure of successive governments to act on the Scarman Report on the Brixton riots (Scarman, 1981) should warn us against making facile predictions about the nature of policy responses. If anything, the experience of the past few decades shows that the translation of policy recommendations into practice is by no means guaranteed, particularly as the policy change depends on broader political agendas. As Lord Scarman himself argued a few years after the publication of his report: 'I constantly ask myself two questions. Has any good resulted from the Brixton Inquiry? And, what now remains to be done?' (Scarman, 1985: 7).

Of course the Macpherson Report may fare somewhat better than the Scarman Report. From a symbolic perspective the commissioning of the inquiry and the government's declared commitment to implementing the report's recommendations signalled New Labour's intention to give questions of race and social justice a higher profile. However trends over the past two decades demonstrate that reform and policy change in these areas tend to be limited. Even in the aftermath of the major urban unrest in 1980–1 and 1985, promises of reform were replaced after a time by complacency and inactivity (Benyon and Solomos, 1987). As Stuart Hall remarked after the 1985 riots:

> I have a reluctance about entering once again into what seems to me a terribly familiar and recurring cycle. The cycle goes something like this. There is a problem that is followed by a conference; the conference is followed by research; the research reinforces what we already know, but in elegant and scholarly language. Then nothing happens (Hall, 1987: 45).

However there are signs that at least some key elements of the Macpherson Report may be implemented, particularly as the government is trying to show that it is taking the question of institutional racism seriously in its own institutions, including the police and the civil service. In terms of agenda setting, it is likely that the public debate on race and public policy will be partly shaped by symbolic and actual responses to the report. However it is also important to bear in mind the likely impact of the Race Relations (Amendment) Act.

Race Relations (Amendment) Act, 2000

During the long period of Conservative domination (1979–97) there were numerous calls for the 1976 Race Relations Act to be strengthened. These calls were backed up by detailed submissions from the Commission for Racial Equality and by research that highlighted the limitations of the 1976 Act, limitations that had become pronounced as early as the 1980s. Despite this the Conservative Party did little to strengthen the legislation, and it was New Labour that took up the question while in opposition. It came as no surprise therefore, particularly in the context of public debates on this issue, that when New Labour came to power it signalled its intention to pass a new Act to remedy past weaknesses and set the agenda for the future.

The 2000 Race Relations (Amendment) Act was the product of this shift in thinking and was the main initiative that New Labour put on the statute books to address racial discrimination and exclusion. The main innovation was to extend the requirements of the 1976 Race Relations Act to all public authorities, so since 1 December 2001, when the Act came into force, public authorities have had a statutory duty to promote racial equality (Home Office, 2001). The expectation embodied in the Act is that public authorities will take action to:

- Prevent acts of racial discrimination before they occur.
- Ensure that when performing their public functions they 'have due regard to the need to eliminate unlawful racial discrimination, and to promote equality of opportunity and good relations between persons of different racial groups'.

The 2000 Act was generally welcomed as a step in the right direction by those concerned with racial discrimination and exclusion. There was, however, some disappointment that the Act did not take up all of the recommendations by the Commission for Racial Equality for strengthening the 1976 Race Relations Act. There was also controversy about the fact that it did not cover the part played by public authorities in respect of immigration, asylum seekers and refugees.

In the past decade some moves have been made to develop policies on racism and racial discrimination at the European Union level (Commission of the European Communities, 1992; European Parliament, 1998). The full extent of the impact of these initiatives on policies pursued by the member countries remains to be seen. In 1998, however, one early indication came with the passing of the Human Rights Act, which specifies that no national laws must contravene the European Convention on Human Rights and Fundamental Freedoms (ECHR). Though passed in 1998 the Act only came into force in October 2000, and by 2002 some provisions had yet to be fully implemented.

It is too early to discuss the likely effects of the Race Relations (Amendment) Act, but the very fact that the government took the step of introducing a new piece of race relations legislation was seen by many as symbolically important, in the sense that it signalled a shift in government thinking in this area. Home Secretary Jack Straw emphasised the political symbolism of the Act as much as its practical impact. As the new legislation works its way through the public sector over the coming years it will be interesting to see how far it represents a genuine advance on the 1976 Race Relations Act. It will also be interesting to see if even stronger legislation becomes a serious item on the political agenda. In light of the debate on institutional racism ignited by the Macpherson Report it is likely that political debates on measures to tackle discrimination and exclusion will remain heated for some time to come.

Summary and conclusion

The very nature of the political debates on race and immigration over the past few decades makes it clear that the development of race relations policies has become part of a wider political process. A central element of that process has been the political and media debates on the impact of black immigration on various aspects of British society. This has meant that major policy initiatives have been largely the result of attempts by successive governments to meet the demands of those calling for action to tackle racial discrimination and to respond to those who oppose such intervention. The end result seems to be an unhappy compromise that pleases few and angers many for a variety of reasons. Antidiscrimination legislation has been in place for nearly five decades and yet there is still widespread evidence of a high degree of discrimination in both the public and the private sector.

Given this it is difficult to be optimistic about the prospects of radical change under the terms of the existing legislation. There is little ground for arguing that the 1976 Race Relations Act, which was seen as a rather radical initiative in its time, achieved the changes it promised. The failure of successive Conservative administrations between 1979 and 1997 to respond positively to calls for greater powers to be given to the Commission for Racial Equality and to remedy the weaknesses of the 1976 Act led to cynicism about the willingness of the state to make racial inequality a central element of the policy agenda. Perhaps the passage of the 2000 Race Relations (Amendment) Act and the policy debates sparked by the Macpherson Report will go some way towards overcoming this cynicism.

In the meantime opposition to state intervention in the problem of racial inequality and exclusion has not disappeared, and advocates of new right social and economic policies have attempted to put doubt on the efficacy of legislative measures to deal with racial inequality. While such ideas have yet to attract the degree of support that the views of liberal market economists such as Thomas Sowell have in the US (Sowell, 1981), there are signs that they are gaining some currency in the work of the new right think tanks. Perhaps these ideas are unlikely to find a hearing in the present political climate, but the arguments put forward by new right commentators remain part of the political scene (Honeyford, 1998). The consequences of this remain to be seen.

The story of race relations policies over the past four decades or so highlights the deep-seated ambiguities and uncertainties that have shaped government thinking on the kind of role the state should play in tackling racial discrimination and exclusion. The new atmosphere created by the 1997 and 2001 Labour administrations holds out some hope that there will be movement towards more active policies. Such hope, however, needs to be tempered by the fact that successive Labour governments since the 1960s have failed to come up with a radical programme of social reform.

5 Urban Politics and Racial Inequality

Previous chapters have noted that the politicisation of public debate on race and immigration in Britain has been partly determined by local political processes. As shown in Chapters 3 and 4, from the very earliest stages of the migration process a number of local authorities, pressure groups and individuals raised the question of the impact of immigration on their localities. Moreover throughout the 1950s and 1960s the political elite in areas such as London, Birmingham, Wolverhampton and elsewhere had to come to terms with the increasingly multiracial composition of their localities. The local political contexts in which these debates took place were often very complex and it was certainly not the case that all local responses to immigration were the same. It is important to emphasise, however, that political debates in this area have never been simply national ones. Rather they have always been deeply influenced by local concerns and preoccupations.

This chapter takes the account a step further by examining the history of the local politics of race through (a) an analysis of the impact of local conditions and processes on the racialisation of the political agenda, and (b) a critical review of legislative and political interventions that have sought to structure race relations at the local level. The main focus of this chapter is therefore on the dynamics of the incorporation of race into the local political agenda. This will allow us to link up with the questions raised at the end of Chapter 4 about the changing role of state intervention in this area and the prospect of transforming the current patterns of racial inequality in Britain through political intervention, both nationally and locally.

Concepts and models of local politics

Since the early 1980s a wide-ranging theoretical debate on local politics and institutions has led to the development of a more dynamic and critical perspective on various aspects of this subject (Dunleavy, 1980; Saunders, 1981; Gregory and Urry, 1985; Thrift and Williams, 1987; Stoker, 2000). The main features of this debate have been (a) a concern to include wider questions about power and society in the study of urban politics, (b) attempts to develop a dynamic analysis of the processes of policy change and formation at the local level, and (c) a focus on the role of conflict and controversy in the shaping of local policy agendas.

A number of writers have argued that many of the crucial features of contemporary class and social relations in advanced capitalist societies cannot be fully understood without reference to the local and spatial context. Studies in both Britain and the US have emphasised the massive impact of changes in the political economies, populations and spatial organisation of urban localities (Katznelson, 1982; Thrift and Williams, 1987; Wilson, 1996). Dearlove (1973) argues that far from being neutral arbiters between competing interests, local authorities are actively engaged in resisting, obstructing and excluding certain groups from decision making. From this perspective the task of local authorities is to make political choices and manage conflicting pressures and interests.

What is notable from the perspective of this book is that, in Britain issues of race and ethnicity have been largely left off the local political agenda. A few writers have begun to acknowledge the significance of racial themes in urban politics, and have attempted to address this issue as an important dimension of contemporary British politics. Stoker, for example, has argued that 'we need to address more systematically the structures of inequality and the history of powerlessness which can lead to the exclusion and non-mobilisation of the working class, women, ethnic minorities and other deprived groups within local politics' (Stoker, 1988: 242; see also Stoker, 2000). There are also signs that the increasing awareness of gender and other forms of non-class-specific social categorisation is resulting in growing interest in local processes of racial categorisation and exclusion. But this is still at a relatively early stage and the local dimension of the politics of racism remains sadly neglected.

Race and local politics in historical perspective

In a controversial statement in 1978 Margaret Thatcher made it quite clear that she was on the side of those who saw black immigrants as swamping British society. When in February 1979 she was asked if she had modified her view on this issue she forcefully restated her basic theme:

> Some people have felt swamped by immigrants. They've seen the whole character of their neighbourhood change .... Of course people can feel that they are being swamped. Small minorities can be absorbed – they can be assets to the majority community – but once a minority in a neighbourhood gets very large, people do feel swamped. They feel their whole way of life has been changed (*Observer*, 25 February 1979).

This statement highlights the important part that images of community and neighbourhood play in political debates on race in British society, and how they can act as symbols of the changing terms of debate on this question. This was referred to in the course of the discussion on the politics of race and immigration in Chapter 3. In this chapter we shall consider the development of political debates and policy change at the local level in more detail.

From the early 1980s to the early 1990s considerable public and media attention was focused on local authorities that had introduced radical policy changes in respect of racial inequality. The most notable cases were the (now abolished) Greater London Council, the Inner London Education Authority and a number of left-wing London boroughs, including Lambeth, Brent, Hackney and Haringey. Away from London a number of other local authorities, including Manchester, Birmingham and Bradford, attracted attention when they adopted comprehensive policies on racial equality and equal opportunity in general.

In the current climate it is all too easy to forget that as late as the 1970s a common complaint by activists and community groups was that local authorities had failed to develop an adequate policy response to the increasingly multiracial composition of their populations. Indeed during the 1970s political intervention in race issues at the local level was mainly restricted to limited support for Community Relations Councils, financial aid to community groups and the distribution of central government funds under Section 11 of the 1966 Local Government Act and the Urban Programme.

During the 1960s political intervention in race issues typically involved a complex interaction between central government, local authorities and voluntary agencies. From as early as the 1950s, as we saw in Chapters 3 and 4, the social policy response to black immigration involved a two-pronged strategy aimed at (a) providing newly arrived immigrants with help in relation to housing, employment, social problems and cultural adjustment, and (b) helping the host community to understand the immigrants and overcome prejudices.

At the local level special officers were appointed in a number of locations to help immigrants cope with their special problems, and local agencies helped to define the policy response to black immigrants in areas such as London, Nottingham and Birmingham. In some areas this led to the formation of voluntary committees that consisted of representatives of statutory and voluntary social services, interested groups and individuals, and trade unions. These committees played a particularly important role in areas of the country where race and related issues had already become politicised and aroused the interest of local politicians, the press and voluntary agencies.

Processes of racialisation

From the early 1960s, questions about race and racism in local political processes took a number of forms. The processes that resulted in the opening up of questions about race in local politics are complex, and to some extent were determined by the specific histories of particular localities. Broadly speaking, however, they can be divided into three stages that correspond to various transformations in the politics of immigration and race from the 1960s onwards.

During the early 1960s and 1970s the local political context of race was a central theme in debates on immigration, particularly in parts of the West Midlands. In addition, as shown in Chapter 4, the direct and indirect impact of racist political mobilisation in Birmingham and the Black Country during the early 1960s pushed the racialisation of political debate to a new level. Indeed the election of Peter Griffiths in Smethwick in 1964 on an openly anti-immigrant platform, was an important symbolic event, since it helped to shape the terms of political debate on immigration and entrench the view that black immigrants were a problem that had to be dealt with through strict immigration control and ameliorative race relations policies.

It is clear from a number of studies that local authorities in London, Birmingham, Bristol, Wolverhampton and other inner city areas developed *ad hoc* initiatives on racial issues from the 1960s onwards. For a number of authorities this involved the development of policies on education, social services and housing. This was often linked to the formation of the voluntary committees described at the end of the previous section. From the late 1960s these committees began to receive the support of the Community Relations Commission and became known by the generic term of Community Relations Councils (Hill and Issacharoff, 1971; Gay and Young, 1988).

The main characteristic of the earliest stages of racialised politics at the local level was the use of race as a symbol of the changing nature of local social and economic conditions. The concerns expressed in local newspapers and by local politicians concentrated on such issues as housing, employment and social problems that were popularly perceived as linked to immigration.

With the emergence of race as a local political issue a steady stream of studies looked at various aspects of race relations and conflicts in particular cities or localities (Rex and Moore, 1967; Richmond, 1973; Lawrence, 1974; Katznelson, 1976; Rex and Tomlinson, 1979). The work of John Rex and his associates during the 1960s and 1970s on the position of black minorities in Birmingham is representative of a major trend in this body of work. One of the issues analysed in this research was the part played by local and national political processes in incorporating black minorities in Birmingham into the institutions of the welfare state and into the employment and housing markets. For example Rex and Moore (1967) investigated the subject of race and housing in an area of Birmingham with a significant black population: Sparkbrook. Their central concerns were to identify the reasons for the concentration of Asian and West Indian immigrants in this declining area, and to assess the impact of Birmingham Housing Department's policies on the incorporation of immigrant communities into the housing market. In a second research project, carried out in the early 1970s, Rex and Tomlinson (1979) investigated the position of the black underclass in the Handsworth area of the city. This time the central concern was to analyse the social position of the community in question and the part played by local and national political processes in determining this position. They also looked in some detail at the political groups that developed within the Asian and West Indian communities in the area, including the history of these groups and their interaction with local political institutions.

Other studies were concerned with aspects of the incorporation of black and ethnic minorities into the local political system. Important studies from this perspective looked at the role of racial and ethnic politics in the political life of cities such as Nottingham, Birmingham and Bristol since the 1950s, the best known examples of which are by Nicholas Deakin (1972), David Beetham (1970), Ken Newton (1976), and Ira Katznelson (1976). Other important studies were carried out by Gideon Ben-Tovim and his associates (1986) in Liverpool and Wolverhampton and by Anthony Messina (1989) in Ealing.

The main themes of this research were the impact of race on local and national politics, the role of the media, the response of local authorities to the race question and the racialisation of electoral politics. An interesting example of this type of study is Susan Smith's (1989) account of the political processes of racialisation and segregation, which explores the diverse political, social and economic dimensions of racial relations in contemporary Britain. Her account of this process highlights the need to situate the analysis of the local politics of race within an understanding of how racialisation of residential space in urban localities has come about, and how the local and national political system has responded to this process.

Models of policy change

Most studies of the local politics of race, however, have been concerned not with broader questions about the dynamics of local political power and change but with the policies and agendas of particular local authorities, and with the specifics of the implementation of particular policies. A good example of this is the work of Ken Young and his associates (Young and Connelly, 1981, 1984; Young, 1985).

The main topics in this body of work are (a) the context and environment of policy change, and (b) the implementation of policy change through particular initiatives and policies. A particular emphasis is placed on the assumptions held by policy makers when developing and implementing policy change. According to the findings, most of the changes in this area have been unplanned and unintended, and have resulted from pressure for change at the local level and from the impact on local authorities of urban unrest since 1981 (Young, 1985: 287).

Young and Connelly (1981) looked at two aspects of policy change in a number of local authorities: (a) the environment of policy change and the local political actors that made up this environment; and (b) the content of policy changes by local authorities and the means by which they sought to bring about change. Young and Connelly identified four different types of local authority in terms of their response to racial issues:

- *Pioneers*: innovative authorities that created a new machinery of policy making and implementation on racial issues.
- *Learners*: authorities that accepted the need for change, and learned from the experience of the pioneers.
- *Waverers*: authorities that issued formal statements but did little in practice.
- *Resisters*: authorities that did not accept the need for specific policies on racial issues (Young and Connelly, 1981: 6–7).

This categorisation influenced much of the subsequent research on the local politics of race, and helped to sharpen researchers' interest in the actual processes of policy making and diffusion in local multiracial settings.

A somewhat different framework of analysis has been offered by Herman Ouseley, who worked at various levels of local government during the 1980s and 1990s and specialised in equal opportunity issues. In his account of policy development in this field Ouseley considers the actions of black communities, local black politicians and administrators, as well as the political debates surrounding the 1981 and 1985 riots (Ouseley, 1981, 1984). From his extensive experience of work in a variety of local government contexts he argues that the key to change in the practices of local authorities lies in pressure from both within and outside the institutions of local politics and policy making.

From this perspective, in order to understand the changing role of local authorities in racial issues it is necessary to look at the part played by black community groups, the voluntary sector, black political leader and community relations councils, as well as shifts in local and central government policies (Ouseley, 1982).

Policy change and conflict

At various stages since the mid 1960s a number of legislative measures have been introduced to give central government a degree of influence over the response of local authorities to race issues. The main measures are shown in Table 5.1. The two measures introduced during the 1960s had a rather limited impact on policy development by local authorities. Section 11 of the 1966 Local Government Act and the 1969 Local Government Grants (Social Need) Act originated from the debates on race and immigration that raged throughout the 1960s (Edwards and Batley, 1978) and were largely aimed at providing financial support to localities with particularly large black populations.

Section 11 of the 1966 Local Government Act as designed to address the financial impact of immigration on particular localities by providing central government money to local authorities to help meet the education and social welfare needs of ethnic minority groups (*Hansard*, vol. 729, 1966: cols 1331–8). Substantial sums were provided to a number of local authorities, although there was some controversy about whether these monies were used directly for the benefit of minority communities.

The 1969 Local Government Grants (Social Need) Act was to some extent a response by the Labour government to the rivers of blood speech by Enoch Powell in April 1968 (Edwards and Batley, 1978; Higgins *et al.*, 1983). The urban programme contained in the act was intended to provide special help to areas where social deprivation was pervasive, including areas inhabited by ethnic minorities. Unlike Section 11 of the 1966 Local Government Act the programme was not presented as concerned only with racial deprivation, but in practice many of the projects funded through it had a strong emphasis on this issue.

Table 5.1 *Legislative measures and the local politics of race*

1966	Local Government Act
1967	Local Government Grants (Social Need) Act
1976	Race Relations Act
1978	Inner Urban Areas Act
1988	Local Government Act

These two Acts were the first of a number of initiatives aimed at providing central government support to local attempts to tackle urban deprivation in multiracial settings (Jacobs, 1986). The full story of these policies would take us beyond the bounds of this volume (but see Ball and Solomos, 1990), though two points need to be emphasised in connection with their impact on the politics of urban racial inequality. First, the scale of these initiatives (and the resources allocated to them) did not in any way match those introduced by the US federal government during the same period. Given the extent of the deprivation they were supposed to tackle, both Section 11 and the urban programme were largely symbolic measures rather than national programmes of action. Second, during the 1960s and early 1970s local authorities themselves showed little interest in developing policies in this area. Although some local authorities were beginning to pay some attention to racial inequality, this rarely went beyond the provision of limited support to Community Relations Councils and the allocation of grants to some local community groups (Ouseley, 1981).

By the mid 1970s most local authorities were still giving little thought to the question of racial inequality. This was why, during the parliamentary debate on the 1976 Race Relations Act, Labour back-bencher Fred Willey argued forcefully that an amendment should be included about the duty of local authorities to promote better race relations. Although Willey's amendment was initially opposed by the government it was eventually included as Section 71 of the Race Relations Act. It consisted of the following general injunction:

> Without prejudice to their obligation to comply with any other provision of this Act, it shall be the duty of every local authority to make appropriate arrangements with a view to securing that their functions are carried out with regard to the need: (a) to eliminate unlawful racial discrimination; and (b) to promote equality of opportunity, and good relations, between persons of different racial groups (Race Relations Act, 1976).

Thus Section 71 of the Act placed a particular onus on local authorities to eliminate unlawful racial discrimination and promote equality of opportunity between persons of different racial groups. This statutory provision did not seem to have an immediate effect on the policies or practices of the majority of local authorities, although a few did take up the opportunity offered by the Act to consolidate their efforts in this area (Young and Connelly, 1981). In addition the CRE attempted from the early days of its existence to encourage local authorities to develop better practices and to learn from the experiences of the more innovative ones.

Whatever the limited effectiveness of Section 71 in the late 1970s, in the aftermath of the urban unrest in Bristol, London and Liverpool in 1980–1 a growing number of local authorities started to develop policies on racial discrimination. As Ouseley (1984) has noted, it seems that the unrest forced some local authorities to respond to the demands of their black communities for action on racial discrimination in employment, service delivery and housing. Although the general impact of Section 71 was patchy during the 1980s and 1990s, it provided the basis for promoting policy change within the existing structure of local government (Young and Connelly, 1981; Young, 1989).

Pressures for change and their impact

Bolstered by the urban unrest of the 1980s, local black politicians and groups sought to bring racial inequality onto the local political agenda and a number of left-wing local authorities saw this as an opportunity to widen their basis of support among ethnic minorities and other constituents (Stoker, 1988: 207–8). However, the failure of the central government to respond to calls for radical reform indicated that relatively little change could be expected from central government actions.

This was reflected in three main policy changes. The first addressed the central question of who would receive what, with an emphasis on equality of treatment and equality of outcome in the allocation process. Procedures were introduced to monitor patterns of access and allocation. For example in relation to housing, authorities such as Hackney and Haringey began to monitor the allocation of local housing stock and its quality, and to change procedures that facilitated discretion and contributed to discriminatory outcomes.

The second addressed the question of local authority employment and resulted in a number of authorities linking allocative equality with the representation of black and ethnic minority people on the staff of local government departments. Racially discriminatory outcomes, it was argued, were not solely the function of organisational procedures but also related to the underrepresentation or exclusion of these groups. Consequently targets were set to increase the proportion of black and ethnic minority staff members.

Finally, a number of local authorities introduced promotional measures to improve communications with and promote awareness of the difficulties faced by black and ethnic minority people. These measures included the translation of policy documents into ethnic languages, the provision of race awareness and equal opportunity training, and the introduction of more effective controls against racial harassment.

Resistance to change

During the early 1980s, at the height of local authority activity in racial matters, much hope was placed on local authorities as agents of change, particularly in light of the neglect of racial equality by the Thatcher administrations. Indeed one study of the local politics of race argued that local political arenas 'provided important sites of struggle, particularly for local organisations committed to racial equality' (Ben-Tovim *et al.*, 1986: 169). Yet the experience of a number of local authorities indicates that any gains in this area were both fragile and vulnerable to pressure from central government.

By the late 1980s there were already signs that even radical local authorities were adopting a lower profile on issues connected with racial equality. This seemed to be partly the result of the increasingly negative publicity given to the policies and programmes pursued by a number of local authorities in London, Manchester, Sheffield and elsewhere. Furthermore the Labour Party increasingly distanced itself from the activities of the more left-wing local authorities and encouraged them to give a lower profile to issues that were seen as controversial or as giving too much support to minority causes.

It was perhaps a sign of the political climate of the time that increasingly it was not racism that was presented as the central problem but the activities of antiracists. Antiracism, a catch-all term to which various meanings were attached, came to occupy a central position in debates on the local politics of race in Britain. It also became the target of critical attack in a number of policy arenas. Indeed there was a noticeable tendency to dismiss the relevance of antiracism and for the new right and the media to articulate an anti-antiracist position in which antiracists were portrayed as a bigger political threat than racists.

In certain arenas, such as education and social welfare, the issue of antiracism became a source of conflict and resistance. This became evident in the late 1980s in particular, when public and media debate on antiracism and multiculturalism reached a high point. It was during this time that the education policies of a number of radical Labour LEAs with antiracist programmes came under close scrutiny. The controversy over what were perceived as the racist views of Bradford head teacher Ray Honeyford in the mid 1980s attracted both local and national political attention to the role and function of antiracist policies in education. Honeyford's views on multicultural and antiracist education policies, as expressed in the pages of the *Salisbury Review* and elsewhere, led to a campaign by local parents and political activists to have him removed from his post. His criticism of the radical initiatives of local authorities in this field involved a wholesale questioning of the political ideologies that he saw as underlying such policies, and the rejection of multicultural education in favour of integration. At the same time other groups voiced support for his views and defended his right to express them. Although he eventually left his teaching job, under pressure from a number of sources, he continued to act as a major critic of radical policies (Honeyford, 1988a).

The ramifications of the Honeyford affair went far beyond the boundaries of Bradford (Murray, 1986; Honeyford, 1988b; Halstead, 1988). For example in 1986 another controversy developed over the attempt by Brent Council to sack another head teacher, Maureen McGoldrick, because of her views on the policy Brent Council was pursuing in relation to antiracist initiatives in education.

More generally, the tragedy at Burnage High School in Manchester added fuel to the controversy over antiracist education policies. In September 1986 Ahmed Iqbal Ullah, a Bangladeshi pupil, was murdered by a white pupil in the school playground. This incident and the response of the local education authority to it became part of a broader national debate on antiracist education that simmered on until 1990. It led to a major report by radical barrister Ian Macdonald, who sought to place the murder in Burnage into the broader context of the complexity of implementing antiracist initiatives in education (Macdonald *et al.*, 1989; Ball and Solomos, 1990). There were numerous other, less well publicised, cases on the issue.

Local authority initiatives mirrored those of central government in that there was a gap between the promises embodied in policy statements and the actual achievements of the policies. However in the early 1980s authorities such as Lambeth and Hackney did make some progress in changing their employment practices and service delivery to reflect the multiracial composition of their populations. Initiatives in specific areas such as social services and housing were also put into effect. In Hackney's case the combination of pressure from the local black communities and a formal investigation by the Commission for Racial Equality had forced the council to rethink its housing policy and introduce major changes. In this period other local authorities were also the site of important debates on the delivery of social services and education.

Other areas of controversy included positive action and contract compliance initiatives, both of which were placed on the political agenda by certain local authorities and became the subject of lively debate.

Positive action and new initiatives

In everyday usage the term positive action has come to be associated with the giving of preferential treatment to black and ethnic minority groups, or with the imposition of quotas and positive discrimination (*Equal Opportunities Review*, 10, 1986: 6–10; Institute of Personnel Management, 1987). This perhaps explains why since the early 1980s it has been the subject of intense debate and has attracted regular media attention.

Terms such as equal opportunity, racial equality and related notions have gained wide currency over the past two decades but there is still considerable confusion about what they mean and, perhaps more fundamentally, about the objectives they are supposed to meet (Young, 1990; Blakemore and Drake, 1996). Some writers see equal opportunity policies as the outcome of a process of political negotiation, pressure group politics and bureaucratic policy making (Ben-Tovim *et al.*, 1986; Young and Connelly, 1981). Others have emphasised the need to look beyond the stated objectives and public political negotiations and to explore the possibility that deeply entrenched processes of discrimination may be resistant to legal and political interventions as long as inegalitarian social relations continue to structure society as a whole (Smith, 1989). From this perspective promises of equal opportunity can easily become largely symbolic political actions that do little to bring about real changes in discriminatory processes.

In Britain, unlike in the US, there has been no intellectual and political tradition to support the view that affirmative action is a legitimate policy tool to tackle the effects of racial and other social inequalities. Rather, successive policies on racial inequality from the 1960s were held together by the notion that the main objectives of state intervention in this field were to secure free competition between individuals and to eliminate barriers created by racial discrimination. These objectives were pursued through legislation aimed at outlawing discrimination and through administrative intervention by quasigovernmental bodies such as the Commission for Racial Equality. Yet a wealth of official reports and academic research findings showed that in practice the impact of public policy in this field was limited even within the limits of this narrow definition of equal opportunity. Research on employment, for example, indicated that equal opportunity policies were having little effect on discrimination in employment, although they did reduce its more overt forms. Similar arguments were made about the impact of equal opportunity policies in housing and education (Brown and Gay, 1985; Jenkins and Solomos, 1989).

It is against this background that interest grew in the use of positive action to improve the likelihood of racial equality policies bringing about positive changes in the employment and service delivery practices of local authorities. Positive action, as practiced in Britain during the 1980s and

1990s, consisted mainly of the following:

- Measures to remove discriminatory barriers to full equality of opportunity, such as rethinking job qualification requirements and placing job advertisements in ethnic minority newspapers.
- Measures to facilitate and encourage minority group participation in education and the labour force, for example by providing additional education and training, using Section 11 of the 1966 Local Government Act to create new posts, and related actions.

The general principle behind these measures was that positive action should be taken to enable certain sections of the community to catch up with other employees or applicants, and to remove barriers that had the effect of excluding some people from employment opportunities (*Equal Opportunities Review*, 14, 1987: 13–18). Part of the rationale for positive action was the argument that even if racial discrimination could be removed overnight, employment opportunities would not be immediately equally available to all members of ethnic communities. Further steps were needed to make up for past disadvantages and discrimination experienced by minority groups. Hence positive action was not meant to be a means of providing direct benefits to minority groups, but a means of promoting equal opportunity in a more effective manner. The Commission for Racial Equality was clear on this point:

> Positive action is a series of measures by which people from particular racial groups are either encouraged to apply for jobs in which they have been under-represented or given training to help them develop their potential and so improve their chances in competing for particular work. The element of competition remains paramount. The Act does not provide for people to be taken on because they have a particular racial origin, except in very limited circumstances where racial group is a genuine occupational qualification (CRE, 1985c: iv).

Within these limits local authorities such as Hackney, Lambeth, ILEA and others attempted to develop positive action initiatives. It is not clear how effective these initiatives were, but there is evidence that limited success was achieved with respect to some of the broad objectives that guided the initiatives, particularly in relation to the provision of training and the reform of recruitment procedures.

What is also clear is that the limits imposed by the 1976 Race Relations Act and the political climate of the time meant that local authorities that wanted to develop positive action strategies were forced to work within very narrow confines. These confines did allow some radical initiatives to be taken, but the authorities that did so were criticised for going too far in the direction of positive discrimination. This can be illustrated by looking at what was perhaps the most radical form of positive action attempted, namely contract compliance.

In Britain contract compliance, as a local-authority strategy to promote racial equality, was not used until the 1980s, though it had a longer history in the US and Northern Ireland. Its main advocates during the early 1980s were the Greater London Council (GLC) and the Inner London Education Authority (ILEA), although the idea was taken up by other left-wing local authorities in London and elsewhere (Hall, 1986; Carr, 1987; IPM, 1987). It attracted considerable attention and a number of local authorities saw it as a way in which effective reforms in the field of equal opportunity could be institutionalised.

The first major initiative came in 1983 when the GLC and ILEA amended their code of practice on tenders and contracts to include an equal opportunities clause. This required tendering companies to adhere to an equal opportunity policy and to develop strategies for implementing this policy. To aid this initiative the GLC/ILEA set up a Contract Compliance Equal Opportunities Unit to ensure that the companies with which they traded understood the equal opportunity policy and were prepared to put it into practice. Companies that failed to comply with the policy were threatened with removal from the GLC's list of approved contractors. Similar initiatives were launched around that time by a number of other local authorities.

Another form of contract compliance was the local labour contract, which required companies in receipt of government grants to carry out capital works in inner city areas to employ mainly or only labour from the local area, thus ensuring that at least some inner city residents would benefit. Such initiatives were developed in cities such as Birmingham and London in the aftermath of the urban unrest of 1981 and 1985. This unrest was considered to be partly related to the employment situation in inner city areas and local labour contracts were seen as a way of remedying the situation (CRE, 1987b).

From the start contract compliance initiatives such as these were unpopular with some major employers and the Thatcher government. They also became a subject of controversy in the popular media and regularly attracted negative publicity. One famous example occurred in 1985 with the news that the ILEA had decided to ban Kit Kat bars from its schools on the grounds that the manufacturers of Kit Kat, Rowntree Mackintosh, had refused to supply information on its compliance with the Sex Discrimination and Race Relations Acts (*Equal Opportunities Review*, 8, 1986: 9–15). This case, along with a number of others, helped to politicise the issue and link it to the broader moral panic about the 'loony left' in local government (Jeffers *et al.*, 1996; Stoker, 2000).

The government also criticised the use of contract compliance as yet another example of the work of 'loony left' local authorities, and as an attack on the workings of the market. Nicholas Ridley, then Minister for the Environment, expressed this view when he argued in October 1986 that:

> Conditions in contracts which have nothing to do with the contractor's ability to carry out work or supply goods ignore a local authority's duty to its rate-payers to obtain value for money, and are merely an attempt by some councils to impose their own social policies on firms who wish to carry out business with them. Such actions have no place in the contractual processes of local government, and early steps will be taken to stamp them out (DoE press notice, 21 October 1986).

This criticism of contract compliance initiatives was maintained even after the abolition of the GLC and in spite of the fact that only a handful of radical authorities were interested in implementing them. Part of the reason for this may have been that contract compliance contradicted the government's avowed intention to roll back the boundaries of the state in favour of market forces. Perhaps the main reason, however, was its concern about the actions of radical left-wing local authorities in the area of race relations.

Whatever the reason it came as no surprise when the government's 1988 Local Government Act prohibited the form of contract compliance practised by some of the more radical local authorities. This new Act prevented local authorities and other specified public bodies from taking account of non-commercial matters when drawing up approved lists of contractors, inviting tenders and making or terminating contracts (*Equal Opportunities Review*, 18, 1988: 31). However, during the passage of the bill through parliament the legislation was amended to permit local authorities to conduct a limited and defined form of contract vetting so as to carry out their duties under Section 71 of the 1976 Race Relations Act as long as they did not take non-commercial criteria into account (*Equal Opportunities Review*, 19, 1988: 24–7; 24, 1989: 26–31).

This intervention reflected the Thatcher government's concern to ensure that local authorities did not implement controversial social policies on issues such as race. It is interesting to note, however, that the Commission for Racial Equality and some radical local authorities found a way of conducting a weak form of contract compliance under the terms laid out in the 1988 Local Government Act (*Equal Opportunities Review*, 28, 1989: 32–5).

Training and racial equality

Controversy also surrounded the thorny question of what was sometimes called 'race awareness training' (RAT), as practised by some local authorities. The provision of race-related training grew rapidly in the 1980s, in line with the growth of local race equality policies. Whether under the rubric of race awareness training or of equal opportunity training local authorities, employers and other agencies introduced courses on race issues as part of their training activities (*Equal Opportunities Review*, 3, 1985: 8–14; 18, 1988: 34–5). Such courses had been around for some time in the US, but in Britain they were basically a new phenomenon. They were conceived as a means of (a) informing decision makers, employers, employees and other important actors of the problems facing black and ethnic minority communities, and (b) challenging individual prejudices and values.

The training programmes took a number of forms but they generally started from the assumption that their purpose was to challenge and change racist attitudes. Following the ideas expressed by Judy Katz (1978), who argued that the root cause of racism was the inherent prejudice of white people combined with power, the proponents of RAT argued that initiatives to deal with racism needed:

- To challenge the individual prejudices upon which racism was based.
- To develop in the people who took part in such courses attitudes which challenge their racism.

They also argued that by challenging racial prejudice among individuals they could help to change the institutional practices that discriminated against black and ethnic minority people. It was perhaps this claim, along with the promise of quick results, that pushed many local authorities into introducing such courses in the early 1980s.

It soon became clear that the claims upon which RAT was based were by no means universally accepted. Indeed opposition came from a broad range of political figures, ranging from avowedly antiracist groups and individuals to spokespersons of the new right (Sivanandan, 1985; Palmer, 1986; Gilroy, 1987, 1990b). The criticisms of the antiracists centred particularly on the assumed link between changes in attitudes and changes in practice, the guilt complex upon which the courses relied and the determinism of seeing all white people as inherently racist. Sivanandan, for example, argued that its proponents ignored the role of socioeconomic, cultural and historical factors, and therefore constructed a deterministic view of racism as an individual problem. He argued:

> Racism, according to RAT, has its roots in white culture, and white culture, unaffected by material conditions goes back to the beginning of time. Hence, racism is part of the collective unconscious, the pre-natal scream, original sin .... It is a circular argument, bordering on the genetic, on biological determinism: racism, in sum, is culture and culture is white and white is racist (Sivanandan, 1985: 29).

For Sivanandan and other critics, RAT's analysis of racism was at best superficial and at worst counterproductive since it ignored the material social and political conditions that helped to reproduce discrimination and racist ideas.

For the new right the RAT courses, along with broader antiracist initiatives, were yet another example of attempts by left-wing local authorities to restrict the freedom of individuals to express certain opinions and to impose multicultural values rather than traditional British ones (Palmer, 1986; Honeyford, 1988b). Along with sections of the popular media they attempted, with some success, to portray the RAT courses as a form of racial brainwashing.

Although numerous local authorities, along with the police and other bodies, adopted forms of RAT as part of their policy on race, surprisingly little information was released about the impact of these courses on the implementation of equal opportunity policies, or on employment and service delivery practices. This lack of concrete evidence about their effectiveness contributed to the controversy that was surrounding them.

Some local authorities attempted to respond to the criticism by locating race-related training within a broader strategy for organisational change. According to Valerie Amos, who was involved in the development of this approach in the London borough of Hackney, the objectives of race-related training were to make clear to staff the objectives of equal opportunity policies and to enable them to gain the necessary skills to implement them. While she rejected the idea that training on its own could be effective in bringing about organisational change, she argued that it could help to develop the conditions needed for the implementation of equal opportunity policies (CRE, 1987a; *Equal Opportunities Review*, 20, 1988: 26–7).

Such training remained a matter of debate and controversy within local authorities and continued to receive regular attention from the media, which forced local authorities to rethink the kind of race-related training they should provide. Nonetheless routinised forms of training became an established part of local authority practices, albeit in a somewhat less politicised form.

Changing forms of local governance

Far from encouraging new initiatives to tackle racial discrimination, legislation on local government by the Thatcher and Major administrations during the 1980s and 1990s was based on the assumption that in future there would be a considerable reduction in (a) the part played by local authorities as direct service providers in education, housing and related fields, and (b) in the ability of local authorities to develop alternative policies and practices from those which were part of the national political agenda. Within this ideological framework the pursuit of egalitarian social objectives by local authorities did not even make first base on the political agenda during this period.

Both the Thatcher and the Major administrations set themselves apart from local authorities in the development of inner city policy and local economic regeneration. This was a key theme after the 1987 general election when Margaret Thatcher undertook a short tour through Britain's inner cities with the aim of declaring her government's commitment to regenerating these areas (Robson, 1988). Throughout the late 1980s and early 1990s the question of regenerating depressed inner city localities was a key issue in political debates between the Labour and Conservative Parties. Whether at the symbolic level, in terms of Thatcher's commitment to do something about 'those inner cities', or at a more practical policy level the question of urban policy remained at the heart of debates on race in British society.

Despite such symbolic gestures, considerable time had elapsed since Lord Scarman called for urgent action to tackle racial discrimination and the social conditions that lay behind the disorders in Brixton and elsewhere, and there was still little evidence of positive changes for the populations of those areas. Whatever the merit of the particular programme proposed by Lord Scarman, and this was the subject of some debate, the one consistent response had little to do with the pursuit of social justice: rather than dealing with the root causes of racial disadvantage and urban unrest, successive governments chose to give more resources, more training and more equipment to the police in order to control the symptoms of urban unrest. During the Thatcher and Major periods the overall objective was to reduce public expenditure for the sake of lower taxation, and to encourage an enterprise culture in the inner cities (see Stewart and Stoker, 1989). In this context aid to inner city areas was dwarfed by the financial cuts applied to their local authorities.

In the aftermath of the 1981 and 1985 urban unrest the central government promised to help inner city areas that had been particularly hard hit by economic restructuring and urban decay. The turning of such promises into practical action was, however, limited and the effectiveness of what little action there was in promoting equal opportunity was minimal to say the least (Benyon and Solomos, 1987; Robson, 1988).

From 1989 the furore over Salman Rushdie's *Satanic Verses* and the consequent spotlight on Muslim fundamentalism added a new dimension to the local politics of race (Samad, 1992; Bhatt, 1997). The wider impact of the Rushdie affair on the local and national politics of race will be addressed in Chapter 10, but the impact on local politics was clear. First, during the 1990s the Rushdie affair gave a new impetus to debates on immigration, integration and public order. Second, it had a direct impact on local politics in terms of both formal and informal political processes. The high profile adopted by Muslim political activists in areas such as Bradford, Leicester and Birmingham in the aftermath of the Rushdie affair can best be seen as a product of the tensions that the affair brought to the surface (Parekh, 1989; Banton, 1989).

Such controversies created a political climate that was much less amenable to antiracist initiatives than had been the case in the early 1980s. Perhaps the most important constraint on the part that local authorities could play in the promotion of racial equality in the 1990s was the curtailing of the political autonomy of local government by the central government. This tended to make local authorities less willing to innovate in areas that were controversial and less responsive to demands for resources by excluded groups. The consequence of this could be seen in the disputed nature of racial equality and antiracist initiatives.

This did not mean, however, that the racialisation of local politics was completely in retreat. Rather the politics of race had become a central feature of the local political scene in many localities, although the impact of questions about race remained more limited in terms of the distribution of resources. When making any assessment about the possibility of bringing about racial equality through the work of local authorities it is important to bear in mind both the fundamental changes in local government since the early 1980s and the legislative and political actions the Thatcher and Major governments took in order to transform the operation of local government finance, housing and education (Stewart and Stoker, 1989).

Local governance and social exclusion

Since the election of New Labour in May 1997 we have seen a somewhat different emphasis in policies on urban regeneration. One of the features of policy change in the past decade has been the linking of questions about racial inequality to wider aspects of social exclusion (London Research

Centre, 1998; Cabinet Office, 2000). Indeed the policies pursued by the government since 1997 have focused on a combination of localised initiatives to deal with multiply deprived communities and community-based strategies to encourage particular communities to become involved in self-help initiatives or policies aimed at tackling social exclusion (Home Office, 1999b; Home Office, Race Equality Unit, 2000). Given the deeply racialised nature of debates on such questions as the 'underclass' and 'urban deprivation', it is not surprising that the government's urban policies have been partly concerned with the question of how race can be made part of its strategy to deal with social exclusion and urban regeneration.

Much of the focus of New Labour's urban policy has been on regenerating the most deprived areas through a national programme to promote area- and community-based initiatives that typically involve central government, local government and community-based organisations working together to tackle specific questions. Even before the election of New Labour the thinking behind many of the policies of the Major government was premised on the need for such interventions, and since 1997 we have seen a proliferation of agencies in this field. These include the Neighbourhood Renewal Unit, Education Action Zones and Health Action Zones. These initiatives are not aimed at black and ethnic minority communities as such; however, it is clear that their work, and the work of the Social Exclusion Unit, will have to address at least some aspects of racialised urban inequality and exclusion (Loftman and Beazley, 1998).

Since 1997 there has been a sustained government attempt to link area-based initiatives with the work of mainstream government departments. For example the Neighbourhood Renewal Unit (NRU) was established to tackle key issues in deprived areas, such as poor schools, unemployment, poor health, educational failure and crime. Two of the objectives of the unit are to involve ethnic minority groups more fully in urban regeneration initiatives and to ensure that racial equality targets are set. At the same time the work of new bodies such as the NRU is seen very much in terms of involving mainstream government departments in meeting the needs of multiply deprived communities and groups.

It is important to remember that responses to urban deprivation and exclusion are shaped by both local and national concerns and it is impossible to reduce all the initiatives that have emerged over the past few decades to the concerns of national government. What national government does do, however, is to provide the financial and ideological context within which policy agendas evolve. Since 1997 the preoccupation of New Labour with questions such as social exclusion and multiple deprivation has resulted in a new policy framework, pointing to a more promising policy context for the development of race equality through urban policies and regeneration programmes. It is also evident that in many local communities initiatives in this field – financed by local and central government as well as by charities – have become part of the local landscape. The success of this endeavour will depend on matching longer-term strategies with people's expectations of reform and change on the ground.

In the aftermath of the 2001 riots and disturbances public discourses have become much more preoccupied by the subjects of social exclusion and urban decay. A recurrent theme in all the key reports produced after the riots is how best to overcome the separation of or lack of everyday contact within communities in Bradford and the other places where the violence was concentrated. It is interesting to note in this respect that Herman Ouseley's report *Community Pride, Not Prejudice: Making Diversity Work in Bradford* (2001) began with the following question: 'Why is community fragmentation along social, cultural, ethnic and religious lines occurring in the Bradford District?' Despite this question Ouseley's report seems to be more concerned with describing this fragmentation than with explaining the reasons for it.

Nevertheless much of the debate that followed the unrest in Bradford, Oldham and Burnley focused on the link between urban deprivation and the relative absence of community cohesion in these localities. In a report by the Ministerial Group on Public Order and Community Cohesion a recurrent theme is the need to take 'a more holistic approach to regeneration and building civic renewal' (Home Office, 2001: 18). The key element of this approach is collaboration between governmental agencies and local communities to improve public services, regenerate run-down areas and deal with crime. We shall return to the impact of the urban unrest in Chapter 7, but it is interesting to note here that future policies on urban renewal are likely to be shaped at least in part by the need to produce the best conditions for community cohesion.

Summary and conclusion

The main topic addressed in this chapter was the impact of local processes on the politics of racism in contemporary Britain. In addressing this the chapter outlined the key elements of and changing responses to questions about race and racism in the local political environment. It is impossible to generalise and say that there has been a uniform pattern of policy responses in this field because since the early 1960s local political and policy responses have been conditioned by national and local determinants that have produced significant variations in the form and content of state interventions (Solomos and Back,

1995; Office for Public Management, 2001). While at a broad level the wider social, political and economic contexts have imposed constraints on the extent of policy change, it is impossible to ignore the part played by local politicians, professionals and bureaucrats in defining policy objectives and priorities.

Perhaps the most important conclusion to emerge from this and the previous chapter is that since the early 1970s the complex process of policy change in this area, whether at the national or the local level, has been in response to pressures from both within and outside the main political institutions. The effectiveness of these policies in reducing the extent of racism and discrimination in British society has been fairly limited, perhaps because during much of the 1980s and 1990s there was intense opposition to antiracist policies at the local level (Small, 1991b; Solomos and Back, 1995). It is important to remember, however, that as a result of policy innovations over the past two decades questions about race and ethnicity have become an established part of the political scene.

Race remains a central feature of local politics in many areas, as demonstrated by the ways in which black and ethnic minority political activists have gained access to power in a number of localities since the 1980s. When making any assessment about the possibility of bringing about greater racial equality through local initiatives, however, it is important to bear in mind both the fundamental changes that local politics has undergone since the early 1980s and the changes that are still taking place. Only by analysing such factors can we begin to think about how local political mobilisations and community-based initiatives can help to transform the racial and ethnic boundaries in urban environments.

6 Race and Policing

Reference was made in the previous two chapters to two issues that have attracted considerable attention in the field of race and racism, namely the effects of policing on ethnic minority communities, and violent urban unrest in multiracial urban areas. It should be clear that no account of the politics of race in contemporary Britain can ignore the role that policing has played in racial issues since the early 1970s. Part of the reason for the growing interest in these issues can be traced back to the impact that the riots of 1981 and 1985 and subsequent outbreaks of violent unrest have had on the politics of race both nationally and locally. Another crucial factor in shaping public debates on race and policing has been the controversy over the killing of Stephen Lawrence and the publication of the Macpherson Report on the case in 1999.

Events such as these have highlighted the tensions between minority communities and the police and other parts of the criminal justice system (FitzGerald, 1998, 1999). They have also highlighted the extent to which contemporary debates on race are shaped by fear of or concern about issues such as crime, urban violence and disorder and the alienation of sections of black and Asian youth in British society. Specific preoccupations have gone through a number of changes since the 1970s, as evidenced by the fact that debates on race and policing are currently couched in terms of 'institutional racism' and 'social exclusion'. It remains the case, however, that such concerns are closely linked to the conflict and tension with the police that has been an intrinsic element of racial situations in urban localities for the past four decades.

It is to these issues that we turn in this chapter. The focus will be on the history and development of public debate on race and policing in British society. We shall begin by exploring the various stages in the history of relations between the police and ethnic minority communities, and then move on to consider the development of public and policy-related positions on this question. This will be followed in Chapter 7 by a critical analysis of the urban unrest that took place in the 1980s, the late 1990s and 2001. Together these two chapters aim to provide an analysis of key dimensions of the political and policy debates on race and racial exclusion in British society.

Race, crime and disorder

Ideologies that link immigrants to crime have a long history in Britain, as discussed briefly in Chapter 2. This is not to say that such ideologies have been constant throughout time, or that they have been monolithic. Rather they have undergone numerous transformations over the years, and the existence of a link between immigrants and crime has not been universally accepted even by those who have opposed immigration. But it is certainly true that whether one considers the Irish immigrants of the nineteenth century, the Jewish immigrants of 1880–1914 or other significant groups of immigrants, crime has been a common theme in the construction of ideologies and policies towards them (Garrard, 1971; Gainer, 1972; Holmes, 1978; Lunn, 1980).

Black seamen who settled in port towns such as Cardiff, Liverpool and London were similarly stereotyped. The areas in which they lived were seen as localities where an immigrant presence combined with social deprivation and poverty to produce not only criminal behaviour but also values that lay outside those of mainstream society. A number of studies of black communities during the early twentieth century noted how important such images were in determining both the form and the content of dominant ideologies on the 'Negro problem' official circles and local voluntary associations (Little, 1947; Banton, 1955; Fryer, 1984).

In an important early study St Clair Drake provided a detailed account of how the Tiger Bay area of Cardiff came to be portrayed in a negative manner. He showed that the inhabitants of the area were generally defined as a problem by outside institutions, and how the black inhabitants were seen as an 'outsider' group. Even though many of the Tiger Bay inhabitants expressed the view that 'the colour-bar is the problem; not the coloured people', the black inhabitants of the area were attributed with characteristics that led them to be defined as a problem, with young 'half-caste' children being seen as a particularly problematic group (Drake, 1954: 69–129).

Other studies have shown how the areas into which post-1945 black settlers moved rapidly became identified with crime-related behaviour and other social problems, including decaying housing, lack of social amenities and a low degree of community involvement (Carter *et al.*, 1987). In areas such as Notting Hill and Brixton in London, Handsworth and Balsall Heath in Birmingham and similar localities in other cities the question of rising crime and lack of law and order became intimately bound up with the broader question of the impact of black immigration on such areas.

Questions about the involvement of specific groups of immigrants in criminal activities were asked both in and out of parliament and became a topic of concern in the press (*The Times*, 28 March 1958). Such questions became even more pronounced during and after the 1958 riots in Notting Hill and Nottingham, which helped to politicise the issue of black immigration and influenced the direction of local and central government policies. Indeed during the late 1950s and early 1960s the issue of immigration control was closely tied to the question of black involvement in criminal activities. Even before the 1958 riots a number of pro-immigration-control MPs had attempted to politicise the issue of black crime (*Hansard*, vol. 578, 1957, cols 743–6; vol. 585, 1958, cols 1415–26), and the political climate in the aftermath of the riots proved conducive to the ideologies of those who blamed growing racial tension on the arrival of 'undesirables' from the colonies. At the 1958 Conservative Party Conference Norman Pannell called for the deportation of such 'undesirables', whom he defined as those migrants who were not of good character, not in good health, or lacked sufficient means to avoid becoming a drain on public resources (*The Times*, 13 October 1958).

Along with the broader process of racialisation, the 1960s saw increased politicisation of this question and continuous attempts by the police and successive governments to deal with the danger of conflict between the police and black people. The main concerns at this stage were the growing number of complaints about racial discrimination by the police against blacks, the future of younger blacks if their social and economic position deteriorated, and that American-style racial violence and disorder might erupt in major cities. In July 1967 the Home Office issued to all chief constables a circular entitled *The Police and Coloured Communities*, which advised them to appoint liaison officers to develop better relations with black communities and educate police officers on the dilemmas of policing such areas. This was followed by a number of consultative meetings to discuss the policing of particular localities and to consider the prospect of future conflict between the police and black people. Between 1967 and 1970 a number of articles appeared in specialist journals that discussed the policing of multiracial localities, the specific problems faced by young blacks and accusations of discriminatory behaviour by the police in parts of London, Birmingham and other localities.

The police gradually began to recognise the need to develop an understanding of policing in multiracial areas. In 1970 a conference of US and British specialists and practitioners was held under the auspices of the Ditchley Foundation to discuss police–community relations on both sides of the Atlantic (Clarke, 1970). This was followed by other meetings and seminars on the issue, and from 1970 onwards the annual reports of the commissioner of the Metropolitan Police contained some discussion of policing in multiracial localities.

An article written by Robert Mark, then deputy commissioner of the Metropolitan Police, provides an enlightening insight into the emergent ideology of the police on the question of race. While stressing that 'there is no evidence to show that migrants commit a disproportionate amount of crime', Mark argued that a minority did come into frequent contact with the police. He linked this to two factors: (a) the involvement of a small number of immigrants in prostitution, gaming and other criminal activities, and (b) the involvement of other immigrants in public order offences, family disputes or noisy parties (Mark, 1970: 4–5). For Mark this was partly the result of the newness of the immigrants and their socioeconomic position in Britain, and partly due to the failure of the police and other institutions to deal with the 'special problems posed by migrants' (ibid.: 5). But he did not think that the situation would permanently damage relations between the police and the immigrant communities:

> Traditionally the protector of all groups and classes, irrespective of race, colour or creed, we believe that we, the police, have done no less than any other public service to promote the welfare and security of the migrant in his transition from his homeland to an alien highly industrial, urban society; and we are not unduly discouraged that we should be attacked and criticised by representatives, self-appointed or otherwise, of the very people that we are trying to help (ibid.)

Mark's optimism about the effectiveness of positive action by the police was not shared, as he pointed out, by a growing number of critics of the force's overall strategy and tactics for policing multiracial areas. In fact it was partly in response to increasingly trenchant criticism of their role from both within and outside black communities that police officers began to develop and articulate an ideological legitimation for their policies on black areas (Lambert, 1970; Humphry, 1972).

The debate on the topic was carried forward by the national media as well as specialist journals such as *Race Today*, which at the time was published by the Institute of Race Relations. The public nature of the debate politicised the question of race and policing to a new level during the early 1970s, particularly as pressure mounted from black communities for the investigation of cases of police harassment and for 'greater equality before the law' (Nandy, 1970; John, 1970; Hall *et al.*, 1978). It should also be remembered that it was during this period that the question of immigration and race came to occupy a central place in debates on domestic social policies at both the national and the local political level. This broader process of racialisation increased the impact of the policy debate on the interrelationship of crime and race, since this issue gave credence to Enoch Powell's claim that immigration was undermining the entire social fabric of inner city areas. The imagery of black involvement in criminal activities and public order offences both fuelled and gave a new direction to the increasingly volatile debate on race relations.

Alienated youth and ghetto life

In the late 1960s concern about the increasing alienation of young blacks from mainstream society was regularly expressed in the media and policy documents, and became a constant refrain in both academic and policy writings on the subject. By the early 1970s it had become clear that this was not merely a passing phenomenon that would disappear with the integration of young blacks into the institutions of British society.

This was so for at least two major reasons. First, calls for action to help 'coloured' school leavers gain equality of opportunity in employment and other areas were not being met by the development of effective policy instruments. Evidence of high levels of unemployment, low levels of attainment in schools and homelessness among young blacks continued to accumulate during the early 1970s, showing that in the space of a few years the picture painted in a report entitled *The Problems of Coloured School Leavers* (1969) had been overtaken by events. Far from the positive measures called for in this report, there had been inaction and a deterioration of the socioeconomic circumstances of young blacks.

Second, the plight of young blacks had become a central concern of black communities themselves. In various local and national forums, black political activists were not only discussing issues such as education, employment and policing in relation to young blacks, they were also criticising the government's failure to take effective measures to tackle the root causes of racism and racial inequality.

At a symbolic level, commitment to the principle of equal opportunity was still part of the political climate. The Conservative home secretary, Robert Carr, restated this commitment during a debate on race relations issues at the 1973 Conservative Party conference:

> Our principle is that there should be no second-class citizens in Britain. Everyone who was born here or has come here legally should be equal before the law and not only that but they should be treated equally in the practices of everyday life. I know we do not live up to that perfectly but that is our commitment and that is what my colleagues and I will do our best to achieve (*The Times*, 11 October 1973).

But such symbolic promises did not answer the fundamental question raised by the portrayal of young blacks, along with their parents, as second-class citizens: why were the inequalities and problems faced by the first generation of black immigrants being reproduced among the second generation? What were the likely medium- and long-term consequences of this both for young blacks and for society as a whole? Vague promises of future action left substantive issues untouched and deflected attention to the prospect of a better future.

The reality of the situation in the early 1970s was made clear in a number of reports that highlighted the dismal prospect for young blacks and the potential of conflict with the police. The year 1970 saw the publication of Gus John's influential study of Handsworth, *Race and the Inner City*, and John Lambert's *Crime, Police and Race Relations*. Both books attracted attention because they came out at a time when relations between black communities and the police and the involvement of young blacks in crime were being widely discussed in the press. Between 1969 and 1973 a number of feature articles and reports addressed various aspects of the growing tension between the police and black communities, both at the national level and in relation to specific communities. Complaints against the police by black communities, which had been articulated as early as 1966 in Hunte's *Nigger Hunting in England*, reached new heights during the early 1970s and were rapidly becoming a major political issue.

John's study of Handsworth was a particularly important document in this growing debate. Written by a black researcher who had spent some time living in the black community in Handsworth, it highlighted the fact that policing and the plight of young blacks were core concerns of local residents. It was written at a time when the police were discussing the task of policing multiracial inner city areas and formulating their ideologies and practices on this issue (Humphry, 1972). In addition there was extensive media coverage of the growing tension between the police and black communities, and in 1969–70 there were a number of minor street confrontations with the police in areas such as Notting Hill. John began his account of Handsworth with an analysis of the area and the contrasting perceptions offered by local residents of the postwar period. But the core element of his report, and the issue that gave rise to a full debate in the press, was the description it offered of relations between the local black community, particularly younger blacks, and the police. He reported that one police official had said to him that the 'growth of black crime' in the area was the work of a 'hard core' of 40 or 50 youngsters (John, 1970: 20). His own perception was that the situation was more complex than portrayed by the police but could be broken down into three main issues:

- The prevalence of rumours and fears of black involvement in criminal activities.
- A tendency by the police to blame a 'hard core' of young blacks for 'giving the area a bad name'.
- Deep resentment by older and younger blacks of their social position and the discrimination they had to endure.

He also warned that there were signs of 'a massive breakdown in relations between the police and the black community', and that if nothing was done the situation was likely to lead to confrontations between black residents and the police and general urban unrest:

> In my view trends in Handsworth are a portent for the future. A decaying area, full of stress and tension, which also happens to be racially mixed, is going to find it increasingly difficult to cope with the root problems because racial animosities and resentments have taken on an independent life of their own. The problem is not, and can never be, simply one of law and order (ibid.: 25).

It was this, argued John, that explained why both young blacks and the police saw the situation in the area as open 'warfare' (ibid.: 28–9). Some aspects of John's account of relations between the police and the black community were criticised as overstated and impressionistic. Yet there is a certain symmetry between his account of the situation and that described later in the 1970s by John Rex and Sally Tomlinson in their detailed empirical analysis of the political economy of race and class in Handsworth (Rex and Tomlinson, 1979). Other studies of the interplay between race and policing during the early 1970s indicated that the relationship between young blacks and the police was becoming an issue of concern in areas other than Handsworth.

Evidence from black communities across the country highlighted three particularly contentious allegations: that young blacks were being categorised as a 'problem group' by the police and were therefore more likely to be questioned or arrested; that the police were using excessive physical violence in their dealings with black suspects; and that police attitudes and behaviour were fuelling popular rumours about the involvement of young blacks in crime and driving a wedge between the white and black communities.

Policing minority communities

Perhaps the most significant factor in the context of my general argument is that the emphasis on young blacks as a problem group for the police and for society as a whole was increasingly being framed in terms of police–community relations. This shift became clear when (a) the question of policing was investigated by the Select Committee on Race Relations and Immigration during 1971–2, and (b) popular and media attention began to focus on the involvement of young blacks in the form of street crime popularly defined as mugging.

As argued above, the politicisation of crime in relation to young blacks is best seen in the broader context of official and public concern about the interplay between ghetto life, the social position of young blacks and criminal activities. The Select Committee on Race Relations and Immigration's investigation of police–immigrant relations, during 1971–2 offers a useful starting point for understanding the concerns of the state, the police and the black communities about policing and law and order. The committee took evidence from community groups, police officials, local authorities and government departments on the causes of the growing tension between the police and sections of the black population. Although the popular press and John's report on Handsworth had claimed that police officers on the ground perceived that a section of the black population was disproportionately involved in criminal activities, the committee concluded that this claim was not supported by the evidence:

> The conclusions remain beyond doubt: coloured immigrants are no more involved in crime than others; nor are they generally more concerned in violence, prostitution and drugs. The West Indian crime rate is much the same as that of the indigenous population. The Asian crime rate is very much lower (Select Committee, 1972: 71).

It did find, however, that relations between the younger generation of West Indians and the police were explosive. This was due to a combination of factors, most notably the attitude of young blacks towards society and the police (ibid.: 68–9). The committee considered that young West Indians were becoming increasingly resentful of society and were venting their anger and frustration against the police because they were an obvious authority symbol. It saw this as arising from three factors (ibid.: 69):

- The pressures faced by young blacks when competing for jobs and housing.
- The nature of West Indian family discipline, which tended to be 'Victorian' for younger children but did not extend to offspring aged 16–25.
- The conflict between the younger and older generations of West Indians.

The committee did accept that young blacks faced discrimination, but significantly it did not prioritise this in its account of the growing tension between them and the police. It stated that while black community groups complained of 'nigger hunting' and a tendency for 'the police to pick on black youths merely because they are black', evidence from the Metropolitan Police showed that 'in London black youths are stopped and/or arrested proportionately no more than white youths'.

On the question of allegations that police officer's engaged in practices ranging from harassment, assault, wrongful arrest and detention to provocation, fabrication, planting evidence and racial insults, the committee was much more reticent to come to conclusion. It accepted that much of the evidence submitted to it by the Community Relations Commission indicated that such practices were common in many localities (Select Committee, 1972, vol. II: 65–8; vol. III: 716–35; vol. III: 765–71), but it found it impossible to prove or disprove this, and considered that the truth probably lay somewhere in between the claims of the police and those of their critics (Select Committee, 1972: 20–1). It saw these claims and counterclaims as the natural outcome of a lack of communication between the police and sections of black youth. This lack of communication helped to build stereotypes and reproduce situations of conflict. The committee explained the process thus:

> There are examples throughout our evidence of the way in which a simple situation builds up to a confrontation. A policeman's mode of address is resented by a black youth sensitive to insult; the youth replies with what the policeman sees as insolence, often accompanied by gesticulation; the policeman counters with what the youth sees as hostile formality. Neither understands the other's point of view; each sees the other as a threat. The youth says he is being picked on because he is black and the policeman is immediately in a dilemma. If he takes firm action he can be accused of racial bias by black people, if he doesn't he is open to the same accusation by white people (ibid.: 69).

The committee recommended that a programme of action be implemented to improve communication, including training and schemes to improve relations with the black community in 'problem areas' (ibid.: 92–5). It concluded that such a positive programme of action could help to establish better relations between young blacks and the police:

> If the best examples of leadership in police and immigrant relations prevailed throughout forces in the United Kingdom, many of the difficulties we have dwelt upon would, within a reasonable space of time, diminish. In some places they could wither away (ibid.: 92).

From this perspective the situation in some localities, although explosive and dangerous, could be defused if the pressures that were causing the tension between young blacks and the police were dealt with.

This hope was to remain unfulfilled throughout the 1970s since the publication of the committee's report coincided with a marked politicisation of the debates on black youth, policing and crime during 1972–6. This politicisation, occurring as it did at a time of controversy over race and immigration more generally, was reflected in frequent media reports, official documents and speeches by politicians, police officers and other opinion leaders. From the summer of 1972 it particularly focused on the supposed involvement of young blacks in mugging.

Mugging and street violence

The social construction of the question of mugging and black youth during the early 1970s offers perhaps the clearest example of how the politicisation of this issue came about. The genesis and development of official, police and media ideologies on mugging has been analysed and commented on from a number of angles and I do not wish to retrace the steps of existing accounts. Hence this section will focus on one aspect of this phenomenon, namely the projected images of black youth and mugging during the early 1970s and the consequences of this for policy and practice in relation to young blacks.

During the 1960s the political debate on the second generation of young blacks became synonymous with images of alienation, despair, lack of equal opportunity and urban disorder. By the early 1970s, as we saw in the previous section, concern was beginning to shift to the involvement of young blacks in mugging and other forms of street crime. This concern reached its peak in 1972–6, when the moral panic over the mugging issue was at its height in the press and official discourses, to the point where Enoch Powell publicly declared mugging to be essentially a black crime (*Guardian*, 12 April 1976).

The media and popular response to the mugging issue has been analysed in some detail by Hall *et al.* (1978). The premise of these authors is that the construction of the black population as a social problem was the ideological bedrock upon which the black youth/urban deprivation/street crime model of mugging was based during the early 1970s. Mugging as a political phenomenon, according to Hall *et al.*, became associated with black youth because they were seen as suffering most from the cycle of poverty, unemployment and social alienation that was afflicting inner city areas, and having the added disadvantage of belonging to a racial group with a 'weak' culture and numerous social problems, such as family breakdown and lack of achievement in school. These images, according to this study, derived partly from commonly held images of race and inner cities, and partly from the feeling of discomfort that was developing in British society as a whole about the position of black communities and their place in the dominant institutions (ibid.: 346–9).

This contradictory response to the growth of permanent black communities in many inner city areas coincided with growing concern about inner city problems and the impact of deprivation on the residents of localities with problems arising out of (a) the rising levels of crime and violence, (b) the emergence of racial disadvantage and inequality, and (c) the development of ghetto areas with distinct cultural values and attitudes towards law and order and the police.

These concerns about the changing character of the inner city areas were imbued with racial overtones since the localities that were defined as particularly problematic – in terms of poverty, poor housing, lack of jobs, broken families and crime – were those with a high degree of black settlement. Inner city problems were therefore often synonymous with questions about race. Hall *et al.* for example, note that even in areas where young blacks constituted a small minority of the total youth, the issue of crime on the streets was intimately tied up with the category of black youth. This construction was possible because from the early 1970s onwards concern about ghetto areas focused on the alleged drift of young blacks into a life of crime and poverty. According to Hall *et al.*:

> For all practical purposes, the terms mugging and black crime are now virtually synonymous. In the first mugging panic, as we have shown, though mugging was continually shadowed by the theme of race and crime, this link was rarely made explicit. This is no longer the case. The two are indissolubly linked: each term references the other in both the official and public consciousness (ibid.: 217).

This projection of concerns about race, crime and ghetto areas onto black youth thus involved a combination of images that linked particular areas to specific types of crime, and these crimes to a specific section of the local population. The definition of criminal areas in everyday police practice thus gained a clear racial dimension, which was further accentuated by the wider social and economic processes that confined black people to inner city localities and excluded them from equal participation in the labour market and society more generally.

The politicisation of the mugging question occurred with reference to a number of issues that preoccupied both government agencies and the police. Chief among these were the breakdown of consent to policing in certain areas, confrontations between the police and young blacks, and concern that Britain was becoming a violent society. We shall look at each of these issues in turn before moving to the broader question of the racialisation of crime and the threat of urban disorder.

A glimpse of the everyday confrontations and conflicts between the police and sections of the black community can be found in the evidence collected by the Select Committee during 1971–2 for its report on police–immigrant relations, in the press coverage of this issue during the early 1970s and in the activities of various groups within black communities for whom the issue of policing was a central concern. But it was during 1972–6 that declining consent to policing and the development of volatile problem areas became major themes in the public debate on policing (Humphry, 1972; Alderson and Stead, 1973; Cain, 1973; Pulle, 1973). This theme was also present in the government's response to the Select Committee's report, which was published in October 1973. After noting that the problems associated with policing black communities were part of a wider question, it went on to argue that:

> The police are of course only one element of the society which is confronted by this challenge. While part of the test is the extent to which coloured people are treated by the police on the same terms as white people, any failure of the rest of society, in employment, in housing and elsewhere, to accept coloured citizens on equal terms would undermine the efforts made by the police and leave them facing forms of discontent which spring from causes outside their control (Home Office, 1973: 5).

This suggestion that wider forces were at work to delegitimise the role of the police pervaded the government's response, although it also pointed out that only a small minority of young blacks were opposed to the police and the majority were law-abiding.

At a more popular level the declining consent to policing was mentioned regularly in both the popular and the serious press. The imagery of American black ghettoes was transposed onto the British scene, with areas such as Brixton, Notting Hill and Handsworth being compared to the streets of Harlem, Watts and other ghettoes. The questions being asked amounted to the following. Why are young blacks being driven to crime? How can they be resocialised into the dominant values of society?

The issue of mugging was therefore intimately linked to wider conceptions about the social problems faced by young blacks in parts of the country that were popularly and officially identified as problem areas. During the early 1970s it also became clear that everyday confrontations over minor issues could easily escalate into open conflict or collective protest on the streets. This phenomenon had already been noted by the media and in the Select Committee's 1971–2 report, but the tension mounted during the mid 1970s in a sequence of incidents that with the benefit of hindsight can be seen as presaging the larger disturbances during the 1980s. This included the widely reported confrontation in June 1973 between black youths, the police and the wider black community in Brockwell Park, south London. The reporting of this event portrayed the events as a race riot and a sign of larger riots and disorders to come. This theme became more pronounced when it became clear that the Brockwell Park confrontation was not an isolated incident and that outbreaks of a similar kind were becoming part of the everyday experience of many inner city localities.

The immediate causes for such outbreaks were often small incidents that escalated through rumour and counter-rumour, leading to the arrival of more police and more young blacks to join in the fray. But the underlying conditions that created the basis for such confrontations were much more complex. In 1970 John had noted in Handsworth that 'the massive breakdown of relations between the police and the black community' held out the potential for violent unrest. When describing black people's feelings about the local police he said:

> The police station in Thornhill Road is one of the buildings most dreaded and most hated by black Handsworth. It is commonplace to hear references made to 'the pigs at Thornhill Road', or 'Babylon House', or 'the place where the thugs hang out' (John, 1970: 22).

John went on to argue that attitudes such as this helped to create a climate of opinion in areas such as Handsworth where the actions of the police were being questioned and at times actively resisted both by young blacks and by older members of the community. At the same time the police were adopting a belligerent attitude towards all forms of black cultural and social activity that they saw as alien or deviant. Thus from 1969 onwards there were numerous confrontations between the police and young blacks in places such as youth clubs, restaurants and other locations that were identified as trouble spots or places where criminal activities thrived. Notable examples include the confrontations at the Mangrove restaurant and Metro youth club in Notting Hill. Confrontations between young blacks and the police also occurred in Brixton, Liverpool, Chapeltown in Leeds, Handsworth in Birmingham and Moss Side in Manchester.

Conflicting interpretations of the relations between young blacks and the police were themselves a reflection of wider preoccupations about the future of race relations in urban localities that were experiencing major economic, social, political and cultural transformations (CCCS Race and Politics Group, 1982; Gilroy, 1987). During this time the racialisation of political debates on urban policy and social policy more generally was reaching new heights through the interventions of Enoch Powell and the articulation of public concern about the immigration of Ugandan Asians. It was also during this period that images of violence and decay became synonymous with the inner city localities in which black migrants had settled.

Politicisation of the mugging issue was part of a wider societal concern about the growing problem of violence and the breakdown of law and order in British society. Although this phenomenon was not always linked to popular and official perceptions of race, crime and policing, the racialisation of political debate during the early 1970s helped to bring the two issues together in popular discourse.

The linking of arguments about black crime to this wider concern became apparent during a debate on the queen's speech in parliament at the height of public alarm about mugging. The debate was ostensibly on the general theme of social problems and had been called by the Labour opposition. But as Shirley Williams pointed out in her opening remarks, this was one of the few sessions in which the House of Commons had discussed in detail 'the future directions in which our society is moving', particularly the 'crisis in the cities' (*Hansard*, vol. 863, 1973, col. 315). For Williams the situation in many inner city localities was more critical than it had been for over a century, particularly in relation to policing, social deprivation, housing, education and juvenile delinquency. The centrality of youth to this scenario was made clear in the following remark:

> Young people, white and black, in increasing numbers [are] moving into cities such as Birmingham and London, often in desperate and futile pursuit of better pay, amenities and conditions. They have themselves become a large floating element among the homeless and ... an element that is particularly disturbing to the police, because it is this reservoir of homeless youngsters who, unless emergency action is taken, will become the young criminals of the next decade (ibid., col. 320).

This theme was taken up throughout the debate by MPs from all political parties, and also by sections of the media covering this and other debates in parliament during this period. Indeed Home Secretary Robert Carr emphasised the importance of ensuring that law and order were maintained in inner city localities, and that disadvantaged groups were not allowed to drift into a vicious circle of disadvantage, alienation, violence and crime (ibid., cols 327–9).

By the mid 1970s, therefore, confrontations on the streets between the police and young blacks had become a central item on the political agenda on race. Yet the impact of this trend on the police remained to be worked out in practice.

Racialisation and popular images

The involvement of young blacks in mugging and other forms of street crime remained a subject of concern, as demonstrated by the regularity with which media reports on mugging referred either directly or in coded terms to the involvement of young blacks. But from the mid 1970s the issue of mugging *per se* was outweighed by other preoccupations about black crime that involved broader issues of race relations as well.

At least two processes were at work. First, the growing politicisation of debates on the social and economic conditions of black communities moved on from a preoccupation with young blacks to encompass the wider communities in which the younger generation lived. In this sense the debates on black crime signalled concern about the crisis of urban black colonies (Hall *et al.*, 1978: 338–9). Second, from the mid 1970s the question of black youth became firmly tied to the broader issues of disorder and violent protest, particularly in localities with large black populations.

The period 1974–8 saw a number of developments that highlighted the impact of these processes. The most important were the attempts by Enoch Powell and other politicians to politicise the debate on black crime, and the occurrence of minor riots in areas such as Notting Hill in 1976 and 1977 and in other localities from 1977 onwards.

As we saw earlier, the 1971–2 Select Committee's report on police–immigrant relations concluded that on balance coloured immigrants were no more involved in crime than others. But it is clear from John's (1970) research in Handsworth and evidence in the report's appendices that the stereotype of areas of black settlement as criminal areas was already deeply entrenched in police thinking. Indeed the report noted that despite the lack of evidence to support a link between blacks and crime, there seems to be a fairly widespread feeling, shared, as we found in informal discussion, by some police officers, that immigrants commit more crime than the indigenous population (Select Committee, 1972: 22). The public debate on mugging helped to amplify and popularise this perception, and the issue of black crime was firmly placed on the political agenda. A number of stages in this process were particularly important.

First, in January 1975 the Metropolitan Police released figures obtained from a study of victims' descriptions of assailants in the Brixton area of London. It was claimed that 79 per cent of robberies and 83 per cent of offences of theft from the person were carried out by black people. This study was widely reported in the media and helped to draw attention to the growing problem of black involvement in crime and the destabilising activities of young disillusioned blacks.

Second, in May 1975 Judge Gwyn Morris jailed five young West Indians for mugging offences in south London. In sentencing them he commented:

> These attacks have become a monotonous feature in the suburbs of Brixton and Clapham, areas which within memory were peaceful, safe, and agreeable places to live in. But immigration resettlement, which has occurred over the past 25 years has radically transformed that environment (*Guardian*, 16 May 1975).

He went on to argue that collectively youngsters such as these were a frightening menace to society, and that they presented immense difficulties to those interested in the maintenance of law and order.

Third, and perhaps more importantly in terms of its public impact, Enoch Powell's speech of April 1976 about mugging being a 'racial phenomenon' articulated wider concern about the interrelationship between race and crime. Powell's words were also linked to evidence submitted by the Metropolitan Police in March 1976 to the Select Committee on Race Relations and Immigration, which was investigating the West Indian community. In its evidence to the 1972 Select Committee the Metropolitan Police had not presented black crime as a major problem, but in the intervening four years it had obviously changed its mind on this issue. In the very first paragraph of its evidence the Metropolitan Police referred to the 'uneasy nature of the relationship between police officers and young blacks' in some localities. After mentioning the social disadvantages that were common in such areas it went on to argue that:

> It is not part of our position that there is a causal link between ethnic origin and crime. What our records do suggest is that London's black citizens, among whom those of West Indian origin predominate, are disproportionately involved in many forms of crime. But in view of their

> heavy concentration in areas of urban stress, which are themselves high crime areas, and in view of the disproportionate numbers of young people in the West Indian population, this pattern is not surprising (Select Committee, 1977, vol. 2: 182).

This analysis proved extremely controversial and it was criticised in the evidence submitted by the Community Relations Commission, to which the Metropolitan Police responded with additional evidence to support its claims. The public debate on these statistics pushed black crime onto the political agenda and legitimised both the public concern about crime on the streets and the arguments of politicians such as Powell, for whom the repatriation of immigrants was the only solution to crime and disorder.

Policing and violent disorder

As argued above, the threat of violent disorder was a common theme in official pronouncements on young blacks from the late 1960s onwards, but in August 1976 this threat became a reality on the streets of Notting Hill. During the annual carnival a major confrontation took place between young blacks (and to some extent young whites) and the police. Although not on the same level as the riots in St Paul's, Brixton, Toxteth, Handsworth and Tottenham during the 1980s, the symbolic significance of this event was clear at the time and has been reiterated with some regularity ever since. For example Kenneth Newman argued that the events at the 1976 Notting Hill carnival were at the time a unique phenomenon and represented an important watershed in terms of the severity of the public disorder dealt with by the police:

> In relation to public disorder, the major changes over the last decade can be easily followed. In 1976, following the riot at the Notting Hill Carnival, defensive shields were introduced; five years later, after petrol bombs were used, we added flameproof clothing and metal helmets; and last year, after the police were shot at, plastic baton rounds were deployed, but not used (Newman, 1986a: 9).

The factor that linked these events together was that all the confrontations involved young blacks in one way or another. In November 1975 less major confrontations took place in Chapeltown (Leeds) and other areas.

During this period police activities under the 'sus' legislation, which allowed them to stop and search suspected criminals, often led to lower-level confrontations between police officers and young blacks. In addition the highly visible operations of the Special Patrol Group in mainly black or multiracial localities gave rise to tension and at times violent confrontation (Demuth, 1978; Hall *et al.*, 1978; AFFOR, 1978). More broadly, concern about the growing problem of black crime served to make the police on the ground suspicious of all black youngsters, with images of violent street crime combining with those of violent street disorders and confrontations to make all young blacks, or particular groups of them (such as Rastafarians), potential suspects in police eyes. They were suspect not only because of social perceptions about their involvement in street crime, but also because they were black, because of the areas in which they lived, because of their style of dress and social contact, and because of their leisure activities. This is certainly how an increasing number of younger blacks, along with their parents and independent researchers, saw the situation in many inner city areas, particularly those designated as 'immigrant areas'.

It was because of this growing problem that Robert Mark, the Metropolitan Police Commissioner, chose to highlight in his annual report for 1975, even before the Notting Hill disturbances, the fact that there was a tendency 'for groups of black people to react in violent opposition to police officers carrying out their lawful duties'. This theme was taken up in police journals and official police documents during this period. The Metropolitan Police's widely publicised evidence to the Select Committee that was investigating the West Indian community revealed official police thinking on the subject:

> Recently there has been a growth in the tendency for members of London's West Indian communities to combine against police by interfering with police officers who are affecting the arrest of a black person or who are in some other way enforcing the law in situations which involve black people. In the last 12 months forty such incidents have been recorded. Each carries a potential for large scale disorder; despite the fact that very few situations actually escalate to the point where local police are unable to cope. Experience indicates that they are more likely to occur during the summer months and that the conflict is invariably with young West Indians. They can occur anywhere in the Metropolitan Police District, but are of course more likely in those areas which have a high proportion of West Indian settlers (Select Committee, 1977, vol. 2: 178).

This perception was mirrored across the country in areas where growing tension and confrontations between young blacks and the police had become a major local issue. In this context references to urban disorder and street violence became a synonym for confrontations between young blacks and the police.

During 1976 and 1977 other widely reported incidents helped to fuel public and policy debates on the issue. First, the killing of an Asian youth, Gurdip Singh Chaggar, in Southall during June 1976 prompted criticism about the lack of concern shown by the police following racial attacks on young blacks, in marked contrast to their preoccupation with black crime. Second, the violence that took place at the Notting Hill carnival in 1976 was repeated in 1977 and led to public concern about violent disorder becoming a regular feature of police–black youth encounters in inner city localities. Third, in August 1977 confrontations took place in the Ladywood area of Birmingham and Lewisham in London. Both these disturbances involved clashes between the National Front and antifascist groups, but it was the involvement of young blacks and the police that became the central issue.

It is clear that the attitude of the police in areas such as Notting Hill, Brixton, Handsworth and Moss Side consolidated the stereotype of young blacks (or at least a section of them) as members of a criminal subculture. Everyday contact between young blacks and the police was interpreted as involving a clash between the cultural values of the majority community and those of minority communities. Such notions were supported by popular attitudes towards the localities in which black people tended to be concentrated ('criminal areas') and the socioeconomic circumstances (for example poverty and unemployment) of young blacks in inner city areas, suggesting that the source of the problem was perceived as laying in the culture and attitudes of young blacks, with racism and discrimination playing only subsidiary roles.

The situation in Handsworth during the late 1970s provides an example of the impact of such thinking on particular localities. The police in Handsworth had long been at the forefront of nationwide initiatives to improve relations between young blacks and the police. However in the evidence it submitted to the Select Committee on police–immigration relations, the Birmingham Police stated that it did not believe that an 'isolated police effort' could deal with the young unemployed West Indians of Handsworth, and it recommended an 'integrated social resources' approach (Select Committee, 1972, vol. 2: 446–7). The area became known as Birmingham's 'angry suburb', with a massive potential for disorder and conflict. During May 1976, in a series of articles on Handsworth the *Birmingham Evening Mail* analysed the underlying tensions in the area, the plight of unemployed young blacks, and the everyday tensions between young blacks and the police. A year later, in the aftermath of the Ladywood riots, the *Observer* printed a vivid description of one confrontation between young blacks and the police:

> Birmingham's Soho Road at half-past nine last Monday night: fluid groups of edgy young blacks on the pavements. A blue-and-white police

> Allegro cruises over the traffic lights. With a sudden jagged movement, a group hurls bricks, sticks and bottles at the car, crunching into the windows and bonking on the metalwork. … Missiles clatter on shop doors and one shatters plate glass. The car slews to a stop and half a dozen youths bombard it from 15 feet. 'Babylon' yells a voice, and the blacks dart outwards, sprinting around corners as a police squad with riot shields and the occasional dustbin lid moves to the stranded panda car (*Observer*, 21 August 1977).

At the same time local papers in Birmingham were full of stories about young West Indians confronting the police in the Bull Ring Shopping Centre and other localities. Such events resulted in the local police becoming overly preoccupied with the issue of young unemployed blacks.

This was later fuelled by a study carried out in 1977 by John Brown on relations between young blacks and the police in Handsworth. Published in November 1977 under the title *Shades of Grey*, the study analysed crime and violence in the area, particularly as it related to a group identified by Brown as consisting of 200 or so 'Dreadlocks' who formed a 'criminalised subculture' and whose actions were serving to perpetuate the tensions between the black community and the police (Brown, 1977: 7–8). In Brown's view the activities of this group of 'criminalised' youngsters could be counteracted by means of improved police contact with local communities combined with broader social policy measures. One consequence of the study was the strategy of 'community policing', developed by Superintendent David Webb from 1977–81, which aimed to bring about more peaceful contact between the black population and the police. But perhaps its broader effect was to popularise the notion that the 'Dreadlock' minority of black youth was the source of the problem. In their detailed sociological study of Handsworth John Rex and Sally Tomlinson commented that *Shades of Grey* fitted in with the popular media image that British society was being threatened by a 'menacing group of strangers', but that they could find no evidence of the existence of a group of 200 'Dreadlocks' terrorising the area and committing crimes (Rex and Tomlinson, 1979: 231–2). This reasoned critique did not prevent Brown's sensational account of Handsworth from continuing to receive wide press coverage and thus helping to popularise dominant police stereotypes of the situation.

The late 1970s saw a further escalation of concern about police–black youth relations, particularly in the context of growing black youth unemployment. Tensions reached new heights and conflict and violent confrontation became more commonplace as time went by. One local resident of Handsworth described the groups of young blacks and other residents who marched on Thornhill Road police station as being 'more pleased than if they'd won the pools' (*Observer*, 21 August 1977). Such intensity of opposition to the police was only partly overcome by the community policing approach adopted from the mid 1970s onwards.

The background to the violent unrest of the 1980s lies precisely in this history of tension and confrontation between young blacks and the police in many localities, with the protests of the 1970s laying the foundations for the severe breakdown of relations between young blacks and the police in the 1980s.

Race, crime and statistics

The 1980s were an important period in the racialisation of debates on law and order, crime and policing in at least two ways. First, the politicisation of the black youth unemployment issue helped to focus attention on the interrelationship between unemployment and crime. Second, the riots of 1980–1 and 1985 forced the issue of crime and violence on the streets onto the mainstream political agenda. The extensive coverage given to the issue of race in connection with the riots opened up a wider debate on issues such as mugging and black crime under the broad rubric of the future of British society.

One of the most important public debates on race and crime started in March 1982 following the decision of the Metropolitan Police to release a previously unpublished racial breakdown of those arrested for street robberies, the statistics having been collected for some time (Scotland Yard press release, 10 March 1982; *Guardian*, 11 March 1982). These figures showed a marked rise in street robberies, but the crucial statistic picked up by the press and other media was the disproportionate involvement of young blacks in crimes such as mugging, purse snatching and robbery from shops. Press reactions varied from sober commentaries on the nature and limitations of the statistics to sensational headlines about black crime and the *Sun's* 'The Yard blames black muggers'. But a common theme was the argument that the statistics, along with the riots of 1980–1, were evidence of the consequences of allowing 'alien' peoples to settle in the very heart of Britain. The *Daily Telegraph* articulated this succinctly:

> Over the 200 years up to 1945, Britain became so settled in internal peace that many came to believe that respect for the person and property of fellow citizens was something which existed naturally in all but a few. A glance at less fortunate countries might have reminded us that such

> respect scarcely exists unless the law is above the power of tribe, or money, or the gun. But we did not look; we let in people from the countries we did not look at, and only now do we begin to see the result. Many young West Indians in Britain, and, by a connected process, growing numbers of young whites, have no sense that the nation in which they live is part of them. So its citizens become to them mere objects of violent exploitation (*Daily Telegraph*, 11 March 1982).

This amounted to a direct link between race and crime. A similar tone was adopted by papers such as the *Daily Mail* and the *Sun*, which went even further in their use of images and harked back to Powell's 1976 definition of mugging as essentially a black crime. A year later Harvey Proctor, a right-wing Tory MP, secured the release of similar figures from the Home Office, leading to a another wave of articles in the press. Since then the Metropolitan Police has been much more reticent about publishing such statistics (although they continue to be kept) because of their potentially volatile effect.

Not surprisingly, however, the involvement of young blacks in criminal or quasicriminal activities remained a key area of concern for the police and other institutions, both locally and nationally. Because of this the issues of crime and violence remain central to our understanding of how ideas about young blacks as a social category were formed and how they are being transformed.

What is clear is that the successive political discourses on black youth from the early 1970s included the issues of policing and black crime as central themes. Whether in terms of specific concerns about street crime or more general concern about the development of subcultures such as Rastafarianism among young blacks, the interplay between race and crime continued to be of symbolic importan in political language. From the late 1970s, and particularly after the 1980–1 riots, political debates on the black crime issue were also heavily weighted by the phenomenon of urban unrest and civil disorder. But even in this context the issues of race, crime and ghettos remained the bedrock of official ideologies and public debate on black youth.

The widespread portrayal of young blacks as being heavily involved in mugging and other forms of street crime prompted the development of strategies to keep them off the streets and maintain police control over localities that were identified in popular and official discourses as crime-prone or potential trouble spots. However it also drew attention to the social and economic alienation of young blacks, as reflected in debates on the impact that unemployment was having on them.

Changing patterns of policing and race

In response to the trends outlined above, over the past two decades the police have been actively seeking to address the challenge of policing multiracial inner city areas by developing new strategies and tactics, and by attempting to recruit more black and Asian police officers. Over the years a number of initiatives have been launched to overcome the reluctance of ethnic minorities to join the police, but with only limited success (Oakley, 1988, 1996; Holdaway and Barron, 1997; FitzGerald and Sibbitt, 1998; Britton, 2000a, 2000b). More fundamentally perhaps, the police have also attempted to develop longer-term strategies to improve relations with various minority communities and to manage unrest and violence in inner city areas (Her Majesty's Inspectorate of Constabulary, 1997, 2000). In this sense the politicisation of police–minority relations, as outlined above, has continued, but at the same time new issues have emerged and become an entrenched part of the scene.

During the 1990s, for example, a key area of concern was the response of the police to racist violence and harassment. The public controversy over the murder of the black teenager Stephen Lawrence in 1993 was perhaps the most important though by no means the only example of the intense debate that emerged on this issue. Much of the discussion on this particular event focused on the horrific nature of the crime, but of equal importance in many people's eyes were the inadequacies of the police response. As the Macpherson Report later made clear, the case of Stephen Lawrence became emblematic of the concern in minority communities about the manner in which the police responded to racist violence, and more generally about how the police perceived minority communities (Macpherson, 1999; see also Cathcart, 1999; Solomos, 1999). It also helped to highlight the limits and contradictions inherent in the reforms instituted in response to the Scarman Report (1981). The main weakness of these reforms was that, despite the rhetoric and the promise of a radical new direction, many of the promised initiatives were only partially implemented, if at all. While the post-Macpherson reforms seem to hold out the promise of more radical reform, it remains to be seen how far we have moved from the cycle of symbolic reforms followed by limited change in practice (Home Office, 1998b, 1999c, 2000).

The history of official responses to racist violence over the past two decades illustrates this dichotomy. Research in a number of countries has highlighted both the state's failure to make racist violence a key issue for state action and the limitations and contradictions of state policies. As a result it is only recently that the police have shown a clear awareness of the need to treat racial violence as a serious matter (Bowling, 1999), but as yet there is little to show for this. Initiatives to tackle racial violence and racist language have been limited and made largely in response to specific events or crises. A case in point is the Metropolitan Police Racial and Violent Crime Task Force in London, which was set up after the killing of Stephen Lawrence and has helped to change everyday police practices in relation to racial violence and terrorism. While it is clear that the task force has had some notable successes in the few years it has been in operation, the belated police response to racist violence remains a point of contention.

While such measures have helped the police to re-establish some degree of credibility for their work, this has been undermined by the death of black and ethnic minority people while being held in police custody, which throughout the 1990s attracted a wave of bad publicity for the police. The cases of Joy Gardner and Roger Sylvester in particular attracted particular media attention, and community-based campaigns on similar cases sprang up regularly. Such public controversies highlighted the degree of mistrust and anger that was still felt by some minority communities about the police.

Although much of the political debate on policing was dominated in one way or another by the Stephen Lawrence case in the 1990s, a number of other issues rose to prominence. For example concern about drug- and gun-related crimes was sparked by the emergence of a new folk devil, namely the 'yardies': criminal gangs from Jamaica who were linked to drug dealing and murder. One of the main themes in public discourses on the yardies was 'black on black' crime, particularly shootings. This was a recurrent cause of police operations during the 1990s and led to the setting up of a special operation, Operation Trident, to deal with gun crimes and murder in black communities.

Some of the most vocal support for measures to tackle black on black crime have come from traditionally radical voices. For example Lee Jasper, the Race Adviser of Ken Livingstone, the Mayor of London, recently called for tough action against crime in black neighbourhoods. Commenting on the emergence of a 'gangsta' culture among young African-Caribbean men, he warned that 'black neighbourhoods have become free trade zones for every kind of drug and illegal contraband, including guns' (*Observer*, 17 February 2002).

Popular images of black gun crime may at one level be seen as feeding a stereotype that has been around for some time, but they also reflect real problems that have emerged in many socially deprived urban areas over the past two decades or so (Bowling and Phillips, 2001). Crime and the fear of crime have become a core concern in many communities, and the everyday occurrence of street crime and drug-related crime has put black on black crime firmly on the policing agenda. What is less clear is whether adequate measures have been taken to deal with the problem.

Summary and conclusion

This chapter has looked at the changing politics of race and policing over the past four decades. As we have seen, public debates on race and policing have tended to emphasise the connection between the social and economic position of the black population and the growth of conflict between the police and certain sections of that population. During the 1970s and 1980s there was a noticeable politicisation of this issue, leading to questions of race and policing occupying a prominent place on the political agenda. Since the 1990s a more complex picture has emerged, shaped in particular by the events surrounding the Stephen Lawrence case and the question of violent crime and drugs. In this changing environment policing remains an important part of the ongoing debate on race and racism in British society.

It is likely that the trends and problems outlined in this chapter will continue to have an impact on immigration policy and race relations in Britain for some time to come. Given that both the experience of crime and the fear of crime remain important matters of public concern, questions about policing, and specifically the relationship between the police and minority communities, will remain a substantial issue in official discourses and in the popular media. At the same time it has become clear over the past three decades that the question of policing is inextricably tied up with wider concerns about the part played by race in shaping violent urban unrest and public disorder. It is to this issue that we now turn.

7 Urban Unrest and the Politics of Protest

One of the striking features of ethnic relations in British society in the past few decades has been the emergence of complex forms of social and political mobilisation by minority communities. As argued in previous chapters, black and ethnic minority groups have by no means been passive political actors; rather they have been an active political force in such issues as immigration policy, race relations policy, social policy and policing. It is important to note, however, that minority communities have not always been able to use mainstream channels of political participation to express their concerns and anger. Rather, during the 1970s and 1980s mobilisation tended to be community-based and focused on specific issues of concern to certain communities or sections of those communities.

In Chapter 6, for example, we looked at how a particular politics emerged during the 1970s and 1980s in respect of policing in multiracial inner city areas. Given the degree of concern in a number of minority communities about the manner policing it is perhaps not surprising that the police as an institution became a specific target of a range of local mobilisations during the 1970s. The politicisation of police–minority relations was taken a step further in the early 1980s with the outbreak of urban unrest on a larger scale than many British cities had experienced for some time. This chapter will analyse the political repercussions of this unrest and its impact on subsequent social and urban policies. This will allow us to consider the extent to which the urban unrest of the 1980s can explain the racialised politics that have emerged in Britain in the past two decades or so. In the concluding section we shall explore more recent incidents of urban unrest and their likely impact on policy and political agendas in the future.

Disorder and urban unrest

Unrest and disorder have become part of the urban scene in Britain since the 1980s. The scale and intensity of the unrest has varied greatly, but it has occurred on a fairly regular basis since the 1980s. The riots of 1981 and 1985 in particular attracted the attention of the media, the police, central and local government, voluntary agencies and black political and community groups on a scale never previously witnessed in the politics of race in Britain.

During 1980 and 1981 there were three major outbreaks of unrest. First, in April 1980 violent confrontations took place in the St Paul's district of Bristol between groups of predominantly black residents and the police. Second, during April 1981 violent confrontations between the police and crowds of mostly black youths occurred in Brixton in London. Finally, in July 1981 there were widespread outbreaks of unrest in the Toxteth area of Liverpool, the Southall area of London and various other localities in London, including Brixton. Other, smaller scale, disturbances took place and attracted some attention in the media and within government (Benyon, 1984).

The violence in Brixton on 10–13 April 1981 caused the Thatcher government to set up the Scarman Inquiry. This was much more limited than the various American inquiries into the violent race riots of the 1960s, but it nevertheless sought to determine what had happened and to suggest what should be done by governmental and other agencies in the future (Scarman, 1981; Benyon, 1984). The more widespread events during July 1981 led to a flurry of activity at both central and local government levels, and to real and symbolic interventions to prevent the disorder and violence spreading further. For example, after years of inaction many local authorities actively sought to develop equal opportunity strategies, and promises were made to reform police training to take account of multiracialism and to tackle the roots of racial disadvantage and discrimination (Joshua and Wallace, 1983).

All of these responses were examples of the symbolic reassurance noted by American analysts (Lipsky and Olson, 1977), but they took different issues as the core variables. At least four explanatory frameworks were used, respectively emphasising race, violence and disorder, the breakdown of law and order, social deprivation and youth unemployment, and political marginalisation.

Further large-scale riots occurred in September and October 1985, with serious outbreaks of violence in Handsworth in Birmingham, Tottenham and Brixton in London, and in Liverpool. Smaller disturbances took place in 1986 and 1987 (Benyon and Solomos, 1987). The scale and locations of the 1985 riots seem to have surprised even some of the most astute observers. Handsworth, for example, was widely perceived as a success story in terms of police–community relations, and therefore the outbreak of violence in this area was seen as an aberration. Similarly the spread of violence in London to areas such as the Broadwater Farm Estate in Tottenham constituted a break from previous events, which had centred on areas such as Brixton. In this sense interpreting the 1985 riots proved as difficult as interpreting the 1980–1 riots.

Explanations of urban unrest

The racialisation of the 1980–1 events was evident from the very first confrontation in Bristol on 2 April 1980, although in a somewhat convoluted manner. Under the headline 'Riot Mob Stone Police' the *Daily Mail* talked of 'mobs of black youths' roaming the streets (3 April 1980). This theme was repeated in the coverage by the *Sun*, the *Daily Star* and the *Daily Express*. The *Financial Times*, however, described the events under the headline 'Bristol: a multiracial riot against the police' (5 April 1980). The *Guardian* was even more ambiguous, its headline being 'The Bristol confrontation: racial but not racist' (5 April 1980).

The tension between the racial and non-racial elements in the media coverage of the Bristol events reflected, according to Joshua and Wallace (1983), the broad divergence of political responses to violent protest: between explanations that treated race and law and order as the main variables and those which saw the riots as a consequence of inner city decay and unemployment. This tension was partly the result of official resistance to the idea that Britain was experiencing race riots on the American model, and partly of the wish to defuse the situation by separating the actions of groups of youths from wider social, economic and political grievances. The fact that Bristol was considered to have good race relations was taken as evidence that the outbreaks of violence were not race riots, with one local paper reporting that William Whitelaw and Tony Benn agreed that the events could not be described as such (*Evening Post*, 3 April 1980).

Reactions to the Bristol riots highlight the changing symbolism attached to race as an explanatory factor in urban violence during the 1980s. Bristol presented a dilemma to those who had warned of the possibility of urban violence, since their predictions had centred on areas such as Brixton, Handsworth, Moss Side and Toxteth rather than St Paul's. Its very unexpectedness made it all the more difficult to cite race and racism as causal factors. But the link between black youth and street violence was already established in popular media images.

This can be seen in the reactions to small-scale street confrontations with the police that took place between the Bristol riots in 1980 and the major outbreak in Brixton on 10–13 April 1981. The most important happened on 3 March 1980 during a protest against the death of 13 young West Indians in a fire in Deptford, South London. The *Daily Express* covered the incident under the headline 'Rampage of a Mob' (3 March 1980), while the *Daily Mail* depicted it as 'When the Black Tide Met the Thin Blue Line' (3 March 1980). The racialisation of the confrontation between the mostly black marchers and the police revolved around the themes of 'mob' and 'young blacks'. As the *Daily Mirror* saw it, 'A peaceful protest by 10 000 of London's West Indians was ruined by the hooliganism of 200 young blacks' (4 March 1981). The ambiguity of the coverage of the events in Bristol was replaced by an emphasis on the involvement of small groups of young blacks in street confrontations with the police, and on black militants and outside agitators fostering violence for their own ends.

Whatever the symbolic importance of the Bristol riots and the Deptford march, there is no doubt that the period between April and July 1981 was the crucial phase in the racialisation of discourses on violent protest. The events in Brixton (10–13 April) and elsewhere in Britain (3–28 July) were often viewed through the prism of race. The starkest use of racial symbols to explain the violence was that by Enoch Powell and a small but vociferous group of Conservative MPs and journalists. Powell had spoken out in a somewhat muted form during the Bristol events, but on a number of occasions in 1981 he claimed that the riots could not be understood without reference to race and immigration. In a confrontation with William Whitelaw in parliament he said that in view of the 'prospective future increase in the relevant population' future outbreaks were inevitable, and that 'Britain has seen nothing yet' (*Hansard*, 1981, vol. 3, col. 25). By July 1981 he had warmed up to this theme and argued his case in a number of articles in the popular press, as well as in parliamentary speeches. During a vigorous speech in parliament he disagreed with Roy Hattersley's assertion that the three main causes of the July riots had been poverty, unemployment and deprivation. Pouring scorn on this suggestion he offered his own explanation and constructed a link with race without actually uttering the word:

> Are we seriously saying that so long as there is poverty, unemployment and deprivation our cities will be torn to pieces, that the police in them will be the objects of attack and that we shall destroy our own environment? Of course not. Everyone knows that, although those conditions do exist, there is a factor, the factor which the people concerned perfectly well know, understand and apprehend, and that unless it can be dealt with – unless the fateful inevitability, the inexorable doubling and trebling of that element of a population can be avoided – their worst fears will be fulfilled (*Hansard*, 1981, vol. 8, col. 1313).

He repeated his argument in a series of graphic warnings in the popular press during this period. Furthermore a number of right-wing Conservative MPs, newspaper columnists and commentators took up Powellite themes and embellished them with different symbols, as did extreme neofascist groupings.

The Powellite usage of race to explain the riots may have been the starkest example but it was by no means the only one, be it in official reports on the riots, in the press and television coverage or in the general public debate. In all of these, race, racial discrimination and black youth were given a central place, either implicitly or explicitly. During the Brixton riot of April 1981 and the nationwide riots of July 1981 the press was full of images, both pictorial and written, that implied that race was a central factor, or even the main one. This was particularly clear during July 1981, when headlines spoke of the hatred that blacks had for the police, their alienation or detachment from the mainstream values of British society, and the growth of racial tension in certain important localities. The *Daily Mail's* headline proclaimed simply: 'Black War on the Police' (6 July 1981). This was perhaps the most extreme example, but the *Sun* was only marginally less direct when it spoke of 'The Cities that Live in Fear'. Meanwhile the *Daily Mirror*, echoing the words of Merseyside's chief constable, Kenneth Oxford, proclaimed that 'This was not a race war. It was blacks versus the police.'

A number of leading articles in both the popular and the serious press from 6–25 July devoted considerable attention to the race issue, which they saw as important in varying degrees. Enoch Powell's statements and those of other politicians in favour of repatriation were widely reported, though usually with a disclaimer that distanced the paper from such extreme views. In the *Daily Mail* on 10 July Ronald Butt argued that for the most part the culprits of the riots were black, and that one could not blame white society for the attitudes that led young blacks to create disturbances. Rather the blame lay with young blacks themselves, and with agitators who directed these attitudes towards their own ends.

The ambivalence about whether the riots in Bristol had been racial was eventually replaced by the certainty that since a sizeable number of the participants were black the riots had indeed been racial, or at least the outcome of bad relations between the police and young blacks. But racism as such was rarely mentioned, since the riots were not seen as linked to real grievances but only to the perceptions that young blacks had of their position in society, and to wider processes that were undermining the rule of law.

Law and disorder

Another important line of argument used in connection with the unrest was the issue of law and order and the difficulty of policing multiracial inner city areas. This was by no means a new issue, since throughout the 1970s a powerful body of media, political, policy and academic opinion had been constructed around the theme of how Britain was drifting into a violent society, and how the basis of consent was being shifted by the pressure of forces that were undermining the moral fabric of British society (Hall *et al.*, 1978). An article by Peregrine Worsthorne during this period underlined this concern:

> The spectre haunting most ordinary people is neither that of a totalitarian state nor Big Brother but of other ordinary people being allowed to run wild. What they are worried about is crime, violence, disorder in the schools, promiscuity, idleness, pornography, football hooliganism, vandalism and urban terrorism (Worsthorne, 1978: 151).

The riots were instrumental in popularising Worsthorne's image of 'ordinary people being allowed to run wild' beyond the readers neoconservative tracts and the *Daily Telegraph*. By forcing the debate on law and order into the public domain they helped give substance to the warning expounded by a number of commentators for over a decade that lawlessness and corrosive violence were undermining traditional British values and institutions.

A glimpse of the impact of the 1980–1 riots at this level can be seen in two important debates in parliament. The first took place in the midst of the July riots and had civil disturbances as its theme. The importance of this debate is indicated by the fact that more than 60 MPs had expressed their wish to participate in it. The tone of the debate was set by William Whitelaw, who in his introductory statement spoke of (a) the need to 'remove the scourge of criminal violence from our streets', and (b) the urgenct need to develope 'policies designed to promote the mutual tolerance and understanding upon which the whole future of a free democratic society depends' (*Hansard*, vol. 8, 1981, col. 1405). Criminal violence was, Whitelaw argued, endangering the whole framework of consent and legality upon which the political institutions of British society were based. In reply Roy Hattersley supported the call for the immediate suppression of street violence, but warned that the roots of such riots could not be dealt with until all people felt they had a stake in society (ibid.: cols 1407–9).

The second debate took place on 26 November 1981 and had law and order as its theme. The part played by the riots in pushing the law and order issue, and specifically policing, onto the main political agenda was alluded to by the Liberal leader, David Steel, who argued that urgent action to prevent a drift into lawlessness was necessary from both a moral and a political perspective (*Hansard*, vol. 13, 1981, cols 1009–11). A subsequent debate on the same issue in March 1982 was also full of references to the experience of 1981 in terms of the impact of street violence, crime, urban decay, the breakdown of relations between the police and many local communities, and the spectre of more violence to come if changes to policing tactics and social policy were not swiftly made (*Hansard*, vol. 20, 1982, cols 1107–81).

The psychological and symbolic importance of the riots was also grasped by Lord Scarman, whose report on Brixton contained the following graphic description:

> During the week-end of 10–12 April (Friday, Saturday and Sunday) the British people watched with horror and incredulity an instant audio-visual presentation on their television sets of scenes of violence and disorder in their capital city, the like of which had not previously been seen in this century in Britain. In the centre of Brixton, a few hundred young people most, but not all of them, black attacked the police on the streets with stones, bricks, iron bars and petrol bombs, demonstrating to millions of their fellow citizens the fragile basis of the Queen's peace. These young people, by their criminal behaviour – for such, whatever their grievances or frustrations, it was – brought about a temporary collapse of law and order in the centre of an inner suburb of London (Scarman, 1981: para. 1.2).

It is perhaps all too easy to forget this sense of shock and the fear that more violence was to come, and this pervaded much of the discussion of the riots during and after 1981. Even a brief glance at the popular and quality press during April and July 1981 reveals the deep sense of shock at the street violence, which was perceived as never having occurred on the same scale during that century. On 13 April *The Times* reported that looters and mobs of young people had virtually taken over Brixton. The *Guardian* saw it somewhat differently, but nonetheless referred to it as 'The Battle of Brixton'. The *Daily Mail* spoke of an 'army of rioting black youths' taking to the street, while the *Daily Star* talked of 'Flames of Hate'. The *Daily Mirror* took a longer-term view and warned that the Brixton disorder was 'The Shape of Things to Come' and that the next riots could come in Birmingham, Manchester and many other inner city localities. Under a picture of groups of youths throwing stones and missiles at the police was the following caption: 'THE BATTLE RAGES: Youths, white and black, hurl their barrage of missiles at point blank range as police attempt to take cover behind their shields.' Similar and more detailed coverage could be found in most papers on 14 and 15 April, and intermittently throughout the rest of April and into May.

The messages that such reports contained were complex and quite often contradictory. But the centrality of the law and order theme and the expressed fear that disorderly street violence would become an established part of British life reflected the fact that the re-establishment of order was the main topic of concern in official political disclosures during this period. Under the headline 'Order Before Research', on (6 July 1981) a *Daily Telegraph* editorial asserted:

> Mob violence must be stopped. Existing laws should be used to the full to punish the offenders and guarantee safety in our cities. If the Public Order Act ... cannot cope with the threat of disorder now, then new riot legislation must be enacted.

The need to support the police was acknowledged by both Labour and Conservative speakers in the parliamentary debate on the riots, and in official responses to the riots long before the Scarman Report was published in November 1981. Most disagreements centred on the part played by social deprivation and unemployment in bringing young people to protest violently on the streets.

A particularly interesting subtheme in the law and order debates was the emergence of outside agitators and middle men, who were seen by some sections of the press as directing the violence. Under the headline 'Search for the Masked Men', on 7 July the *Daily Mail* reported:

> Masked figures on motor cycles were seen issuing instructions to groups of rioters on the second night of violence in the predominantly black district [of Toxteth]. They appeared to be giving tactical orders to sections of the 500 strong mob of mainly white youths. As the battle developed, groups armed with petrol bombs and stones were moved quickly from street to street.

During July 1981 a whole mythology grew up around this image of outside forces directing the actions of mobs on the street, and of the purposes they had in mind. As we shall see later, this was taken up and reworked in 1985 to become one of the main factors in analyses of the causes of the riots in Handsworth, Brixton and Tottenham.

Racial disadvantage and urban unrest

Threaded through the discourses on race and law and order were constant references to unemployment, particularly among the young, and various forms of social disadvantage and poverty. The attack by Enoch Powell on the arguments articulated by Roy Hattersley was but one example of the clash between opponents and proponents of the idea that the riots were a result of social deprivation. Throughout 1980 and 1981 debates on the riots in the media, parliament and various official reports hinged on the interrelationship between racial and social factors. An important aspect of this debate was the political capital that could be made by the opposition by linking the social and economic malaise of the country at large with violent street disturbances. Hence throughout this period numerous government ministers strenuously denied that unemployment and social deprivation were the most important causes of urban unrest.

The tone of this debate and the ambiguities contained in social explanations of the riots highlight the dilemmas faced by the political establishment during 1980–1. These dilemmas became even greater when the Scarman Report was published in November 1981, as it was followed by a vigorous public debate on how the recommendations in the report could be implemented, what other policy initiatives were necessary and what immediate measures could be taken to prevent a recurrence of the July 1981 events.

Although the Scarman Report is often taken as the first text to link poor social conditions with disorder, the terms of the debate were by no means set by Scarman. During April and July 1981 vigorous exchanges took place both in the press and in parliament about the role that deteriorating social conditions and unemployment might have played in the riots. During the 16 July parliamentary debate on civil disturbance, Roy Hattersley's formulation of this link provided a useful summary of the social conditions argument. After some preliminary remarks about the Labour Party's support for the police, he went on to outline his opposition to the idea that the riots were essentially antipolice outbursts:

> I repeat that I do not believe that the principal cause of last week's riots was the conduct of the police. It was the conditions of deprivation and despair in the decaying areas of our old cities – areas in which the Brixton and Toxteth riots took place, and areas from which the skinhead invaders of Southall come (*Hansard*, vol. 8, 1981, col. 1408).

He went on to outline four common features in such areas:

- Inadequate housing and insufficient government spending on improvements.
- A lack of social, cultural and welfare amenities.
- Inadequate provision of remedial education for deprived families.
- High levels of unemployment, particularly youth unemployment.

Much of the subsequent controversy over Hattersley's analysis, apart from Powell's retort (discussed above), centred on the question of youth unemployment. Hattersley suggested that the riots were a direct product of the high level of youth unemployment, and a furious debate ensued in both parliament and the media about this assertion. A similar debate took place after the publication of the Scarman Report, when many of the report's arguments were linked with Hattersley's version of the social conditions argument.

An interesting aspect of this debate was the different emphases that were put on the four common features identified by Hattersley. While William Whitelaw and Margaret Thatcher accepted that the social conditions in many inner city areas were bad, they disputed, that these conditions had led to the violent confrontations on the streets between youths and the police. Furthermore Thatcher responded angrily to Labour's suggestion that unemployment was a primary cause of the riots:

> If you consider that unemployment was the only cause – or the main cause – of the riots I would disagree with you. Nothing that has happened to unemployment would justify these riots (quoted in *Financial Times*, 15 April 1981).

A number of similar exchanges took place during July 1981 about unemployment and urban poverty. Although the existence of unemployment could not be denied, its impact was disputed and the link between high levels of youth unemployment and urban disorder remained a hotly debated issue.

Alienation and powerlessness

The final symbolic cue used to make sense of the 1980–1 protests is more difficult to categorise, but it can be captured by the term political marginality. While a number of studies of the roots of the urban unrest in the US had noted the salience of political marginality to participation in violent protests (Skolnick, 1969; Fogelson, 1971; Edelman, 1971), this issue received relatively little attention in Britain and during the 1980–1 events and their aftermath the political context was discussed from a number of other perspectives.

The Scarman Report, for example, laid part of the blame for the riots on the feeling of alienation and powerlessness experienced by young blacks living in depressed inner city areas. A successful policy for tackling the roots of urban disorder was seen as one that would involve all members of a community in dealing with the problems of the area so that they would feel they had a stake in its future (Scarman, 1981: para. 6.42).

A number of examples of the political marginality argument could also be found in media reports during 1980–1. After the Bristol riot, for example, the *Observer* quoted a 'lanky Rastafarian with dangling dreadlocks', who argued that:

> Discrimination accumulates; chickens come home to roost. They wanted to strike fear in people's hearts with law and order. You have no say in your life. People may give you some grant, some urban aid, but they are not really interested in getting to the root of the situation (*Observer*, 6 April 1980).

The question of politics and power also entered into some aspects of the public debate on the causes of urban violence. However the issue of political marginality was difficult to handle as it touched upon the thorny question of whether the riots were in fact a form of political action.

The ambiguities and tensions to which the 1980–1 riots gave rise meant that though the statements of 'lanky Rastafarians' were sometimes reported and to an extent were taken on board, they were not accorded the detailed coverage that other factors were given. When such arguments did not fit in with the overarching themes of race, violence, disorder and social deprivation they were either sidelined or pushed into subclauses of official reports. The Scarman Report, for example, contained the following policy proposal:

> I … recommend that local communities must be fully and effectively involved in planning, in the provision of local services, and in the management and financing of specific projects (Scarman, 1981: para. 8.44).

Lord Scarman saw such a move towards greater political integration as essential if the differences between inner city residents and the forces of law and order were to be resolved and cooperation developed.

But the subject of political marginality remained on the sidelines of the main public debate because it contradicted the idea that the rioters had been driven by irrational, uncivilised and criminal instincts. According to Martin Kettle (1982: 404):

> The attempt to depict the riots as irrational was very important. It denied legitimacy to the rioters, their actions and their views. It made them

events without cause, and events that therefore posed no direct threat to any existing assumption.

This did not, however, entirely prevent the question of political marginality and the need to reform existing policies from being raised, as demonstrated by the numerous attempts after 1981 to introduce local and national measures to address some of the grievances of the rioters and to ensure that further disturbances did not occur. It is to this issue that we now turn.

Power, legitimacy and political disorder

Perhaps the most important lesson of the 1980–1 riots was the way they emphasised the role of political protest as a channel for challenging racial injustice. But many of the issues raised and the reforms that were promised failed to be given a central place on the political agenda of the Thatcher administration. Part of the reason for this may have been the hope that the events of 1980–1 were a one-off aberration and were not likely to recur.

Between 1982 and 1985 the partial nature of the government's response to the riots became clear and a matter of comment both in the media and in academic research. Writing in 1985 John Clare, the BBC's community affairs correspondent, noted that although the government had carried out many changes in relation to the police after 1981 it had done remarkably little in respect of political, social and economic problems. Indeed during this period many of the social conditions that had commanded attention during 1981 had steadily worsened, particularly unemployment, housing and welfare provision. For example the government's policies, far from remedying the employment situation, had pushed unemployment in inner city areas to levels that were two or three times higher than during the 1980–1 disorders (Cross and Smith, 1987). Perhaps even more disastrously, the government had steadfastly refused to strengthen the legislation on race relations or to take administrative measures to tackle racial inequality. Instead it seemed to believe that it had the situation under control, and that future violent disorders were unlikely.

It is clear from the language used that the government was not only seeking to establish the senselessness of violent protest but also to argue that the lessons of 1980–1 had been learned and that solutions were being applied to the main problems. In response to the Handsworth events Douglas Hurd argued with some force that such events reflected more on those who participated in them than on the society in which they took place:

> The sound which law abiding people in Handsworth heard on Monday night, the echoes of which I picked up on Tuesday, was not a cry for help but a cry for loot (*Financial Times*, 13 September 1985).

The chief constable of the West Midlands Police, Geoffrey Dear, took this argument further by pointing out that the day before the riots a successful carnival had taken place with the support of local community leaders, so the riot had come 'like a bolt out of the blue' (*Guardian*, 21 November 1985). Attention was focused on those individuals or groups who were 'breaking the law', 'committing criminal acts' and threatening the interests of the law-abiding 'majority'.

There was also a reworking of some of the main themes that had emerged in the aftermath of the 1980–1 events in relation to law and order: race and social disadvantage; urban decline and unemployment; crime, drugs and hooliganism; and internal enemies and political disorder. Take the political debate on race and urban unrest in the aftermath of the 1985 riots. While there were many continuities between 1980–1 and 1985 in respect of the race issue, the responses in 1985 were different in terms of degree, and probably in terms of the riots being seen as a racial phenomenon by a wider body of opinion. The ambiguities and subtext in much of the press coverage during 1980–1 had at least served to counter the more extreme forms of discourse that put the blame entirely on blacks. During the 1985 riots and their immediate aftermath, however, the imagery of race was used by sections of the press without the ambiguity found in 1980–1. The silence about race was breached in 1980–1, but in a more limited way than in 1985.

An example of this greater openness on racial issues is the way new right commentators used the urban unrest in 1985 to question whether a multiracial society could develop without conflict. Peregrine Worsthorne, for example, argued that the ferocity of the confrontations in Handsworth, Brixton and Tottenham put a major question mark over the possibility of the 'coloured population' assimilating mainstream British values (*Sunday Telegraph*, 29 September 1985). While there was still strong opposition to Enoch Powell's call for repatriation from all shades of political opinion, the racialisation of public debate on the riots went even further than in 1980–1. Consider for example the following headlines of 11 September, which appeared on the day after the violence in Handsworth:

> Bloodlust (*Daily Mail*)
> Hate of Black Bomber (*The Sun*)

War on the Streets (*The Mirror*)
Torch of Hate (*The Star*)
England, 1985 (*Daily Express*)

All five headlines were accompanied by a picture of a black petrol bomber, who was variously described as 'stalking the streets of Handsworth' or as a 'prowling West Indian'. These images fitted the official view that this was not a social phenomenon but crime, which was also reported by the press on the same day. They established a much more firm link between race, crime and disorder than the riots of 1980–1 had done.

In this context it was the alienness of West Indians and Asians that was highlighted rather than the racist institutions and processes that worked against blacks at all levels of society. During the 1985 riots race took on new meanings that had little if anything to do with the effects of racism as such, since the emphasis was on the cultural characteristics of the minority communities themselves. After Handsworth some newspapers blamed the riot on rivalry between West Indians and Asians, and even when this was denied by local residents and community leaders it was still used to explain what had happened. Furthermore the question of whether the culture and values of black people, their family structure and their political attitudes bred violence was constantly raised.

The question of whether the majority of rioters were black or white was hardly debated since it was assumed that most were black, unemployed and involved in crime. The newspaper image of the black bomber in Handsworth was extended to imply that groups of alienated and criminalised young blacks had seen the riots as a chance to engage in an orgy of looting. The Dear Report on Handsworth captures this image and links it to the social circumstances of young blacks:

> The majority of rioters who took part in these unhappy events were young, black and of African Caribbean origin. Let there be no doubt, these young criminals are not in any way representative of the vast majority of the African Caribbean community whose life has contributed to the life and culture of the West Midlands over many years and whose hopes and aspirations are at one with those of every other law abiding citizen. We share a common sorrow. It is the duty of us all to ensure that an entire cultural group is not tainted by the actions of a criminal minority (Dear, 1985: 69).

This black criminal minority was portrayed not only as the leading force behind the riots, but sometimes as the only force, and throughout the following months the imagery of race continued to dominate debates on the causes of and policy responses the riots.

As pointed out above, the social causes argument was another major plank in the public debate on the 1980–1 riots, particularly in relation to the highly politicised issue of unemployment. This issue was raised again in 1985, by which time the degree of unemployment and urban de-industrialisation and decay had worsened. Images of urban decay, tinderbox cities and ghettos linked up with images of racial inequality to produce an analysis based on complicated and contradictory sets of arguments.

An interesting mixture of the various images was provided by a story in the *Daily Telegraph* under the heading 'Broadwater Farm: Like the Divis Flats with Reggae' (8 October 1985). The *Mirror* described the estate as 'Living Hell', and quoted one resident as saying that 'You've no idea how awful daily life is' (8 October 1985). Such images were reworkings of those used for Toxteth and Brixton in 1981, but now they were being used much more widely. Even the *Daily Mail*, which made the clearest use of racial and outside agitator arguments, ran a major story on Broadwater Farm under the heading 'Burnt-out hulks litter this concrete jungle … despair hangs heavy' (8 October 1985). Similar stories appeared in the quality press during this period, and the images they contained were reflected in parliamentary debates (*Hansard*, vol. 84, 1985, cols 30–46, 368–88) and even in official police reports on the riots in Birmingham and London.

The following editorial from the *Mirror*, printed after the Brixton riot, illustrates the point:

> The fires in Brixton have been damped down but the spark that ignited them is still glowing in every inner-city area with a large black population. That spark will not be extinguished easily or painlessly.
>
> There is no excuse for what happened on Saturday and there can be no mercy for those who committed crimes …
>
> But bad conditions make bad people of some who would otherwise be good. If they had pleasant housing, secure jobs and favourable prospects, they would be far less likely to behave as they did on Saturday (*Mirror*, 1 October 1985).

The suggestion that as well as tackling the criminal acts the government should be doing something about housing, employment and leisure facilities challenged the notion that the riots were a mere excuse for looting, and that a broader explanation of the roots of the disorder was needed.

The despair felt in inner cities was seen as breeding disorderly protest, and however hard the government tried to deny a causal link it was forced to accept the necessity of restoring order not only through police action but also through the provision of help to deprived inner city areas. Much as in 1980–1, the social causes argument could not be taken separately from the broader debate on the future of the British economy and society more generally. The Thatcher government's record on unemployment was a highly contentious issue, and just as in 1981 it vehemently denied that its pursuit of free-market policies had anything to do with the riots. But the government did find a way of accepting a link between the riots and social problems without bringing its main policies into the debate, namely by linking the growth of violent disorder to crime and drugs.

Policing after the riots

The arguments in the official responses to the 1985 riots took a general and a specific form. The general argument was that the riots had not been a protest against the dire conditions in inner city areas or the actions of the police, but had been a criminal act or an excuse cry for looting. This argument was put most succinctly by Geoffrey Dear, chief constable of the West Midlands Police (Dear, 1985), and Home Secretary Douglas Hurd in relation to Handsworth, but it was also a recurring theme in official and press statements on the other riots. The specific argument was that the violence in Handsworth and Brixton had been instigated by drug barons in response to police attempts to curb their activities and control their territory. Numerous examples of this line of argument can be found in Dear's report on Handsworth and in a number of major press stories during the riots.

The emphasis on criminal acts and the need for law and order resonated throughout a long parliamentary debate on 23 October 1985. Rejecting the Labour Party's call for an independent inquiry into the causes of the riots the government succeeded in pushing through the following resolution:

> That this House recognises the crucial importance of the maintenance of public order; applauds the courage and dedication of the police and responsible community leaders in restoring order; and welcomes Her Majesty's government's commitment to early effective action in the light of the recent urban disturbances (*Hansard*, vol. 84, 1985, col. 388).

The law and order argument was also prominent in Douglas Hurd's numerous calls for people to rally round the police in order to defend the rule of law, and a measure of the popularity of the argument was that virtually all the media accepted that, in the short term at least, restorating police authority on the 'streets of fear' was the first priority.

The argument that drug barons had instigated the riots seems to have served two purposes First, it distanced the riots from the social, economic, political and other grievances that had been linked to them by locating their cause outside the social problems of inner city dwellers and in the simple greed of drug barons. Second, just as Dear's image of a few hundred 'young black criminals' was used to explain what happened in Handsworth, the problem of drugs was used to explain what happened at the national level. The issue of drugs provided an everyday image, already a national issue through saturation media coverage and public debate, with which the police, the Home Office and other institutions could desocialise the riots.

It is clear, therefore, that the branding of the riots as criminal acts and an excuse for looting was only one element of a wider ideological construction of the events as a drift towards crime. While the branding of the riots as criminal seemed to depoliticise them, it is quite clear that a more complex analysis of why crime and disorder were growing phenomena influenced police and other official ideologies.

The blaming of outside agitators had been common place after the 1980–1 riots, and this was resurrected in 1985 to explain the attacks on the police. Take for example the treatment by the press of Bernie Grant and other local Labour Party leaders. Having been labelled by Douglas Hurd as the 'high priests of race hate', lurid press stories claimed that 'GLC leftists', 'black activists' and 'reds' were behind a campaign to undermine the police, stimulate urban violence and bring about the collapse of law and order. Such stories served (a) to give credibility to the claim that even if the riots had not been planned by outsiders they had been agitated by outside leftists and other folk devils; and (b) to separate the riots from the issue of racism and the social plight of inner city black communities by laying the blame for racial hatred squarely at the door of extreme left-wing and black activists. Indeed according to Ronald Butt, a regular columnist for *The Times* and other papers on racial issues during 1980–1 and 1985, race had become a new weapon in the class war.

The theme of outside agitators subsequently took on extreme forms. A classic example is the following story in the *Daily Express* about the death of PC Blakelock on Broadwater Farm:

> **Moscow-trained hit squad gave orders as mob hacked PC Blakelock to death**
>
> The thugs who murdered policeman Keith Blakelock in the Tottenham riots acted on orders of crazed left-wing extremists. Street-fighting experts trained in Moscow and Libya were behind Britain's worst violence.

> The chilling plot emerged last night as detectives hunted a hand-picked death squad believed to have been sent into North London hell-bent on bloodshed.
>
> They include men and women from Commonwealth countries like Jamaica, Barbados and Nigeria, who have been trained in Russia and Libya in street revolutionary tactics (*Daily Express*, 8 October 1985).

A number of similar stories resonated in the pages of the popular press, even though there was no evidence and the links seemed to be pure speculation. Looking for the 'men behind the riots' turned out to be less a matter of the individual 'leftists' who were named in such stories and more of the construction of symbolic cues about the threat posed to Britain by 'outside agents', such as 'men and women from Commonwealth countries'. What is interesting about the *Daily Express* story, apart from the sensationalist headline, is the way it highlights the supposed use of 'immigrants' by Russia and Libya to undermine order and stability.

The symbolic political value of such metaphors has been noted in studies of riot responses in the US, where the 'outside agitator' argument was used to deflect attention away from social, economic and policing issues (Edelman, 1971; Lipsky and Olson, 1977). The experience of 1980–1 and 1985 in Britain suggests that such an analysis needs to be put into a broader historical perspective, since 'outside agitator' arguments did not seem to bear any relation to the facts of the riots. Rather they were part of a wider use of symbolic political language to help make sense of the crises facing British society. Ambiguous political situations such as riots may boost anxiety about external threats to order, but they do not create this anxiety. Nonetheless, when they are contextualised against the wider political debates on race and immigration in post-1945 Britain it becomes easier to see the interconnection between the image of outside agitators and the popular stereotype of blacks as 'alien'.

The notion that street violence was the product of various social problems combining to cause the emergence of a 'criminal element' and 'hooliganism' was one of the main themes in accounts of the 1980–1 riots, as pointed out above. In the responses to the 1985 riots there was not only a popular resurrection of such ideas but they were also used by sections of the police. Some reference to this was made in Dear's (1985) report on Handsworth. A more developed version was offered after the 1985 riots by Sir Kenneth Newman, commissioner of the Metropolitan Police. During 1982–5 he had already made a series of influential speeches on the issue of disorder and the growth of violence. For example in a paper delivered in 1983 he had stated that in many inner city areas the police were under threat and unable to maintain order:

> In many multi-ethnic areas police encounter not merely apathy and unhelpfulness when making enquiries or engaging in order maintenance, but outright hostility and obstruction (Newman, 1983: 28).

He had gone on to warn that this could result in a further increase in crime and law-breaking, and in the reinforcement of urban decay.

In the aftermath of the 1985 riots Newman extended his analysis by arguing that crime and the fear of crime helped to reinforce attitudes towards the police and society that encouraged violent protests to break out and challenges to be made to the legitimacy of the established order (Newman, 1986a,b). Crime, according to Newman, was not so much a cause of riots but just one element of the broader crisis in social policy and control. He saw this as particularly important in multiethnic areas where hostility towards the police was growing.

Scarman and beyond

As discussed above, the 1980–1 riots prompted a wide variety of responsive measures by central and local government and other agencies. There are, however, three distinct responses that need to be analysed: (a) the Scarman Report, (b) policing and law and order, and (c) economic and social policies.

In the aftermath of the April 1981 riots in Brixton, Home Secretary William Whitelaw used his powers under the 1964 Police Act to appoint Lord Scarman to inquire into the events, produce a report and make recommendations. This brief was subsequently broadened to cover other disturbances during July 1981. Scarman's inquiry was not on the same scale as the famous Kerner inquiry into the US riots, but after the publication of his report in November 1981 his views and prescriptions played an important part in fashioning political debate on riots. It is therefore important to look into the basic analysis put forward in the report in order to understand how the political agenda for riot response developed after 1980.

The starting point of Scarman's explanation of the riots is important here. He began his analysis by distinguishing between the background factors that had created the potential for urban disorder in areas such as Brixton and the action or event that had sparked off the riots. Scarman identified two commonly held views about the cause of the disorders. The first explained them in terms of oppressive policing, and in particular the harassment of young blacks. The second explained them as a protest against society by deprived people who saw violent attacks on the forces of law and order as a way of calling attention to their grievances. For Scarman both views were a simplification of a complex reality, or at least 'not the whole truth'. He linked the social and policing aspects of the complex reality of areas such as Brixton in an analytic model that emphasised the following issues:

- The problems faced when policing and maintaining order in deprived, multiracial, inner city localities.
- The social, economic and related problems faced by all residents of such areas.
- The social and economic disadvantages suffered particularly by black residents, especially young blacks (Scarman, 1981, paras 2.1–2.38).

He saw the existence of all these factors in certain deprived areas as 'creating a predisposition towards violent protest', which could be sparked off by confrontations between local residents and the police or by rumours about the actions of the police or other authority figures.

Scarman concluded that once a 'predisposition towards violent protest' had taken hold it was difficult to reverse the situation. Talking about the position of young blacks, he noted that because they felt neither socially nor economically secure many of them had drifted into situations where confrontations with the police were more or less the daily norm. Noting that despite the fact that academic and government reports had pointed to widespread discrimination against young blacks, very little had been done to remedy the situation, Scarman concluded that many young blacks believed that violence was an effective means of protesting against their conditions, and that far from the riots being a meaningless event, they were 'essentially an outburst of anger and resentment by young black people against the police' (ibid., paras 3.110, 2.38). What is important here is that aside from Scarman's condemnation of the criminal acts committed during the riots, he strongly argued in favour of a historical and social explanation of the riots.

Another line of argument embodied in the report related to the social and family structures of black people in inner cities, particularly West Indian families. Explaining the drift towards violence and crime it painted the following picture of the life of a young black in Brixton:

> Without close parental support, with no job to go to, and with few recreational facilities available, the young black person makes his life on the streets and in the seedy commercially run clubs of Brixton. There he meets criminals, who appear to have no difficulty in obtaining the benefits of a materialist society (ibid., para. 2.23).

Though the report went on to emphasize that by no means all young black people resorted to crime, it nonetheless used the image of the rootless black youngster as a symbol of the despair and injustice suffered in areas such as Brixton. This despair had to be remedied through central and local government measures to help the minority communities overcome their special problems.

Given the close link that Scarman established between questions of policing and the wider social context, he outlined proposals not only for the reform of the police and the introduction of new methods of policing and riot control, but also for employment policy, social policy and policies on racial discrimination. In a telling paragraph he argued that:

> The social conditions in Brixton do not provide an excuse for disorder. But the disorders cannot be fully understood unless they are seen in the context of complex political, social and economic factors which together create a predisposition towards violent protest (ibid., para. 8.7).

Although some of these issues went beyond the remit of his inquiry he considered that only a government-led initiative to deal with problems of policing, unemployment, poor housing and racial disadvantage could tackle the roots of the unrest. Parliamentary and media responses to the report varied widely, although it was widely seen as making an important contribution to the question of how to respond to riots and prevent their outbreak in the future.

It soon became clear that the government was not going to implement Scarman's recommendations uniformly. Some aspects of his proposals for reforming the police and rethinking police tactics were implemented during 1982 and 1983 (Reiner, 1985), but the urgent action he called for in other areas seemed to be ignored (Benyon, 1984; Benyon and Solomos, 1987).

This returns us to the point made earlier about the other major forces that contributed to the political responses to the riots: the media, parliament, political parties and popular debate. The Scarman Report formed a part – and a vital one – of the political debate, but its role cannot be understood in isolation. This can be seen if we look more closely at the issues of policing and economic and social problems.

Although the report influenced the nature of subsequent government responses in the area of policing, it should be clear from the discussion in Chapter 6 that the construction of the law and order response was influenced by a wider set of pressures. For example the police expressed doubts about whether Scarman's proposals for new methods of policing could be implemented, and whether they would be effective in preventing further violence and unrest. Sim (1982) argues that the police were particularly worried by Scarman's recommendations that they should (a) tackle racial prejudice and harassment, (b) improve their methods of policing multiracial inner city areas, and (c) develop new methods of managing urban disorder. According to Sim the police, sections of the media and right-wing parliamentarians launched an offensive to counteract criticisms of the police's handling of the riots and their relations with the black community in general.

Indeed even before the publication of the report the police and sections of the media were painting a rather different picture of the riots and its participants. During July 1981 a number of accounts of the events focused on the family background of the participants and the lack of 'firm parental control'. For example Kenneth Oxford, the chief constable for Merseyside, repeatedly argued that the main responsibility for the riots lay with parents who either could not control their children or did not care. On 8 July 1981 the *Daily Telegraph* reported him as saying:

> What in the name of goodness are these young people doing on the streets indulging in this behaviour and at that time of night? Is there no discipline that can be brought to bear on these young people? Are the parents not interested in the futures of these young people?

Hence for Oxford the cause of the riots was not the conflict between young people and the police but the failure of families to control the actions of their children. This argument, which was articulated with regularity throughout the period of the riots, was supported by the prime minister and the home secretary. On 10 July 1981 *The Times* reported the prime minister as saying that if parents could not control the actions of their children the government could do little to stop them engaging in hooliganism and a 'spree of naked greed', and the home secretary as saying that the government was looking at plans to involve parents in 'the consequences of offences committed by their children'.

Such arguments were not necessarily linked to race, but as we saw earlier Lord Scarman himself partly explained the drift of black youngsters into crime and violence by reference to West Indians' weak family units, and considerable media coverage was given to the supposed pathology of the West Indian family and the isolation of young blacks from both their families and society as a whole. Moreover, as shown in earlier chapters, historically the political response to black immigration was deeply infused with the notion that blacks represented a problem in social and cultural terms. Thus even when such arguments were not racialised *per se*, popular common sense linked the notion of weak family structure to the West Indian communities, and it was a short step from this to explaining the riots as an outcome of pathological family structures.

The question of the family was also linked to other issues, such as the crisis of youth, the growth of violence in society in general, the phenomenon of youth hooliganism and the drift of young people into crime. Whether this was based on factual evidence or not it became part of the public debate on the 1980–1 riots and helped to construct an image of them as the outcome of causes beyond the control of both the government and the police, thus deflecting attention away from the broader social context of the Scarman Report and towards specific social problems that were seen as undermining law and order.

In terms of economic and social policies the impact of the 1980–1 riots was equally ambiguous and contradictory. Part of this ambiguity, as was shown earlier, resulted from the government's strenuous efforts to deny any link between its policies and the outbreak of violence and disorder. This denial was particularly important, since at the time the Thatcher administration was going through a bad patch in terms of public opinion on unemployment, social services and housing (Leys, 1989; Thompson, 1986). While Scarman was careful not to enter the political dispute between the Thatcher government and the Labour Party on these issues, his call for direct action to deal with these problems, along with racial disadvantage, posed a challenge to the political legitimacy of the policies the government had followed from 1979 onwards. It also posed a delicate problem for the home secretary, since Scarman had been appointed by him to carry out the inquiry. Having spent the whole summer denying any link between its policies and the riots, the government had to tread carefully when responding to the economic and social policy proposals contained in the report when it was published in November 1981.

In parliamentary debate on the report the home secretary adopted a two-pronged strategy. While, he accepted many of the report's recommendations, particularly in respect of policing and the need to tackle racial disadvantage and other social issues, he emphasised the government's view that the immediate priority was to restore and maintain order on the streets. Therefore, when the home secretary talked of the need for the government to tackle racial disadvantage he saw this as longer-term project. On the other hand he was much more specific about the reform of the police and the development of new tactics to manage urban disorder (*Hansard*, vol. 14, 1981, cols 1001–8).

The changing politics of policing

The policy responses after the 1985 riots shared some of the same characteristics as those in 1980–1, but an even stronger link was made between lawlessness and crime and the supposedly pathological characteristics of inner city residents. This resulted in a sharper contrast than in 1980–1 between (a) responses that emphasised the need to strengthen and buttress the role of the police and (b) responses that called for greater emphasis on the rejuvenation of the social and economic fabric of inner cities. As Douglas Hurd argued after the 1985 Handsworth disturbances, this was not a case history for sociologists to pore over, but a case for the police (*Guardian*, 23 September 1985).

The home secretary's statement, which was backed up by numerous government ministers and MPs, reflected the most important shift in political thinking between 1981 and 1985, namely that riots were criminal enterprises and more suited to investigation by the police than by social analysts or judicial experts such as Lord Scarman. While the question of policing and law and order had been central in 1981 as well, it had been balanced to some extent by an emphasis (for example in the Scarman Report and the interventions of opposition parties) on the wider social policy context.

In 1985 the government specifically rejected calls for another Scarman-type inquiry, arguing that since the riots were a criminal enterprise it was useless to search for social explanations or to have yet another report advising the government about what to do. Implicitly the government was saying that it knew what the problems were, and how they could be tackled.

While some senior policemen, including Kenneth Newman of the Metropolitan Police, wanted to stress the link between policing and other areas of social policy, the government attempted to decontextualise the riots and portray them as the actions of a small minority who were either criminalised or influenced by extreme political ideas. The government emphasised two main arguments:

- That the riots were 'a lust for blood', an 'orgy of thieving', 'a cry for loot and not a cry for help'.
- That the riots did not reflect a failure to carry out the 'urgent programme of action' recommended by Lord Scarman in 1981, but were the outcome of a spiral of crime and disorder in inner city areas.

Hence the riots were portrayed as both unjustifiable and a criminal activity. Doughlas Hurd made this point clear in a widely reported speech to police chiefs at the time of the Handsworth riot:

> Handsworth needs more jobs and better housing. But riots only destroy. They create nothing except a climate in which necessary development is even more difficult. Poor housing and other social ills provide no kind of reason for riot, arson and killing. One interviewer asked me whether the

> riot was not a cry for help by the rioters. The sound which law-abiding people heard at Handsworth was not a cry for help but a cry for loot. That is why the first priority, once public order is secure, must be a thorough and relentless investigation into the crimes which were committed (*Daily Telegraph*, 14 September 1985).

Such arguments resonated throughout the media and parliamentary debates during September and October, and became part of the symbolic political language through which the riots were understood by policy makers and the public.

The ascription to rioters of 'wickedness' and 'pure naked greed' did not go unchallenged, as the analysis in the previous section has shown. Indeed Lord Scarman and numerous other commentators sought implicitly or explicitly to challenge such simplifications. However the American experience shows that the official explanation of riots as irrational outbursts of criminal activity cannot be easily countered by oppositional forces, however well founded and empirically sound their arguments are (Edelman, 1971; Lipsky and Olson, 1977). This certainly seemed to be the case after the 1985 riots, particularly if one looks at the nature of the response to the social and economic issues that underlay the riots.

The emphasis on law and order measures did not preclude initiatives on other issues, most notably inner city and employment policies. Parliamentary exchanges during September–December 1985 were full of declarations by the government and the opposition that they were interested in transforming the social conditions of inner city areas (*Hansard*, vol. 84, 1985, cols 348–88; vol. 88, 1985, cols 929–1004). The media expressed similar concerns, and a number of feature articles analysed the problems of inner city, 'ghettoes' and the lives of people living in such areas. In a feature article on the Broadwater Farm Estate the *Mirror* described it as a 'Living Hell', and went on to summarise what it saw as the feelings of the local people:

> If you don't live in desolate apartments where no one seems to care – and even the police have declared a no-go area, you have no idea how awful your daily life can be (*Mirror*, 8 October 1985).

When combined with no jobs, inadequate social facilities and no real help from either central or local government, the *Mirror* went on, such areas can become 'another world', a world where disillusionment and violence are everyday facts of life.

During the late 1980s and early 1990s successive governments announced initiatives to tackle inner city problems and employment, and presented these as part of an effort to rejuvenate depressed areas on a sound basis. Examples of such plans included the provision of government finance to encourage the establishment of black business enterprises, the regeneration of inner city localities, the setting up of task forces to generate jobs in problem areas, and attempts to integrate black youngsters into the various training schemes run by quasigovernmental bodies. In addition, having done little if anything about Lord Scarman's recommendation for 'positive action', successive administrations belatedly promised to consider new initiatives to tackle racial discrimination in employment and other areas.

However there was a major discrepancy between these promises of action and the allocation of resources to them. This had also been the case after the 1981 riots. Indeed a number of researchers and commentators have pointed out that a common response to unrest is the symbolic announcement of policies to deal with the causes of the unrest, but that concrete measures often fail to materialise (see Benyon and Solomos, 1987). A number of local authorities did attempt to take action on the issues raised by the 1985 riots, but these initiatives were often severely constrained by the actions of central government and the police, and by broader economic and political pressures. We shall return to this issue in Chapter 12, which looks specifically at the possibilities for reform and the constraints faced both nationally and locally.

The end of urban unrest?

In the aftermath of the 1981 and 1985 riots it was generally thought that a key objective of the state, the police and local authorities would be to ensure that similar events would not happen in the future. This was certainly the assumption behind the recommendations made in the Scarman Report and a whole range of other official reports on the riots. Perhaps because the unrest was perceived as an atypical deviation from British culture it was expected that, as long as appropriate remedial action was undertaken, violent protest would not become a regular feature of urban life.

For most of the late 1980s and 1990s this seemed to be the case as there were no large-scale outbreaks of urban unrest. However smaller outbreaks did occur. For example in July 1992 there were violent confrontations between groups of young people and the police in Burnley, Coventry and Blackburn (*Observer*, 26 July 1992; *Independent on Sunday*, 26 July 1992). In June 1995 similar confrontations took place in Bradford, with reports that 'alienated Asian youth' had engaged in battles with the police (*Guardian*, 12 June 1995). The Bradford events were the first time that public attention had focused on Asian youths rather than black youths, and were the forerunner of a series of events in the late 1990s that led to increasing public concern about the drift of some young Asian men into criminality and confrontations with the police. The images projected did not necessarily present a rounded picture of the changing position of young Asians in British society, but they helped to politicise and amplify existing concerns about minority communities in general. While these events were not on the same scale as the unrest in 1981 and 1985 and did not attract the same amount of media or government attention, links were made between them and the circumstances that had led to the violent protests of the 1980s, particularly the treatment of minorities by the police.

A new contributory factor in the 1990s was death in police custody. For example the death of Wayne Douglas while being held in police custody in Brixton in December 1995 sparked violent confrontations with the police on a scale that the area had not witnessed since 1985. There was particular concern about this because after the Scarman Report the police and central and local government had worked closely together to prevent any future recurrence of the tensions that had developed in the area during the 1970s and 1980s (*Guardian*, 14 December 1995; *Observer*, 17 December 1995). Interestingly, although there was general agreement that the events were solely a response to the death of Wayne Douglas and others in police custody, the *Daily Mail*, (15 December 1995) covered the violence under the headline 'Mob Plot to Shoot Police'. Such coverage reflected the lack of sensitivity among sections of the media and the police themselves to the issue, and caused some minority groups to feel marginalised and excluded from equal treatment by the police and other institutions.

The unrest that took place in the 1990s kept the subject of urban unrest on the public agenda, although it was generally thought that such localised outbreaks were containable and would not spread. Certainly in both academic and policy discourses there was little expectation that there would be urban unrest on a larger scale. Between April and July 2001, however, the scale of the violence on the streets of Bradford, Oldham and Burnley reminded many commentators of earlier events. It is perhaps too early to comment on the longer-term impact of the 2001 events, but it is worth noting some of the issues they helped to highlight. The first point to note is that in terms of location and context the events in 2001 were markedly different from the unrest of 1981 and 1985. In 2001 the core events took place in a number of relatively deprived cities in the north of England, and the minority participants were largely from a South Asian background. More importantly perhaps, although confrontations with the police remained at the heart of the unrest there was the added dimension of conflict between the

Asian and white communities. Finally, the British National Party and other extreme right-wing groups were implicated in the events. Certainly in Oldham and Burnley there was evidence that the BNP was gaining support in local white communities, and it garnered a respectable vote in the June 2001 general election (*Observer*, 15 July 2001).

Given all this it is not surprising that the events in 2001 were seen through a somewhat different lens than the unrest of the 1980s. In Oldham and Burnley, and to some extent Bradford, the unrest was seen in a number of ways:

- As 'race riots' involving conflict between different racial and ethnic groups.
- As partly the result of mobilisation by the BNP and extremist ethnic groups.
- As the product of decades of segregation and lack of contact between white majority and minority, particularly Asian, communities.

While media coverage and official reports produced after the events looked at the state of police–community relations in these localities, this was seen as a less central factor than it had been during the 1980 and 1990s. Therefore rather than seeing the events of 2001 as a continuation of the unrest of the 1980s and 1990s, it is better to put them in the context of the political, cultural and social changes that had taken place since then in the towns in question. If we look at the BNP, for example, it seems clear that in Burnley and Oldham it played at least some part in shaping the tensions that ignited in 2001. It is also evident that it has remained active in these localities and has attempted to gain the support of the white electorate by nationalistically claiming to represent their 'rights', as opposed to those of the minority communities. Such mobilisations need to be analysed in terms of the specific contexts in which they emerged, and they represent a significant break from the urban unrest of the 1980s.

It is interesting to note in this regard that a core concern in the series of official reports that were produced after the 2001 unrest was the lack of social cohesion (Burnley Task Force, 2001; Cantle, 2001; Oldham Independent Review, 2001; Ouseley, 2001). While this notion was never fully defined in the reports it became part of a mantra that has been repeated with some regularity by the Blair government and by local politicians and community groups. In particular the reports focused on what they perceived to be a 'white–Asian divide', meaning that there was relatively little contact between these populations and no shared sense of belonging to and pride in the local community. These concerns were most clearly articulated in the report by the Ministerial Group on Public Order and Community Cohesion, chaired by John Denham:

> Our central recommendation is the need to make community cohesion a central aim of government, and to ensure that the design and delivery of all government policy reflects this. We recognise that in many areas affected by disorder or community tensions, there is little interchange between members of different racial, cultural and religious communities and that proactive measures will have to be taken to promote dialogue and understanding (Home Office, 2001: para. 7).

This argument did not represent a radical departure from previous government policies on race relations. What was new was concern about the consequences of social segregation, the entrenchment of cultural and religious differences and the erosion of 'common values'. These concerns had been shaped by the social and political changes that had come to the fore in the 1990s, most notably the emergence of new patterns of racialised inequality, ethnic differences in terms of opportunities and employment, and tensions over new patterns of migration and transnational identity politics. The riots of 2001 were thus read through a political language that was deeply imbued with concern about the emergence of new forms of conflict and tension in British society.

Summary and conclusion

Since the late 1980s there has been much discussion about whether the lessons of the urban unrest of 1980–1 and 1985 have been learned, whether the political responses to the riots were adequate and whether collective violence might become a permanent feature of British political life. The array of inner city initiatives, expressions of government concern, police reforms and promises of action to tackle unemployment and urban disadvantage can be seen as responses to the overriding concern about how to manage and depoliticise the impact of urban unrest.

The effect of these initiatives on the lives of inner city residents has varied with localities, and they have had a limited impact on communities caught up in the web of inner city deprivation. This is not to say that the political objectives of state intervention have not been achieved. Indeed symbolic promises of reform seem to have reassured the general public that something is being done and thus helped to ensure the 'political viability of unsuccessful policies' (Edelman, 1977). But symbolic action does little to change the underlying problems, and there have been persistent cries from black and ethnic minority communities and other inner city residents that the promise of reform without actual change is not acceptable.

It is clearly impossible to separate the unrest from wider social and economic changes in contemporary Britain. Nor is it possible to ignore the deep political and ideological shifts that have taken place, particularly the emergence of nationalistic and neofascist ideologies since the 1980s (Troyna and Williams, 1986; Gilroy, 1987; Thurlow, 1998). Such developments have inevitably affected the possibility of implementing reforms aimed at tackling inequalities, however limited these reforms may be. It seems clear that if this continues, the symbolic value of violent protest will become even more important for minority communities, and for political movements that claim to represent the interests of the white majority. The reforms needed to address these issues may well be beyond the limits of the current political reality, but as the violent confrontations in 2001 show, it would be foolhardy not to take action to tackle the root causes of urban violence and unrest. It is to the limits and possibilities of political action that we now turn.

8 Racism, Nationalism and Political Action

The post-1945 debates on black immigration and the definition of national identity and Britishness were discussed in some detail in Chapters 3 and 4, but a number of dimensions of this issue have yet to be analysed, including the changing forms of racial ideology between the 1970s and the 1990s, the transformation of ideologies of race and nation, and the emergence of what is sometimes called a new racism. While these processes have been hinted at in previous chapters, this chapter presents a detailed analysis of their development.

In Chapter 3 we looked at how Powellism, as a form of political mobilisation, helped to redefine the terms of the political discourse on race relations in Britain during the late 1960s and early 1970s. The responses of the Labour government from 1964 to 1970 and the Conservative government from 1970 to 1974 in their different ways showed how politically powerful this mobilisation was. Both administrations responded to the approval of Powell's ideas on immigration and race by certain sections of the population by openly addressing these issues (Freeman, 1979; Layton-Henry, 1984). The two most important manifestations of this were the acceptance by both the Labour Party and the Conservative Party of the need for tighter restrictions on immigration and the necessity of allaying the fears of those who were influenced by Powell's ideas.

In this sense the late 1960s and early 1970s have been rightly characterised as a period in which Powellite ideas helped to racialise British political life. Apart from the impact of Powell's interventions at the political level, it is important to acknowledge a less obvious aspect of his activities, namely his influence on the political language used to discuss race and immigration issues. His emphasis on the social and cultural changes brought about by immigration helped to create or recreate an understanding of Englishness or Britishness that was based on the notion of shared history, customs and kinship, which effectively excluded black and ethnic minorities from membership (Powell, 1969, 1972).

From the late 1960s to the 1990s Powell continually returned to two themes. The first of these was the rapid growth of the black and ethnic minority population, and the prospect that by the end of the twentieth century a large proportion of Britain's population would consist of black immigrants and their descendants. From the 1960s onwards this concern with the size of the black and ethnic minority population became part of broader political thinking on immigration. Second, Powell claimed that the magnitude of black and Asian immigration meant that the entire social and cultural fabric of British society was under threat from foreign cultures and religions. This second theme occupied a central place in Powell's rhetoric during the 1970s and beyond.

A good example of the emphasis in Powell's discourse can be found in his interventions during the urban unrest of 1981 and 1985, when he constantly emphasised the danger of civil war on the streets of Britain's cities and other threats posed to the nation by the growth of multiracialism. More generally he reiterated some of the themes from his 1968 'rivers of blood' speech in a series of articles that coincided with the twentieth anniversary of that speech. As already indicated, for Powell the main threat to the British nation came from the volatile mixture of nationalities and cultures that immigration had created in many inner city areas, rather than from external enemies. He returned repeatedly to this issue in 1988. For example in a speech in Birmingham he spoke on the theme of 'Englishness' and the current threats to its survival. He identified a number of factors that he saw as endangering the threat to English culture, including the presence 'of those who not only visibly do not share with them a common identity but are to be encouraged to maintain and intensify their differences' (*Independent*, 23 April 1988).

By the 1980s, therefore, the language Powell used to describe the politics of race in Britain had as much to do with the definition of Englishness or Britishness as it had with characteristics of the minority communities themselves. He made no claim to knowledge of all the sources that 'since neolithic times, or earlier, have contributed to the gene pool of the English people' (ibid.), but he warned of the 'spectre of a Britain that has lost its claim to be a nation':

> The spectacle which I cannot help seeing … is that of a Britain which has lost, quite suddenly, in the space of less than a generation, all consciousness and conviction of being a nation: the web which binds it to its past has been torn asunder, and what has made the spectacle the more impressive has been the indifference, not to say levity, with which the change has been greeted (*Guardian*, 9 November 1981).

From this perspective the loss of Britain's national identity was due to the failure of the nation to recognise the repercussions of immigration on the national culture.

Such arguments were by no means limited to Powell, and during the early 1980s and 1990s his thoughts on national identity and culture were given respectability by the increasingly influential new right, who adopted race as one of the main components of their political discourse.

Conceptions of race and nation

As in other areas of political life, from the 1980s the new right began to influence public debates on racial questions. They were particularly influential during the long period of Conservative domination from 1979 to 1997. Through channels such as the Centre for Policy Studies, the Social Affairs Unit and the *Salisbury Review*, a number of new-right commentators criticised what they saw as incorrect dogmas and policies in areas such as multiracial education, housing and antiracism generally (Flew, 1984; Palmer, 1986). These writings are a clear example of how ideologies on race are not static, but constantly changing.

The political language of the new right continued to resonate with Powellite themes, such as immigration and stereotypes of 'black muggers', 'aliens' and 'black criminals'. But as with Powell's political language, there were two main shifts in the concerns of the new right. First, there was a move away from the language of nativism and anti-immigration. In the late 1970s the concern expressed about the social position of young African-Caribbeans signalled a new preoccupation with the danger that the political and social alienation of sections of the black and ethnic minority populations presented to the polity as a whole (Keith, 1987; Solomos, 1988). The image of inner city areas becoming 'black enclaves' where British law and order could not be easily enforced was a recurrent theme in new right writings on the subject. The very presence of black and ethnic minority communities was presented as a threat to the way of life and culture of white citizens.

Second, new right racial discourses increasingly presented minority communities as 'enemies within' who were undermining the moral and social fabric of society. In both popular and elite discourses on immigration and race, black and minority communities as a whole, or particular groups, such as young blacks, were depicted as being involved in activities that posed a threat to social order and political stability. Hence the new right's ideological constructions, like those of Powell, did not necessarily rely on notions of racial superiority in the narrow sense. In practice the most resonant themes in racial discourses were not absolute notions of racial superiority, but the threats that black and minority communities presented to the cultural, political and religious homogeneity of white British society.

Commonly held ideas about black and ethnic minority people included assumptions about differences between the culture, attitudes and values of minorities compared with the white majority. In addition the attempts by black and ethnic minority groups to assert their rights and lay claim to social justice were often presented in the media as a sign of the failure of immigrants to adapt to British society, and not as a sign that racial injustice was deeply embedded.

This type of argument has been summarised by van Dijk (1988) as amounting to a claim that the demands of black minorities were not legitimate, that they were in fact attempts to claim special privileges and hence were a threat to the majority. Because such claims came from groups that were seen as removed from the traditions and culture of British life they were easily portrayed as challenging the values of the majority of the population, and by a twist of logic as unjust.

As we saw in Chapter 7 the emergence of urban unrest during the 1980s, and the widely publicised involvement of young blacks in this unrest, led to the increased use of racial symbols by sections of the popular media and the extreme right. The media coverage of the 1985 riots in particular did much to reinforce the popular image of young blacks as involved in antisocial acts such as crime, and to allow the extreme right to present them as a threat to social and political stability.

The notion that the seeds of racial conflict had been sown by the failure of successive governments to tackle immigration was a major theme in the statements made by Enoch Powell from the 1960s. The outbreak of urban unrest enabled Powell to expand his anti-immigration theme to include the notion that the entire nation was under the imminent threat of civil war, and that the cause of this was the imposition of what he called 'alien cultures' on British society. This theme proved particularly attractive to the new right, as will be discussed in more detail in Chapter 10.

New right ideologies and national identity

It became increasingly clear during the 1980s that racial discourses were rarely concerned only with the presence of minority communities and cultures, but were also an attempt to define the characteristics of the dominant national culture and the ways in which these differed from those of racial and ethnic minorities. It was precisely on this issue that new right ideologists began to concentrate, though this was by no means a new phenomenon.

For example, over the centuries, the meanings attached to 'Englishness' and 'Britishness' had changed constantly, or as one account put it: 'Englishness has had to be made and re-made in and through history' (Colls and Dodd, 1986: i). This included ideas about shared language, customs, religion, colour, family and numerous other assumed attributes of the national culture. In contemporary debates on race and immigration a recurrent issue was the definition of the historical and cultural attributes of the 'British way of life'. While the position of black minority communities in the inner cities may have been the immediate point of reference in discussions of crime and disorder, the overarching concern was the supposed threat posed to the majority culture by the development of multiracial communities.

One example of this was the attention given to young African-Caribbeans, who were at the centre of much political debate during the 1980s, particularly in the aftermath of urban unrest (Solomos, 1988). Although the immediate concern of the new right was violent unrest on the streets of major cities, their underlying concern was that the permanent settlement of black immigrants, a phenomenon that young, British-born blacks symbolised, was threatening the unity of British society.

John Casey, writing in 1982 in the *Salisbury Review*, reflected this view when he argued that black immigration had broken down the social order established during the Victorian era and was therefore a threat to the way of life of the majority of the population. He concluded that the source of the problem was a failure to understand the role of national identity in the development of British society:

> There is no way of understanding British and English history that does not take seriously the sentiments of patriotism that go with a continuity of institutions, shared experience, language, customs, kinship. There is no way of understanding English patriotism that averts its eyes from the fact that it has as its centre a feeling for persons of one's own kind (Casey, 1982: 25).

This 'feeling for persons of one's own kind' was Casey's way of arguing that any opposition to the settlement of black migrants in Britain was not necessarily based on racial antipathy but was a 'natural' response to outsiders.

The famous 'swamping' statement made by Margaret Thatcher on television in February 1978 was another example of how the perceived threat posed by black immigration could be utilised to mobilise political support without resorting directly to racist language. Referring to trends in immigration, Thatcher argued that if the present rate of immigration continued, by the end of the twentieth century there would be four million people from the Commonwealth and Pakistan in Britain:

> That is an awful lot, and I think it means that people are really rather afraid that this country might be swamped by people of a different culture. The British character has done so much for democracy, for law, and done so much throughout the world that if there is any fear that it might be swamped, then people are going to be rather hostile to those coming in.

In the same interview she said that the support achieved by the National Front during the 1970s was the result of mainstream political institutions' failure to deal with immigration. She went on:

> We are a British nation with British characteristics. Every nation can take some minorities, and in many ways they add to the richness and variety of this country. But the moment a minority threatens to become a big one, people get frightened (*Guardian*, 31 January 1978).

The voicing of notions such as 'British nation' and 'British character' served to highlight Thatcher's concern to protect the interests of the nation against what she saw as threats from within and without, and there is evidence that this helped the Conservative Party to attract National Front sympathisers, who saw the party as a more likely channel for translating their views into policy (Layton-Henry, 1986).

In this way the new right helped to redefine the terms of political discourse on race in British politics. What is interesting about this is that, unlike Powell's declarations during the late 1960s and 1970s, the new right's views on race and nation achieved a certain respectability in both popular and political circles. This does not mean that their more extreme arguments did not arouse anger and opposition. But in the prevailing political climate their ideas on culture, nation and identity constituted a potent political force whose impact has yet to be fully understood.

Neofascist politics

One of the most important features of the politics of racism was the emergence from the early 1970s of the National Front – and other minor neofascist groups – as a more or less credible political force. Indeed there was serious concern during the late 1970s that the National Front might become an established entity on the formal political scene. The history and political impact of the National Front have been given considerable attention by academics. There have been numerous studies of its rise and decline, and of the social context of the support received by it and other neofascist and racist political groups. In addition a number of studies have explored the role of racialised ideologies and of the prospect of the future mobilisation of racist beliefs and ideologies by political parties and movements (for example Walker, 1977; Billig and Bell, 1980; Husbands, 1983). These studies, written mostly between the 1970s and the early 1990s, focus on the impact of the National Front on both local and national political life.

The National Front was founded in 1967 as a united organisation of groups with neofascist and anti-immigration views (Walker, 1977). One of the primary motivations for its formation seems to have been the relative neglect of immigration and race-related issues by the mainstream political parties. This was seen as providing an opportunity for a party openly committed to the defence of racial purity and to a clear anti-immigration stance to capture support from both of the main political parties.

As a union of the right-wing British National Party and the League of Empire Loyalists, the National Front inherited the ideological baggage of anti-Semitism and resistance to Britain's postwar decolonisation, two prominent themes among far right-wing political groups in the 1960s. In its political rhetoric it made clear its links with the politics of anti-Semitism and its commitment to a nationalist ideology based on racial purity (Thurlow, 1975; Edgar, 1977; Kushner, 1994b).

Research on the social basis of support for the National Front and other racist political groups revealed two important features. First, Phizacklea and Miles (1980), in their study of working-class racism, argued that it was important to look at social and economic factors in order to understand the attraction of sections of the white working class to the politics of the National Front. Drawing on research conducted in London they argued that one of the most important factors in the growth of support for racist political groups was the economic and social restructuring of many inner-city working-class areas.

Based on a study of National Front support in localities such as the East End area of London, Husbands (1983) argued that it was particularly important to look at the influence of such issues as the presence of black communities, changes in the national and local politics of race and the restructuring of local political economies in order to understand the level and solidity of National Front support in some areas and its relative weakness in others (see also Samuel, 1998).

Hence these studies emphasised the need to locate the support for racism in a wider social, economic and geographical context. A similar theme was taken up by Cashmore (1987) in his detailed analysis of the social basis of racism in Birmingham and its environs during the 1980s. But it is important not to lose sight of the part played by politics and ideology in the mobilisation of this support.

It is interesting to remember, for example, that during the 1970s both the Conservative Party and the Labour Party lost voters to the National Front. Throughout the 1970s the National Front's membership and level of electoral support ebbed and flowed with the tide of political debate on and public controversy over racial questions. Its membership rose from 14 000 to 20 000 between 1972 and 1974, at the height of the arrival of the Ugandan Asians. In 1973 it achieved a vote of 16.2 per cent in the West Bromwich by-election, and it also achieved respectable results in local elections in 1976 and the London local elections in 1977 (Taylor, 1982).

This level of support was not maintained, however, and fell dramatically after Thatcher's 'swamping' statement in 1978 and the attempt by the Conservative Party to draw in National Front sympathisers. Between 1977 and 1979 the activities of the National Front also became the focus of antiracist political actions orchestrated by the Anti-Nazi League and Rock Against Racism, which helped to counter the National Front's claim to be a defender of the national interest and spread awareness of the political dangers that its growth as a major political force presented.

From its foundation the issue of black immigration occupied a central place in the National Front's political rhetoric and propaganda. Despite periodic attempts by its leadership to broaden the movement's appeal and political platform, immigration and race remained the single most salient issue among its members and sympathisers during the 1970s. It was the ability of the party to play on this issue at both the local and the national level that enabled it to mobilise electoral support and attract members.

The political discourses of the National Front, as well as those of subsequent neofascist political groupings, resonated with references to racial purity, cultural superiority or difference and defence of 'the nation'. Indeed according to the National Front the main threats to Britain were immigration and racial mixing. The alien, the stranger and the 'subhuman' were common themes, and the anti-Semitism embedded in the pages of the main neofascist journals tied them closely to Nazi ideology. What was also at play in the ever changing politics of the extreme right was an attempt to create a mass nationalist movement that would attract popular support on a scale never before witnessed in Britain.

After the election of the first Thatcher government in 1979 there was a decline in the electoral success of the National Front, and during the 1980s it splintered into various factions. This has been interpreted from a number of perspectives as (a) indicating the marginalisation of the racist message the National Front was propounding, (b) the outcome of the adoption of some of the National Front's ideas by mainstream political parties, and (c) the result of factional strife and conflict within the racist groups themselves. Whatever the reason, during the 1980s and 1990s they failed to have any significant impact on electoral politics (Cronin, 1996; Eatwell, 1996, 1998; Durham, 1998).

Most of the small groups that emerged from the splintered National Front had little impact on either national or local politics. Perhaps the most successful organisation to emerge was the British National Party, which was founded by John Tyndall in 1982. Tyndall, who had left the National Front in 1980, was linked to the neo-Nazi political groupings of the 1960s and 1970s. In his personal monthly journal *Spearhead* he espoused a mixture of anti-immigration politics, anti-Semitism and ethno-national politics. The BNP never achieved the degree of national attention garnered by the National Front in the 1970s, but it did have some success in particular localities.

In 1993, for example, BNP member Derek Beackon briefly held the Millwall ward in the London borough of Tower Hamlets. After his surprise victory in the by-election, Beackon commented 'I put my own people first – by that I mean white people' (*Independent on Sunday*, 19 September 1993). Beackon's success was short-lived and the BNP did not gain the foothold in local politics it had hoped for. It continued to be active in some localities throughout the 1990s, but it too suffered from factionalism and splits. Part of its political agenda during the 1990s was its adoption of a nationalist rhetoric. In its newspaper, the *British Nationalist*, there was constant emphasis on the need for the party to fight for the interests of the white majority in British society, and a call for the adoption of the Union Jack by its members as a symbol of their political stance. By the late 1990s the BNP was also showing an interest in developing an electoral strategy to gain influence in both national and local politics.

This was perhaps reflective of a broader shift by sections of the extreme right towards a more overt nationalist political stance, and particularly by one of the rising young leaders of the organisation, Nick Griffin, who had been active in the National Front and was a member of one of the 'third position' factions that had emerged from the split in the early 1980s. In the mid 1990s he became active in the BNP and was involved in the editing of *Spearhead* and another journal called *Rune*. He gained a sufficient power base to challenge Tyndall for the leadership of the BNP and became leader in 1999. Although Griffin retained some of the National Front's political rhetoric on race and immigration he sought to reinvent the party in order to give it a broader electoral appeal.

As part of its 'electoral road to power' the BNP sought to gain a higher profile in both national and local elections. This became evident in the 1997 general election and was taken a step further during the 2001 general election. The urban unrest in Oldham, Burnley and Bradford featured prominently in the BNP's electoral strategy for the 2001 election and it stood for 33 seats, gaining an average of 3.9 per cent of the votes. Its most successful result was Nick Griffin's 16.4 per cent in Oldham West and Royton. The BNP also did relatively well in Burnley, Bradford and in parts of the West Midlands and east London (*Searchlight*, July 2001).

This relative success encouraged the BNP to move further towards presenting itself as essentially a white nationalist party. Interestingly the official magazine of the BNP is now called *Identity*, and it is attempting to construct an ideological focus for the party based on attacks on Islam and asylum seekers, and gaining rights for whites on a range of social and economic issues, including housing, crime and the environment (*Identity*, 14 October 2001; 15 November 2001). The terrorist attacks in America on 11 September 2001 encouraged the BNP to give a higher profile to its attacks on Islam, framed around its idea that the West needed to be defended against enemies within as well as without.

In the mid to late 1990s, while the BNP concentrated on its electoral strategy a number of small, extreme right-wing groups drifted towards violence, including Combat18, a BNP splinter group. Much of the activity of Combat 18 remains clouded in secrecy and it is not clear that it was ever a large group, but was committed to the use of violence to achieve its objectives. The main elements of its political stance were antiblack racism and anti-Semitism, and a deep hatred of gays, the IRA and 'race mixers', among others (*Combat18*, no.1, no date). The activities of groups such as Combat18 attracted the attention of antiracist groups and the police, but they received relatively little public attention for most of the 1990s. This changed, however, with a series of bombings during April 1999 in Brixton, Brick Lane and Soho. The bombs focused attention on the activities of such groups and led to a wide-ranging debate on the dangers they presented. Eventually a man named David Copeland was arrested for the bombings, found guilty and sentenced to six life terms in prison. Copeland had been on the fringes of both the BNP and Combat18, and saw the bombings as a way to start a race war that would bring about a more racially pure society.

The BNP and other extreme-right groups remain relatively small and it is unlikely that they will have much impact on national politics. However they have been active in a number of localities up and down the country, and it seems clear from trends in a number of towns and cities that the appeal of the extreme right will remain closely intertwined with the state of race relations in British society as a whole. However they cannot be seen in isolation from other forms of political mobilisation around the symbols of race and nation, which can be illustrated by considering the question of racial attacks.

The politics of racial attacks

Racially motivated attacks have a long history, but during the late 1970s and 1980s increasing public attention was given to the phenomenon (House of Commons, Home Affairs Committee, 1994; Virdee, 1995; Bowling, 1999). The context in which such attacks took place was complex, and far-right groups were not always involved, but there is no doubt that they had a profound effect on the lives of many black and ethnic minority people in Britain. The following are fairly typical cases:

> As a boy sleeps, a pig's head, its eyes, ears, nostrils and mouth stuffed with lighted cigarettes, is hurled through the window of his bedroom. A family do not leave their home after 7 in the evening; they stay in one large room, having barricaded their ground floor. A family are held prisoner in their own flat by a security cage bolted to their front door by white neighbours. A youth is slashed with a knife by an older white boy as he walks along a school corridor between classes. A family home is burned out and a pregnant woman and her three children killed. A ticket collector is stabbed in the eye with a metal stake and killed simply because he refused to take racial abuse from some white passengers (Gordon, 1986: v).

A number of surveys by the Home Office, the Commission for Racial Equality and local authorities throughout the 1980s and 1990s confirmed the widespread nature of such attacks, as well as everyday forms of racial harassment (Home Office, 1981; GLC, 1984; CRE, 1987a, 1987b; Sibbitt, 1997). The involvement of far-right racist groups in some of these cases has been clearly demonstrated. What seems to have happened is that when the National Front found itself electorally isolated after 1979 sections of its membership, along with supporters of other far-right groups, turned to more direct forms of racial attack (Björgo and Witte, 1993; Witte, 1996).

This is not to say, of course, that all racial attacks were and are carried out by extreme-right political movements. It is quite clear from research carried out in a number of localities that racial violence needs to be set against the background of local histories of race and racism and everyday relations in specific urban environments. Indeed one of the problems faced by the police and other agencies is that in responding to racial violence they have to take account of a whole range of local as well as national factors.

This may explain the low-key nature of the response to racial attacks by the government and the police for most of the past two decades, but it contrasts sharply with their oft-expressed views on the criminal activities of young blacks, and with the amplification of black crime in the popular media on an almost daily basis. What is clear is that racial attacks underwent a dramatic increase during the 1990s. Between the late 1980s and the 1990s official Home Office statistics showed that racial incidents had risen dramatically, and during the same period a British crime survey found that recorded incidents represented only 10 per cent of the real total. In evidence to the Select Committee into Racial Attacks and Harassment, Herman Ouseley stated that 49 per cent of victims were Asian, 23 per cent were African-Caribbean, 22 per cent were white and 7 per cent were Jewish (*Independent*, 2 December 1993).

In the 1990s and 2000s a number of high-profile cases revealed the reality of racial violence. While the case of Stephen Lawrence attracted the most attention, among the many other victims were Quddus Ali, Michael Menson, Ricky Reel and Mukhtar Ahmed. A report in 1997 by Human Rights Watch highlighted the extent of racial violence in Britain and the relative weakness of legislation and other measures taken to tackle it (*Observer*, 11 May 1997), and subsequently the government and the police sought to develop a more coordinated response to the issue.

The Macpherson Report on the murder of Stephen Lawrence received widespread public attention, particularly because it resulted in both the government and the police developing strategies to tackle racial violence and setting up mechanisms to monitor their effect. Another important development was the inclusion in the 1998 Crime and Disorder Act of the category of 'racially aggravated' offences. It is too early to determine the effectiveness of this Act, but it did help to bring the issue of racial violence more fully into the open. In addition the Metropolitan Police has attempted to transform its practice in this field by means of a Racial and Violent Crime Task Force. All this holds out at least some hope that an integrated strategy for effectively tackling racist violence will develop, both nationally and for specific local environments.

New forms of racist mobilisation

Perhaps the most important lesson to be learnt from the experiences of the past decade or so is that racist mobilisations are constantly evolving and changing, as demonstrated by the emergence of new forms of racist politics, violent attacks on ethnic minority people and a rapid expansion of the use of cultural symbols by racist and neofascist movements. This has been the subject of considerable journalistic attention and research over the past few years (Back *et al.*, 1996; Eatwell, 1998), with wide-ranging discussions in the press and among researchers and policy makers on the origins of these new racist activities and their impact in specific environments (Björgo and Witte, 1993; Wrench and Solomos, 1993).

One particular issue that has drawn the attention of writers in recent years is that far-right movements across Europe and other parts of the globe have set up international networks whilst simultaneously reinforcing their own virulently nationalistic patterns of racism. This has been facilitated by modes of mass communication that transcend national boundaries, such as the internet and other forms of electronic communication. The growth of new types of racism, whether directed at new targets or expressed through different media, and the resurgence of traditional racist movements has caused great concern among those involved in fighting racism and ensuring that racist ideologies do not become a dominant political force.

What has also become evident over the past two decades is an extension of racist stereotyping, with the derogatory term being joined by 'Pakis', 'refugees' and 'economic migrants', all of whom are attributed with negative social and cultural characteristics. Recent theoretical work has emphasised that racism needs to be conceptualised according to the historical context in which it is expressed (Solomos and Back, 1996). In short one must speak of racisms in the plural. From this perspective the targets of racism differ from one national context to another, and this often depends on the historical relationship between the host society and the countries of origin of the target groups. Hence alliances between different groups of racists (and antiracists) reflect particular contexts, and images of hate and otherness are an intrinsic element of racist discourses.

The cultures of the extreme right pose real difficulties with regard to definition and classification. A wide range of terms, including neo-Nazi, white supremacist, fascist and racist, are used to describe a diversity of ideologies, movements and groups. However while these movements are diverse they often share the following features:

- A rhetoric of racial and/or national uniqueness and common destiny.
- The idea of racial supremacy and superiority.
- A conception of racial otherness.
- A utopian revolutionary world-view that promotes the overthrow of the existing order.

For some conventional scholars of the far right the current interest in the relationship between xenophobia, popular culture and new technologies is little more than a fashionable intellectual pursuit. They caution that the real issue is what is happening in terms of the ballot box and the macroeconomic and political trends that underpin political mobilisations. While this warning has a point, in order to understand racism in all its manifestations it is crucial to adopt a much wider view that embraces politics, culture, and the mass media and more.

In historical terms, racism has been expressed over the past two centuries through the construction of symbolic boundaries between racially constituted or racialised categories. Its binary system of representation marks and attempts to fix the difference between belongingness and otherness, and while 'we' might remain constant, 'other' has the potential to expand and include any or all 'others'. A principal means of accomplishing this is to perceive the self as carried in the genes rather than transmitted via culture; as distilled through what appears most 'natural' and immediate: the body. Corporeal properties, and particularly skin colour, thus furnish an 'epidermal schema' not only for anchoring difference but also for distinguishing the pure from the impure, the included from the excluded.

To the extent that the body signifies difference, it becomes a site and target for strategies of normalisation and discipline, a site for an obsessive imperative to expunge any kind of syncretism that destroys the authenticity of 'truth propositions' about the embodied polar identities of 'black' and 'white'. We can see this in the rules of interaction in Victorian and Edwardian society (and indeed even today) that governed sexual relationships between constructed categories of black and white people. It was there that the marriage of information and myth making reached its apogee: interracial sex was presented as an act of bestiality, miscegenation as a curse against civilisation and both as the product of folly and physical immorality (Mosse, 1985).

Racialised politics and the enemy within

Perhaps the most important theme in contemporary political discourses on race in Britain, even after successive attempts to institutionalise antidiscrimination policies, is the portrayal of black and ethnic minority communities as a whole, or particular groups of them, as a threat to the unity and order of British society. Cohen (1988) notes that one way in which this tendency is expressed is in attempts to attribute the persistence of racial inequality not to racism but to the presence of black minorities and the problems that result from their presence.

This is by no means unique to the post-1945 period, nor to Britain. Edelman (1971), writing about the US, shows how in situations of conflict and protest one of the ways in which dominant groups or political institutions defend themselves is to rationalise the events as the product of outsiders whose social and moral values are removed from those of society as a whole. For example, referring to the race riots of the 1960s he argues that the dominant elite attempted to reduce the political impact of the events by portraying them as the work of enemies of American society and its values. In Britain in the 1990s the new right portrayed black and ethnic minority communities not as an enemy from without but as an enemy within: as endangering the cultural and political values of the nation. Meanwhile the media depicted them as a threat to the way of life of the white population and difficult to integrate into mainstream British society. More recently Muslims have been portrayed as a kind of fifth column, particularly at times of global tension, and other racialised groups, such as refugees and asylum seekers, have been said to pose a threat to cultural and religious unity.

Two of the main influences on political debates on race since the 1980s have been new right discourses on the naturalness of racial antipathy and increasingly vociferous attacks on antiracism by the popular media. It is to these issues that we now turn.

The naturalisation of racism

Barker (1981) notes that an important aspect of racial ideologies in Britain in the late 1970s was the tendency to obscure or deny the meaning and implications of the deployment of racial categories. This fitted in with the wider tendency (a) to deny the importance of racism in British society and (b) to deny that hostility to the presence of black people in Britain was a form of racism. According to this line of argument it was only natural that, given the choice, people preferred to live with their own kind and not in a multiracial society. This preference was not seen as a manifestation of racialist attitudes, but as a natural response to the presence of people of a different cultural and racial background.

When in 1978 Margaret Thatcher expressed the view that 'the moment a minority threatens to become a big one, people get frightened', she was giving voice to an argument that subsequently became part of the accepted common sense of new right writings on racial questions. A more virulent expression of this kind of argument can be found in the arguments developed in the *Salisbury Review*. Mishan (1988), for example, argued that opposition to the emergence of a multiracial society was not necessarily an 'irrational or superstitious reaction':

> Opposition to the creation of a multi-racial society may well spring primarily from a deep concern about the future of one's country, one arising from a belief that its transformation over a short period from a relatively homogeneous population to one of a particular racial mix may, on balance, have adverse effects on its institutions and character or, at any rate, may be more likely to do harm than good (ibid.: p. 18).

Therefore for Mishan, and other new right commentators on racial issues, opposition to immigration and support for the repatriation of black people who had settled in Britain was a 'natural' response to the new racial mix in British society, and not a sign of racism.

Some of the policy suggestions by the new right were not fundamentally different from those espoused by Enoch Powell. For example John Casey, writing in the *Salisbury Review*, argued that the only feasible solution to the supposed problems caused by the presence of black people was the voluntary repatriation 'of a proportion of the immigrant and immigrant-descended population', or the withdrawal of the right of black immigrants to citizenship and the creation of a status analogous to the position of 'guest workers' in Europe (Casey, 1982: 27).

Even those on the right who did not go along with this accepted that the social problems that they thought were caused by black immigrants required constructive measures to encourage repatriation or to ensure the integration of those who wished to remain in Britain. What is interesting is that such arguments were presented not as extreme solutions but as a rational political response to what the new right saw as an intractable problem. In the logic of the politics of the new right, any attempt to create a multicultural society could only lead to social conflict and threaten the values and culture of the majority.

Anti-antiracism

In the 1980s and early 1990s some of the most strident voices in the mass media and academia were raised not against racism but against one of the favourite targets of the new right, namely antiracism. Almost daily, sections of the media concerned themselves with aspects of the work of local authorities or agencies such as the Commission for Racial Equality

(Honeyford, 1998a, b). It also became an important focus of concern for the various right-wing think tanks, who saw antiracism as an intrusion into individual freedom and a threat to the interests of the white majority.

According to van Dijk (1988) the purpose of these attacks on antiracism was to defend the assumed British virtues of tolerance and decency against attacks from enemies within:

> Within a more embracing framework of defending white British culture and its values, the targets of such press campaigns were obvious: assumed positive discrimination, ethnic projects, cultural pluralism, multicultural education, and in general each initiative based on the recognition that Britain is no longer white (ibid.: p. 184).

These were precisely the targets that sections of the popular media and new-right pressure groups singled out for particular attention, and there were numerous controversies over the actions of local authorities that took a positive stance on racial equality and antiracism (Smith, 1994; Ansell, 1997). What the new right called the ideology of antiracism became the subject of virulent attack, and indeed the whole notion of racism was dismissed in some circles as an invention of the loony left and the race relations industry.

Russell Lewis's *Anti-Racism: A Mania Exposed* (1998) was one of the most strident attacks on the work of what he called antiracist fanatics. With a preface by Enoch Powell, it was taken up by the new right as a fundamental critique of antiracist politics. Starting with a denial of the importance of racism in contemporary Britain, Lewis argued that the source of the current problems was Britain's failure to control immigration, and the creation and perpetuation of a race relations industry by successive Labour and Conservative governments. Indeed for Lewis, race relations had been damaged not by racism but by the lunatic outrages committed in the name of antiracism and the failure of the black minorities to respect the way of life and customs of the white majority.

Arguments such as these were only expressed by a minority but they represented an important phase in the politics of racism in post-1945 Britain. By attacking the activities of antiracists they shifted public attention away from racial discrimination and racism and focused it instead on the activities of black communities and antiracists, who were seen as having a vested interest in claiming that Britain was a racist society.

One consequence of these attacks on antiracism is that they served to legitimise the relative inaction of the three Conservative administrations from 1979 onwards. In a commentary on Lewis's book, William Deedes, a former Conservative minister, argued that it proved that Britain needed to feel less guilty about racism and to hold more open discussions on the impact of minority communities on majority values (*Daily Telegraph*, 30 June 1988).

Interestingly the debate on antiracism also led to attempts by people on the left and in the Labour Party to rethink the politics of racial equality. In the late 1980s the controversy over the events at Burnage High School in Manchester prompted a debate among sections of the left about the role and future of antiracist initiatives (*New Statesman*, 9 May 1988; *New Socialist*, 27 July 1988). During the 1990s, and particularly after New Labour took power in 1997, this process of rethinking antiracism was influenced by a desire to distance the mainstream labour movement from electorally unpopular debates on racism in British society.

Nationalism and the interests of the majority

It was perhaps no accident that antiracism was a prevalent theme in political debates in the 1980s and 1990s, given the mobilisation of national symbols and the attack on 'enemies' that Thatcherism as a political philosophy did much to foster. As Thatcher's swamping statement in 1978 made clear, she was committed to defending the interests of the white British majority against the claims of minority communities. Her rhetoric on the shared history, customs and values of Britons was an attempt to provide a social basis for her political project. This was illustrated to some extent during the Falklands war with the mobilisation of nationalist sentiments against the 'Argies'.

With regard to multiculturalism, Thatcher's declared sympathy for the fear of the majority about the impact of immigration and race on 'their' localities, 'their' schools and 'their' cultural heritage was not an isolated rhetorical statement. Rather it was part of a wider debate on the politics of national identity, to which we shall return in Chapter 10. Extreme right wing movements used similar arguments to justify their political agendas. For example in both the 1997 and the 2001 general election campaigns the BNP attempted to portray itself as a party that was interested in the plight of the white majority. Under such slogans as 'rights for whites' it argued that far from being a racist party it was seeking to prevent whites from becoming 'second class citizens'. This strategy became even more pronounced when Nick Griffin replaced John Tyndall as leader of the BNP.

Summary and conclusion

Much of this chapter has been concerned with unravelling and exploring the part played by ideology and political language in the process of racialisation. In addition the various forms of racist mobilisation, at both the theoretical and the practical level, analysed in this chapter have provided a basis for understanding how policy issues as diverse as urban change, law and order, unemployment and youth policy are racialised and constantly transformed.

The transformations in racist ideologies that have taken place since the 1980s point to the need for a deeper understanding of the logic of these ideologies and their associated mobilisations, particularly by those who are interested in challenging the roots of racism and its everyday manifestations. The prevalence of racialised ideas about Englishness and national identity shows how far we have to go to achieve racial justice and equality, and it also highlights the importance of understanding the complex forms of racial thought in contemporary British society.

9 Race, Politics and Mobilisation

Previous chapters have shown that since 1945 the politicisation of race and race-related issues has been a complex process involving interventions by successive governments, political parties, pressure groups, individual politicians and other political actors. In other words, the associated events we have witnessed since 1945 have been the product of political mobilisation of one sort or another, rather than the inevitable consequence of processes beyond political control. What is even more clear is that since the 1980s ethnic minority communities have engaged in politics in a variety of ways and forged their own forms of political mobilisation at the local and national levels, be this in terms of mainstream politics, community-oriented action over specific issues such as the Stephen Lawrence campaign, or alternative forms of political organisation. There has also been a resurgence of identity politics premised on religious faith, ethnicity or regional or local identity.

These are not entirely new phenomena. Although it is sometimes ignored in accounts of post-1945 history, from the earliest days of postwar migration black and ethnic minority people played an active part in political action and debates on race and immigration, both locally and nationally (James and Harris, 1993; Ramdin, 1999). Black and ethnic minority mobilisation took the form of community or ethnic associations, local campaigns on specific issues of concern, or alliances between minority and white organisations. Some of these mobilisations were linked to political activism in the immigrants' countries of origin. In the early stages of migration and settlement many of these mobilisations focused on initiatives to counteract the activities of racist groups and to promote measures to improve racial justice and equality (Pearson, 1981; Sivanandan, 1982; Anwar, 1986, 1994; Carter, 1986; Saggar, 1992, 2000; Solomos and Back, 1995). Later mobilisations involved putting pressure on the mainstream political parties to respond to the needs of ethnic minority communities (Sewell, 1993; Shukra, 1998).

Such mobilisations were as controversial as the activities of extreme right-wing groups, and the actions of black and ethnic minority political activists in some localities attracted widespread media attention. Perhaps the best known of the related controversies was the debate that took place in the

Labour Party throughout the 1980s and early 1990s on antiracist measures and the creation of a 'black section' in the party to voice the concerns of minority groups. Another controversy, and one that was by no means resolved, was about the selection of minority candidates to run in national and local elections. This issue came to the fore in the 1980s in the context of growing minority political influence in certain localities in London, Birmingham, Bradford and other major urban conurbations (Anwar, 1994, 1998; Solomos and Back, 1995; Saggar, 1998b), and resulted in the increased presence of minority political activists in all the main political parties, particularly at the local level. After 1987 this included limited black and ethnic minority representation in parliament. Ultimately both of these issues related to the question of how inclusive political institutions were in respect of minority communities, and how they could become more inclusive in the future.

Part of the reason for the perception that minority political mobilisation was a threat was that everyday political rhetoric and media coverage often portrayed it as endangering the fabric of British society. Indeed one of the ironies of the situation was that antiracists were often depicted as doing more harm to race relations than extreme right-wing racists. Peregrine Worsthorne reflected this view when he argued that the future of the Notting Hill Carnival was threatened not by white racists or the police, but by black racists who were keen to use the occasion for their own political ends (*Sunday Telegraph*, 28 August 1988). Hence according to the logic of this argument the greatest threat to racial harmony lay in the politicisation of racial issues by black activists and politicians or race relations professionals. This served both to marginalise the issue of white racism and to highlight the perceived threat posed by black racism. It thus fitted in with the view, articulated later in the language of the new right, of black communities being a threat to the political and social unity of British society.

This chapter examines the nature and impact of black and minority political mobilisation, and the responses to it. The focus is on the basic forms of black and ethnic minority mobilisation, the interplay between race and class, the activities of antiracist political alliances, minority political participation and the impact of minority politics on local political processes. The final section considers the future prospects for black and minority politics, particularly in light of the social changes that are taking place within minority communities at the present time. Before moving on to the central concerns of the chapter, however, it is necessary to introduce some general arguments about political participation and forms of mobilisation.

Political participation and exclusion

Political participation and action are essential elements in the development of political systems and institutions, which historically has involved the integration of disparate groups into the polity and the institution of channels of participation and inclusion. In liberal democratic societies such as Britain the most obvious means of enabling, as well as constraining, participation are elections, parties, trade unions and pressure groups. Such processes and institutions tend to reinforce identification with the rules, procedures and values of the polity, they enable the articulation of demands, they facilitate consent and they strengthen acceptance of the legitimacy of the political system (Edelman, 1977; Alford and Friedland, 1985).

However it is clear that not all groups have the same opportunity to participate through 'legitimate' channels (Piven and Cloward, 1977; Bowles and Gintis, 1987). According to Katznelson and Weir (1985: 204), different groups may (a) be incorporated fully and equally into the political process and possess the capacity to affect the contours of policy, (b) be incorporated fully and equally but have relatively little influence over the political system, (c) be incorporated in a partial and structurally subordinate way, but possess the capacity to influence policy outcomes on some occasions, or (d) be structurally subordinate and lack the resources needed to influence what the state does.

Thus when individuals or groups gain access to channels of political participation they do not necessarily gain influence over agenda setting and decision making. Some groups and individuals have far greater power to place issues on the agenda. Indeed it has been argued that certain types of problem and certain groups of people are systematically excluded from participation; that is, there is a mobilisation of bias whereby some issues and people are organised into politics while others are organised out.

Prevailing social and political values can also limit the political agenda. A good example of this is the way in which, with the shift in political values to the right during the period of Conservative Party rule from 1979 to 1997, calls for action to promote racial equality and positive action were politically marginalised. Because such calls did not fit in with the ethos and culture of the Conservative Party, successive administrations systematically refused to introduce any major initiatives to increase the political representation of minority groups. They also paid little attention to calls to strengthen race relations legislation or to allocate more resources to bodies charged with promoting greater racial equality. Yet it is clear that such neglect acted as a spur to various minority communities to press for a greater political voice.

The context of minority political mobilisation

As discussed in previous chapters, racist political mobilisations, whether in the form of Powellism or the actions of extreme right-wing groups, have attracted considerable attention since the 1960s. Yet during the same period black and antiracist political mobilisations played an important part in shaping the politics of race in Britain. Such mobilisations remain, however, largely underresearched and little understood.

The relative neglect of this important facet of the politics of race and racism in Britain stems partly from the fact that until the mid 1970s it was commonly assumed that there was little if any political mobilisation by the ethnic minority people at the political level. This assumption seemed to be supported by national studies of electoral behaviour and local political studies. For example Newton's (1976) study of Birmingham found no significant evidence of political mobilisation.

Another factor that worked against the serious study of black and minority politics was the sensitivity of research on political issues. Research on both the national and the local politics of race could prove to be highly controversial so there was a marked reluctance by social scientists to carry out such research. This reluctance was also partly the result of antipathy by local black community groups and activists towards outside researchers (Jenkins, 1971; Rex and Tomlinson, 1979; Mullard, 1985; Nelson, 2000), but whatever the reason, during the 1970s and 1980s political participation by black and Asian people was little understood or analysed. A handful of studies did look at the experiences of specific cities or ethnic minority organisations, but they remained very much the exception.

From the mid 1970s onwards, however, the issue of black and minority political participation attracted the attention of a number of researchers. Although this research was not clearly focused it helped to clarify some aspects of minority political organisation and electoral participation, and the response of political parties and institutions to minority political action (FitzGerald, 1984; Anwar, 1986; Solomos and Back, 1995; Adolino, 1998).

One of the main concerns of a number of studies was the future development of minority politics, particularly when black and ethnic minorities became more established and incorporated into political processes. These studies have suggested three possible patterns for the future political incorporation of minority communities into the British political system.

First, it was argued that with the passing of time immigrants and their descendants would become incorporated fully, if unequally, into Britain's political institutions, including political parties, pressure groups and trade unions. Second, it was suggested that immigrant groups might be incorporated into the political system through their own ethnically or regionally based organisations. Such organisations would seek to advance the interests of particular ethnic groups by political means. Third, it was argued that in response to institutional racism and the politicisation of racial issues in British society minority communities, whatever their ethnic origins, might develop a common political identity as an excluded 'black' minority.

There was little agreement about the most likely course that the political incorporation of minorities would take, or about the degree of choice they would have in this, but it was generally agreed by neo-Marxists and pluralists that black and minority political participation was likely to follow one of the above three courses.

For example Phizacklea and Miles (1980), based on their fieldwork in London during the late 1970s and utilising a Marxist framework, concluded that what seemed to be happening in Britain involved a combination of class-based and ethnically based political mobilisation. Because of their class composition minority communities showed a strong interest in traditional forms of working-class participation in the political system, expressed through their support for the Labour Party and involvement in trade unions. But because of the pervasiveness of racial exclusionism at all levels of society they were also forced to organise autonomously on ethnic or racial lines to defend their interests. In broad terms this was also the argument developed by Layton-Henry (1984), although he laid more stress on the incorporation of minority politics into political parties and electoral processes.

As there are few research-based studies of the political incorporation of or autonomous political mobilisation among the various minority communities it is difficult to make firm predictions about the future of minority politics in Britain, so in the rest of this chapter we shall outline some of the main aspects of ethnic minority political involvement since the 1940s and look briefly at possible prospects for the future. In the course of this account we shall return to the themes outlined in this section.

Origins of minority political mobilisation

During the 1940s and 1950s the political position of newly arrived migrants can be seen in terms of exclusion and marginalisation from the political system as minority organisations and groups had few or no resources to influence the state's actions. This does not mean that immigrants had no involvement in politics, indeed throughout this period there was a lively interest in both mainstream British politics and community-based associations and groupings (Sivanandan, 1982; Ramdin, 1987; Gilroy, 1987).

In the 1960s a number of minority groups and individuals began to challenge this exclusion and invoke fundamental issues of citizenship and equality. Black and Asian immigrants formed a series of local and national organisations that sought in various ways to challenge their exclusion from equal participation in British society. Such organisations included the (previously established) Indian Workers' Association, the West Indian Standing Conference and other ethnically based groups (Pearson, 1981; Jacobs, 1986; Carter, 1986).

The organisation that received the most public attention during the 1960s was the Campaign Against Racial Discrimination (CARD), which was formed in 1964–5 by a coalition of black political groups, white liberals and campaigners against racism. Its main objectives were to eliminate racial discrimination, oppose racially discriminatory legislation and coordinate the work of local and national organisations that were fighting racial discrimination (Heineman, 1972: 20–35). It collapsed after a brief and highly controversial internal power struggle during 1967, but before this it took part in public debates on policies to tackle racial discrimination and served as a catalyst for a wide-ranging debate on the need for an autonomous black political organisation to tackle the roots of racial inequality at all levels of British society.

Forms of minority political involvement

From the early 1970s there was a noticeable expansion of political involvement and mobilisation among black and Asian people, with a rich diversity of political and cultural expression at the local level in electoral politics, community mobilisation and political party involvement, and later at the national level in parliamentary politics.

Electoral politics

During the 1970s and 1980s the politics of various minority communities began to attract the attention of political parties and academic researchers alike. A study carried out by the Community Relations Commission on the importance of the minority vote in certain constituencies during the general election of 1974 helped to arouse media and public interest in this issue.

In the period leading up to the 1979 general election the race issue was further politicised, particularly in respect of party allegiance. The Conservative Party's attempt to draw in white National Front supporters did not prevent it from seeking the support of minority voters in some constituencies, particularly Asian voters.

During the late 1970s and early 1980s all the major political parties showed some interest in attracting the support of minority communities, particularly in important inner city constituencies where the minority vote could make a considerable difference to the outcome. However in practice both Asian and black voters tended to vote Labour in both national and local elections. This trend went back to the 1950s, although there is clear evidence only from the 1970s. In the general elections of 1974 and 1979 the Labour Party received strong support from Asian and black voters, with some variation according to class position. This trend continued with a few changes, in the 1983, 1987 and 1992 general elections. Since then there has been a reduction in Asian support, but compared with the white electorate, black and Asian people are overwhelmingly likely to support the Labour Party.

However other factors do need to be taken into account. For example there is evidence of a lower electoral turnout by some sections of minority communities, particularly the young. Such groups are more likely to be disillusioned with the ability of politicians to bring about changes in major areas that concern them. It is also important to look at generational differences in party preference. The Asian swing towards the Conservative Party may not be uniform, so there is a need to look into class and generational patterns of voting behaviour (Crewe, 1983; Layton-Henry and Studlar, 1985; Anwar, 1986, 1998; Saggar, 1998a, 2000).

Interestingly, during the 1983 and 1987 general elections there was considerable speculation about a major move towards the Conservative Party by middle-class Asian and black voters, but the scale of the change did not support such a generalisation. At the time Layton-Henry (1988) argued that the trend towards class-based voting would be more limited than some studies suggested:

> In the future, one would expect that class voting will increase among members of the black electorate but there are a number of reasons why this is likely to be rather slow. These include Mrs Thatcher's determination to bring New Commonwealth immigration to an end, her lack of sympathy for anti-discrimination measures and her willingness to allow the Labour Party to be identified with what she regards as unpopular minorities (ibid.: 22).

Whether the shift towards class-based voting by minority communities will become more pronounced is the subject of much academic debate, and naturally it is of interest to the major political parties. But before analysing this issue in detail we need to look more deeply at the sociology of the black and Asian electorate and its various component parts.

Community politics

Since the 1950s a feature of black and Asian self-organisation has been the array of communal, religious, political and issue-oriented groups that have arisen (Vertovec, 1996; Kalilombe, 1997; Toulis, 1997). Such organisations have frequently been of a local or community-based character, and have involved a variety of forms of autonomous organisation in a number of contexts, rather than being unified ethnic movements.

While there are few detailed studies of the history and political ideologies of such groups, during the 1960s and 1970s some studies of Asian political and cultural organisations were conducted, particularly in relation to their political involvement and ideological commitment. A more limited number of studies of black organisations and groups were also carried out during that time, but these were limited both in scope and geographically.

Part of the reason for the neglect of this dimension of minority political action may have been the assumption that such organisations and groups were not very influential at higher political levels. Goulbourne (1987), however, argued forcefully that without looking at the activities of such groups it would be impossible to understand the growing impact of minority politics on the major political parties and mainstream institutions. He saw this as particularly important in placing such issues as the education of black children, police relations with black people, black unemployment and racial attacks on the political agenda at both the local and the central government level.

Other studies of black community organisations in the 1980s revealed that active self-organisation was an everyday feature of the political life of various black communities. Cheetham (1988) noted that the most important feature of ethnic associations in Britain was their extraordinary vitality, energy and commitment. She concluded from her study of a sample of ethnic associations that two issues were of particular importance to most of the groups she studied: questions of culture, language and ethnic identity, including the politics of the country of origin of the associations' members; and how to achieve greater equality and integration into British society without losing traditions and values (ibid.: 150–1).

The importance of the part played by community-based associations in the politics of larger ethnic minority organisations is only now being fully appreciated. This is likely to lead to more detailed studies of the processes of political mobilisation and community organisation, in relation both to issue-centred politics and to electoral and party politics. For example attention has already been given to the growth of political activity by ethnically and religiously based community groups. The two most important examples in this context are the Muslim and Sikh communities, which have engaged in a considerable degree of political organisation and community-based action on issues relating to British politics and the politics of their countries of origin. There is also evidence that forms of religious and ethnic mobilisation are taking shape in Hindu communities in various towns and cities (Bhatt, 1997).

The Labour Party and the black sections

As we have already seen, from the earliest days of postwar immigration black and Asian immigrants tended to give their electoral support to the Labour Party. Yet it is clear that until the mid 1970s the Labour Party itself made no serious attempt to incorporate its black and ethnic minority supporters into its own organisations or to tackle racism in the party structure.

From the mid 1970s, however, both black and white Labour Party members began to press for action to be taken on racial inequality and racism. In 1975 the Labour Party Race Action Group was established as an internal pressure group, and along with the efforts of other individuals it helped to increase awareness of the politics of racism within the party. From the late 1970s internal debates and policy changes brought racial inequality, along with other previously neglected issues, onto the general political agenda of the party at both the national and the local level.

These pressures were given greater force during the early 1980s in the aftermath of the urban unrest. In many local Labour constituencies, as well as at the national level, race-related issues became the focus of intense policy debate. The early 1980s were a period of innovation as a number of left-wing Labour local authorities developed racial equality policies, promoted antiracist initiatives and tackled racism within their own institutions.

It was in the context of these changes that black and ethnic minority Labour politicians and activists began to demand greater minority representation in local and national political institutions. This was seen as a way of putting black and ethnic minority issues on the political agenda and providing a voice for those who were excluded from political participation (Geddes, 1993; Solomos and Back, 1995; Fielding and Geddes, 1998).

Attention then began to turn to the formation of a black section within the Labour Party, which was seen as a way of increasing the influence of black and Asian party members on policy making and encouraging more minority people to become involved in politics. A resolution calling for the recognition of a black section was debated at a number of annual conferences from 1983 onwards. However the leadership of the party spoke out against the idea, largely on the grounds that it could be seen as divisive and as a form of apartheid. There also seems to have been a fear among the leadership such that a section could become a political liability if it was led by radical left-wing black groups.

Marc Wordsworth, a leading figure in the black section campaign, expressed the thinking behind the campaign when he warned:

> If the Party did not begin actively to take the issue of black representation seriously, it must face the possibility of increased abstentions, a tide of black independents and perhaps a tendency, particularly amongst black youth, to redress their grievances through extra-parliamentary action (*The Times*, 16 April 1984).

It was argued that the setting up of a black section would help to institutionalise black representation and give black members a channel through which to press for changes in the political programme of the party, both locally and nationally.

According to Diane Abbott, a leading figure in the movement who was elected to parliament in 1987, a number of factors helped to make the issue a central theme: the long-standing institutionalised racism in the party and the glaring contradiction between the party's reliance on the black and ethnic minority vote and the fact that the party structures were dominated by whites; the way in which in the late 1970s the left wing of the party had used constitutional means, such as mandatory selection, to organise against the *status quo*; and 'the emergence in the Labour Party of a different generation of black activists, who took for granted that they should organise themselves as black people' (*Marxism Today*, September 1985: 31).

Despite the failure of the black section movement to achieve formal recognition by the party, calls for greater representation of minority interests continued to influence political debates within the party throughout the 1980s and 1990s (Jeffers, 1991; Sewell, 1993; Adolino, 1998). A number of active groups developed in various localities, and their influence was noticeable in areas of London and Birmingham. These groups continued to campaign for formal recognition and to meet regularly at both the local and the national level. In 1988 they produced a detailed *Black Agenda* that put forward proposals on such issues as inner city policy, education, policing and housing (Labour Party Black Section, 1988). However the agenda had little influence on the policies pursued by the Labour Party. As minority representation became more established in local and national politics during the 1990s, pressure for minority incorporation into political institutions continued and had at least some effect on the thinking of the Labour Party (Back and Solomos, 1992a, b; Solomos and Back, 1995).

Today the question of minority participation in the Labour Party has moved beyond the matter of a black section as such. Many black and ethnic minority politicians and activists who were not active in the movement during the 1980s and 1990s are demanding increased minority representation in party institutions and elected posts. Despite official opposition this demand is beginning to bear fruit, particularly at the local level. Increased minority representation in local authorities such as Birmingham and Tower Hamlets since the 1990s is a case in point.

Representation in parliament

The final aspect of black and ethnic minority political involvement that needs to be considered is the question of representation in parliament. The breakthrough in this context came in the 1987 general election, when four minority Labour MPs were elected: Bernie Grant (Tottenham), Diane Abbott (Hackney North and Stoke Newington), Paul Boateng (Brent South) and Keith Vaz (Leicester East). For the first time in 60 years blacks and Asians were represented in parliament, and this was popularly presented as a major change in British political life.

In the 1992 general election the number of ethnic minority Labour MPs increased to five, the first Conservative minority MP was elected (*Runnymede Trust Bulletin*, May 1992) and all the political parties claimed that race was no longer an issue in British political life. All of those who had been elected in 1987 were returned to parliament, two of them with significantly increased majorities: Bernie Grant with a 9.4 per cent increase and Keith Vaz with a 10.4 per cent increase. While Ashok Kumar, who had been elected as Labour MP for Langaugh in a 1991 by-election, lost his seat, two new minority MPs were elected: Piara Khabra took over her Labour predecessor's seat Ealing Southall, and in Brentford and Isleworth Nirj Deva became the first minority Conservative MP.

In all, 23 black and Asian candidates stood in the 1992 general election: ten for Labour, eight for the Conservatives and four for the Liberal Democrats. The electoral success of black and Asian candidates was offered as evidence that Britain was becoming a multiracial society. This was contrasted with the experience of other European societies where immigration was becoming a highly politicised issue and there was relatively little integration of minorities to the political system.

Part of the reason for the widespread interest in the election of the minority MPs in 1987 was the controversy surrounding their selection, which was popularly presented as the result of pressure by the black section movement and sections of the left wing of the Labour Party. In addition many of the black and ethnic minority politicians elected at the national and local levels were depicted in the media and in popular political discourse as either representatives of black power and the extreme left, or as representing specific religious and ethnic communities.

When in the lead-up to the 1987 general election the Labour Party selected a number of ethnic minority candidates for winnable seats there were clear signs of unease about the possible impact of minority representation in parliament. The *Sun* warned that the election of minority MPs would not help the majority of the ethnic minority population since they were 'all holders of loony left ideas which have shocked the nation' (*Sun*, 14 February 1987). At a broader level the selection of minority candidates became embroiled in the wider controversy over the influence of the 'loony left' on Labour Party politics and the activities of left-wing local authorities such as Lambeth and Brent. The controversy over the selection and deselection of Sharon Atkin as the candidate for Nottingham East in the lead-up to the election was a clear example of how these issues coalesced in popular political debates.

After the 1987 and 1992 general elections considerable attention was paid to the parliamentary performance of the minority MPs and to their impact on debates in parliament and on committees. There were also clear signs that black and Asian MPs were facing unique pressures that were rendering their position very difficult both as constituency MPs and as ethnic minority politicians. On the one hand they were under pressure to become integrated into the norms of parliamentary politics, while on the other hand they were expected to act as spokespersons on a variety of race and ethnic issues. A similar situation faced the increasing number of minority politicians who had been elected as local councillors, and who were often thought of as speaking for entire communities regardless of ethnic, cultural or religious differences (Solomos and Back, 1991, 1993, 1995; Werbner and Anwar, 1991).

In the May 1997 general election 44 ethnic minority candidates stood for the mainstream political parties – 14 for Labour, 11 for the Conservatives, and 19 for the Liberal Democrats – but only nine were successful, all for the Labour Party. The situation in the June 2001 general election was broadly similar, though there was some increase in the number of minority candidates standing for the Conservatives, the Liberal Democrats and more marginal parties. Of the 25 Liberal Democrat, 16 Conservative and 16 Labour candidates, only 12 (from a range of minority backgrounds) were successful, all of them for the Labour Party. Though this was by no means a significant increase in the number of minority MPs at Westminster it indicated the entrenchment of at least some degree of minority political representation.

The success of New Labour in the 1997 election led some to hope that the political representation of minorities would gain a higher profile. Certainly during its first term of office the Blair government talked of the need for more black and Asian role models in political life, but recent research has revealed the limited and rather patchy progress that minority representation has made in both local and national institutions (Office for Public Management, 2001; Ali and O'Cinneide, 2002). More worryingly, there seems to be no consensus about how this relatively slow rate of progress is to be tackled, let alone plans for substantive reforms.

Antiracist politics and political alliances

A recurrent theme in debates on the development of minority political action is the question of political alliances between minority and antiracist political groups. The need for such alliances is based on two assumptions. First, it is argued that the relatively small size of the minority population means that their demands would have a greater chance of success if they had the support of sections of the majority white population. The second assumption is that racism in Britain is as much a problem for the white majority as it is for the ethnic minorities, and that racist political groups can best be dealt with by an alliance between minority and white antiracist groups.

One example of a national attempt to develop an alliance of antiracist political groups was the Anti-Nazi League (ANL), which was founded in 1977. The league was particularly active from 1977 to 1979, when it concentrated on political action to counter the propaganda of the National Front and other extreme right-wing groups. It drew its support from members of the Labour Party, the Socialist Workers Party and from other left-wing organisations who were concerned about the growing popularity of racist political groups. One of these organisations was Rock Against Racism, which since 1976 had been attempting to turn young people against the National Front and other racist organisations, and which helped to draw many supporters to the ANL (Widgery, 1986; Gilroy, 1987).

The ANL used two particular modes of action to oppose the National Front. First, extraparliamentary initiatives such as rallies and demonstrations helped to publicise its arguments on racism and the political dangers the extreme right presented. Emphasis was put on the links between the ideologies of the National Front and the Nazi Party, and on the National Front's connection with underground fascist groups. This helped to mobilise opposition to the Front in the period leading up to the 1979 election.

Second, during 1978 and 1979 it held a series of successful musical events in association with Rock Against Racism. These were aimed at attracting to the antiracist cause young people who were seen as particularly vulnerable to National Front propaganda. The speedy rise of the ANL was matched by its rapid decline as a political force from 1979 onwards. Although it continued to function for some time afterwards its high point was over and it had little impact on public debates on racism and immigration.

However this does not mean that antiracist political alliances ceased to exist. For example Ben-Tovim *et al.* (1986) found that locally based antiracist alliances in Liverpool and Wolverhampton were doing much to promote minority political demands and mobilise opinion against racist organisations. From this they concluded that, at the local level at least, antiracist political alliances remained an important part of the politics of racism in Britain. Furthermore research carried out by Solomos and Back (1995) in Birmingham during the early 1990s revealed that coalition politics was doing much to shape minority political agendas during this period.

At another level, issue-centred campaigns on matters of concern to minority communities remained an important part of local and national political mobilisation. An interesting example of this was the work carried out by the National Coalition of Anti-Deportation Campaigns, a body that grew out of local campaigns on immigration and related issues.

During the 1990s there were various attempts to set up a national umbrella organisation to bring together these local groups. The Anti-Nazi League was reformed with this in mind, but it soon became clear that interests had diverged and a number of rival bodies, such as the Anti Racist Alliance and the National Assembly Against Racism, were formed to give voice to the various factions of the now divided antiracist movement (*Fighting Talk*, Anti-Fascist Action, 1995–2000). The aftermath of the Stephen Lawrence case saw the launch in April 1999 of the National Civil Rights Movement, which modelled itself on the American Civil Rights Movement of the 1950s and 1960s (*Observer*, 28 March 1999).

The politics of race and class

The interplay between race and class in the formation of minority political action has been one of the most resonant themes in studies of this question. As we saw in Chapter 1 the theoretical debate on how race and class interact is far from resolved and the subject is still a cause of heated debate among social scientists. Underlying the theoretical controversy, however, are more practical questions about the relationship between autonomous minority mobilisation and class-based politics.

This theme was central, for example, in the 1980s controversy over the electoral behaviour of minority communities and the formation of a black section in the Labour Party. Similar questions have been raised about the development of black politics in the US, particularly in the debate between Marxists and black nationalists (Marable, 1981).

In Chapter 1 we looked at some of the ways in which scholars have attempted to overcome the dichotomy between race and class relations. At that stage no attempt was made to provide full answers to the problems. After the above discussion, however, we are in a better position to look more deeply into this issue.

There are two broad questions we have to address when rethinking the terms of political debate on race and class. First, there is the question of what is meant by class. The role of political mobilisation in determining the formation of class consciousness, national consciousness and other identities has been the subject of lively debate over the years. One of the sharpest formulations of this can be found in a study of the politics of schooling in the US by Ira Katznelson and Margaret Weir (1985: 62), who argue that:

> It is important to think of the formation of a class as a conditional process. Whether people who share objective traits in the material organisation of society will form a class in action cannot be predicted from the profiles of the social structure, nor can the rhetorical and practical bases of their action be deduced from such profiles.

From this perspective, what is important in the development of political mobilisation is not the position of political actors in the social structure but their actual experiences and responses to the social, economic and political processes of the societies in which they live.

Second, and following on from the above, there is a need to understand the connection between race as a political category and wider social processes and conflicts. In Britain the main problem with trying to view minority politics from a purely class perspective is that it is impossible to separate contemporary forms of minority political mobilisation from the everyday experiences of discrimination and exclusion that have operated over five decades. The particular experiences of African-Caribbeans, Asians and other minority groups therefore need to be understood, and this necessarily takes us beyond a dogmatic conception of class formation. At the same time it is important to remember that their distinctive historical experiences are joined by a common thread: full or partial denial of citizenship and the rights that accompany it (Phillips, 1991, 1995).

Politics, social movements and reform

Central questions that underlie all accounts of minority political mobilisation are what impact can ethnic minority communities have on the political agenda, and what are the prospects that an effective challenge to racism can be mounted in the current political environment? These questions have certainly become common reference points in debates on specific policy issues such as education and policing, which have been areas of active concern among the various minority communities for some time.

It is clear, however, that there is by no means a uniform answer to these questions. Responses range from deep scepticism about the possibility of ethnic minorities having a major influence on the mainstream political agenda, to a degree of optimism about the ability of minority politicians to transform political institutions.

Perhaps the most notable political development in recent years has been the attempt by minority politicians to gain positions of political patronage and power at both the national and the local level. The assumption behind this strategy is that it is only through integration into the mainstream channels of political power and patronage that minority communities will be able to move beyond political exclusion and powerlessness to the situation where they are incorporated equally into the political system and have the resources needed to bring about policy changes in their interest.

Such an optimistic view of the possibility of black advancement through the political system is not shared by all commentators. The relative failure of the mainstream political institutions to tackle the root causes of racial inequality and racism in British society has led some commentators to look beyond the channels of formal politics for a solution to these problems.

Gilroy (1987), for example, concludes his account of urban social change and black community struggles in the 1980s by arguing that:

> In the representation of the recent riots, it is possible to glimpse a struggle, a sequence of antagonisms which has moved beyond the grasp of orthodox class analysis. Unable to control the social relations in which they find themselves, people have shrunk the world to the size of their communities and begun to act politically on that basis (ibid.: 245).

While it is difficult to find a clear political strategy in this rather general and cryptic statement, Gilroy seems to be suggesting that (a) the idea that minority people are becoming increasingly incorporated into the existing class-based political institutions is inadequate, and (b) excluded groups are likely to develop forms of political involvement at the micro rather than the macro level.

This argument stands in direct contrast to the attempts by other minority radicals to prioritise direct minority involvement in national and local political institutions. This tension was also reflected in the debate on the formation of a black section in the Labour Party and the wider debate on increased minority representation in the mainstream political institutions.

At the present time, even the presence of twelve ethnic minority MPs and a sizeable number of minority councillors in many local authorities is unlikely to have much effect on the allocation of resources and political influence. This seems to have been implicitly recognised in the so-called Black Agenda issued by the black section movement during 1988 (Howe and Upshal, 1988).

Minority demands for full citizenship will not be achieved easily in the present political climate. Urban unrest such as that which occurred sporadically throughout the 1980s and 1990s may be better managed in the future, but the underlying conflicts that produced it are not going to disappear. Ordinary methods of dispute resolution have so far proved incapable of managing conflict with this degree of meaning and intensity, and the prospects for the future are not good.

Yet it is also important to note that this situation is not likely to result in wholesale withdrawal from all types of political activity. This is perhaps the best hope in the long struggle by minority communities for equality and full citizenship. Reflecting on the history of attempts to form a national body to fight for minority interests at the political level, Hall (1985b) argues that one reason for the failure of such attempts is the gap between such organisations and the 'actual day-to-day experience of repression and exploitation which the black community has gone through'.

Summary and conclusion

This chapter has focused on two key topics. First, it has explored minority political mobilisations and the changing boundaries of race, ethnicity and religion that have helped to shape them over time. The chapter started by looking at ethnic minority and antiracist political mobilisation in the context of the racialisation of British political life since 1945. Second, it has sought to show that, far from being helpless victims, black and ethnic minority people have actively challenged racism and injustice. Indeed the events of the past few years indicate that the participation and involvement of Asian and black people in mainstream as well as community politics is likely to increase.

Antiracist political mobilisations have also been important at various stages since the 1950s and have attracted widespread sympathy and support from outside the minority communities. Local and national attempts to create alliances against racism have been inherently contradictory and have proved unstable, but the formation of groups such as the Anti-Nazi League and Rock Against Racism in the 1970s, along with various locally based initiatives, indicate that the potential for political mobilisation against racism is there.

With regard to the future, concern seems to be particularly focused on young blacks and other disaffected minority groups. For example Rose (1985: 59) asks whether public policy will succeed in bringing about greater social integration or the situation where 'a small, politically alienated and active group will identify themselves as blacks rather than Britons'. From a rather different perspective, Gilroy (1987: 246) argues that the immediate prospect of change from the present situation is to be found among 'those groups who find the premises of their collective existence threatened'.

Perhaps the most important lesson to be learnt from the experiences of the past two decades is that it is far too simplistic to present one model of black or of antiracist political mobilisation. Rather it is important to recognise the volatile, and to some extent unpredictable, nature of political struggles over race and to determine whether such struggles have a racist or an antiracist political objective. Once this is done it becomes clear that the active involvement of black and ethnic minority communities must be an integral part of any realistic strategy for challenging the political agenda on race in British society.

10 Race, Culture and Identity Politics

In the previous two chapters the analytical focus was on the various forms of political mobilisation that have emerged over the past few decades. In particular they explored aspects of identity formation based on ethnoracial political movements and political action within black and ethnic minority communities. In this chapter the focus shifts to another feature of the changing face of contemporary race relations, namely the meaning of British national identity in an increasingly multicultural society. Since the 1990s this has been a recurrent theme of both Conservative and Labour political discourses. A case in point was the vociferous debate in the period leading up to the 2001 general election on the nature of multiculturalism in contemporary Britain. This debate highlighted the extent to which questions about cultural difference were inextricably linked to ideas about race. This was but the latest addition to the ongoing debate on the meaning of Englishness and Britishness, which seems to have its roots in a deep uncertainty about national identity since the end of colonialism (Solomos, 1998).

The question of our changing understanding of British national identity has provoked an increasingly vociferous public debate. At the same time there can be little doubt that the question of just what is happening to our national identity is intimately linked to questions about the consequences of growing multiculturalism. This is an issue that has preoccupied politicians, journalists and commentators alike (Nairn, 1981, 1988; Crick, 1991; Werbner and Modood, 1997; Alibhai-Brown, 1999) and about which there have been recurrent controversies, such as that over the role of religion in public life following the Rushdie affair (Appignanesi and Maitland, 1989; Asad, 1990a; CRE, 1990; Ruthven, 1990; Ahmed, 1992; Samad, 1992; Bhatt, 1997). At a broader level, there have been a whole range of other spheres in which this debate has taken place, including religion, sport and popular culture (Dodd, 1995). Public controversies about such diverse issues as the Gulf War in 1990–1, immigration, the arrival of refugees and asylum seekers, urban unrest and violence, the 2001 war in Afghanistan highlight the tensions about the changing basis of national identity. Such concerns have a long history, but there seems little doubt that they have become more prominent since the 1990s (Solomos and Back, 1995; Knox, 1995; Kushner and Knox, 1999).

In this chapter we shall deal with some of the key aspects of the changing dynamics of culture, religion and identity in contemporary Britain. The focus will be on the implications of emergent forms of identity politics for an understanding of the logic of national culture and ideas of nationhood. We shall also look at some broader features of multiculturalism, religious diversity and transnational political ideologies. All of these trends form part of the wider environment that has led to the emergence of a more complex definition of what it means to be part of the national culture.

In addition to the above, there have been vigorous public debates on the changing balance between civil society and the state in Britain, the need to redefine citizenship rights to take account of minority communities, desire to protect their religious and cultural identity, and the extent to which minorities are really accepted as an intergral part of a multiracial, multicultural Britain. There has also been a questioning of the possibility of achieving such objectives through the types of policy and initiative pursued by successive governments since the 1960s (Parekh, 1991; Asad, 1990b; Werbner and Modood, 1997; Wayland, 1997; Favell, 2001).

Such preoccupations link up with the concerns expressed in academic studies of culture and identity (Rutherford, 1990; Grossberg *et al.*, 1992), including the growing body of literature on the relationship between racial and gender identities (Grewal *et al.*, 1989; Brah, 1992, 1996; Anthias and Yuval-Davis, 1992; James, 1992; James and Harris, 1993). Many radical writers in this field point to the need to analyse the dynamics of racial and ethnic identities in Britain and other European societies (Hall, 1991a; Gilroy, 1991; Rattansi, 1992), and an increasing number of scholars have questioned the appropriateness of using general categories such as 'black' and 'Asian' to describe highly differentiated ethnic and racial minorities with quite separate cultural and religious traditions.

Whatever the reasons for the growing preoccupation with identity politics, there is a need to explore the likely consequences of this trend for racial and ethnic politics in Britain. It is to this issue that we now turn.

Culture, nation and identity

One way to begin to grapple with the range of issues covered in this chapter is to ask the following question: what is the acid test for who is and who is not English or British? Simple as it sounds, in practice this has been a difficult question to answer in light of the significant social changes that have taken place in British society over the past few decades. There is no longer, if there ever was, any certainty about the meaning of Englishness and Britishness, since in many ways the boundaries of national identity have been subject to constant change and political manipulation (Samuel, 1989b; Colley, 1992; Dodd, 1995). What we are seeing at present, however, is a profound debate on the definition of the nation and its boundaries in the context of internal processes of social change and external patterns of political transformation.

According to Talal Asad (1990b, 1993), modern nation states offer minorities two basic options: complete assimilation or despised difference and exclusion. Asad's argument may seem extreme as in practice minority groups occupy various positions in between, but it is reflective of the ongoing argument about who belongs and who does not (Dodd, 1995; Alibhai-Brown, 1999, 2000). More importantly it reflects the deep uncertainty felt by many countries, including our own, about the types of strategy and policy they should adopt to deal with the position of racial, ethnic and cultural minorities within their boundaries. Even Britain, which first declared itself multicultural in the mid 1960s, still faces the dilemma of what kind of multicultural society it should become.

What is interesting is that widely publicised cases were only the tip of the iceberg. Alluding to popular youth cultures and other contemporary forms of cultural expression a number of writers have argued that during the 1990s there was a flowering of 'new ethnicities' that challenged the boundaries of national identity. Perhaps the most important symbol of this change was the assertion that it was possible to be both black and British (Mercer, 1990, 1994; Hall, 1991a; Alexander, 1996). In addition a large number of feminist writers began to explore the changing dynamics of culture, race and identity in determining the position of both white and ethnic minority women in British society (Parmar, 1990; Brah, 1992; Ware, 1992).

Against this background the definition of Britishness or Englishness became a matter of political controversy. The furore caused by Nicholas Ridley's remarks in July 1990 about the threat posed to Britain by the 'German nation' highlighted the increasing importance of national identity in political discourses (*Spectator*, 14 July 1990). In a sense Ridley was expressing the much broader concern within the Thatcher administration and the Conservative Party about the implications of (a) the progress towards political and economic unity in the European Union, and (b) the unification of Germany.

For example, in a speech in Bruges in September 1988 Margaret Thatcher had warned of the danger of diluting Britain's national identity under the rubric of a wider European identity. She had argued that although Britain's future was as part of Europe it was important to protect the uniqueness of its national culture. She had also pointed to the danger of

Europe falling under 'the dominance of a single power' (Thatcher, 1988: 2). A few months before Ridley made his remarks Thatcher had organised a meeting of experts to discuss the implications of German reunification for Britain and other societies. The minutes of this meeting were subsequently published and sparked a controversy over the language used to describe the German nation and the dangers that might result from reunification (*Independent on Sunday*, 15 July 1990).

Another clear example of the preoccupation with national identity was Norman Tebbit's suggestion in April 1990 that a 'cricket test' be used as a benchmark to measure migrants' loyalty to Britain. According to Tebbit many migrants were disloyal to Britain because they failed to support the English cricket team in matches against their countries of origin (*Daily Express*, 21 April 1990). Despite ferocious criticism of his remarks, Tebbit chose to stick to his words and has subsequently expressed similar views.

Such controversies highlighted the fact that ideas about race and nationhood were as much to do with the 'others' in Europe as with those outside. Ridley's comments and the wide-ranging debate surrounding them can be seen as symbolic of the uncertainty of the future of Britishness and Englishness in a period of global change in economic and political power relations. This uncertainty was by no means new and went back to the decline of Britain's imperial role and economic power over the preceding century (Rich, 1986; Goulbourne, 1991).

Multiculturalism, identity and the nation

One of the trends that became clear during the 1980s and 1990s was the attempt to reinvent a British national identity in line with its historical image as an 'island race'. The media and politicians continually used this image to construct a picture of national identity in line with myths of origin and cultural uniqueness.

A number of events highlighted the ways in which nationhood connected with the politics of race and racism in Britain. The death of the nation state was proclaimed in public discourse simultaneously with the recirculation of a national image that was increasingly chauvinistic, defensive and racially exclusive. New and not so new expressions of national identity dominated the public imagination as it grappled with the changes occurring in the world geopolitical order.

The furore over Salman Rushdie's *The Satanic Verses* (1989) in the late 1980s and early 1990s can be seen as a significant turning point in popular and policy debates on the changing boundaries of national and ethnoreligious identities in societies such as Britain. The first notable public response in Britain was a staged book burning in Bradford in January 1989. This was followed by protests in Bradford and other major cities and towns. Demonstrations against the book also took place in Pakistan and other Islamic countries, culminating in Ayatollah Khomeini's *fatwa* on Rushdie in February 1989. Such events politicised the debate on *The Satanic Verses* and influenced popular and elite discussions on the future of minority communities in British society.

The Rushdie affair reinforced public interest in fundamentalism among sections of the Muslim community in various localities and gave new life to debates on cultural differences and the process of integration and assimilation (Bhatt, 1997). The impact of the Rushdie affair on both the local and national politics of race was evident throughout the 1990s, particularly in respect of shaping public discussions on such issues as multiculturalism and antiracism (Asad, 1990b; Ruthven, 1990; Samad, 1992). This could be seen at two broad levels:

- At the national level, where the Rushdie affair gave new impetus to debates on issues such as immigration, integration and public order.
- At the level of local politics in terms of both formal and informal political processes, with local Muslim political activists adopting a high profile in areas such as Bradford, Leicester, Birmingham and elsewhere (Akhtar, 1989; Appignanesi and Maitland, 1989).

In the aftermath of the affair local political discussions on race and ethnicity had to take on board a range of issues to do with religious identity, which had not been a priority in the policies of local authorities during the 1980s. Research in Birmingham highlighted the complex ways in which the affair had influenced broader debates on race and ethnicity in the local political context (Back and Solomos, 1992b; Solomos and Back, 1995).

Political mobilisations over *The Satanic Verses* also brought to the fore organisations such as the Bradford Council of Mosques and other Muslim communal and religious organisations. Such bodies consciously mobilised on the basis of representing particular religious communities, and rejected the idea of organising within the limits of traditional party politics. In Bradford the Council of Mosques symbolised attempts to use the Rushdie affair as a means of mobilising Muslims as a specific political constituency.

The affair also led to reappraisal of the role of gender in the politics of race and ethnicity (Sahgal and Yuval-Davis, 1992). A number of black and Asian feminist organisations and other groups questioned the idea that there was a united Muslim response to the Rushdie affair, regardless of gender and politics. In particular groups such as Women Against Fundamentalism sought to support Rushdie while at the same time challenging the stereotyping of Asian and Muslim women.

The hostile media coverage of the political mobilisations over *The Satanic Verses* served to reinforce the view that minorities who did not share the dominant values of British society posed a threat to social stability and cohesion (Asad, 1990b). Some commentators argued that as a result of the affair more attention should be given to the divergent political paths adopted by sections of the black and Asian communities. The affair also gave added impetus to debates on the multiple cultural and political identities that were included in the broad categories of 'black' and 'ethnic minority' (Hall, 1991a; Modood, 1992; Bhatt, 1997).

In his response to the events John Patten, minister of state at the Home Office, argued that:

> The last few months have been difficult ones for British Muslims. The issue of race relations has been thrown into sharp relief and all of us have had to think deeply about our objectives and priorities; about what it means to be British, and particularly what it means to be a British Muslim (*The Times*, 5 July 1989).

Patten then went on to argue that it was important to link the rights of Muslims to their responsibilities to British society:

> [If Muslims] are to make the most of their lives and opportunities as British citizens, then they must have a clear understanding of the British democratic processes, of its laws, the system of government and the history that lies behind them, and indeed of their own rights and responsibilities (ibid.).

Pronouncements along the same lines were common in many media discussions of and political debates on the affair during 1989 and the early 1990s. These highlighted the racialisation of political debates in general and the tension between ideas about race and ideas about national belonging. They also demonstrated the interplay of nation, culture and xenophobia in shaping ideas about Britishness.

Some media responses focused specifically on the implications for race relations in the future. The *Daily Telegraph*, for example, alleged in an editorial headed 'Races Apart' that the events that followed the publication of *The Satanic Verses* highlighted the 'difficulty of integrating Moslem communities into British life'. It went on: 'In the wake of *The Satanic Verses*, there must be increased pessimism about how far different communities in our nation can ever be integrated, or want to be' (*Daily Telegraph*, 17 May 1989).

Statements such as this show how the Rushdie affair helped to push back onto the agenda questions about the integration of minority communities and aided the cause of those who questioned the viability of an ethnically plural society. They also gave added impetus to the argument that the development of ethnic pluralism would interfere with the social and political cohesion of British society.

Partly in response to media attacks on fundamentalism, supporters of the political stance taken by some radical Muslim groups defended an absolutist definition of what a Muslim was and criticised opponents as defenders of Western liberalism and secularism (Akhtar, 1989). Other writers argued that the politicisation of Islam was the result of a process that had started long before the publication of *The Satanic Verses*. They pointed to the long history of racism, discrimination and exclusion and cited this as one of the reasons for the emergence of radical Islamic groups (Modood, 1992; Commission on British Muslims and Islamophobia, 1997).

The affair also illustrated the limitations of some left-wing conceptions of multiculturalism and antiracism. Some on the left, including the black and Asian MPs Bernie Grant and Keith Vaz, openly supported the criticisms of Rushdie and argued that the blasphemy laws should be extended to cover Islam. They justified their stand by saying that they were supporting the wishes of the Muslim community and antiracist activists in general, thus portraying the Muslim protests against Rushdie as progressive and antiracist.

Yet it was also clear that many on the left found it impossible to sympathise with the arguments of the radical Islamic groups. This was partly to do with the issues of free speech and basic civil rights, but it was also because many on the left mistrusted the political values and objectives of these groups (Bhatt, 1997). The impact of the events surrounding the Rushdie affair continued to be felt both locally and nationally in the decade that followed. In this sense the Rushdie affair can be seen as the forerunner of a series of controversies that helped to shape ideas about race and ethnic relations to the present time.

The boundaries of national identity

The events sparked by the Gulf War in 1990–1, and more recently the war in Afghanistan in 2001, provided a stark reminder, if any were needed, of how the question of national identity had become inextricably linked to the politics of race. Perhaps the main social impact of the Gulf War, especially when taken together with the Rushdie affair, was to enhance the idea that there was some kind of unitary Muslim community in Britain that could pose a threat to national identity.

An interesting example of the ways in which these tensions were experienced locally emerged during the course of a research project on ethnic minority political mobilisation that I was engaged in during the time of the Gulf War. As it involved fieldwork in Birmingham on the main political groupings in the city, particularly the Labour and Conservative Parties, we were able to observe at close hand the ramifications of the Gulf War on local as well as national political agendas (for a full discussion of this research see Solomos and Back, 1995). With the declaration of war the Labour-run council decided to fly the United Nations flag above Council House as a gesture of solidarity with the troops fighting in the Gulf. This displeased many Conservative members, who protested by producing 17 Union flags during the course of a council meeting. A motion was put forward that the United Nations flag be replaced with the Union flag. As one Conservative councillor put it:

> It should be the right of the city to fly our flag, it is our flag, we are all British. ... I believe it is time to take it back from the National Front. It belongs to all of us whether we belong to Labour, Liberal Democrat or Conservative parties. ... I don't understand why people are asking us not to fly our flag. [He then mentioned the sense of embarrassment he had felt about the incident when travelling around the country.] This I understand from the press has not just happened in this City Council. If people are offended by us flying our flag then I ask why? [Shouting from the Labour benches]: Who? I don't see what the problem is with flying the flag. I have been told that it may cause problems within the immigrant population as they used to be called ... [shouts from the Labour benches]. I'll withdraw that ... there are forces from 28 nations in the Gulf ... [shouts from Labour benches]. I therefore ask the Labour members opposite as to why our flag isn't being flown.

The most important symbol in this speech was 'our flag', which was closely associated with a commitment to the nation. This was rhetorically directed towards those who were assumed to have divided loyalties – that is, minority people in general – but in the context of the council chamber it was specifically aimed at Asian councillors, particularly those who were Muslim. The atmosphere in the chamber was intense and it seemed to trigger defensive declarations of commitment to Britain by Muslim councillors.

Later in the meeting the Conservative group put forward a motion to convey the goodwill of the people of Birmingham to the troops fighting in the Gulf. In the debate that followed a Muslim councillor spoke, and in the content of his speech we can see resistance to the war alongside passionate commitment to Britain. He started by stating that he was against the war as he saw it as 'a war for oil'. He then said that although he had been born in Pakistan:

> I am British and a Brummie and I am very proud to be British and a Brummie. I am also a Muslim. I believe that giving my life for England is the greatest thing that anyone can do. If I had a thousand lives I should die a thousand times for Britain. [A prominent white Labour councillor calls out 'Good man'.] But this is an unjust war – it is a war for a new world order. But it is not just me who is saying this.

He then digressed to say that America had invaded and illegally occupied a number of small countries, and he asked what the United Nations was doing about the Kashmiri people's struggle for freedom. Returning to the subject of the Gulf War he said:

> I started to pray for peace and harmony the moment I saw mothers and wives waving to their children as the forces were leaving for the Gulf. I started to pray. I hope and pray that common sense will prevail. Why can't politicians use their brains rather than their guns and sorties. It was Gandhi who said when someone asked him 'what did he think of western civilization?' He said 'it will be a good idea' [Labour members laugh]. I believe in the power of prayer. I pray for peace, justice and harmony.

Eventually the Labour group decided to send a message of goodwill to the troops and to fly the Union flag above a building adjacent to Council House until a second flagpole was erected.

Events such as this and, in a wider context, some media coverage of the Gulf War focused specifically on the question of which side the Muslims in Britain were on. More broadly, they raised important questions about the changing dynamics of race, culture and ethnicity in British society (Joly, 1995). There was also a renewed interest in the question of religious and cultural identity among black and ethnic minority communities.

Nationality and immigration

Other developments in political discourses on race, immigration and national identity highlight the complex ways in which these issues were being debated. The debates on immigration and refugee policies and Norman Tebbit's 'cricket test' are interesting examples of this, although the issues they raised were somewhat different from those raised by the Rushdie affair and the Gulf War. More recently the renewed preoccupation with refugees, asylum seekers and multiculturalism has shown that uncertainty and confusion still hang over the question of British national identity.

In the 1990s questions about immigration focused specifically on two issues. The first concerned immigration from the ex-colonies, particularly Hong Kong in the period leading up to the handover of the colony to China, when the issue was widely discussed in the media and in parliament (*Hansard*, 19 April 1990). The second was the influx of refugees and asylum seekers, which was also an important topic of public concern in other European countries (Wrench and Solomos, 1993; Joppke, 1998). As we have seen, both of these issues continued to be important elements of political discussions on race and racism throughout the 1990s and into the 2000s.

These debates evoked images from earlier discourses on immigration, particularly when populist Conservative politicians such as Norman Tebbit used this issue to emphasise their commitment to the values and interests of the white British majority. Both Conservative and Labour politicians saw the electoral value of taking a hard or at least an ambiguous line on immigration, but it is clear that the debate on immigration was as much about perceived dangers to British national identity as it was about the potential number of immigrants.

For example Norman Tebbit went as far as to claim that 'most people in Britain did not want to live in a multicultural, multiracial society, but it has been foisted on them' (*Evening Standard*, 21 December 1989). He also reiterated Thatcher's declaration in 1978 that the British people were fearful of being swamped by immigrants with different cultures and values. During the parliamentary debates on immigration from Hong Kong the Labour Party was keen to show that it too had a tough policy stance on immigration, no doubt with an eye to allaying fears that it would allow increased immigration if it were elected.

During the 1990s the issue of immigration became inextricably linked to the perceived impact of European integration on British national identity (Asad, 1990a; Goulbourne, 1998), which was an ongoing theme in the popular media and in parliamentary and local politics. For example, in 1990 Norman Tebbit insisted:

> In recent years our sense of insularity and nationality has been bruised by large waves of immigrants resistant to absorption, some defiantly claiming a right to superimpose their culture, even their law, upon the host community. All this in the era when the great Euro legal and cultural magimixer of Brussels is trying to blend us into a Continental culture,

> abusing our linguistic heritage with crude Eurospeak such as pigmeat and sheepmeat in place of the pork, lamb and mutton which had adorned our table talk for centuries past. Sterling – not just a currency but an adjective of excellent worth, having been debauched, devalued and even deformed into the politicians' money, 'Green Pounds' – looks set to be masticated by EMUs, ERMs and ECUs before becoming more fodder for that monetary successor of the Panzer, the Deutsches Bundesbank (*The Field*, May 1990: 81).

Views such as these may have represented only one segment of political opinion in Britain, but their role in amplifying broader concerns about threats to the national character cannot easily be dismissed. Indeed from the early 1990s such sentiments gained wider currency in the context of public concern about asylum seekers.

Tebbit returned to the question of multiculturalism after the 1997 general election, when he warned that multiculturalism was likely to lead to the entrenchment of new forms of ethnic identity:

> Multiculturalism is a divisive force. One cannot uphold two sets of ethics or be loyal to two nations, any more than a man can have two masters. It perpetuates ethnic divisions because nationality is in the long-term more about culture than ethnics. Youngsters of all races born here should be taught that British history is their history, or they will forever be foreigners holding British passports and this kingdom will become a Yugoslavia (*Guardian*, 8 October 1997).

Such sentiments were rejected by Conservative Party leader William Hague, who attempted to portray Tebbit and his associates as 'dinosaurs' whose views were out of tune with modern Conservatism. Whatever the merits of this depiction, the ongoing debates within the Conservative Party, and more recently New Labour, about race and multiculturalism reflect a deep sense of uncertainty about cultural and religious differences in British society.

New ethnicities, culture and identity

From the mid 1990s it became evident that concern about national identity was not restricted to the Conservative Party and neofascist political movements, as the Labour Party also became entangled in the debate on the changing meaning of Britishness and Englishness in the current environment. Under Tony Blair's leadership New Labour was particularly concerned to portray itself as a party that did not shy away from expressions of love for its country, albeit accompanied by acceptance that Britain was a multicultural society.

It therefore came as no surprise when, after its victory in the 1997 general election, it attempted to define a new sense of patriotism and pride in national symbols such as the flag. At the same time, however, it was alert to the need to link such imagery to the increasingly multicultural environment that had developed over the past few decades. In the period leading up to the 2001 general election there was a series of attempts by New Labour to link aspects of multiculturalism to the subject of national identity. An interesting, if idiosyncratic attempt to flesh out such a perspective was made by Robin Cook, then foreign secretary: 'Chicken tikka masala is now Britain's true national dish, not only because it is the most popular, but because it is a perfect illustration of the way Britain absorbs and adapts external influences (*Evening Standard*, 19 April 2001). While many commentators took this seriously and pondered whether chicken tikka masala had indeed replaced fish and chips as the national dish, Cook's statement is best seen as an expression of New Labour's concern to popularise the idea that the British national identity was capable of assimilating other cultural practices and identities.

In the aftermath of the race riots of 2001 and the terrorist attacks on the US on 11 September 2001 there was a noticeable shift in political language on immigration and race relations. The new home secretary, David Blunkett, continued to argue in favour of multiculturalism combined with tough controls on immigration, but at the same time he raised the idea of migrants and refugees being given a 'British test' in order to assess whether they were suited to become part of the social and cultural fabric of Britain. Ignoring the irony of the link between the 'cricket test' and the 'British test', Blunkett forcefully argued that it was necessary to combine a strong sense of identity with knowledge of the English language and cultural norms if social cohesion was to be maintained (*Guardian*, 18 February 2002).

Since Blunkett's interventions it has become evident that there is a broad sense of unease about the boundaries of multiculturalism. One expression of this was the warning given by Matthew Taylor of the Institute for Public Policy Research that policies relating to multiculturalism were in fact constructing a kind of 'consenting apartheid'. Taylor's argument was buttressed by references to areas of the country where there was little contact between the minority and majority communities (*Guardian*, 4 December 2001). Since the race riots in Oldham, Burnley and Bradford in 2001 warnings such as these have become a recurrent theme in political debates, and it is likely that they will influence the government's thinking on immigration and race relations policies.

Summary and conclusion

This chapter has shown that since the early 1990s there has been a deep questioning of what it is to be British, and therefore what it means to be a minority in racial, ethnic or religious terms. Not only has there been increased debate on the politics of identity, but a number of events have emphasised the tensions that exist in constructed identities such as 'black', 'Muslim' and 'Asian' (Modood *et al.*, 1994). It is likely that such tensions will be heightened in the future, particularly when seen in terms of the broader debate on the position of Britain in the European Union.

There has also been an interesting coalescence of left and right on such issues as separate ethnicities and essential cultural difference. Concern with the politics of identity can be found among both radicals and reactionaries (Keith and Pile, 1993; Appiah and Gutmann, 1996; Bhatt, 1997). The left-wing preoccupation with the politics of identity seems to be partly a result of the decline of the labour movement and the rise of new social movements, while the preoccupation of those on the right stems from a fear that Britishness or Englishness is being diluted by multiculturalism.

Moreover it is becoming increasingly clear that the search for cultural, religious or ethnoracial identity is taking on new and complex forms in Britain and other European countries. In this uncertain environment there is a need for a critical analysis of the language of race and nation and the part it plays in shaping our notions of who belongs or does not belong. It is likely that we shall have to rethink our conceptual frameworks for these issues and develop a grounded understanding of what kinds of political identities are likely to influence our understanding of racial and ethnic differences in contemporary societies.

11 Race, Class and Social Change

In the three preceding chapters we have explored the changing dynamics of political mobilisation and identity politics based on claims about race and ethnicity. In this and the concluding chapter we shift our attention to a related set of issues, namely social changes and their likely impact on both the current situation and the future of race and racism in British society. This has been the subject of much debate and reflective comment in the popular media, as well as a focus of scholarly research (Peach, 1996; Coleman and Salt, 1996; Ratcliffe, 1996; Modood *et al.*, 1997). It has also become an area of concern for local and national policy makers as they look at the kinds of policy agenda needed to address the requirements of minority communities that have become increasingly diverse in terms of class and social position. It is perhaps because of this diversity that we are now beginning to see more debate on the patterns of racial inequality that are likely to emerge in the coming years.

It is to these issues that we turn in this chapter. Up to this point the analysis has concentrated on two core issues: how various theoretical paradigms have attempted to account for the impact of immigration and racialised politics in contemporary Britain; and the key arenas in which ideas about race and the position of minorities in British society have been mobilised. Both of these themes are closely related to a somewhat broader question, namely the links between racism and social inequalities that have been characterised as either racial in origin or racial in character (Karn, 1997; Mason, 2000). In developing the account of these issues, previous chapters have inevitably touched the ways in which racial ideologies and practices have helped to structure social and political relations in post-1945 Britain, and have in turn been shaped by specific discourses on immigration and race relations. Indeed it is clear that much of the sociological literature on race and racism has been concerned with this question. At the same time the changing morphology of racial inequality has been a core preoccupation in public policy debates on racism. This is evidenced by the panoply of policies and legislative measures on racial inequality.

Race, racism and social change

Perhaps no other feature of contemporary racial and ethnic relations in Britain has attracted as much attention in recent years as the intersection of race, class and gender relations. Part of the reason for this can be traced back to a concern among some commentators that while attention had been focused on issues of culture and identity there had been relatively little empirical research on the changing social relations within black and ethnic minority communities (Miles, 1993; Williams, 1995). Since then a wealth of empirical research has pointed not only to the persistence of racial inequalities more generally, but also to the emergence of patterns of social differentiation within and between minority communities (Mason, 2000; Cabinet Office, 2001).

It is precisely because of this developing body of work that there has been much more analytical and policy discussion about the social relations that have emerged during the past half century or so of immigration and settlement, as well as a wide-ranging conceptual debate on the intersection of race and class (Mac an Ghaill, 1999; Virdee, 2000) and of race, class and gender (Mama, 1989, 1992; Bhavnani and Phoenix, 1994; Mirza, 1997; Sudbury, 1998; Bhavnani, 2001). In addition a number of empirical studies have provided evidence of important changes in the social structure of racial minorities (Owen and Green, 1992; Jones, 1993; Owen 1994a, b; Modood *et al*., 1997).

The question of the impact that racism has on social relations has preoccupied many sociologists working within a variety of theoretical paradigms. The focus of much empirical research on contemporary race relations has been on specific aspects of inequality, such as in housing or employment, or on the development and impact of antidiscrimination measures. Certainly the bulk of research in Britain, the US and other advanced industrial societies has been on the changing face of racialised inequalities (Wilson, 1996; Winant, 2001). In Britain, for example, studies have been conducted on virtually all aspects of racial inequality both nationally and locally. These are supplemented by studies that explore the complex ways in which various migrant communities experience inequality and disadvantage in their daily lives (Small, 1994; Parekh, 2000b; Bhattacharyya *et al*., 2002).

In relation to all these areas there is an obvious need for greater conceptual clarity and sustained empirical research on the role of social differentiation and modes of incorporation within minority communities. There are also a number of older questions that need to be addressed more fully. For example, how does one account for the emergence and persistence of racialised inequalities in employment, housing, social welfare and education, as well as evident inequalities in other areas? What processes help to explain the structuring of inequalities along racial lines? What can liberal democratic societies do to ensure that racialised inequalities do not lead to the social and economic exclusion of minorities? These questions have been raised in one way or another by researchers and politicians for at least three decades, yet we do not seem to have moved much closer to resolving them.

The highly politicised nature of debates on the origins of and remedies for racial inequality is partly the result of the fact that the interrelationship between racism and social inequality is a deeply controversial question and has given rise to quite divergent theoretical and political perspectives over the years. Part of the problem is that there is very little agreement on how to conceptualise the interrelationship between racism and specific sets of racialised social relations. While some writers have used the notion of racism in a very broad social and political sense to cover sets of ideas and institutional practices, this approach is by no means universally accepted. Indeed some writers have criticised the way in which the general category of racism and the more specific notion of institutionalised racism have been used to describe forms of social relations and types of inequalities. Yet others have argued that racism should be defined as essentially an ideological phenomenon. Over the past decade the lack of a commonly accepted notion about what racism is has become even more apparent, particularly in the wake of the controversy on the application of neo-Marxist and post-modernist perspectives to the study of race and racism.

Such debates and disagreements signal real difficulties with the ways in which the links between racist theories and practices have been conceptualised. For example, terms such as institutional racism have been used as catch-all phrases to describe quite diverse and complex patterns of exclusion. At the same time such notions tend to be underpinned by instrumentalist ideas about the relationship between racist ideas and specific types of inequality in a very undifferentiated sense. Such problems do not mean that we should ignore the part played by racism in structuring social relations. Rather they point to the need for a more open and critical framework for analysing such processes.

Racism and racial discrimination

There are divergent perspectives on the definition of racism and racial discrimination. Some argue that racism can best be perceived as sets of ideological values that propound either biological or cultural explanations of racial difference. From this perspective racial discrimination may or may not be the outcome of racist ideologies. Michael Banton (1992) articulates this clearly when he criticises the tendency to treat racism and racial discrimination as interchangeable notions. For Banton and others there is a clear danger that racism will become a catch-all term for quite disparate social, political and economic practices. A similar point has been made by Miles (1989), who warns of the dangers of 'conceptual inflation' in relation to the usage of the term in the social sciences.

Yet it is clear that in much contemporary political discourse and research the concepts of racism and racial discrimination have been merged to such an extent that in practice they have come to mean almost the same thing. This is perhaps not surprising as links between racist ideologies and social and economic relations have existed in many societies during the past two centuries. But it is also clear that the relationship between racist ideas and specific practices is by no means simple, and from a historical perspective it is obvious that racism as an exclusionary practice can take various forms. It is therefore important for a distinction to be maintained between the terms racism and racial discrimination. As David Goldberg cogently argues:

> Racism excludes racially defined others, or promotes, or secures, or sustains such exclusion. Often racist exclusions will be undertaken or expressed for their own sakes, for the recognition of the putatively inherent value the expressions are claimed to represent. In the case where persons insist that they are acting for the sake of racist principles, it is conceivable that exploitative acts will be a means of sustaining racist principles (Goldberg, 1993: 101).

It follows from this that the relationship between racism and forms of exploitation has to be demonstrated and cannot be assumed *a priori*. In other words the processes that structure the relationship between racism and social exclusion have to be seen in the context of specific historical circumstances. As we have seen in previous chapters, one of the key lessons to be learnt from analyses of the changing forms of racial politics over the past half century is that it is quite impossible to conceptualise racism as a monolithic phenomenon that remains unchanged by historical and cultural circumstances. Indeed one can go further and say that the force of historical research points clearly in the opposite direction.

A wealth of historical research has illustrated how racism has interacted with specific social and political processes to produce racialised forms of inequality in a wide variety of societies. In the British context, a broad range of empirical studies have examined how racist ideologies have helped to create deeply entrenched racial inequalities in employment, housing, welfare provision and related areas. Many of the early studies were concerned with the ways in which racial discrimination affected the social and economic position of immigrants in localities such as London and Birmingham. A classic example is Rex and Moore's study of race, social change and conflict during the 1960s in Birmingham. These authors conducted a sociological analysis of the social and housing conditions of immigrants in the Sparkbrook area of the city, and their book is still an influential text for those interested in the dynamics of racial discrimination and exclusion in urban environments. They provide a particularly sharp analysis of the process of exclusion in council house allocation and point to the existence of a housing class system. For example, Pakistani landlords occupied a 'pariah position' and were in a different housing class from those who lodged with them, who were predominantly West Indian (Rex and Moore, 1967: 165). Running alongside this was the development of 'immigrant colonies' in response to the 'anomie' and 'personal demoralisation' to which migrants were subjected in urban environments (ibid.: 277). In this context community and immigrant organisation took on political meanings. Rex and Moore refer in particular to the political work that took place in organisations within immigrant colonies and to the development of organisations to act for particular housing class interests.

In more recent years a number of community studies and surveys have explored the changing contours of racialised discrimination and inequality at both the local and the national level. Much of this research has been concerned with racial discrimination against migrants and their descendants in employment, housing and education, and with the ways in which certain economic, social, racial and political relations have helped to shape minority communities in cities such as London, Birmingham, Leicester, Bradford and elsewhere (Small, 1991a, 1994; Rex, 1991; Cohen, 1993; Keith, 1993; Solomos and Back, 1995).

Whether in conceptual debates on the sociology of racial relations or more policy oriented research on racial inequality the main question remains the same: what role does race play in shaping key facets of social relations in contemporary societies? In Britain studies on this subject have taken a variety of forms, ranging from quantitative overviews of racial inequality in British society as a whole to qualitative accounts of the changing experience of black and ethnic minorities or certain sections of these groups. It has become evident that in key areas of social policy, including health and community care, complex patterns of racialisation and exclusion have emerged that shape everyday social relations (Ahmad, 1993; Ahmad and Atkin, 1996; Berthoud, 1997; Nazroo, 1997; Beishon *et al.*, 1998).

Similarly in the US, research by historians and sociologists has focused on the relationship between racial ideology and structured segregation and exclusion, particularly in respect of African-Americans. These studies have considered the general historical context of the socioeconomic exclusion of African-Americans, and an increasing number have looked at the part played by the civil rights movement and antidiscrimination legislation in transforming their position in American society. These studies have shown that the question of racial inequality has become heavily politicised and is likely to become even more so in the future. This is partly because there has been a noticeable backlash against the affirmative action programmes and civil rights initiatives introduced during the mid 1960s, leading to heated debates between liberals and neoconservatives about the utility of public policies in this field. We shall discuss this issue later in the chapter, but it has been mentioned here to highlight the centrality of racial inequality to the sociology of race relations.

At a broader level the development and persistence of racialised inequalities is a feature of many advanced industrial societies. For example, there is growing recognition in a number of West European countries that migrant workers and their families suffer from a variety of exclusionary practices in employment and housing. More broadly, processes of racial and ethnic discrimination are seen as instrumental in the racialisation of poverty. It is therefore not surprising that considerable intellectual energy and political debate has been directed at this question in recent years.

Race, class and social exclusion

This leads us to questions about the workings of exclusionary practices and racialised inequalities. How should we define and analyse the workings of specific types of racial inequality? How should the interrelationship between racism, social relations and politics be conceptualised? What processes help to structure contemporary racial inequalities and patterns of discrimination? All these questions point to important political dilemmas and it would be wrong to pretend that there is agreement on what racial inequality is and how it can be explained and dealt with. In this sense the experience of the past three decades has shown that racial inequality remains a contested concept, both in political and policy debate and in academic research.

This makes it all the more important to remember that when we talk of racial inequality and racial discrimination we are not referring to static and unchanging phenomena, and that numerous and complex social, economic and political processes are at work. Patterns of direct and indirect racial discrimination are only part of the story and it is essential to recognise that class, gender and spatial processes also shape the ways in which racialised inequalities are formed and reproduced over time (Williams, 1995). As we saw above in relation to the situation in the United States and Britain, wide social and economic processes can interact with racial processes to produce entrenched forms of racial inequality that are not amenable to race-specific policies as such.

It is interesting to note in this regard that as well as providing statistical evidence on patterns of inequality, researchers have provided insights – through qualitative research – into the detail and processes of hidden discrimination and the economic and political pressures that lie behind racist judgements and acts. Some commentators have emphasised the need for more of this type of investigation. As Banton argues, we also need to understand racial inequality in terms of the levels at which decisions are taken that consciously or otherwise, either increase or reduce inequality:

> It is necessary to understand the workings of social institutions, such as those which socialise children, which channel job seeking and employee selection so that particular sorts of people end up in particular jobs (Banton, 1992: 84).

Such detailed investigations have highlighted the complex processes that have helped to shape racialised inequalities in both the institutional and the everyday context.

Interesting examples of the interactions between historical and contemporary forms of racial exclusion and segregation have been provided by the ongoing debate in the US about the changing patterns of ghettoisation and social exclusion. A challenging account of such transformations can be found in Loic Wacquant's study of new forms of spatial segregation in American cities. Referring to what he calls the 'new urban colour line', he points out that after the gains made by the black middle class from the 1960s onwards, 'the economic, social and cultural distance between inner-city minorities and the rest of society has reached levels that are unprecedented in modern American history as well as unknown in other advanced societies' (Wacquant, 1994: 233). At the same time, however, he rejects the argument that today's urban ghettos are merely a continuation of the 'same old story' of the exclusion of African-Americans from mainstream American society. He points to two substantive differences between the situation in the 1950s and the 1990s:

- *first*, the inner city urban ghettos of the 1990s have become spatially split from the working class and middle class suburbs that surround them;
- *second*, these inner city areas are experiencing accelerating physical degradation, economic exclusion and increasing levels of physical violence (ibid.: 237–8).

This collapse of the social and economic institutions in inner city localities and the increasing separation between those living in these areas and the rest of American society has been commented on by other researchers who have studied developments since the reforms of the 1960s. But Wacquant's account of what he terms the 'hyperghettos' of the 1990s serves to highlight the complex web of economic, racial and political processes that have caused the marginalisation and exclusion of the poorest American blacks at a time when political institutions have supposedly committed themselves to tackling the root causes of racial inequality and discrimination.

The situation in the US is to some extent unique among the advanced industrial societies. But this is not to say that some of the trends that have emerged so markedly in the US since the 1980s are not present in other societies. Take, for example, the changing job patterns among black and Asian workers in Britain since the 1950s. In the 1950s and 1960s migrants were primarily recruited to work in sectors that were experiencing labour shortages, such as foundries in the Midlands, textile mills in the North, transport industries in major cities, and the health service. In common with migrant workers across Europe, these workers experienced a high degree of exploitation, discrimination and marginalisation in their economic and social lives. Despite the need for their labour, their presence aroused widespread hostility at all levels, from trade union branches to the government level. Employers recruited immigrants only when there were no white workers to fill the jobs, and white workers, through their unions, often came to an agreement with their employers about the sorts of work that immigrants should be offered (Duffield, 1988). At that time a preference for white workers was perceived as quite natural and legitimate, while immigrant workers were seen as 'an inferior but necessary labour supply' (Brown, 1992: 48).

Over the years these workers remained in a restricted range of occupational areas, being overrepresented in low-paid and insecure jobs and working antisocial hours in unhealthy or dangerous environments. Although by the 1970s African-Caribbean and Asian people had access to a broader range of occupations, these were still jobs that were 'deemed fit' for ethnic minority workers rather than white workers (ibid.: 52). In 1984 the Policy Studies Institute published a major survey on the state of racial inequality in Britain, covering housing, education and employment. It was shown that black and Asian workers were still generally employed below their qualification and skill level, earned less than white workers in comparable jobs, and were still concentrated in the same industries as 25 years earlier (Brown, 1984).

On top of this, black and ethnic minority workers had a higher unemployment rate, a rate that was increasing faster than that of the white population. Young ethnic minority people were particularly badly hit. As a 1986 statistical review reported:

> While employment prospects are discouraging for all young people, the evidence ... shows that black youth unemployment has reached astronomical proportions in some areas. The differential unemployment rates between blacks and whites are in fact generally greater for this age group than for any other. When account is taken of the fact that black people are far more likely to go into further education than whites, we can see that young black people in the 1980s are facing a desperate situation (Newnham, 1986: 17).

In the context of rapid economic restructuring in the industrial sectors in which black and ethnic minority workers were concentrated from the 1950s to the 1970s, these trends were likely to create further problems and pressures over the following years.

One feature of the past two decades has been growing social differentiation within minority communities. One indication of this is provided by the growth of self-employment among some South Asian groups and smaller ethnic groups such as the Chinese (Metcalf *et al.*, 1998).

A recurring theme in the surveys carried out each decade by the Policy Studies Institute is the relative concentration of certain ethnic minority workers in lower-level, poorly paid jobs compared with the white labour force. Even after effect of qualifications is taken into account, African-Caribbean and South Asian women tend to occupy substantially lower job levels than whites. However in general African-Asian, Indian and Chinese male employees have similar or better job levels than whites. What is of interest in this top category is that most of these employees are twice as likely as white men to be in professional jobs whereas more white men are employed as managers by large establishments. It therefore seems that ethnic minority men have penetrated certain professions but are still relatively excluded from senior management positions in large organisations.

White workers are generally less prone to unemployment than ethnic minorities but the overall figures hide marked differences among the various ethnic minority groups, particularly in the case of South Asians. Whilst African-Asians and Indians have similar unemployment rates to whites, Bangladeshis and Pakistanis have higher rates than any other group. African-Caribbeans' rates are higher than those of Indians and African-Asians but lower than those of Pakistanis and Bangladeshis. The differences are magnified amongst those aged 16–24. Young Pakistanis have a particularly high unemployment rate. This phenomenon is partly due to the fact that workers in lower job levels are more vulnerable to unemployment, but even among non-manual groups Pakistanis have a higher rate.

Thus controlling for job levels explains some but not all the variations in employment between ethnic groups. When comparisons are made within job levels, the differences between white and ethnic minority groups as a whole are reduced, but the differences between specific minorities become more striking. This might suggest that the circumstances of ethnic minorities are beginning to diverge.

There is a substantial body of evidence to show that people of African-Caribbean and South Asian origin are much more likely to be in education after the minimum school leaving age than are white people. Amongst South Asians, males are generally more likely to be in full-time education after 16 than are females. The reverse is true of whites and African-Caribbeans.

The picture emerging from research in both Britain and the US is that there has been a hardening of racial and ethnic cleavages among lower class groups. This is borne out by evidence of racial disadvantage in major urban conurbations and by what some have defined as the 'racialisation of poverty'. But at the same time there has been a noticeable growth of the black professional middle class and of ethnic minority small businesses, with an impact at all levels of society (Farley and Allen, 1989; Daye, 1994; Small, 1994). This has prompted much greater academic attention to the economic and social processes that help to transform the class position of sections of minority communities.

One of the most important topics in policy debates on race in the US, and to some extent in Britain and other European countries, has been the question of the underclass. References in public debates and the media to the underclass have become so commonplace that 'the concept, has virtually become a household term within the past five years' (Heisler, 1991: 455). This term, which was first used by Myrdal (1962), is used to describe people who occupy a class that lies beneath the standard social scale, permanently removed from the labour market and with no power or stake in the economic system. In the US the term has particularly come to depict the black urban poor. There are other distinct usages of the notion, ranging from the attempts by William Julius Wilson to give it a strong empirical basis to its use by neoconservatives such as Charles Murray as a general catch-all term in their critiques of the welfare state and affirmative action programmes.

While the debate on the underclass in the US has a particular history that cannot easily be applied to the European context, it is of some significance that the notion is beginning to be used in Europe to describe the position of migrant communities. This has been stimulated by recent economic and social developments in Europe: economic stagnation and recession, deindustrialisation, high unemployment, welfare state contraction and new ethnically and racially distinct migrant populations. Contemporary debates in Europe on the changing patterns of social exclusion have highlighted the links between new forms of poverty and the circumstances of migrant workers and their communities. Recent research in Germany has highlighted the severe impact that deindustrialisation and labour market restructuring have had on the economic and social position of Turks and other groups of migrant workers. It has also pointed up the relevance of the underclass thesis to the analysis of the class position of migrant workers more generally.

In Britain too there is growing interest in the question of the underclass, although the concept is by no means as deeply racialised as it is in the US (Rex, 1988; Smith, 1992). Some of this interest can be seen as the result of attempts to apply the arguments of Charles Murray and other neoconservatives to the British situation, largely inspired by right-wing think tanks such as the Institute of Economic Affairs and the Centre for Policy Studies. But there has also been a much broader debate on the underclass in both academic and popular discourses, stimulated in part by a fear that the situation in Britain's inner cities may be moving closer to that which prevails in the US. It is also the outcome of a concern that processes of racial exclusion are causing some ethnic minority groups to be socially and culturally excluded from mainstream British society.

It is of interest to note that the move towards in-depth studies of social differentiation within minority communities has not resulted in more detailed accounts of the position of black and ethnic minority women in the labour market and other important social arenas. What little research has been done indicates that gender is an important factor in shaping racial inequality, and some of the most innovative research has focused specifically on the position of black and other ethnic minority women in respect of employment, education, welfare provision and related social policy issues. There is a clear need, however, for more theoretically informed research on the part played by the race–gender interplay in structuring contemporary racial relations (Sudbury, 1998).

Some of the most important studies in this field have focused on the position of black and ethnic minority women in the US but there is a rich and rapidly growing body of literature on the situation in other countries, including Britain, other European countries and South Africa. It is clear from this research that gender is a crucial determinant of the life chances of minorities in terms of education, employment, income and related issues. It is also evident that there are quite marked differences within and between racial and ethnic groups in relation to the role that gender plays in structuring social relations and in influencing political and community mobilisation.

Diversity and racialised exclusion

Public policy responses to racial inequality has been another important area of analysis. Since the 1960s there has been an ongoing debate on the form and substance of policy initiatives to tackle racial discrimination, and on inequalities shaped by historical patterns of racism and domination. This debate has been particularly vibrant in the US and Britain, which have witnessed numerous waves of policy initiatives to deal with various aspects of racialised inequality. Although no clear solutions have emerged from the debate it has at least revealed some of the dilemmas that have to be confronted when formulating policies and programmes to tackle the root causes of racial inequality. It has also highlighted the politically controversial nature of policies in this field and the fact that there is little likelihood of reaching a universal agreement on the kinds of policy that need to be developed. Such controversy is not surprising, given the politically sensitive nature of all policies to address racial issues.

As mentioned above, a number of commentators have pointed to the limitations of race relations legislation and other initiatives. This prompts a number of questions. First, what kinds of policy might be able to tackle discrimination more effectively? Second, what links can be made between immigration policy and policies on social and economic issues? What social policy agenda could be developed to deal with the position of both established communities and future immigrants? There are no easy answers to these questions and the experience of recent decades indicates that no set of policies will receive the unanimous support of society as a whole. But a good starting point would be to recognise the need for a coordinated public policy to deal with the various social, political and cultural factors contributing to the situation of black and ethnic minorities in British society today. At best, past policy initiatives have been *ad hoc* and piecemeal. This is partly due to the fact that although public policy has been committed for some time to equal opportunity and multiculturalism there is no clear political and social consensus about what this means, either ideologically or in practice. There is little agreement, for example, about the type of public policies that should be developed to deal with discrimination in areas such as education, social policy and employment. In addition, as recent debates on antiracism indicate, there is denial that racial inequality and racism are integral features of British society.

Whatever the merits of such arguments it is clear that there is considerable confusion about the objectives of public policy. Because of the *ad hoc* nature of policy development in this field it is difficult to talk of coherent strategies to deal with the changing economic and social dynamics we face today. Perhaps more fundamentally there is confusion about the links between:

- antidiscrimination legislation and its role in creating greater opportunities and providing remedies for ethnic minorities and new migrants;
- multicultural and antiracist initiatives to address the problems in employment, education, social services, housing and so on;
- national policies and initiatives by local authorities and community groups to address specific issues.

The lack of coordination in these areas needs to be overcome if the oft-repeated call for more effective policies is to become a reality. The process of change is not likely to be easy. The very plurality of the categories used in current debates indicates that the notions being pursued are by no means clear and are in fact contested. In particular researchers and practitioners do not concur on the meaning of such terms as equality of opportunity and racial equality, or on what they see as evidence of a move towards the stated goals of policies. Some argue that the development of equal opportunity policies is the outcome of political negotiation, pressure group politics and bureaucratic policy making. Others emphasise the need to look beyond the stated objectives and public political negotiations, and point out that deeply entrenched processes of discrimination may be resistant to legal and political intervention as long as inegalitarian social relations continue to structure society as a whole.

Despite intense debate there has been surprisingly little detailed analysis of the workings of public policy on racial inequality, and we still know relatively little about the workings of the race relations legislation and related social policies. Such research as has been carried out has shed some light on the workings of public policy in this field, particularly in relation to the labour market. But more detailed analyses of the everyday workings of specific policies and programmes will have to be conducted if we are to resolve the questions raised above.

As this chapter has tried to show, racial inequalities are produced and reproduced via a range of social, economic and political processes. They are also subject to constant change and are by no means fixed in time and space. Irrespective of whether one looks at employment, housing or other institutional areas it is clear that racialised inequalities are both reproduced and challenged at the same time. In liberal democratic societies racialised inequalities have been the subject of political conflict and controversy, a clear outcome of which has been the development of antidiscrimination policies and initiatives in various national political contexts.

Nevertheless it is likely that the question of racial inequality will remain at the heart of the public policy agenda. Aspects of the situation in the US and Britain have been highlighted in this chapter, but there has been substantial debate in countries as diverse as Holland, France, Germany, Italy and the Scandinavian countries on the measures needed to remedy the discrimination suffered by racialised minority communities and migrant workers and refugees. There are also ongoing discussions at the EU level about the need for common antidiscrimination initiatives and policies.

In practice, of course, there are numerous models of policy action to tackle racial inequality. Persistent public debates on and controversy over the limits of affirmative action programmes in the US have provided evidence of the variety of policy agendas on offer. In recent years aspects of these debates have begun to be reproduced in Britain, albeit in a different ideological and political climate. But what is beyond doubt is that we cannot take the boundaries of public policy debate on racial inequality as fixed and given. Rather they are the subject of constant debate on and conflict over the kinds of legislation that are necessary and how they should be implemented. Consequently the institutionalisation of antidiscrimination policies and practices still has a long way to go.

What is clear is that the processes that help to structure racialised inequalities are by no means static and are constantly being transformed. A case in point is the restructuring of industries and jobs in Europe and the US and the impact of this on employment opportunities for minorities. Recent discussions on the underclass have suggested that this restructuring may have a major impact on those racial and ethnic minority groups who are most vulnerable and least likely to benefit from equal opportunity policies. Unfortunately we still know relatively little about the ways in which such processes affect social and economic conditions in particular communities and localities.

In certain social policy areas there have been important developments in the study of the position of minorities. For example the interplay between race and class in shaping people's experience of the health service has been highlighted in recent research. It is precisely because it is not possible to look at the question of health purely through the prism of either race or class that a number of commentators have insisted that their combined role should be the focus of any rounded analysis of this issue (Ahmad, 1993; Ahmad and Atkin, 1996).

Part of the problem with many existing accounts is that their analysis of racial inequality tends to start from an overly deterministic position or looks at the subject in isolation from other social relations. This has produced a rather static picture of the interrelationship between racial inequality and racism. Such accounts also tend to say little to help us understand the transformation of social, cultural and political relations in contemporary Britain and other societies. What, for example, are the processes that have helped to produce the new politics of race and ethnicity? What impact have these processes had on the articulation of new political discourses on race at the local and national levels? Questions such as these must be addressed if we are to gain a clearer understanding of the present dynamics of racial inequality and social change.

Summary and conclusion

The interrelationship between the changing politics of race and wider processes of economic, social and cultural change has been touched upon at a number of points in this book. A complete analysis of this vexed question is not yet possible as the issue still has to be researched in detail at both the national and the local level. Race and ethnicity are experienced and negotiated in quite disparate ways in contemporary Britain, and there is no one common perspective that can characterise British society as a whole. Ideas on race and the meanings attached to it enter particular social contexts in complex forms (Back, 1991; Gilroy, 1991; Ballard, 1996), and this makes it impossible to conceptualise the discourse on race and identity as monolithic and unchangeable.

This is not the place to explore this question in depth, but two general points arise from the discussion in this chapter. The first is that if we conceive of racialisation as a process, we need to understand how racial relations are affected by the underlying process of social, economic and cultural change in advanced capitalist societies. This point has been emphasised by radical geographers who have begun to explore the ways in which the restructuring of labour markets and regional economic spaces is reproducing new forms of incorporation and division along racial and gender-specific lines (Harvey, 1989; Smith, 1989; Soja, 1989). Other research has pointed to the construction of new identities (Keith and Pile, 1993).

The second point is that with the fundamental restructuring of economic and social relations in Britain, racial and national symbols have re-emerged as important factors in political mobilisation. The wholesale reorganisation of regions and localities to boost the enterprise culture has, if anything, helped to strengthen mythological claims about national culture and the threats it faces. It is not surprising that the quest for more fixed boundaries for the nation coincides with perceived threats to national identity from within and without.

More generally, it seems clear that along with the transformation of social and economic relations we are seeing the emergence of new forms of racism in a number of European countries (Wrench and Solomos, 1993). According to Michel Wieviorka (1993) the rise of social movements that openly articulate xenophobic political views, and engage in direct action against migrants and refugees is but one aspect of a much wider process in a number of countries. He argues that the growth of such movements can be partly explained by the decline of the labour movement as a key social force and by the transformation of class relations more generally as a result of economic and social change. No doubt there are other factors that have contributed to the resurgence of racism, but it is important to look closely at the part played by social and economic changes.

12 New Directions and Perspectives

This book has analysed key trends and developments in the area of race and racism over the past half-century or more, particularly in respect of political debates, public policies and legislative processes. In particular it has sought to show that the processes that have shaped our understanding of race and racism in British society have not proceeded in a linear fashion. Rather the present state of race relations is the outcome of often messy and complex political, social and economic processes. In the course of the analysis we have looked at the main ways in which questions about race, immigration and racism have been debated and acted upon. We have also considered a number of questions about the likely future of race relations and the evolution of political ideologies in this area. These questions include the following. What is the relationship between racial ideologies and politics? How far have social and economic factors influenced the racialisation of political life? What is the prospect of fundamental reforms to challenge racism in political institutions and tackle the root causes of racial inequality? What is the likely trajectory of policies on race and immigration in Britain?

We have grappled with these questions in the course of this study by exploring specific areas of political debate, conflict and policy change. What remains to be discussed is the extent to which the processes and issues that dominated public debate in the past century will continue into the twenty-first century. It is to these issues that we now turn in order to conclude our analysis and consider some of the dilemmas that are likely to confront us as the century unfolds. By looking backwards as well as forwards we shall situate current preoccupations against a broader set of issues that are likely to remain part of our political culture for some time to come.

Race, identity, politics

In one way or another much of the public debate on race and racism in Britain is framed around one key question: what is the likely course of race and ethnic relations during the first part of the twenty-first century? This question has been asked by academic scholars and by politicians and activists who are involved in matters of race and immigration. It is also the underlying concern behind the current preoccupation with immigration and the position of refugees and asylum seekers across Western Europe. It has certainly given rise to intense scholarly debate in recent years, and to heated political debate at times of conflict and public concern, for example after the Stephen Lawrence murder and the outbreak of violent urban unrest and disorder during 2001.

The intensity of such debates is not surprising in the light of recent trends. There can be little doubt that in the last decades of the twentieth century the issue of race, or what is popularly called race relations, became an important social and political topic in Britain. Part of the reason for this was that British society was still attempting to come to terms with the end of the Empire and the emergence of postcolonial racial relations in British cities and towns. Another crucial factor was that after the 1950s many of the immigrants who arrived were visibly different in racial or ethnic terms. Whatever the reasons for the growing salience of questions about race and racism in Britain, the outcome can be seen in the everyday discourses on race that have become part of the social fabric of all major urban localities. It can also be observed in media and political discourses on immigration and race relations, and in the racial and ethnic stereotypes instilled in the popular imagination.

There seems little doubt at the beginning of the twenty-first century that race and racism are likely to continue to give rise to public debates and controversies at both the national and the local level. The debates on the core meaning of Britishness and Englishness that have come to the fore in recent years are just one sign of the continuing salience of race and ethnicity. Likewise the controversy over asylum seekers and refugees, and the playing of the 'race card' before and after the 2001 general election, are but the latest examples of the volatile and powerful part that ethnoracial imagery continues to play in British political culture.

One problem with much of the public debate on race relations is that it tends to be at best speculative and at worst linked to dark predictions about the future. There is remarkably little discussion of the kind of political and social policy measures that need to be developed in response to the increasing presence of racial and ethnic minorities in Britain. In place of informed debate there are confused, angst-ridden discussions about the kind of multiculturalism that should be encouraged and the limitations of public policies and legislation as tools for tackling the roots of racial inequality. These discussions have also been rather limited in terms of the way they have defined the parameters of public discourse on the dynamics of social and cultural change. Because of these limitations there has been very little positive debate about the parameters of policies aimed at developing a clear direction for the future (Favell, 2001).

There have been some signs of change in this situation since the publication of Macpherson's (1999) report on the Stephen Lawrence case and Parekh's (2000b) report on the future of multi-ethnic Britain. Both of these reports pushed forward the public debate on what it means to live in a society with diverse communities and cultural/religious practices. In this sense their influence can be compared with that of the Scarman Report some two decades earlier. In their different ways both the Macpherson Report and the Parekh Report helped to increase public awareness that Britain as a society is both shaped by racism and increasingly multicultural.

The Parekh Report, in particular, provided a basis for rethinking the underlying rationale of policies on race and immigration. Perhaps the most interesting part of the report (Part 1), is entitled 'A Vision for Britain'. This attracted critical attention from the popular press for proposing that the notion of what it means to be British needs to be rethought in light of Britain's increasing multiculturalism (Parekh, 2000b: 14–15). The report went on to argue:

> Britishness, as much as Englishness, has systematic, largely unspoken, racial connotations. Whiteness nowhere features as an explicit condition of being British, but it is widely understood that Englisness, and therefore by extension Britishness, are racially coded (ibid.: 38).

The report does not provide clear suggestions about how to move beyond the 'racially coded' images of national identity that it criticises, although it does point out the limitations of much of the political debate on 'the nation' and what it means to be part of the fabric of British society. More importantly, perhaps, it provides a basic critique of the nature of policy agendas on a whole range of questions that lie at the heart of current anxieties about race relations, including race relations legislation.

Whatever the merits of the Parekh Report, however, there is little doubt that the Macpherson report has had the greatest impact in terms of policy agendas and reforms. It is certainly the case that for both central government departments and local authorities the question of how to respond to institutional racism and other issues highlighted in the report has been at the heart of debates on racial inequality and exclusion since 1999. All the key civil service and local government departments, along with bodies such as the police, have had to address the question of whether they are 'institutionally racist' and to propose measures to deal with racist practices in their own ranks. Perhaps more importantly, the report provided the necessary impetus for the 2000 Race Relations (Amendment) Act to reach the statute books.

Both of these reports, however, need to be placed in a broader context, namely the ongoing attempt to come up with national and local strategies for tackling racism and racial inequality and developing a more inclusive and avowedly multicultural society. In the rest of this chapter we shall look at likely future trends in this area. We shall begin by reflecting on the implications of the preceding account of the morphology of race and racism in British society for the way we think about present and future race relations in Britain and elsewhere. This is a particularly pertinent question at a time when the boundaries of the politics of race seem to be shifting, alongside other important shifts in political and cultural relations. We shall then explore the kinds of policy change that are necessary to address the dilemmas we currently face, including the need to question many of the assumptions that have dominated the debate on race and racism for the past half century and more (Appiah and Gutmann, 1996; Modood and Werbner, 1997; Solomos, 1998).

Racism, politics and ideology

In thinking about this issue it is worth considering a point made by Sami Zubaida when the academic study of race and racism in Britain was in its infancy. Zubaida was writing at a time when questions about immigration and race relations were becoming the subject of highly charged political debate, especially in light of Enoch Powell's expressed views on the matter during the late 1960s. Zubaida warned social scientists that one of the main dangers when analysing policy interventions in this field lay in adopting society's dominant definitions of the problems concerned:

> It is no criticism of a field of study to say that it is concerned with social problems, but it is a criticism of that field to say that it defines its own sociological problems in accordance with the definition of social problems prevalent in that society. Thus, for a long time, race-relations research was primarily concerned with prejudice and discrimination, defined as problems by the 'liberal' agencies of the wider society (Zubaida, 1970: 3).

Zubaida's warning remains pertinent today, though perhaps not in ways that could have been foreseen in 1970: the experience of both the long period of Conservative domination from 1979 to 1997 and the more recent post-1997 New Labour policies on race and immigration highlight how little attention we have given to the danger of defining the problems associated with race and racism in 'accordance with the definition of social problems prevalent in that society'. More worryingly there has been a consistent tendency to decontextualise social problems that the state or other institutions or individuals define as racial. Previous chapters have provided a number of examples of how particular racial questions have been officially constructed as 'social problems', and how issues as diverse as race relations legislation, urban policy, policing, urban unrest, political mobilisation and racial inequality have tended to be seen through the lense of official discourses that show little understanding of historical and contemporary forms of racism and discrimination (Blackstone *et al.*, 1998; Favell, 1997, 2001).

When attempting to make sense of the current situation it is important to reflect on the changing forms of racial discourse and political debates on ethnoracial boundaries in countries such as Britain. As we saw in Chapters 10 and 11, there have been a number of important changes to the themes of political and popular discourses on race and nation. However this is not to say that these themes are completely distinct from those which dominated earlier debates. For example immigration, asylum seekers and refugees are still constant points of reference, and there is still an all too common tendency to perceive minority communities or specific groups within them as sources of social problems and conflict. The recurrent theme of young black, involvement in criminal activities is but one case in point. A more recent concern has been the alienation of groups of young Asians, particularly Muslims, from mainstream British society.

This takes us to another key question: why have political and ideological discourses on race become so entrenched in Britain? Perhaps the most important point to make in this regard is that these discourses have been shaped by the changing context of everyday events and conflict situations. Take for example the issue of policing urban multiracial areas. We can make little sense of current preoccupations if we do not situate them against the background of the urban unrest of the 1980s and minority communities' disenchantment with the police. More recently, protests about the Stephen Lawrence case, the race riots in 2001 and other events have highlighted the volatile nature of relations between the police and many multiracial communities.

On a broader level, public debates on multiculturalism and antiracism highlight the fact that the visible growth of multiethnic communities is perceived by some as challenging the hegemony of Anglo-Saxon cultural values in areas such as education, religion and popular culture. This has resulted in attempts to mobilise political support to defend conservative and monocultural definitions of Englishness.

Hence in recent years the development of debates on antiracism has shown the importance of ideological and political mobilisation around the meaning of local, national, ethnic or religious identity in British society.

Such mobilisations do not take place in a vacuum. They are conditioned by local and national state institutions, by political movements and parties, and by community organisations. As David Goldberg (2002) has reminded us, 'the racial state' in all its forms is a crucial factor in the makeup of contemporary racial and ethnic relations in a wide range of societies. It is worth noting, however, that antiracist mobilisation may in turn help to shape state institutions and policy agendas.

Equality or symbolic reforms?

This book has presented a critical and in some ways pessimistic account of the processes that have shaped racial politics in Britain since the late 1940s. This does not mean, however, that it has ruled out the possibility of either radical or more limited reforms. One of the book's main conclusions is that there is a need to develop a dynamic analysis of the policy environment in which race relations policies have been implemented over the past five decades, and of the achievements and limitations of these policies. A key point that the various chapters have emphasised is that we have to move beyond the conception of racism as a fixed and unchanging feature of social and political relations in contemporary societies. However this should not prevent us from developing a critical analysis of the limitations and contradictions of dominant policy agendas and strategies for reform.

The limitations of policies aimed at tackling racial discrimination from the 1960s onwards were threefold. First, antidiscrimination legislation was based on the assumption that the enactment of measures outlawing discriminatory acts would end everyday discriminatory practices in employment. Little attention was given to the need for wider administrative and political strategies against discrimination, or to the development of positive action programmes by central government. This meant that antidiscrimination policies operated in a vacuum and in an environment that was generally negative, if not hostile (Freeman and Spencer, 1979; Gordon, 1982, 1989b; Jenkins and Solomos, 1989; Parekh, 2000b).

Second, successive governments promised reform while doing very little to remedy the structural separation between organisations such as the CRE, or to give them the powers needed to bring about fundamental changes. Hence there was no linking of the various elements of state intervention, even though this had been called for in various government reports from the mid 1970s. Referring to the situation after the 1976 Race Relations Act, Bindman (1980) argues that at best the 1976 Act only achieved 'the perpetuation of existing inequalities', and that this was unlikely to change without a radical policy package covering the major policy areas:

> The most pressing need … is not for change in the law but for a substantial strengthening of the legal and economic powers and inducements to apply effective equal opportunity policies. This will only come about if there is greater readiness by the courts and the law to enforce the law, if more resources are provided for law enforcement, and if the government demonstrates its commitment to racial equality by using its executive powers (ibid.: 258).

This analysis is remarkably similar to the CRE's own comments on the problems it faced during the 1980s and 1990s (CRE, 1985a, 1991, 1998). It was also supported by a number of other studies of the operation of the 1976 Race Relations Act (McCrudden, 1987; Jenkins and Solomos, 1989; McCrudden *et al.*, 1991; Bhavnani, 2001), which highlighted the difficulty of bringing about fundamental reform through piecemeal actions rather than coordinated public policies. Yet throughout the 1980s and 1990s there was little sign of positive initiatives to strengthen the antidiscrimination legislation. The passage of the 2000 Race Relations (Amendment) Act may prove an important turning point in governmental interventions in this field, although this Act too is somewhat limited in scope and intent.

Third, broader structural limits were put on the implementation of the 1976 Race Relations Act by the economic and social policies pursued by successive administrations, particularly during the period of Conservative domination from 1979 to 1997. Although the broader economic environment cannot be seen as fully determining the effectiveness of government policies, there is still a link between state actions and the demands placed on resources by wider pressures, for example economic downturn and high unemployment. It is clear from recent experiences that equality of opportunity, as a goal of government policy, cannot be realised if no account is taken of the economic and political forces in society as a whole.

Given these limitations a number of questions need to be asked. Are these limitations an inherent aspect of social policies in capitalist societies, such that reform policies will always be symbolic in character? Or can initiatives be taken to counter these limitations and allow a more radical package of social policies on race and other issues to be implemented?

Much more detailed research will have to be conducted before these questions can be answered satisfactorily, but the existing evidence suggests that race relations policies have been constrained by the above factors since 1965, although slightly less so since 1976. However this is not to say that they have had no impact at all. Research points to at least some success in the public and private sectors in respect of employment, and research by the Policy Studies Institute supports this conclusion (Modood *et al.*, 1997). It is clear, however, that in-depth studies are needed of the role of state and government institutions in the development of race relations policies, the reasons why certain definitions of the race problem have gained currency, and the reasons why a large gap has developed between the promise of equality and the reality of widespread discrimination and systemic racism. Detailed knowledge of these factors would allow us to go beyond the limits of existing analyses and provide a more reasoned and critical account of various strategies for tackling the roots of racism.

In this regard it is interesting to note the CRE's thoughts on the Conservative government's response to Lord Scarman's report on the 1981 disturbances in Brixton:

> So far the response [to the Scarman Report] by the government and others has been disappointingly inadequate. It lacks the sense of urgency that runs through Lord Scarman's report in particular. Of course, it is more difficult in a time of recession, when unemployment is high and resources are scarce, for a massively expensive effort to be made. But it is precisely at such a time that the vulnerable sections of society suffer most, and even steps that require only a comparatively modest outlay are not being taken by the government (CRE, *Annual Report*, 1981: 3).

While this analysis was written over twenty years ago, it remains important if we are to make sense of trends and developments over the past two decades. Similarly, while much was promised in the aftermath of the 1980–1 and 1985 riots and some policy changes were implemented, the promises of reform did not result in a major change in direction and the long term impact of the policy changes was somewhat limited.

After New Labour was elected to government in May 1997 there was a flurry of activity in this field, giving rise to an expectation that it would carry out the reforms laid out in existing policies as well as introduce new ones. That there was indeed to be a change of direction was signalled by the setting up of the Macpherson Inquiry and the reform of the 1976 Race Relations Act. It was also evidenced by the fact that questions about race and ethnicity became an integral part of governmental initiatives in areas such as urban regeneration, policing, social exclusion, education and employment. However, while it is still too early to determine the likely impact of these initiatives in the medium term, the experience of the past four decades should warn us against complacency in this regard.

Protest and social change

The political language used to explain the urban unrest of the 1980s, 1990s and 2001 provides a clear example of the inherently contradictory nature of political legitimacy when confronted with questions about race and racism. This is particularly so in a political context that allows only limited reform of the fundamental social and power inequalities that shape the fate of inner city residents. It could well be argued that all political language is symbolic reassurance that the government is in control of the situation. But this does not mean that it will be able to justify unsuccessful policies on a permanent basis.

This conclusion is supported by events over the past two decades. A combination of symbolic reassurance and promises of reform helped to bring a temporary halt to large-scale street violence, but urban protest did not disappear altogether. The smaller outbreaks of unrest during the late 1980s, early 1990s and in 2001 point to the limitations of such policy responses and the volatile nature of racial and ethnic-mobilisations, particularly when combined with deeply entrenched class inequality and urban poverty.

This is not to say that no attempts have been made to deal with racism and racial inequality, urban decline, unemployment and community involvement. For example, as discussed in Chapters 6 and 7, there have been numerous pronouncements by government departments and ministers about the need to tackle the law and order issue not in isolation but alongside the questions of unemployment, inner city decline, the provision of leisure and social facilities, and private initiatives. Indeed after her third election victory in 1987 Margaret Thatcher put the question of inner city policy at the top of her agenda, and a number of initiatives were introduced to tackle aspects of urban deprivation. Similar pronouncements were made after the Conservative victory in May 1992, with a variety of promises being made by the government to regenerate inner city localities through private initiatives and central government assistance.

Since 1997 New Labour has also prioritised the issues of urban deprivation and social exclusion. The work of the Social Exclusion Unit and numerous other governmental bodies is premised on the idea that deprived urban communities present a potential threat in terms of crime and violent disorder, and a recurrent theme in New Labour's pronouncements on 'joined up' government is the use of multi-agency intervention strategies to tackle deeply rooted and seemingly intractable social problems. Whether these measures will be successful in dealing with the underlying issues that prompt violent protest is a burning question. The experiences of the 1980s and early 1990s show that promises of reform do not necessarily lead to coordinated programmes of change.

After the 1980s urban riots there were numerous promises to deal with the underlying problems, but while the riots did lead to a review of inner city and employment policies, the emphasis on law and order as the first priority was unmistakable: 'There can be no economic or sociological justification for throwing a petrol bomb. That is crime and must be dealt with as such, wherever it occurs' (Nigel Lawson Chancellor of the Exchequer, quoted in the *Guardian*, 6 November 1985).

It is notable also that whilst in 1980–1 it was quite often the Department of Environment that led the way in terms of public pronouncements, by 1985 the Home Office was serving as the leading department. Other government departments were called in to play their part in restoring order and preventing future disturbances, but only in the context that their actions were just part of the answer. This tells us something about the inherent contradictions in responses to urban unrest, be it in Britain during the 1980s or the US during the 1960s. Both sets of responses represented an attempt to reassure the public that the government was still very much in control while minimising the political impact of the protests. In addition, and this has perhaps been more clear in Britain since 1985, the restoration of law and order has been achieved through the imposition of tough measures to support the police. Such a strategy has necessitated that riots be branded as criminal acts, senseless outbursts or the work of drug barons. Against such political symbols the language of liberal reform has been pushed into a corner.

In the late 1980s and early 1990s there were numerous calls to look more closely at the recommendations in the Scarman Report and the reasons for their non-implementation, but perhaps unsurprisingly these calls were not heard. The reimposition of order on the streets was seen as an objective that could be achieved without the economic and political reforms called for by the liberal project, at least in the medium term. In the long term the strong free-market economy that the Conservative administrations espoused throughout the 1980s and most of the 1990s was seen as the best insurance against social disorder, rather than short-term reform measures.

Since the 2001 riots in Oldham, Bradford and Burnley we have been faced with somewhat similar dilemmas. In the wake of the riots a flurry of *ad hoc* investigations produced reports that explored the background of the unrest and provided a wide range of proposals for tackling the root causes as well as the catalysts of the violence. Yet it is evident that concrete changes will take some time to come about, leading to dashed expectations and new tensions in both minority and majority communities.

Rethinking the politics of racism

There are few academic analyses of the relationship between racism, politics and society in Britain and other advanced capitalist societies. This is in marked contrast to a wealth of studies of the relationship between class structure and the state, and between gender relations and the state. This omission has serious consequences for the adequacy of accounts of racism in contemporary societies in that there are few detailed studies upon which to draw when considering the role of state institutions and agencies in the reproduction of racial inequalities and ideas. It is only recently that David Goldberg and others have made a rigorous attempt to theorise the role of the 'racial state' (Goldberg, 2002).

At the beginning of this book it was argued that there is a need for greater theoretical clarity about the interplay between racism, politics and society, and it has been shown throughout that the basic problem confronting any study of the complex relationship between race, class and the state is the very nature of racism in contemporary capitalist societies. From the brief survey in Chapter 1 of the competing approaches to this question in sociological, neo-Marxist and political discourses it should be clear that at least two problems have defied resolution: the interplay between racial and ethnic categorisations and economic and class determination; and the part played by the state and its institutions in the reproduction of racism. The latter includes state intervention to control immigration, the mismanagement of race relations and, more broadly, the failure to integrate racial and ethnic groupings into the wider society. This chapter will outline some of the fundamental questions that have arisen from case studies of racialised politics in contemporary Britain.

Michael Omi and Howard Winant, in their analysis of the politics of race in the US, suggest that it is wrong to conceive of the state as an external factor in the shaping of racial relations. On the contrary, they argue:

> The state is inherently racial. Far from intervening in racial conflicts, the state is itself increasingly the pre-eminent site of racial conflict. … Every state institution is a racial institution, but not every institution operates in the same way. In fact, the various state institutions do not serve one co-ordinated racial objective; they may work at cross-purposes. Therefore, race must be understood as occupying varying degrees of centrality in different state institutions and at different historical moments (Omi and Winant, 1994: 76–7).

Such arguments have been made in a number of other theoretical analyses of the politics of racism (see for example Solomos and Back, 1996;

Goldberg, 2002). Whatever the merit of these theoretical propositions, they have not been systematically used to inform historical and empirical analyses of particular racial situations. There have been some *ad hoc* attempts to do this, but they have been both partial and based on limited research on the dynamics of racism across historical and spatial boundaries. While not wishing to diminish the importance of these studies, the relative absence of empirical analysis has left a major gap in writings on this subject. Without analysing the interaction between racist structures and other social structures in capitalist societies it is difficult to explain how certain racialised ideologies and inequalities develop and help to shape the fundamental institutions of society.

Part of the problem has been the lack of a fruitful dialogue on theoretical and methodological issues among those involved in research into and scholarship on these issues. Another problem is the absence of detailed studies of the genesis, development and transformation of racial institutions. An example of the failure to integrate theory with research is presented in the work of Stuart Hall. In his account of the interplay between racism and other social relations in capitalist societies, he argues:

> At the economic level, it is clear that race must be given its distinctive and 'relatively autonomous' effectivity, as a distinctive feature. This does not mean that the economic is sufficient to found an explanation of how these relations concretely function. One needs to know how different racial and ethnic groups were inserted historically, and the relations which have tended to erode and transform, or to preserve these distinctions through time – not simply as residues and traces of previous modes, but as active structuring principles of the present society. Racial categories alone will not provide or explain these (Hall, 1980: 339).

Hall implicitly criticises approaches that assume there is a harmonious articulation between racism and the capitalist relations of production. His emphasis on the ways in which racial and ethnic groups are historically incorporated into society, and how their position changes over time, suggests that the relationship between racism and wider social relations should be seen as historically and spatially variable and contradictory.

Such broad generalisations, however, need to be tested out and analysed in studies of the processes of racialisation in particular historical situations. In order to develop a dynamic framework that can help us understand the historical and contemporary intersection between racism and politics in specific societies it is necessary to focus on the processes that politicise racial and ethnic issues. Yet there is no attempt in Hall's work, or in many of the conceptual works that have emerged over the past two decades, to go beyond general theoretical propositions by analysing the development of racism in particular societies. This failure to integrate theory with detailed historical and political analysis is a shortcoming of much of the radical literature on racism. Hence there are a plethora of theoretical studies that have little to say about the specific mechanisms that structure and shape racial ideas and practices in local and national politics, in specific institutions and in key areas of social life.

The separation of theoretical analysis from political analysis has to be overcome if we are to understand the history of racialised politics and its present forms in Britain. There is also a need to move away from the notion that racialisation is uniform across different societies. The paradox inherent in attempts to construct a uniform conception of racism is that they lose the ability to explain the dynamics of change and conflict, and in so doing they fail to analyse the processes that lead to the racialisation of social relations.

This has been a main concern of this book. In particular it has focused on two broad questions. First, how do political structures and institutions in Britain function in relation to race and in what ways do they produce, reproduce or help to overcome racism? Second, how does racism shape the ways in which class, gender and other social relations are experienced, and how do they structure political action? The above discussion provides a basis upon which to begin to answer to these questions.

Racism and nationalism in Europe

The resurgence of racist and extreme nationalist movements in a number of European societies has been widely commented upon in public and media debates on the new Europe. The Front National in France, the Vlaams Blok in Belgium and a number of similar movements in Germany have enjoyed growing support, mainly because of their opposition to immigration and their manipulation of nationalistic symbols (Lloyd, 1991, 1998; Miles, 1992; Wrench and Solomos, 1993; Crowley, 1993; Joppke, 1998).

Interestingly, however, extreme right-wing political parties have not enjoyed similar success in Britain, despite the fact that immigration and race remain heavily politicised issues. According to Husbands (1992) this is due to (a) the limited appeal of extreme-right groups such as the National Front and the British National Party outside a few specific localities, and (b) the ability of the Conservative Party to retain the support of voters who might otherwise be attracted to the extreme right. Others have pointed out that the electoral system in Britain makes it difficult for small parties to become major political forces at the national level.

In Robert Miles' (1989) view it is important to move beyond descriptive accounts of racism and to explore the forms that racism actually takes in contemporary societies. He argues that what is novel about contemporary racism is not the proliferation of racist social movements but the intensification of ideological and political struggles that express racism but claim not to be racist. It is certainly clear that racism is taking on new forms in the present political environment, where there is widespread confusion about the boundaries of national identity and the effect of cultural, religious and linguistic differences (Castles, 1993; Joppke, 1998, 1999; Castles and Miller, 1998). The experience of former Yugoslavia is a case in point. After the break-up of Yugoslavia there was not only 'ethnic cleansing' but also the articulation of new types of cultural racism based on the construction of fixed religious and cultural boundaries.

This raises the question of what is meant by racism in contemporary British society. This question has been hotly debated, with some writers arguing that we can no longer use the term racism while others point to the emergence of more subtle forms of racism that eschew notions of racial supremacy in favour of patriotism and the fixing of cultural boundaries. Whatever the merits of these arguments, events in a number of European countries have highlighted the persistence of neofascist political ideas that are virulently anti-Semitic and antiforeigner. This indicates that it is best to see racism not as a monolithic set of ideas but as an ideology that takes particular forms in certain social and political situations (Wieviorka, 1993; Miles, 1994; Macey, 1994).

Despite the absence of a mass racist political movement, political discussions on immigration and race relations in Britain have much in common with debates in the rest of Europe (Spencer, 1994; Soysal, 1994). For example there is increasing concern about the arrival of asylum seekers and refugees. Despite claims by the Major administration and the post-1997 Blair administrations that they are interested in developing a non-racial response to these issues, political debates about them remain heavily racialised.

Studies show, however, that there is no simple model to explain the power and effect of the new types of racism in Europe and elsewhere (Miles, 1989; Goldberg, 1990a; Ansell, 1997). That is, simplistic notions of racism, or notions derived from one specific sociohistorical context, cannot be used to explain the growing popularity of racist ideologies and movements in today's Europe, and that the rise of the Front National in France and similar movements elsewhere need to be contextualised against particular national political settings and trends in European societies more generally. Researchers have generally not been good at combining these two levels of analysis and ensuring that they explain as well as describe the development of new forms of racism.

Perhaps the most glaring absences are serious debates on the best ways to tackle the growth of racism and appropriate suggestions for antiracist initiatives. These are certainly difficult aspects of policy in this field, as evidenced by the confused and conflicting accounts of antiracism that are currently found in Britain. In the present climate it is impossible to ignore the pressing need for measures to tackle the growth of racism and challenge the visions articulated by racist movements and parties.

What kind of future?

As this book has shown, race is one of the most controversial and volatile issues in contemporary British society and politics. Indeed it is clear from the analysis of trends over the past fifty years or so that race has been a divisive issue at all levels of British society and is likely to remain so in the future. For example, since the early 1990s the increasingly politicised debates on asylum seekers and refugees have once again emphasised the complex forms that mobilisations around ethnoracial identity can take (IPPR, 1997; Kushner and Knox, 1999; Blake and Fransman, 1999; May, 1999; Papastergiadis, 2000). More generally, the ongoing debate about the meaning of 'Englishness' and 'Britishness' in an increasingly multicultural society hinges on concerns about who really 'belongs' within the imagined boundaries of the national collectivity.

One of the ironies of the current situation is that at the same time as the symbols of multiculturalism are becoming an integral part of youth culture and popular culture in general, the racialised boundaries of 'Englishness' are still left largely unquestioned (Alibhai-Brown, 1999, 2000; Philo and Beattie, 1999). It is evident both from media discourses and from research on specific aspects of popular culture and sport that the emergence of multiculturalism has not displaced racism and racialised discourses. Rather, multiculturalism and racism can be seen as part of the broader sets of social relations that have emerged in Britain over the past few decades.

This point is perceptively made by Andrea Levy, a writer born in London of Jamaican parents:

> Since the War, the changes in this country have been staggering. When we think back to my childhood in little grey socks in Highbury, it's a completely different planet. These changes mean that the English identity has devolved: if the word Englishness doesn't define me,

> then the word needs to be redefined (*Independent on Sunday*, 28 February 1999).

For some, Levy's words may sound overtly optimistic, but it is impossible to look back at the processes that have shaped race relations in British society over the past few decades and not comment on the changes and transformations that have remade British society in a very fundamental way.

The failure thus far to tackle the roots of racism and racial inequality means that it is difficult to be optimistic about the future of racial relations. The need for urgent political action on this issue is clear, but there is no commonly accepted political basis for such action. Indeed during the 1980s and 1990s the most notable features of government policy were the strengthening of immigration controls and a complete failure to promote positive measures to overcome racial inequality and injustice. The politics of the Conservative administrations from 1979 to 1997 was such that it was difficult to imagine fundamental changes being made to the political priorities and policies in this area.

Ironically, since 1997 New Labour has proved as keen to be seen as tough on immigration and asylum issues as were the Conservatives. Despite Labour's opposition to the Conservatives' policies on immigration and asylum during the 1980s and early 1990s, when it took power it offered no radical alternative to these policies. Indeed in practice it has shown itself to be in favour of a tough stance against what the new right once called 'economic migrants' 'bogus asylum seekers'.

What, then, are we to make of New Labour's policies on immigration and race relations? Do they obscure a turning point in state policies in this field that is likely to lead in a radically new direction? We have attempted to deal with both of these questions in the course of the analysis in Chapters 3 and 4, but a general appraisal may be useful in order to pull the threads of our argument together. The first point to make is that there have been some positive developments, particularly in relation to measures to tackle racial inequality and discrimination. More generally, the governments' inclusion of questions of race and ethnicity in its wider agendas on social exclusion and urban deprivation may bear some fruit in the medium term. As we have attempted to show, however, there are fundamental contradictions in its policies on immigration, refugees and asylum seekers.

More worryingly, it has become evident that rather than questioning and challenging the moral panic that has broken out over the question of refugees and asylum seekers New Labour has, if anything, added to it. Perhaps the saddest aspect of this is that it has increased the fear and racist violence suffered by these groups themselves.

It is perhaps not surprising that the 2002 white paper *Secure Borders, Safe Haven: Integration with Diversity in Modern Britain* has little to say on Labour's vision of multicultural Britain. Instead it speaks of the need to 'maintain and develop social cohesion and harmony within the United Kingdom' (Home Office, 2002: 27). Terms such as integration, inclusion and exclusion have been deployed in various policy discourses, such as those on education, poverty and health, so that they have become commonplace and their ubiquity obviates any need for a discussion of their meaning – they have acquired the status of common sense. Hence in the government's view it is 'obviously' desirable and in 'everyone's' interest that everyone speaks English – who in their right mind could argue against that? Likewise it is clear that those who settle in Britain should respect and embrace 'our values' and seek to share our 'sense of belonging and identity' (ibid.: 3). Citizenship classes, already introduced for school children, are now to be made compulsory for naturalisation applicants in order to help them fit into 'our' society. There has been little discussion on definition of the values, sense of belonging or identity that will be acquired, or of how these will create the sense of security that is a recurrent theme in the 2002 white paper.

It is clear that the current preoccupation with social cohesion and integration has already begun to have an impact on policies and practices in this field. In 2002 Gurbux Singh, then head of the Commission for Racial Equality, mirrored official thinking when he called for 'public policies which actively encourage integration' (*Guardian*, 18 March 2002). Underlying Singh's call was a sense of frustration that after four decades of race legislation there was little sign of greater understanding between the communities living in deprived inner city localities. At the same time his call for for what amounted to forced integration reflected concern about the limits of multiculturalism as an ideology for dealing with racial conflict and tension.

New Labour came to power with an extraordinary mandate, and at a time when the Conservative Party was in such disarray that it was unlikely to return to office at the next general election. This confluence meant that Labour was presented with a historic opportunity to 'think the unthinkable' and 'do the undoable'. This did not happen, and Labour's time in power may come to be seen as a tragic missed opportunity for all sections of British society, especially the established minority communities and new arrivals. New Labour could have shifted the terms of the debate, but in practice its policies on migration and race relations have displayed marked continuities with those of previous Labour and Conservative governments. While the 2000 Race Relations Amendment Act may make some difference in the medium term, any progress in this area is likely to be undermined by legislation on migration and asylum. The 1999 Immigration and Asylum Act may prove to be as faulty and as ineffectual as the legislation passed by the

Conservatives. It is also unlikely that the next Immigration and Asylum Act will lead to any improvement for migrants or minorities. This is because the same flawed logic underpins all legislation on migration and race relations, namely that good race relations depend on strict immigration controls.

The present political climate therefore suggests that the prospect of a radical reorientation of policies is slim. Rather, what we are likely to see is a limited strengthening of race relations policies combined with stronger measures to regulate the flow of refugees and asylum seekers. The outbreaks of urban unrest during the 1980s gave rise to a short-lived flurry of remedial activity, but this did little to tackle the problems of racial inequality and urban neglect. The 2001 race riots led to similar public debates and promises for action at both the national and the local level. Yet it remains to be seen whether longer-term initiatives to tackle the inadequacies of the policies of the past few decades will emerge.

One area where there has been some change in recent years is minority political representation. The number of local politicians from minority backgrounds has grown over the past two decades, and in some localities they have started to exercise a degree of influence. At the national level, the current presence of 12 black and ethnic minority MPs in the House of Commons may have some effect on the nature of the politics of race, but on present evidence their influence is likely to be limited, particularly as minority politicians with ambitions to join the higher echelons of government are unlikely to speak out forcefully on immigration issues or racism. In the longer term, however, increased black and ethnic minority political involvement and representation, and alliances with other political forces, may help to transform the terms of political debate on racial inequality in Britain, particularly in respect of New Labour's limited commitment to antiracism (Mactaggart and Phillips, 1995). The experience of the United States during the 1990s under the Clinton administration highlights the limitations of this kind of reform strategy in tackling deep-seated racial inequalities (Reed, 1999).

On the basis of current evidence, public opinion is still divided on the matter of race. A public opinion survey conducted by MORI after the 2001 general election found that almost a fifth of people surveyed saw immigration and race relations as one of the most serious issues the country was likely to face in the future (*Guardian*, 22 June 2001). Subsequent events, such as the terrorist attacks in the United States on 11 September 2001 and the consequent allied actions in Afghanistan, further politicised the issues of immigration and multiculturalism and led to a higher-profile debate on the future of race relations in British society. More worryingly it also allowed the British National Party to portray itself as having national interests at heart and as defending British society from attacks within as well as without.

Hence it is all the more important for those interested in tackling the roots of racism and racial inequality and developing a truly multicultural society to look more deeply into the dilemmas and political questions discussed in this book. The lessons learned since the 1950s need to be acted upon if racism is to cease to structure the life chances of Britain's black and ethnic minority citizens and shape the values of sections of the white population.

A reality of the past few years is that no matter what steps have been taken to make race and community relations part of the agenda of central government departments it has proved difficult to put appropriate strategies into practice. A report produced by the Institute for Public Policy Research helpfully points out that 'race equality and community relations seem obvious areas meriting a cross-cutting and joined up approach to the identification and delivery of outcomes' (Collins, 2002: 23). Yet experiences since 1997 have shown that such an approach will remain an ideal rather than a reality as long as the government continues to treat race relations and immigration as two separate policy areas.

Indeed part of the lesson to be learnt from the experiences of the past half century or so is that the achievement of a more just and egalitarian civil society remains the best hope for achieving greater racial justice.

I hope that this book has helped to situate Britain's experience of race and racism in a wider social and political framework and raised questions that will provoke further thought and debate on this vital issue. If it has done so it will have achieved its main objective.

Guide to Further Reading

Since the first edition of this book was published there has been a rapid growth of scholarly literature on all key aspects of racial and ethnic relations in British society, including racism, immigration, employment, political participation, social policy and education. There has also been a marked growth of texts that provide alternative theoretical perspectives on race, racism and ethnicity. Much of this literature is written by sociologists, but growing bodies of related research have developed in the fields of political science, cultural studies, geography, history, the humanities and anthropology.

There has also been a notable expansion of public debates on policies in this field, and this has prompted a number of studies of the dynamics of policy change and innovation. In addition a wide range of reports and documents on key aspects of race and racism in Britain have been produced by government departments, public bodies and local authorities. These can be important resources when trying to make sense of changing political agendas, and they provide insights into modes of thinking on specific policy issues and current dilemmas. A growing number of central and local government reports are easily accessible on the internet.

Key facets of scholarly and public policy debates are contained in the sources used in this volume. For detailed overviews of trends and developments across a range of disciplines see Back and Solomos (2000), Bulmer and Solomos (1999a,b) and Goldberg and Solomos (2002). All of these works consider historical and contemporary trends and debates. For a concise overview of conceptual and political debates see Solomos and Back (1996).

The purpose of this guide to further reading is to help you to follow up important pieces of research and scholarship that add to the arguments developed in this volume. It is not intended as an exhaustive review of the literature (although the Bibliography provides quite a full coverage of the literature on the topics covered in this book), Rather the object is to direct you to works that present up-to-date analyses of specific topics. Consideration of these will enable you to gain some familiarity with divergent perspectives and an awareness of the political and policy implications of recent research.

You may find it useful to look at recent issues of the growing number of journals that consider questions of race and racism, including: *Ethnic and Racial Studies* (the main international scholarly journal covering questions of race, ethnicity and nationalism), *Ethnicities* (a journal oriented towards the interface between politics and sociology), *Immigrants and Minorities* (the main historical journal on questions of race and immigration), *Journal of Ethnic and Migration Studies* (formerly known as *New Community*, and with a broadly European focus on questions of immigration and race), *Patterns of Prejudice* (a journal that focuses on questions to do with anti-Semitism, prejudice, and racism), *Race and Class* (a radical journal with a Third World orientation), *Sage Race Relations Abstracts* (contains abstracts of research on race, racism and related issues) and *Social Identities* (a journal that focuses on the construction of social identities based on race and nation).

Other more specialised journals have emerged in recent years, covering subfields such as history, education, health and area studies. An overview of trends and developments on the extreme right and among neofascist movements can be found in the monthly magazine *Searchlight*. During the 1980s and 1990s the Runnymede Trust provided a regular overview of trends and developments in the area of race and ethnicity in Britain in its monthly *Bulletin*. For more recent developments in race relations and equal opportunities legislation see the *Equal Opportunities Review*, a bimonthly publication that provides up-to-date reviews of equal opportunity policies.

A sizeable number of relevant sources can be accessed electronically. Most government departments, including the Home Office, and bodies such as the Commission for Racial Equality provide reports and research findings on their web sites, as do the mainstream political parties and extreme right-wing groups such as the British National Party. It is also possible to find relevant sources on particular topics through online databases such as *Bids, Ingenta* and *ISI Web of Science*.

Introduction

To follow up the key issues covered in the Introduction you can begin by looking at Bulmer and Solomos (1999a,b), Castles and Miller (1998) and Wrench and Solomos (1993). You may also find it useful to look at Cohen (1994), Goulbourne (1991, 1998) and Solomos and Back (1995, 1996). For a discussion of political and ethical aspects of research on race see Back and Solomos (1993) and Connolly and Troyna (1998). For a collection of recent and thought provoking American perspectives on the dilemmas faced when carrying out research in this area see Twine and Warren (2000).

1 Theorising Race and Racism

The literature on this is vast and growing all the time. The historical and contemporary literature on race and racism is covered in full in Bulmer and Solomos (1999b). A useful overview of key aspects of recent debates can be found in Back and Solomos (2000) and Goldberg and Solomos (2002), and a range of disciplinary perspectives can be found in Bulmer and Solomos (1999a). A more specific but still useful overview of divergent theoretical perspectives is contained in Rex and Mason (1986). Other important texts are Banton (1998), Gilroy (1987, 1993), Mac an Ghaill (1999), Miles (1989, 1993), Rattansi and Westwood (1994) and Rex (1983). An interesting collection of feminist perspectives on contemporary British debates can be found in Mirza (1997).

Useful reviews of American debates can be found in Cornell and Hartmann (1998) and Omi and Winant (1994). Other useful American studies are Marable (1985) and Wilson (1980, 1988). For more recent debates in America see Cornell and Hartmann (1998), Goldberg (1990a, 1993), Reed (1999) and Winant (2001).

2 Historical Background and Context

For the history of race and immigration in Britain the best starting points are Holmes (1988) and Smith (1999). Two important collections of original papers are contained in Holmes (1978) and Lunn (1980). For the history of Irish immigration and attitudes towards the Irish see Curtis (1968), Hickman (1995) and Swift and Gilley (1985). For more contemporary evidence of discrimination against the Irish see Hickman and Walter (1997). For a polemic against what he sees as the 'invisibility' of the Irish in much scholarly writing see Mac an Ghaill (2001). For the politics of Jewish immigration see Cheyette (1993), Cheyette and Marcus (1998), Feldman (1994), Gainer (1972) and Gartner (1973). Fryer (1984, 1988) takes a historical view of the black presence in British society, and other important sources on this subject are Ramdin (1987, 1999), Rich (1986) and Walvin (1992, 1999). Developments in the early part of the twentieth century are the focus of Bush (1999) and Tabili (1994). A fascinating account of the invention of images of Africa in the popular imagination can be found in Coombes (1994). For the question of race, femininity and sexuality in Victorian Britain see Brody (1998). For anticolonialism as a movement and an ideology see Howe (1993).

3 The Politics of Race and Immigration since 1945

For further reading on the wide range of issues raised in this chapter you could begin by looking at Cohen (1994), Freeman (1979), Layton-Henry (1984) and Paul (1997). Phillips and Phillips (1998) provide an overview of the experiences of West Indian migrants in the immediate postwar period and subsequently; see also Wambu (1998). Other studies that are widely consulted to are Foot (1965), Miles and Phizacklea (1984), Sivanandan (1982) and Spencer (1994). To get a feel for the political debates on immigration during the 1940s and 1950s look at Panayi (1999). The sociolegal context is covered fully in Macdonald and Blake (1995). Key aspects of recent policy changes in relation to refugees and asylum seekers are covered in Kushner and Knox (1999). A good account of the comparative politics of immigration can be found in Castles and Miller (1998), and a challenging account of the British and French experiences is contained in Favell (2001). For a strident, not to say vitriolic, critique of much of the research conducted since 1945 see Hansen (2000b).

4 Race Relations Policies and the Political Process

This field has recently begun to attract more interest. An interesting overview of the early history of legislation on this issue can be found in Lester and Bindman (1972), while the papers in Abbott (1971) look at various aspects of race relations policies during the 1960s. On the legal context since the passage of the 1976 Race Relations Act see the divergent perspectives of McCrudden (1982), McCrudden *et al.* (1991), Edwards (1995) and Lustgarten (1980). The Commission for Racial Equality produces regular annual reports that look at the implementation of policies, as does the *Equal Opportunities Review*. For the political and social context see Glazer and Young (1983), Hepple (1983), Law (1996) and Jenkins and Solomos (1989). For the politics of equal opportunity policies see Blakemore and Drake (1996). Banton (1996) provides an overview of international legislation on racial discrimination, while recent trends and developments in Europe can be found in European Parliament (1998). Recent debates on the best way to tackle racism are usefully reviewed in Bhavnani (2001).

5 Urban Politics and Racial Inequality

A number of books have looked at various aspects of the local politics of race during the 1980s and 1990s, though this area remains surprisingly underresearched. A pioneering work in this respect was Rex and Moore (1967). Good overviews of the history and background can be found in Ball and Solomos (1990), Ben-Tovim *et al.* (1986) and Law (1996). For trends and developments in the 1990s see Geddes (1993) and Solomos and Back (1995). For policy agendas since 1997 see Cabinet Office (2000) and Home Office, Race Equality Unit (2000). More specific case studies can be found in Reeves (1989) and Saggar (1991). For a comparative perspective see Cross and Keith (1993).

6 Race and Policing

Because of the frequent controversies over relations between black communities and the police there is a large body of literature on this subject. Good starting points are Reiner (1985) and Smith and Gray (1987). Other important studies include Hall *et al.* (1978) and Humphry (1972). More recent trends in police and minority relations are analysed in Holdaway (1996) and Holdaway and Barron (1997). For the history of police relations with young blacks see Solomos (1988). For the politics of urban unrest see: Benyon (1984), Benyon and Solomos (1987), Keith (1993) and Scarman (1981). For the issues surrounding the Stephen Lawrence case see Bowling (1999), Bowling and Phillips (2001) and Cathcart (1999).

7 Urban Unrest and the Politics of Protest

The urban unrest and social change that have taken place since the 1980s have sparked a growing interest in the politics of protest and violent unrest. For the historical background and context see Panayi (1996). For a review of some of the main issues see Benyon (1984) and Benyon and Solomos (1987). For other perspectives see Joshua and Wallace (1983) and Kettle and Hodges (1982). A discussion of some of the major problems with popular discussions of urban unrest can be found in Keith (1993). Good starting points for looking at issues linked to more recent outbreaks of urban unrest in the north of England are Cantle (2001) and Ouseley (2001).

8 Racism, Nationalism and Political Action

Much of the literature on this relatively neglected topic is fairly limited in scope. A good starting point for the theoretical aspect of this question is Miles (1989). Useful attempts to analyse the changing political language on race and nation are made in Ansell (1997), Gordon and Klug (1986), Seidel (1986b) and Smith (1994). For the politics of the neo-fascist right see Husbands (1983) and Miles and Phizacklea (1979). For more recent developments see Back *et al.* (1996), Cronin (1996), Durham (1998), Eatwell (1996, 1998) and Thurlow (1998). For a selection of new-right perspectives on these issues see Palmer (1986). You may also find it useful to look at copies of the journal *Searchlight*, which covers the activities of neofascist and extreme right-wing groups. Some interesting papers on racial violence across Europe can be found in Björgo and Witte (1993). See also Cheles *et al.* (1995).

9 Race, Politics and Mobilisation

Due to the relative neglect of this topic there is no detailed up-to-date study of all its dimensions. For an early critique of this neglect in traditional studies of the subject see CCCS Race and Politics Group (1982). Useful considerations of aspects of black and Asian political mobilisation can be found in Anwar (1998), Carter (1986), FitzGerald (1987), Pearson (1981) and Saggar (1998b). Recent developments are examined in Back and Solomos (1992a,b), Shukra (1998) and Solomos and Back (1991, 1995). Another useful collection is James and Harris (1993). The role of black women in political mobilisation is looked at in Sudbury (1998). For the development of religious and fundamentalist ideologies see Bhatt (1997). The topic of antiracism has also been relatively neglected, but see Bonnett (2000) and Lloyd (1991, 1998).

10 Race, Culture and Identity Politics

The best overviews of the issues covered in this chapter are contained in Alibhai-Brown (1999), Brah (1996) and Donald and Rattansi (1992). See also Anthias and Yuval-Davis (1992), Appignanesi and Maitland (1989), Asad (1990a,b) and James (1992). For a more theoretical and comparative perspective see Goldberg (1990a). On the role of the media see van Dijk (1991). For perspectives drawing on feminist as well as other sources see Bhavnani and Phoenix (1994). For the changing dynamics of race and urban identities among young people see Back (1996).

11 Race, Class and Social Change

A good starting point for the issues covered in this chapter is Modood *et al.* (1997). There are a number of overviews of social trends based on 1991 census data, including Coleman and Salt (1996) and Karn (1997). Ballard (1996) provides a useful discussion of key themes that arise from this data, as does Owen (1994b). For another overview of social trends see Mason (2000). An interesting review of developments in the US and England can be found in Small (1994). A journalistic insight into contemporary debates is provided in Alibhai-Brown (2000).

12 New Directions and Perspectives

Good starting points for looking at the issues covered in this chapter are Appiah and Gutmann (1996) and Solomos and Back (1996). An exhaustive collection of classic and contemporary pieces on these issues can be found in Bulmer and Solomos (1999b). For more recent conceptual debates and policy trends in Britain see Blackstone *et al.* (1998) and Cohen (1999). For useful American comparisons see Marable (1985), Reed (1999) and Wilson (1988). Debates on the reinvention of British and English national identities are discussed in Dodd (1995) and Gilroy (1993). For the topic of multiculturalism see May (1999) and Modood and Werbner (1997). Global trends in and processes of migration are explored in Papastergiadis (2000). For contemporary conceptual debates on the future of racial and ethnic relations see Goldberg and Solomos (2002). A feeling for current scholarly research agendas and debates can be gained by browsing through some of the journals mentioned earlier.

Bibliography

Abbott, S. (ed.) (1971) *The Prevention of Racial Discrimination in Britain* (Oxford: Oxford University Press).

Adolino, J. R. (1998) *Ethnic Minorities, Electoral Politics and Political Integration in Britain* (London: Pinter).

AFFOR (1978) *Talking Blues* (Birmingham: AFFOR).

Ahmad, W. I. U. (ed.) (1993) *'Race' and Health in Contemporary Britain* (Buckingham: Open University Press).

Ahmad, W. I. U. and Atkin, K. (eds) (1996) *'Race' and Community Care* (Buckingham: Open University Press).

Ahmed, A. S. (1992) *Postmodernism and Islam* (London: Routledge).

Akhtar, S. (1989) *Be Careful With Muhammad! The Salman Rushdie Affair* (London: Bellew).

Alderman, G. (1983) *The Jewish Community in British Politics* (Oxford: Clarendon Press).

Alderson, J. and Stead, P. (1973) *The Police We Deserve* (London: Wolf).

Alexander, C. (1996) *The Art of Being Black: The Creation of Black British Youth Identities* (Oxford: Clarendon Press).

Alford, R. and Friedland, R. (1985) *Powers of Theory: Capitalism, the State and Democracy* (Cambridge: Cambridge University Press).

Ali, R. and O'Cinneide, C. (2002) *Our House: Race and Representation in British Politics* (London: Institute for Public Policy Research).

Alibhai-Brown, Y. (1999) *True Colours: Public Attitudes to Multiculturalism and the Role of Government* (London: Institute for Public Policy Research).

——(2000) *Who Do We Think We Are? Imagining the New Britain* (London: Allen Lane).

Amin, K. and Oppenheim, C. (1992) *Poverty in Black and White* (London: Child Poverty Action Group).

Amin, K. and Richardson, R. (1992) *Politics for All: Equality, Culture and the General Election 1992* (London: Runnymede Trust).

Ansell, A. E. (1997) *New Right, New Racism: Race and Reaction in the United States and Britain* (New York: New York University Press).

Anthias, F. (1990) 'Race and Class Revisited – Conceptualizing Race and Racism', *Sociological Review*, 38, 1: 19–42.

——(1992) 'Connecting "Race" and Ethnic Phenomena', *Sociology*, 26, 3: 421–38.

Anthias, F. and Yuval-Davis, N. (1992) *Racialized Boundaries: Race, Nation, Gender, Colour and Class and the Anti-racist Struggle* (London: Routledge).

Anwar, M. (1986) *Race and Politics* (London: Tavistock).

——(1994) *Race and Elections: The Participation of Ethnic Minorities in Politics* (Warwick: Centre for Research in Ethnic Relations, University of Warwick).

——(1998) *Ethnic Minorities and the British Electoral System* (Warwick: Centre for Research in Ethnic Relations, University of Warwick).

Appiah, K. A. and Gutmann, A. (1996) *Color Conscious: The Political Morality of Race* (Princeton, NJ: Princeton University Press).

Appignanesi, L. and Maitland, S. (eds) (1989) *The Rushdie File* (London: Fourth Estate).

Appleby, G. and Ellis, E. (1984) 'Formal Investigations: The Commission for Racial Equality and the Equal Opportunities Commission as law enforcement agencies', *Public Law*, Spring: 58–81.

Asad, T. (1990a) 'Multiculturalism and British Identity in the Wake of the Rushdie Affair', *Politics and Society*, 18, 4: 455–80.

——(1990b) 'Ethnography, Literature, and Politics: Some Readings and Uses of Salman Rushdie's *The Satanic Verses*', *Cultural Anthropology*, 5, 3: 239–69.

——(1993) *Genealogies of Religion: Discipline and Reasons of Power in Christianity and Islam* (Baltimore, MD: Johns Hopkins University Press).

Audit Commission (2000) *Another Country: Implementing Dispersal Under the Immigration and Asylum Act 1999* (London: Audit Commission).

——(2002) *Equality and Diversity* (London: Audit Commission).

Back, L. (1996) *New Ethnicities and Urban Culture: Racisms and Multiculture in Young Lives* (London: UCL Press).

Back, L., Keith, M. and Solomos, J. (1996) 'Technology, Race and Neo-Fascism in a Digital Age: The New Modalities of Racist Culture', *Patterns of Prejudice*, 30, 2: 3–27.

Back, L. and Solomos, J. (1992a) 'Who Represents Us? Racialised Politics and Candidate Selection', *Research Papers No. 3* (London: Department of Politics and Sociology, Birkbeck College).

——(1992b) 'Black Politics and Social Change in Birmingham, UK: An Analysis of Recent Trends', *Ethnic and Racial Studies*, 15, 3: 327–51.

——(1993) 'Doing Research, Writing Politics: The Dilemmas of Political Intervention in Research on Racism', *Economy and Society*, 22, 2: 178–99.

——(eds) (2000) *Theories of Race and Racism: A Reader* (London: Routledge).

Baldwin-Edwards, M. (1991) 'Immigration After 1992', *Policy and Politics*, 19, 3: 199–211.

Balibar, E. (1991) 'Es Gibt Keinen Staat in Europa: Racism and Politics in Europe Today', *New Left Review*, 186: 5–19.

Balibar E. and Wallerstein, I. (1991) *Race, Nation, Class* (London: Verso).

Ball, W. and Solomos, J. (eds) (1990) *Race and Local Politics* (Basingstoke: Macmillan).

Ballard, R. (1996) 'Negotiating Race and Ethnicity: Exploring the Implications of the 1991 Census', *Patterns of Prejudice*, 30, 3: 3–33.

Ballis Lal, B. (1990) *The Romance of Culture in an Urban Civilisation* (London: Routledge).

Banton, M. (1955) *The Coloured Quarter: Negro Immigrants in an English City* (London: Jonathan Cape).

——(1959) *White and Coloured* (London: Jonathan Cape).

——(1967) *Race Relations* (London: Tavistock).

——(1983) *Racial and Ethnic Competition* (Cambridge: Cambridge University Press).

——(1985) *Promoting Racial Harmony* (Cambridge: Cambridge University Press).

——(1989) 'Minority Rights and Individual Rights', paper presented at the CRE PSI Seminar on Freedom of Speech, 28 September.

——(1991) 'The Race Relations Problematic', *British Journal of Sociology*, 42, 1: 115–30.

Banton, M. (1992) 'The Nature and Causes of Racism and Racial Discrimination', *International Sociology*, 7, 1: 69–84.

——(1996) *International Action Against Racial Discrimination* (Oxford: Clarendon Press).

——(1998) *Racial Theories*, 2nd edn (Cambridge: Cambridge University Press).

Barkan, E. (1992) *The Retreat of Scientific Racism* (Cambridge: Cambridge University Press).

Barker, M. (1981) *The New Racism* (London: Junction Books).

Bauböck, R. (1991) *Immigration and the Boundaries of Citizenship, Monographs in Ethnic Relations, No. 4* (Warwick: Centre for Research in Ethnic Relations, University of Warwick).

Beetham, D. (1970) *Transport and Turbans* (Oxford: Oxford University Press).

Beishon, S., Modood, T. and Virdee, S. (1998) *Ethnic Minority Families* (London: Policy Studies Institute).

Bell, D. (1987) *And We Are Not Saved: The Elusive Quest for Racial Justice* (New York: Basic Books).

Benedict, R. (1943) *Race and Racism* (London: Routledge).

Ben-Tovim, G. and Gabriel, J. (1979) 'The Politics of Race in Britain: a Review of the Major Trends and of the Recent Literature', *Sage Race Relations Abstracts*, 4, 4: 1–56.

Ben-Tovim, G., Gabriel, J., Law, I. and Stredder, K. (1986) *The Local Politics of Race* (Basingstoke: Macmillan).

Benyon, J. (ed.) (1984) *Scarman and After* (Oxford: Pergamon Press).

Benyon, J. (1986) 'A Tale of Failure: Race and Policing', *Policy Papers in Ethnic Relations No. 3* (Warwick: Centre for Research in Ethnic Relations, University of Warwick).

Benyon, J. and Solomos, J. (eds) (1987) *The Roots of Urban Unrest* (Oxford: Pergamon Press).

Berghahn, M. (1984) *German–Jewish Refugees in England* (Basingstoke: Macmillan).

Berghe, P. L. van den (1967) *Race and Racism* (New York: Wiley).

Berkeley, H. (1977) *The Odyssey of Enoch* (London: Hamish Hamilton).

Berthoud, R. (1997) 'The Mental Health of Ethnic Minorities', *New Community*, 23, 3: 309–24.

Bevan, V. (1986) *The Development of British Immigration Law* (London: Croom Helm).

Bhabha, H. K. (1990a) 'Interrogating Identity: The Postcolonial Prerogative', in D. T. Goldberg (ed.), *Anatomy of Racism* (Minneapolis, Min.: University of Minnesota Press).

Bhabha, H. K. (ed.) (1990b) *Nation and Narration* (London: Routledge).

Bhachu, P. (1991) 'Culture, Ethnicity and Class Amongst Punjabi Sikh Women in 1990s Britain', *New Community*, 17, 3: 401–12.

Bhatt, C. (1997) *Liberation and Purity: Race, New Religious Movements and the Ethics of Postmodernity* (London: UCL Press).

Bhattacharyya, G., Gabriel, J and Small, S. (2002) *Race and Power: Global Racism in the Twenty-First Century* (London: Routledge).

Bhavnani, K. K. (ed.) (2001) *Feminism and 'Race'* (Oxford: Oxford University Press).

Bhavnani, K. K. and Phoenix, A. (eds) (1994) *Shifting Identities, Shifting Racisms* (London: Sage).

Bhavnani, R. (2001) *Rethinking Interventions to Combat Racism* (Stoke on Trent: Commission for Racial Equality with Trentham Books).
Billig, M. (1978) *Fascists: A Social Psychological View of the National Front* (London: Academic Press).
Billig, M. and Bell, A. (1980) 'Fascist Parties in Post-War Britain', *Sage Race Relations Abstracts*, 5, 1: 1–30.
Bindman, G. (1980) 'The Law, Equal Opportunity and Affirmative Action', *New Community*, VIII, 3: 248–60.
Björgo, T. and Witte, R. (eds) (1993) *Racist Violence in Europe* (Basingstoke: Macmillan).
Blackstone, T., Parekh, B. and Sanders, P. (eds) (1998) *Race Relations in Britain: A Developing Agenda* (London: Routledge).
Blake, N. and Fransman, L. (eds) (1999) *Nationality and Asylum Under the Human Rights Act of 1998* (London: Butterworths).
Blakemore, K. and Drake, R. (1996) *Understanding Equal Opportunity Policies* (London: Prentice-Hall/Harvester Wheatsheaf).
Bloch, A. (2000) 'A New Era or More of the Same? Asylum Policy in the UK', *Journal of Refugee Studies* 13, 1: 29–42
Bonnett, A. (2000) *Anti-Racism* (London: Routledge).
Bovenkerk, F., Miles, R. and Verbunt, G. (1990) 'Racism, Migration and the State in Western Europe. A Case for Comparative Analysis', *International Sociology*, 5, 4: 475–90.
Bowles, S. and Gintis, H. (1987) *Democracy and Capitalism* (London: Routledge & Kegan Paul).
Bowling, B. (1999) *Violent Racism: Victimisation, Policing and Social Context*, revd edn (Oxford: Clarendon Press).
Bowling, B. and Phillips, C. (2001) *Racism, Crime and Justice* (Harlow: Longman).
Bozzoli, B. (ed.) (1987) *Class, Community and Conflict* (Johannesburg: Ravan).
Brah, A. (1992) 'Difference, Diversity and Differentiation', in J. Donald and A. Rattansi (eds), *'Race', Culture & Difference* (London: Sage).
——(1996) *Cartographies of Diaspora: Contesting Identities* (London: Routledge).
Britton, N. J. (2000a) *Black Justice? Race, Criminal Justice and Identity* (Stoke on Trent: Trentham Books).
——(2000b) 'Examining Police/Black Relations: What's in a Story?', *Ethnic and Racial Studies*, 23, 4: 692–711.
Brody, J. D. (1998) *Impossible Purities: Blackness, Femininity and Victorian Culture* (Durham, USA: Duke University Press).
Brown, A. R. (1999) '"The other day I met a constituent of mine": A Theory of Anectodal Racism', *Ethnic and Racial Studies*, 22, 1: 23–55.
Brown, C. (1984) *Black and White Britain* (London: Heinemann).
——(1992) '"Same Difference": The Persistence of Racial Disadvantage in the British Employment Market', in P. Graham, A. Rattansi and R. Skellington (eds), *Racism and Antiracism. Inequalities, Opportunities and Policies* (London: Sage).
Brown, C. and Gay, P. (1985) *Racial Discrimination: 17 Years After the Act* (London: Policy Studies Institute).
Brown, J. (1977) *Shades of Grey* (Cranfield: Cranfield Police Studies).

Brownill, S., Razzaque, K., Stirling, T. and Thomas, H. (2000) 'Patterns of Inclusion and Exclusion: Ethnic Minorities and Urban Development Corporations', in G. Stoker (ed.), *The New Politics of Local Governance* (Basingstoke: Macmillan).

Browning, R. P., Marshall, D. P. and Tabb, D. H. (1984) *Protest is Not Enough* (Berkeley, CA: University of California Press).

Brubaker, W. R. (1990) 'Immigration, Citizenship, and the Nation-State in France and Germany: A Comparative Historical Analysis', *International Sociology*, 5, 4: 461–74.

Bryan, B., Dadzie, S. and Scafe, S. (1985) *The Heart of the Race: Black Women's Lives in Britain* (London: Virago).

Bulmer, M. and Solomos, J. (eds) (1999a) *Ethnic and Racial Studies Today* (London: Routledge).

——(eds) (1999b) *Racism* (Oxford: Oxford University Press).

Burgess, J. R. (1985) 'News from Nowhere: The Press, the Riots and The Myth of the Inner City', in J. R. Burgess and J. R. Gold (eds), *Geography, the Media and Popular Culture* (London: Croom Helm).

Burleigh, M. and Wippermann, W. (1991) *The Racial State: Germany 1933–1945* (Cambridge: Cambridge University Press).

Burnley Task Force (2001) *Report* (Burnley: Task Force).

Bush, B. (1999) *Imperialism, Race and Resistance: Africa and Britain, 1919–1945* (London: Routledge).

Butler, Lord (1971) *The Art of the Possible* (Harmondsworth: Penguin).

Cabinet Office, Performance and Innovation Unit (2001) *Ethnic Minorities in the Labour Market* (London: Cabinet Office).

Cabinet Office, Social Exclusion Unit (2000) *Minority Ethnic Issues in Social Exclusion and Neighbourhood Renewal* (London: Cabinet Office).

——(2001) *Preventing Social Exclusion* (London: Cabinet Office).

Cain, M. (1973) *Society and the Policeman's Role* (London: Routledge & Kegan Paul).

Cambridge, A. X. and Feuchtwang, S. (eds) (1990) *Antiracist Strategies* (Aldershot: Avebury).

Cantle, T. (2001) *Community Cohesion: A Report by the Independent Review Team* (London: Home Office).

Carr, J. (1987) *New Roads to Equality: Contract Compliance for the UK?*, Fabian Tract 517 (London: Fabian Society).

Carter, B. (2000) *Realism and Racism: Concepts of Race in Sociological Research* (London: Routledge).

Carter, B., Harris, C. and Joshi, S. (1987) 'The 1951–55 Conservative Government and the Racialisation of Black Immigration', *Policy Papers in Ethnic Relations No. 11* (Warwick: Centre for Research in Ethnic Relations, University of Warwick).

Carter, T. (1986) *Shattering Illusions* (London: Lawrence & Wishart).

Casey, J. (1982) 'One Nation: The Politics of Race', *The Salisbury Review*, Autumn: 23–8.

Cashmore, E. (1987) *The Logic of Racism* (London: Allen & Unwin).

Castles, S. (1993) 'Migrations and Minorities in Europe. Perspectives for the 1990s: Eleven Hypotheses', in J. Wrench and J. Solomos (eds), *Racism and Migration in Western Europe* (Oxford: Berg).

Castles, S. with Booth, H. and Wallace, T. (1984) *Here for Good: Western Europe's New Ethnic Minorities* (London: Pluto).

Castles, S. and Kosack, G. (1985) *Immigrant Workers and Class Structure in Western Europe* (Oxford: Oxford University Press).
Castles, S. and Miller, M. J. (1998) *The Age of Migration*, 2nd edn (Basingstoke: Macmillan).
Cathcart, B. (1999) *The Case of Stephen Lawrence* (London: Viking).
CCCS Race and Politics Group (1982) *The Empire Strikes Back: Race and Racism in 70s Britain* (London: Hutchinson).
Cesarani, D. (ed.) (1990) *The Making of Modern Anglo-Jewry* (Oxford: Basil Blackwell).
Cesarani, D. (1992) *Justice Delayed: How Britain Became a Refuge for Nazi War Criminals* (London: Mandarin).
Chambers, I. (1989) 'Narratives of Nationalism: Being British', *New Formations*, 7: 88–103.
Cheetham, J. (1988) 'Ethnic Associations in Britain', in S. Jenkins (ed.), *Ethnic Associations and the Welfare State* (New York: Columbia University Press).
Cheles, L., Ferguson, R. and Vaughan, M. (eds) (1995) *The Far Right in Western & Eastern Europe*, 2nd edn (London: Longman).
Cheyette, B. (1993) *Constructions of 'the Jew' in English Literature and Society: Racial Representations, 1875–1945* (Cambridge: Cambridge University Press).
Cheyette, B. and Marcus, L. (eds) (1998) *Modernity, Culture and 'the Jew'* (Cambridge: Polity Press).
Clare, J. (1985) 'Time to dust off the Scarman report', *The Listener*, 3 October: 6–7.
Clarke, C. F. D. (1970) *Police/Community Relations: Report of a Conference at Ditchley Park*, (Ditchley Park: Ditchley Foundation).
Clarke, J. and Speeden, S. (2000) *Measuring Up* (London: Commission for Racial Equality).
——(2001) *Then and Now: Change for the Better?* (London: Commission for Racial Equality).
Coates, D. (1984) *The Context of British Politics* (London: Hutchinson).
Cohen, A. (1993) *Masquerade Politics: Explorations in the Structure of Urban Cultural Movements* (Oxford: Berg).
Cohen, P. (1988) 'The Perversions of Inheritance: Studies in the Making of Multi-Racist Britain', in P. Cohen and H. Bains (eds), *Multi-Racist Britain* (Basingstoke: Macmillan).
Cohen P. (ed.) (1999) *New Ethnicities, Old Racisms?* (London: Zed Books).
Cohen, R. (1991) 'East–West and European Migration in a Global Context', *New Community*, 18, 1: 9–26.
——(1994) *Frontiers of Identity: The British and the Others* (London: Longman).
Coleman, D. and Salt, J. (eds) (1996) *Ethnicity in the 1991 Census, Volume One, Demographic Characteristics of the Ethnic Minority Populations* (London: Office for National Statistics).
Colley, L. (1992) *Britons: Forging the Nation 1707–1837* (New Haven, CT: Yale University Press).
Collins, C. (2002) *Separate Silos: Race and the Reform Agenda in Whitehall* (London: Institute for Public Policy Research).
Collins, P. H. (1990) *Black Feminist Thought* (Boston: Unwin Hyman).
Colls, R. and Dodd, P. (eds) (1986) *Englishness: Politics and Culture 1880–1920* (London: Croom Helm).

Commission for Racial Equality (CRE) (1977–2001) *Annual Reports* (London: Commission for Racial Equality).
——(1983) *The Race Relations Act 1976 – Time for a Change?* (London: Commission for Racial Equality).
——(1985a) *Review of the Race Relations Act 1976: Proposals for Change* (London: Commission for Racial Equality).
——(1985b) *Immigration Control Procedures: Report of a Formal Investigation* (London: Commission for Racial Equality).
——(1985c) *Positive Action and Equal Opportunity in Employment* (London: Commission for Racial Equality).
——(1987a) *Training: The Implementation of Equal Opportunities at Work* (London: Commission for Racial Equality).
——(1987b) *Principles of Practice for Contract Compliance* (London: Commission for Racial Equality).
——(1990) *Free Speech. Report of a Seminar* (London: Commission for Racial Equality).
——(1991) *Second Review of the Race Relations Act 1976* (London: Commission for Racial Equality).
——(1998) *Reform of the Race Relations Act 1976: Proposals from the Commission for Racial Equality* (London: Commission for Racial Equality).
——(2001a) *Strengthening the Race Relations Act* (London: Commission for Racial Equality).
——(2001b) *The General Duty to Promote Racial Equality* (London: Commission for Racial Equality).
——(2001c) *The Code of Practice on the Duty to Promote Race Equality* (London: Commission for Racial Equality).
Commission of the European Communities (1992) *Legal Instruments to Combat Racism and Xenophobia* (Brussels: Commission of the European Communities).
Commission on British Muslims and Islamophobia (1997) *Islamophobia: A Challenge for Us All* (London: The Runnymede Trust).
——(2001) *Addressing the Challenge of Islamophobia* (London: Commission on British Muslims and Islamophobia).
Connolly, P. and Troyna, B. (eds) (1998) *Researching Racism in Education: Politics, Theory and Practice* (Buckingham: Open University Press).
Coombes, A. (1994) *Reinventing Africa: Museums, Popular Culture and Popular Imagination in Late Victorian and Edwardian England* (New Haven, CT: Yale University Press).
Cornell, S. and Hartmann, D. (1998) *Ethnicity and Race: Making Identities in a Changing World* (Thousand Oaks, CA: Pine Forge Press).
Coussey, M. (2002) *Tackling Racial Equality: International Comparisons* (London: Home Office Research, Development and Statistics Directorate).
Cox, O. C. (1948) *Caste, Class and Race* (New York: Monthly Review Press).
Crewe, I. (1983) 'Representation and the Ethnic Minorities in Britain', in N. Glazer and K. Young (eds), *Ethnic Pluralism and Public Policy* (London: Heinemann).
Crick, B. (ed.) (1991) *National Identities* (Oxford: Blackwell).
Cronin, M. (1996) *The Failure of British Fascism: The Far Right and the Fight for Political Recognition* (Basingstoke: Macmillan).
Cross, M. and Keith, M. (eds) (1993) *Racism, the City and the State* (London: Routledge).

Cross, M. and Smith, D. I. (eds) (1987) *Black Youth Futures* (Leicester: National Youth Bureau).

Crossman, R. (1975) *Diaries of a Cabinet Minister*, vol. 1 (London: Hamish Hamilton).

Crowley, J. (1993) 'Paradoxes of the Politicisation of Race: A Comparison of the UK and France', *New Community*, 19, 4: 627–43.

Curtis, L. P. (1968) *Anglo-Saxons and Celts* (Connecticut: University of Bridgeport).

——(1971) *Apes and Angels: The Irishman in Victorian Caricature* (Washington, DC: Smithsonian Institution Press).

Curtis, L. (1984) *Nothing But the Same Old Story* (London: Information on Ireland).

Dangerfield, G. (1976) *The Damnable Question: A Study of Anglo-Irish Relations* (Boston, Mass.: Little, Brown).

Daniel, W. W. (1968) *Racial Disadvantage in England* (Harmondsworth: Penguin).

Daye, S. (1994) *Middle Class Blacks in Britain: A Racial Fraction of a Class or a Class Fraction of a Racial Group?* (Basingstoke: Macmillan).

Deakin, N. (1965) *Colour and the British Electorate* (London: Pall Mall Press).

——(1968) 'The Politics of the Commonwealth Immigrants Bill', *Political Quarterly*, 39, 1: 24–45.

——(1970) *Colour, Citizenship and British Society* (London: Panther).

——(1972) 'The Immigration Issue in British Politics', unpublished PhD thesis, University of Sussex.

Dean, D. (1987) 'Coping with Colonial Immigration, the Cold War and Colonial Policy', *Immigrants and Minorities*, 6, 3: 305–34.

——(1993) 'The Conservative Government and the 1961 Commonwealth Immigration Act: The Inside Story', *Race and Class*, 35, 2: 57–74.

Dear, G. (1985) *Handsworth/Lozells, September 1985: Report of the Chief Constable, West Midlands Police* (Birmingham: West Midlands Police).

Dearlove, J. (1973) *The Politics of Policy in Local Government* (Cambridge: Cambridge University Press).

——(1982) 'The Political Science of British Politics', *Parliamentary Affairs*, 35: 436–54.

Dearlove, J. and Saunders, P. (1991) *Introduction to British Politics*, 2nd edn (Cambridge: Polity Press).

Deedes, W. (1968) *Race Without Rancour* (London: Conservative Political Centre).

Demuth, C. (1978) *'Sus': A Report on the Vagrancy Act* (London: Runnymede Trust).

DO (1957) Commonwealth Immigration: Social and Economic Problems, DO 35/5219 (London: Public Record Office).

Dodd, P. (1995) *The Battle Over Britain* (London: Demos).

Donald, J. and Rattansi, A. (eds) (1992) *'Race', Culture and Difference* (London: Sage).

Drake, St Clair (1954) 'Value Systems, Social Structures and Race Relations in the British Isles', unpublished PhD thesis, University of Chicago.

Duffield, M. (1988) *Black Radicalism and the Politics of De-industrialisation* (Aldershot: Avebury).

Dummett, A. and Nicol, A. (1990) *Subjects, Citizens, Aliens and Others: Nationality and Immigration Law* (London: Weidenfeld & Nicolson).

Dunleavy, P. (1980) *Urban Political Analysis* (Basingstoke: Macmillan).

Dunleavy, P. and O'Leary, B. (1987) *Theories of the State* (Basingstoke: Macmillan).
Durham, M. (1998) *Women and Fascism* (London: Routledge).
Eade, J. (1989) *The Politics of Community* (Aldershot: Avebury).
Eatwell, R. (1996) *Fascism: A History* (London: Vintage).
——(1998) 'The Dynamics of Right-wing Electoral Breakthrough', *Patterns of Prejudice*, 32, 3: 3–31.
Edelman, M. (1971) *Politics as Symbolic Action: Mass Arousal and Quiescence* (Chicago: Markham).
——(1977) *Political Language: Words that Succeed and Policies that Fail* (New York: Academic Press).
——(1985) 'Political Language and Political Reality', *Political Studies*, XVIII, 1: 10–19.
Edgar, D. (1977) 'Racism, Fascism and the Politics of the National Front', *Race and Class*, 19, 2: 111–31.
Edwards, J. (1995) *When Race Counts: The Morality of Racial Preference in Britain and America* (London: Routledge).
Edwards, J. and Batley, R. (1978) *The Politics of Positive Discrimination* (London: Tavistock).
Elton, Lord (1965) *The Unarmed Invasion* (London: Godfrey Bles). (1985–2001) *Equal Opportunities Review* (London: Industrial Relations Services).
Essed, P. (1987) 'Academic Racism Common Sense in the Social Sciences', Working Paper No. 5 (Amsterdam: Centre for Race and Ethnic Studies).
——(1990) *Everyday Racism* (Claremont, NH: Hunter House).
——(1991) *Understanding Everyday Racism* (Newbury Park, CA: Sage).
Essed, P. and Goldberg, D. T. (eds) (2002) *Race Critical Theories* (Oxford: Blackwell).
European Commission (2000) *European Conference on Combating Racism at European Level* (Luxembourg: Office for Official Publications of the European Communities).
——(2001) *European Union Action to Combat Racism at European Level* (Luxembourg: Office for Official Publications of the European Communities).
European Parliament (1998) *EU Anti-Discrimination Policy: From Equal Opportunities Between Women and Men to Combating Racism* (written by Mark Bell) (Brussels: European Parliament).
Evans, J. M. (1983) *Immigration Law* (London: Sweet & Maxwell).
Evans, N. (1980) 'The South Wales Race Riots of 1919', *Llafur*, 3, 1: 5–29.
——(1985) 'Regulating the Reserve Army: Arabs, Blacks and the Local State in Cardiff 1919–45', in K. Lunn (ed.), *Race and Labour in Twentieth Century Britain* (London: Frank Cass).
Evans, P. B., Rueschemeyer, D. and Skocpol, T. (1985) *Bringing the State Back In* (Cambridge: Cambridge University Press).
Farley, R. and Allen, W. R. (1989) *The Color Line and the Quality of Life in America* (New York: Oxford University Press).
Favell, A. (1997) 'Citizenship and Immigration: Pathologies of a Progressive Philosophy', *New Community*, 23, 2: 173–95.
——(2001) *Philosophies of Integration: Immigration and the Idea of Citizenship in France and Britain*, 2nd edn (Basingstoke: Macmillan).
Feldman, D. (1994) *Englishmen and Jews: Social Relations and Political Culture 1840–1914* (New Haven: CT Yale University Press).

Feuchtwang, S. (1990) 'Racism: Territoriality and Ethnocentricity', in A. X. Cambridge and S. Feuchtwang (eds), *Antiracist Strategies* (Aldershot: Avebury).
Fielding, N. (1981) *The National Front* (London: Routledge).
Fielding, S. and Geddes, A. (1998) 'The British Labour Party and "Ethnic Entryism": Participation, Integration and the Party Context', *Journal of Ethnic and Migration Studies*, 24, 1: 57–72.
Fighting Talk (1995–2000) issues 11–23.
FitzGerald, M. (1984) *Political Parties and Black People* (London: Runnymede Trust).
——(1987) *Black People and Party Politics in Britain* (London: Runnymede Trust).
——(1998) '"Race" and the Criminal Justice System', in T. Blackstone, B. Parekh and P. Sanders (eds), *Race Relations in Britain: A Developing Agenda* (London: Routledge).
——(1999) *Final Report Into Stop and Search* (London: Home Office).
FitzGerald, M. and Layton-Henry, Z. (1986) 'Opposition Parties and Race Policies: 1979–83', in Z. Layton-Henry and P. Rich (eds), *Race, Government and Politics in Britain* (Basingstoke: Macmillan).
FitzGerald, M. and Sibbitt, R. (1998) *Ethnic Monitoring in Police Forces: A Beginning* (London: Home Office).
Flett, H. (1981) 'The Politics of Dispersal in Birmingham', *Working Paper on Ethnic Relations No. 14* (Warwick: Centre for Research in Ethnic Relations, University of Warwick).
Flew, A. (1984) *Education, Race and Revolution* (London: Centre for Policy Studies).
Fogelson, R. M. (1971) *Violence as Protest* (Garden City, NY: Anchor Books).
Foot, P. (1965) *Immigration and Race in British Politics* (Harmondsworth: Penguin).
Forbes, I. and Mead, G. (1992) *Measure for Measure: A Comparative Analysis of Measures to Combat Racial Discrimination in the Member Countries of the European Community* (London: Department of Employment).
Ford, G. (ed.) (1992) *Fascist Europe: The Rise of Racism and Xenophobia* (London: Pluto).
Fredrickson, G. M. (1981) *White Supremacy: A Comparative Study of American and South African History* (Oxford: Oxford University Press).
Freeman, G. (1979) *Immigrant Labor and Racial Conflict in Industrial Societies* (Princeton, NJ: Princeton University Press).
Freeman, M. D. A. and Spencer, S. (1979) 'Immigration Control, Black Workers and the Economy', *British Journal of Law and Society*, 6, 1: 53–81.
Fryer, P. (1984) *Staying Power: The History of Black People in Britain* (London: Pluto).
——(1988) *Black People in the British Empire: An Introduction* (London: Pluto).
Gaffney, J. (1987) 'Interpretations of Violence: The Handsworth Riots of 1985', *Policy Papers in Ethnic Relations No. 10* (Warwick: Centre for Research in Ethnic Relations, University of Warwick).
Gainer, B. (1972) *The Alien Invasion: The Origins of the Aliens Act of 1905* (London: Heinemann).
Gallagher, T. (1985) 'A Tale of Two Cities: Communal Strife in Glasgow and Liverpool Before 1914', in R. Swift and S. Gilley (eds), *The Irish in the Victorian City* (London: Croom Helm).

Gamble, A. (1981) *Britain in Decline* (Basingstoke: Macmillan).

Gamble, A. (1988) *The Free Economy and the Strong State* (Basingstoke: Macmillan).

Garrard, J. A. (1971) *The English and Immigration 1880–1914* (Oxford: Oxford University Press).

Gartner, L. P. (1973) *The Jewish Immigrant in England 1870–1914* (London: Simon Publications).

Gates, H. L. (ed.) (1986) *'Race', Writing and Difference* (Chicago, Ill.: University of Chicago Press).

——(1988) *The Signifying Monkey* (Oxford: Oxford University Press).

Gay, P. and Young, K. (1988) *Community Relations Councils* (London: Commission for Racial Equality).

Geddes, A. (1993) 'Asian and Afro-Caribbean Representation in Elected Local Government in England and Wales', *New Community*, 20, 1: 43–57

Genders, E. and Player, E. (1989) *Race Relations in Prisons* (Oxford: Clarendon Press).

Gerzina, G. (1995) *Black England: Life Before Emancipation* (London: John Murray).

Gifford, Lord (1986) *The Broadwater Farm Inquiry* (London: Karia Press).

Gilley, S. (1978) 'English Attitudes to the Irish in England 1789–1900', in C. Holmes (ed.) *Immigrants and Minorities in British Society* (London: Allen & Unwin).

——(1980) 'Catholics and Socialists in Glasgow, 1906–1912', in K. Lunn (ed.), *Hosts, Immigrants and Minorities* (Folkestone: Dawson).

Gilroy, P. (1987) *There Ain't No Black in the Union Jack* (London: Hutchinson).

——(1990a) 'One Nation Under a Groove: The Cultural Politics of "Race" and Racism in Britain', in D. T. Goldberg (ed.), *Anatomy of Racism* (Minneapolis, Min.: University of Minnesota Press).

——(1990b) 'The End of Anti-Racism', in W. Ball and J. Solomos (eds), *Race and Local Politics* (Basingstoke: Macmillan).

——(1991) 'It Ain't Where You're From, It's Where You're At… The Dialectics of Diasporic Identification', *Third Text*, 13: 3–16.

——(1993) *Small Acts: Thoughts on the Politics of Black Cultures* (London: Serpent's Tail).

——(1998) 'Race Ends Here', *Ethnic and Racial Studies*, 21, 5: 838–47.

Glasgow Media Studies Group (1997) *'Race', Migration and Media* (Glasgow: Glasgow Media Studies Group).

Glass, R. (1960) *Newcomers: West Indians in London* (London: Allen & Unwin).

Glazer, N. and Young, K. (eds) (1983) *Ethnic Pluralism and Public Policy* (London: Heinemann).

Glover, S. *et al* (2001) *Migration: An Economic and Social Analysis* (London: Home Office).

Goldberg, D. T. (ed.) (1990a) *Anatomy of Racism* (Minneapolis, Min.: University of Minnesota Press).

Goldberg, D. T. (1990b) 'The Social Formation of Racist Discourse', in D. T. Goldberg (ed.), *Anatomy of Racism* (Minneapolis, Min.: University of Minnesota Press).

——(1992) 'The Semantics of Race', *Ethnic and Racial Studies*, 15, 4: 543–69.

——(1993) *Racist Culture* (Oxford: Blackwell).

——(2002) *The Racial State* (Oxford: Blackwell).

Goldberg, D. T. and Solomos, J. (eds) (2002) *A Companion to Racial and Ethnic Studies* (Oxford: Blackwell).

Gordon, P. (1982) 'Racial Discrimination: Towards a Legal Strategy', *British Journal of Law and Society*, 9, 1: 127–35.

——(1985) *Policing Immigration: Britain's Internal Controls* (London: Pluto).

——(1986) *Racial Violence and Harassment* (London: Runnymede Trust).

——(1989a) *Fortress Europe? The Meaning of 1992* (London: Runnymede Trust).

——(1989b) *Citizenship for Some? Race and Government Policy 1979–1989* (London: Runnymede Trust).

——(1990) 'A Dirty War: The New Right and Local Authority Anti-Racism', in W. Ball and J. Solomos (eds), *Race and Local Politics* (Basingstoke: Macmillan).

Gordon, P. and Klug, F. (1986) *New Right/New Racism* (London: Searchlight).

Goulbourne, H. (1987) 'West Indian Groups and British Politics', paper presented at the Conference on Black People and British Politics, University of Warwick, November.

——(ed.) (1990) *Black Politics in Britain* (Aldershot: Avebury).

——(1991) *Ethnicity and Nationalism in Post-imperial Britain* (Cambridge: Cambridge University Press).

——(1998) *Race Relations in Britain Since 1945* (Basingstoke: Macmillan).

Greater London Council (GLC) (1984) *Racial Harassment in London* (London: Greater London Council).

Greenberg, S. B. (1980) *Race and State in Capitalist Development* (New Haven, CT: Yale University Press).

Gregory, D. and Urry, J. (eds) (1985) *Social Relations and Spatial Structures* (Basingstoke: Macmillan).

Gregory, J. (1987) *Sex, Race and the Law: Legislating for Equality* (London: Sage).

Grewal, S., Kay, J., Landor, L., Lewis, G. and Parmar, P. (1989) *Charting the Journey* (London: Sheba).

Griffiths, P. (1966) *A Question of Colour* (London: Leslie Frewin).

Grossberg, L., Nelson, C. and Treichler, C. (eds) (1992) *Cultural Studies* (London: Routledge).

Guillaumin, C. (1980) 'The idea of race and its elevation to autonomous scientific and legal status', in UNESCO, *Sociological Theories: Race and Colonialism* (Paris: UNESCO).

Gurnah, A. (1984) 'The Politics of Racism Awareness Training', *Critical Social Policy*, 11: 6–20.

Hall, S. (1977) 'Pluralism, race and class in Caribbean society', in UNESCO, *Race and Class in Post-colonial Society* (Paris: UNESCO).

——(1980) 'Race, Articulation and Societies Structured in Dominance', in UNESCO (ed.), *Sociology Theories: Race and Colonialism* (Paris: UNESCO).

——(1985a) 'Gramsci's Relevance to the Analysis of Racism and Ethnicity', unpublished paper.

——(1985b) 'The gulf between Labour and Blacks', *Guardian*, 15 June.

——(1987) 'Urban Unrest in Britain', in J. Benyon and J. Solomos (eds), *The Roots of Urban Unrest* (Oxford: Pergamon Press).

——(1991a) 'Old and New Identities, Old and New Ethnicities', in A. D. King (ed.), *Culture, Globalization and the World System* (Basingstoke: Macmillan).

——(1991b) 'The Local and the Global: Globalization and Ethnicity', in A. D. King (ed.), *Culture, Globalization and the World System* (Basingstoke: Macmillan).

Hall, S., Critcher, C., Jefferson, T., Clarke, J. and Roberts, B. (1978) *Policing the Crisis: Mugging, the State, and Law and Order* (Basingstoke: Macmillan).

Hall, W. (1986) 'Contracts Compliance at the GLC', *Local Government Studies*, 12, 4: 17–24.

Halstead, M. (1988) *Education, Justice and Cultural Diversity: An Examination of the Honeyford Affair* (London: Falmer).

Hammar, T. (ed.) (1985) *European Immigration Policy: A Comparative Study* (Cambridge: Cambridge University Press).

Hammar, T. (1990) *Democracy and the Nation State, Aliens, Denizens and Citizens in a World of International Migration* (Aldershot: Avebury).

Hansen, R. (2000a) 'British Citizenship after Empire: A Defence', *Political Quarterly*, 71, 1: 42–9.

——(2000b) *Citizenship and Immigration in Postwar Britain* (Oxford: Oxford University Press).

Harris, C. (1988) 'Images of Blacks in Britain: 1930–60', in S. Allen and M. Macey (eds), *Race and Social Policy* (London: Economic and Social Research Council).

Hartley-Brewer, M. (1965) 'Smethwick', in N. Deakin (ed.), *Colour and the British Electorate 1964* (London: Pall Mall Press).

Harvey, D. (1989) *The Condition of Postmodernity* (Oxford: Blackwell).

Haseler, S. (1992) *The English Tribe: Identity, Nation and Europe* (Basingstoke: Macmillan).

Hechter, M. (1975) *Internal Colonialism* (London: Routledge).

Heineman, B. (1972) *The Politics of the Powerless: A Study of the Campaign Against Racial Discrimination* (Oxford: Oxford University Press).

Heisler, B. S. (1991) 'A Comparative Perspective on the Underclass: Questions of Urban Poverty, Race and Citizenship', *Theory and Society*, 20, 4: 455–83.

Henderson, J. and Karn, V. (1987) *Race, Class and State Housing* (Aldershot: Gower).

Hepple, R. (1968) *Race, Jobs and the Law in Britain* (Harmondsworth: Penguin).

——(1983) 'Judging Equal Rights', *Critical Legal Problems*, 36: 71–90.

Her Majesty's Inspectorate of Constabulary (1997) *Winning the Race: Policing Plural Communities* (London: Home Office).

——(2000) *Policing London – 'Winning Consent', A Review of Murder Investigation and Community and Race Relations Issues in the Metropolitan Police Service* (London: Home Office).

Hickman, M. J. (1995) *Religion, Class and Identity: The Irish in Britain* (Aldershot: Avebury).

Hickman, M. J. and Walter, B. (1997) *Discrimination and the Irish Community in Britain* (London: Commission for Racial Equality).

Higgins, J., Deakin, N., Edwards, J. and Wicks, M. (1983) *Government and Urban Poverty* (Oxford: Basil Blackwell).

Hill, M. and Issacharoff, R. (1971) *Community Action and Race Relations* (Oxford: Oxford University Press).

Hill, R. and Bell. A. (1988) *The Other Face of Terror: Inside Europe's Neo-Nazi Network* (London: Grafton Books).

Hirschfeld, G. (1984) *Exile in Great Britain: Refugees From Hitler's Germany* (Leamington Spa: Berg).

Hirst, P. (1985) *Marxism and Historical Writing* (London: Routledge).

Hobsbawm, E. (1990) *Nations and Nationalism Since 1780: Programme, Myth, Reality* (Cambridge: Cambridge University Press).

Holdaway, S. (1996) *The Racialisation of British Policing* (Basingstoke: Macmillan).
——(1997) 'Constructing and Sustaining "Race" Within the Police Workforce', *British Journal of Sociology*, 48, 1: 19–34.
Holdaway, S. and Barron, A.-M. (1997) *Resigners? The Experience of Black and Asian Police Officers* (Basingstoke: Macmillan).
Holmes, C. (1978) *Immigrants and Minorities in British Society* (London: George Allen & Unwin).
——(1979) *Anti-Semitism in British Society 1876–1939* (London: Edward Arnold).
——(1988) *John Bull's Island* (Basingstoke: Macmillan).
Home Office (1973) *Police/Immigrant Relations in England and Wales* (London: HMSO).
——(1975) *Racial Discrimination*, Cmnd 6234 (London: HMSO).
——(1977) *A Guide to the Race Relations Act 1976* (London: Home Office).
——(1981) *Racial Attacks* (London: Home Office).
——(1998a) *Fairer, Faster and Firmer: A Modern Approach to Immigration and Asylum* (London: The Stationery Office).
——(1998b) *Statistics on Race and the Criminal Justice System* (London: Home Office).
——(1999a) *Immigration and Asylum Act 1999* (London: The Stationery Office).
——(1999b) *Race Equality: The Home Secretary's Employment Targets* (London: Home Office).
——(1999c) *Statistics on Race and the Criminal Justice System* (London: Home Office).
——(2000) *Stephen Lawrence Inquiry: Home Secretary's Action Plan, First Annual Report on Progress* (London: Home Office).
——(2001) *Race Relations (Amendment) Act 2000* (London: Home Office).
——(2002) *Secure Borders, Safe Haven: Integration with Diversity in Modern Britain* (London: The Stationery Office).
Home Office, Ministerial Group on Public Order and Community Cohesion (2001) *Building Cohesive Communities* (London: Home Office).
Home Office, Race Equality Unit (2000) *Connecting Communities: Proposals for Race Equality Support Programmes* (London: Home Office).
Honeyford, R. (1983) 'Multi-Ethnic Intolerance', *Salisbury Review*, 4: 12–13.
——(1984) 'Education and Race: An Alternative View', *Salisbury Review*, 6: 30–2.
——(1988a) *Multi-Ethnic Education: The Burnage High School Lesson* (York: Campaign for Real Education).
——(1988b) *Integration or Disintegration. Towards a Non-Racist Society* (London: Claridge Press).
——(1998) *The Commission for Racial Equality: British Bureaucracy and the Multiethnic Society* (New Brunswick, NJ: Transaction Books).
hooks, b. (1981) *Ain't I A Woman: Black Women and Feminism* (Boston, Mass.: South End Press).
——(1990) *Yearning: Race, Gender, and Cultural Politics* (Boston, Mass.: South End Press).
——(1992) *Black Looks: Race and Representation* (London: Turnaround).
House of Commons, Home Affairs Committee, Sub-Committee on Race Relations and Immigration (1981a) *Racial Disadvantage* (London: HMSO).

House of Commons, Home Affairs Committee, Sub-Committee on Race Relations and Immigration (1981b) *Commission for Racial Equality* (London: HMSO).
——(1982) *Racial Attacks* (London: HMSO).
——(1994) *Racial Attacks and Harassment* (London: HMSO).
House of Commons, Home Affairs Committee (2001) *Border Controls* (London: HMSO).
House of Lords (1999) *Race Relations (Amendment) Bill* (London: The Stationery Office).
Howe, D. (1973) 'Fighting Back: West Indian Youth and the Police in Notting Hill', *Race Today*, December: 333–6.
Howe, S. (1993) *Anticolonialism in British Politics: The Left and the End of Empire, 1918–1964* (Oxford: Clarendon Press).
Howe, S. and Upshal, D. (1988) 'New Black Power Lines', *New Statesman & Society*, 15 July.
Hubbuck, J. and Carter, S. (1980) *Half a Chance? A Report on Job Discrimination Against Young Blacks in Nottingham* (London: Commission for Racial Equality).
Humphry, D. (1972) *Police Power and Black People* (London: Panther).
Hunte, J. (1966) *Nigger Hunting in England* (London: West Indian Standing Conference).
Husbands, C. (1983) *Racial Exclusionism and the City* (London: Allen and Unwin).
——(1991) 'The mainstream right and the politics of immigration in France: major developments in the 1980s', *Ethnic and Racial Studies*, 14, 2: 170–98.
——(1992) 'Why has there been no extreme right in Great Britain', *LSE Magazine*, Spring 1992: 4–8.
Huxley, E. (1964) *Back Street New Worlds* (London: Chatto & Windus).
Ignatiev, N. (1995) *How the Irish Became White* (New York: Routledge).
Immigration Law Practitioners' Association (1993) *The Asylum and Immigration Appeals Act 1993* (London: ILPA).
——(1996) *The Asylum and Immigration Act 1996* (London: ILPA).
——(1999) *Evidence to the Special Standing Committee on the Immigration and Asylum Bill 1999* (London: ILPA).
Institute for Public Policy Research (IPPR) (1997) *Survey on Prejudice* (London: Institute for Public Policy Research).
Institute of Personnel Management (IPM) (1987) *Contract Compliance: The UK Experience* (London: IPM).
Institute of Race Relations (IRR) (1960–69) *Newsletter*.
Jackson, J. A. (1963) *The Irish in Britain* (London: Routledge).
Jacobs, B. (1986) *Black Politics and Urban Crisis in Britain* (Cambridge: Cambridge University Press).
Jacobson, M. F. (1998) *Whiteness of a Different Colour: European Immigrants and the Alchemy of Race* (Cambridge, Mass.: Harvard University Press).
James, W. (1992) 'Migration, Racism and Identity: The Caribbean Experience in Britain', *New Left Review*, 193: 15–55.
James, W. and Harris, C. (eds) (1993) *Inside Babylon: The Caribbean Diaspora in Britain* (London: Verso).
JanMohamed, A. R. and Lloyd, D. (eds) (1990) *The Nature and Context of Minority Discourse* (Oxford: Oxford University Press).
Jeffers, S. (1991) 'Black Sections in the Labour Party: The End of Ethnicity and "Godfather" Politics?', in P. Werbner and M. Anwar (eds), *Black and Ethnic Leaderships in Britain* (London: Routledge).

Jeffers, S., Hoggett, P. and Harrison, L. (1996) 'Race, Ethnicity and Community in Three Localities', *New Community*, 22, 1: 111–26.

Jenkins, R. (1971) 'The Production of Knowledge in the Institute of Race Relations', unpublished paper.

Jenkins, R. and Solomos, J. (eds) (1989) *Racism and Equal Opportunity Policies in the 1980s*, 2nd edn (Cambridge: Cambridge University Press).

Jenkinson, J. (1985) 'The Glasgow Race Disturbances of 1919', in K. Lunn (ed.), *Hosts, Immigrants and Minorities* (Folkestone: Dawson).

Jessop, B. (1982) *The Capitalist State* (Oxford: Martin Robertson).

Jewson, N. and Mason, D. (1994) ' "Race", Employment and Equal Opportunities: Towards a Political Economy and an Agenda for the 1990s', *Sociological Review*, 42, 4: 591–617.

John, G. (1970) *Race in the Inner City: A Report from Handsworth* (London: Runnymede Trust).

Joint Council for the Welfare of Immigrants (1989) 'The European Community's unequal treatment of migrants and refugees', *Policy Papers in Ethnic Relations*, No. 13 (Warwick: Centre for Research in Ethnic Relations, University of warwick).

Joly, D. (1995) *Britannia's Crescent: Making a Place for Muslims in British Society* (Aldershot: Avebury).

Jones, S. (1996) *In the Blood: God, Genes and Destiny* (London: HarperCollins).

Jones, T. (1993) *Britain's Ethnic Minorities* (London: Policy Studies Institute).

Joppke, C. (ed.) (1998) *Challenge to the Nation-State: Immigration in Western Europe and the United States* (Oxford: Oxford University Press).

——(1999) *Immigration and the Nation-State: The United States, Germany, and Great Britain* (Oxford: Oxford University Press).

Joshi, S. and Carter, B. (1984) 'The role of Labour in the creation of a racist Britain', *Race and Class*, xxv, 3: 53–70.

Joshua, H. and Wallace, T. (1983) *To Ride the Storm: The 1980 Bristol 'Riot' and the State* (London: Heinemann).

Kalilombe, P. (1997) 'Black Christianity in Britain', *Ethnic and Racial Studies*, 20, 2: 306–24.

Karn, V. (ed.) (1997) *Ethnicity in the 1991 Census, Volume Four, Employment, Education and Housing among the Ethnic Minority Populations of Great Britain* (London: Office for National Statistics).

Katz, J. (1978) *White Awareness* (Norman: University of Oklahoma Press).

Katznelson, I. (1976) *Black Men, White Cities* (Chicago, Ill.: University of Chicago Press).

——(1982) *City Trenches* (Chicago, Ill. University of Chicago Press).

——(1986) 'Rethinking the silences of social and economic policy', *Political Science Quarterly*, 101, 2: 307–25.

Katznelson, I. and Weir, M. (1985) *Schooling for All* (New York: Basic Books).

Kay, D. and Miles, R. (1992) *Refugees or Migrant Workers? The Recruitment of Displaced Persons for British Industry 1946–1951* (London: Routledge).

Keith, M. (1987) ' "Something Happened": The Problems of Explaining the 1980 and 1981 Riots in British Cities', in P. Jackson (ed.), *Race and Racism* (London: Allen & Unwin).

——(1993) *Race, Riots and Policing: Lore and Disorder in a Multiracist Society* (London: UCL Press).

Keith, M. and Pile, S. (eds) (1993) *Place and the Politics of Identity* (London: Routledge).

Kennedy, P. and Nicholls, A. (eds) (1981) *Nationalist and Racialist Movements in Britain and Germany Before 1914* (Basingstoke: Macmillan).

Kennedy, R. (1997) *Race, Crime and the Law* (New York: Vintage).

Kettle, M. (1982) 'Will 1982 See More Riots', *New Society*, 18 February.

Kettle, M. and Hodges, L. (1982) *Uprising!* (London: Pan).

Kirp, D. (1979) *Doing Good by Doing Little* (Berkeley, CA:University of California Press).

Knopf, T. A. (1975) *Rumors, Race and Riots* (New Brunswick, NJ: Transaction Books).

Knowles, C. (1992) *Race, Discourse and Labourism* (London: Routledge).

Knox, K. (1995) 'The Gulf War and Race Relations in Britain', *Patterns of Prejudice*, 29, 1: 29–51.

Kushner, T. (1994a) *The Holocaust and the Liberal Imagination: A Social and Cultural History* (Oxford: Blackwell).

——(1994b) 'The Fascist as "Other": Racism and Neo-Nazism in Contemporary Britain', *Patterns of Prejudice*, 28, 1: 27–45.

Kushner, T. and Knox, K. (1999) *Refugees in an Age of Genocide: Global, National, and Local Perspectives During the Twentieth Century* (London: Frank Cass).

Kushner, T. and Lunn, K. (eds) (1989) *Traditions of Intolerance: Historical Perspectives on Fascism and Race Discourse in Britain* (Manchester: Manchester University Press).

Labour Party Black Section (1988) *The Black Agenda* (London: Labour Party Black Section).

Lambert, J. R. (1970) *Crime, Police and Race Relations: A Study in Birmingham* (Oxford: Oxford University Press).

Law, I. (1996) *Racism, Ethnicity and Social Policy* (London: Prentice-Hall/Harvester Wheatsheaf).

Lawrence, D. (1974) *Black Migrants, White Natives* (Cambridge: Cambridge University Press).

Layton-Henry, Z. (1980) 'Immigration', in Z. Layton-Henry (ed.), *Conservative Party Policies* (Basingstoke: Macmillan).

——(1984) *The Politics of Race in Contemporary Britain* (London: Allen & Unwin).

——(1986) 'Race and the Thatcher Government', in Z. Layton-Henry and P. Rich (eds), *Race, Government and Politics in Britain* (Basingstoke: Macmillan).

——(1988) 'The Black Electorate and the General Election of 1987', paper presented at the Conference on Black People and British Politics, University of Warwick, November.

——(ed.) (1990) *The Political Rights of Migrant Workers in Western Europe* (London: Sage).

——(1992) *The Politics of Immigration: Immigration, 'Race' and 'Race' Relations in Post-War Britain* (Oxford: Blackwell).

Layton-Henry, Z. and Rich, P. (eds) (1986) *Race, Government and Politics in Britain* (Basingstoke: Macmillan).

Layton-Henry, Z. and Studlar, D. (1985) 'The Electoral Participation of Black and Asian Britons', *Parliamentary Affairs*, 38: 307–18.

Lebow, R. N. (1976) *White Britain and Black Ireland* (Philadelphia, PA: Institute for the Study of Human Issues).

Lebzelter, G. (1978) *Political Anti-Semitism in England* (Basingstoke: Macmillan).

——(1981) 'Anti-semitism: A Focal Point for the British Radical Right', in P. Kennedy and A. Nicholls (eds), *Nationalist and Racialist Movements in Britain and Germany Before 1914* (Basingstoke: Macmillan).

Lee, A. (1980) 'Working Class Response to Jews in Britain, 1880–1914', in K. Lunn (ed.), *Hosts, Immigrants and Minorities* (Folkestone: Dawson).

Lees, L. H. (1979) *Exiles in Erin: Irish Migrants in Victorian London* (Manchester: Manchester University Press).

Le Lohe, M. J. (1989) 'The Performance of Asian and Black Candidates in the British General Election of 1987', *New Community*, 15, 2: 159–70.

Lenton, J., Budgen, N. and Clarke, K. (1966) *Immigration, Race and Politics: A Birmingham View* (London: Bow Publications).

Lester, A. and Bindman, G. (1972) *Race and Law* (Harmondsworth: Penguin).

Levitas, R. (ed.) (1986) *The Ideology of the New Right* (Cambridge: Polity Press).

Lewis, R. (1988) *Anti-Racism: A Mania Exposed* (London: Quartet).

Leys, C. (1989) *Politics in Britain: From Labourism to Thatcherism*, revd edn (London: Verso).

Lindeborg, R. H. (1994) 'The "Asiatic" and the Boundaries of Victorian Englishness', *Victorian Studies*, 37, 3: 381–404.

Lipman, V. D. (1954) *Social History of Jews in England 1850–1950* (London: Watts).

Lipsky, M. and Olson, D. (1977) *Commission Politics: The Processing of Racial Crisis in America* (New Brunswick, NJ: Transaction Books).

Little, K. (1947) *Negroes in Britain: A Study of Racial Relations in English Society* (London: Routledge & Kegan Paul).

Lloyd, C. (1991) 'Concepts, Models and Anti-racist Strategies in Britain and France', *New Community*, 18, 1: 63–73.

——(1998) *Discourses of Antiracism in France* (Aldershot: Ashgate).

Loftman, P. and Beazley, M. (1998) *Race and Regeneration* (Birmingham: University of Birmingham and LGIU).

London Diversity Partnership (1999) *From the Margins to the Mainstream: Delivering Diversity in London* (London: London Development Partnership).

London, L. (2000) *Whitehall and the Jews 1933–1948* (Cambridge: Cambridge University Press).

London Research Centre (1998) *Getting the Measure of Social Exclusion* (London: London Research Centre).

Lowe, L. (1991) *Critical Terrains: French and British Orientalisms* (Ithaca, NY: Cornell University Press).

Lunn, K. (ed.) (1980) *Hosts, Immigrants and Minorities* (Folkestone: Dawson).

——(1985) *Race and Labour in Twentieth-Century Britain* (London: Frank Cass).

——(1989) 'The British State and Immigration, 1945–51: New Light on the *Empire Windrush*', *Immigrants and Minorities*, 8, 1 and 2: 161–74.

Lustgarten, L. (1980) *Legal Control of Racial Discrimination* (Basingstoke: Macmillan).

Mac an Ghaill, M. (1999) *Contemporary Racisms and Ethnicities: Social and Cultural Transformations* (Buckingham: Open University Press).

Mac an Ghaill, M. (2001) 'British Critical Theorists: The Production of the Conceptual Invisibility of the Irish Diaspora', *Social Identities*, 7, 2: 179–201.

Macdonald, I. (1983) *Immigration Law and Practice in the United Kingdom* (London: Butterworth).

Macdonald, I., Bhavnani, R., Khan, L. and John, G. (1989) *Murder in the Playground: the report of the Macdonald Inquiry into racism and racial violence in Manchester schools* (London: Longsight Press).

Macdonald, I. and Blake, N. (1995) *Macdonald's Immigration Law and Practice* (London: Butterworths).

MacDougall, H. B. (1982) *Racial Myth in English History: Trojans, Teutons and Anglo-Saxons* (Hanover, NH: University Press of New England).

MacEwen, M. (1995) *Tackling Racism in Europe: An Examination of anti-Discrimination Law in Practice* (Oxford: Berg).

Macey, M. (1994) '"Same Race" Adoption Policy: Anti-Racism or Racism?', *Journal of Social Policy*, 24, 4: 473–91.

Macmillan, H. (1973) *At the End of the Day* (Basingstoke: Macmillan).

Macpherson of Cluny, Sir William (1999) *The Stephen Lawrence Inquiry: Report of an Inquiry by Sir William Macpherson of Cluny* (London: The Stationery Office).

MacRaild, D. M. (1999) *Irish Migrants in Modern Britain, 1750–1922* (Basingstoke: Macmillan).

Mactaggart, F. and Phillips, T. (1995) 'Anti-racism: New alliances, New agendas', *Renewal*, 3, 3: 63–71.

Malik, K. (1996) *The Meaning of Race: Race, History and Culture in Western Society* (Basingstoke: Macmillan).

Mama, A. (1989) 'Violence Against Black Women: Gender, Race, and State Responses', *Feminist Review*, 32: 30–48.

——(1992) 'Black Women and the British State: Race, Class and Gender Analysis for the 1990s', in P. Graham, A. Rattansi and R. Skellington (eds), *Racism and Antiracism. Inequalities, Opportunities and Policies* (London: Sage).

Marable, M. (1981) 'Race, Class and Conflict', *Sage Race Relations Abstracts*, 6, 4: 1–38.

——(1983) *How Capitalism Underdeveloped Black America* (London: Pluto).

——(1985) *Black American Politics* (London: Verso).

Mark, R. (1970) 'The Metropolitan Police: Their Role in the Community', *Community*, July: 3–5.

Martiniello, M. (1991) 'Racism in Paradise?', *Race and Class*, 32, 3: 79–84.

Mason, D. (2000) *Race and Ethnicity in Modern Britain,* 2nd edn (Oxford: Oxford University Press).

Mason, D. and Jewson, N. (1992) 'Race, equal opportunities policies and employment practice: Reflections on the 1980s, prospects for the 1990s', *New Community*, 19, 1: 99–112.

Matar, N. (1999) *Turks, Moors and Englishmen in the Age of Discovery* (New York: Columbia University Press).

May, R. and Cohen, R. (1974) 'The Interaction Between Race and Colonialism: A Case Study of the Liverpool Race Riots of 1919', *Race and Class*, 16, 2: 111–26.

May, S. (ed.) (1999) *Critical Multiculturalism: Rethinking Multicultural and Antiracist Education* (London: Falmer Press).

McAdam, D. (1982) *Political Process and the Development of Black Insurgency: 1930–1970* (Chicago, Ill.: University of Chicago Press).

McClintock, A. 1995) *Imperial Leather: Race, Gender and Sexuality in the Colonial Context* (New York: Routledge).

McCrudden, C. (1982) 'Institutional Discrimination', *Oxford Journal of Legal Studies*, 2: 303–67.

——(1983) 'Anti-discrimination goals and the legal process', in N. Glazer and K. Young (eds), *Ethnic Pluralism and Public Policy* (London: Heinemann).

——(1987) 'The Commission for Racial Equality', in R. Baldwin and C. McCrudden (eds), *Regulation and Public Law* (London: Weidenfeld & Nicolson).

——(1988) 'Codes in a Cold Climate: Administrative Rule-Making by the Commission for Racial Equality', *Modern Law Review*, 51, 4: 409–41.

McCrudden, C., Smith, D. J. and Brown, C. (1991) *Racial Justice at Work* (London: Policy Studies Institute).

McIntosh, N. and Smith, D. J. (1974) *The Extent of Racial Discrimination* (London: Political and Economic Planning).

Mercer, K. (1990) 'Welcome to the Jungle: Identity and Diversity in Postmodern Politics' in J. Rutherford (ed.), *Identity: Community, Culture, Difference* (London: Lawrence & Wishart).

——(1994) *Welcome to the Jungle: Essays in Black British Cultural Studies* (London: Routledge).

Messina, A. (1985) 'Race and Party Competition in Britain', *Parliamentary Affairs*, 38, 4: 423–36.

——(1987) 'Mediating Race Relations: British Community Relations Councils Revisited', *Ethnic and Racial Studies*, 10, 2: 187–202.

——(1989) *Race and Party Competition in Britain* (Oxford: Clarendon Press).

Metcalf, H., Modood, T. and Virdee, S. (1998) *Asian Self-Employment: The Interaction of Culture and Economics in England* (London: Policy Studies Institute).

Metropolitan Police (1986) *Public Order Review – Civil Disturbances 1981–1985* (London: Metropolitan Police).

Miles, R. (1982) *Racism and Migrant Labour* (London: Routledge & Kegan Paul).

——(1984) 'The Riots of 1958: Notes on the Ideological Construction of "Race Relations" as a Political Issue in Britain', *Immigrants and Minorities*, 3, 3: 252–75.

——(1986) 'Labour Migration, Racism and Capital Accumulation in Western Europe Since 1945', *Capital and Class*, 28: 49–86.

——(1987) 'Recent Marxist Theories of Nationalism and the Issue of Racism', *British Journal of Sociology*, XXXVIII, 1: 24–43.

——(1988) 'Racism, Marxism and British Politics', *Economy and Society*, 17, 3: 428–60.

——(1989) *Racism* (London: Routledge).

——(1992) 'Migration, Racism and the Nation State in Contemporary Europe', in V. Satzewich (ed.), *Deconstructing the Nation. Immigration, Multiculturalism and Racism in 90s Canada* (Toronto: Garamond Press).

——(1993) *After 'Race Relations'* (London: Routledge).

——(1994) 'A rise of racism and fascism in contemporary Europe? Some sceptical reflections on its nature and extent', *New Community*, 20, 4: 547–62.

Miles, R. and Phizacklea, A. (eds) (1979) *Racism and Political Action in Britain* (London: Routledge & Kegan Paul).

——(1984) *White Man's Country* (London: Pluto).

Millward, P. (1985) 'The Stockport Riots of 1852: A Study of Anti-Catholic and Anti-Irish Sentiment', in R. Swift and S. Gilley (eds), *The Irish in the Victorian City* (London: Croom Helm).

Mirza, H. S. (ed.) (1997) *Black British Feminism: A Reader* (London: Routledge).
Mishan, E. J. (1988) 'What Future for a Multi-Racial Britain?', *Salisbury Review*, 6, 4: 18–27.
Modood, T (1988) '"Black" racial equality and Asian identity', *New Community*, XIV, 3: 397–404.
——(1992) *'Not Easy Being British': Colour, Culture and Citizenship* (London: Trentham Books and Runnymede Trust).
Modood, T., Beishon, S. and Virdee, S. (1994) *Changing Ethnic Identities* (London: Policy Studies Institute).
Modood, T., Berthoud, R., Lakey, J., Nazroo, J., Smith, P., Virdee, S. and Beishon, S. (1997) *Ethnic Minorities in Britain: Diversity and Disadvantage* (London: Policy Studies Institute).
Modood, T. and Werbner, P. (eds) (1997) *The Politics of Multiculturalism in the New Europe: Racism, Identity and Community* (London: Zed Books).
Moore, R. (1975) *Racism and Black Resistance in Britain* (London: Pluto).
Moore, R. and Wallace, T. (1975) *Slamming the Door: The Administration of Immigration Control* (Oxford: Martin Robertson).
Moran, M. (1985) *Politics and Society in Britain* (Basingstoke: Macmillan).
Morley, D. and Robins, K. (1990) 'No Place Like Heimat: Images of Home (Land) in European Culture', *New Formations*, 12: 1–23.
Mosse, G. L. (1985) *Toward the Final Solution: A History of European Racism* (Madison, Wis.: University of Wisconsin Press).
Mullard, C. (1985) *Race, Power and Resistance* (London: Routledge & Kegan Paul).
Murdock, G. (1984) 'Reporting the Riots: Images and Impact', in J. Benyon (ed.), *Scarman and After* (Oxford: Pergamon Press).
Murray, N. (1986) 'Anti-racists and Other Demons: The Press and Ideology in Thatcher's Britain', *Race and Class*, XXVII, 3: 1–19.
Myrdal, G. (1962) *Challenge to Affluence* (New York: Pantheon).
——(1969a) *Objectivity in Social Research* (London: Duckworth).
——(1969b) *An American Dilemma: The Negro Problem and Modern Democracy* (New York: Harper & Row).
Nairn, T. (1981) *The Break-Up of Britain* (London: Verso).
——(1988) *The Enchanted Glass* (London: Radius).
Nandy, D. (1970) 'Immigrants and the Police', *Runnymede Trust Bulletin*, October.
Nazroo, J. (1997) *The Health of Britain's Ethnic Minorities* (London: Policy Studies Institute).
Nelson, W. E. Jr (2000) *Black Atlantic Politics: Dilemmas of Political Empowerment in Boston and Liverpool* (Albany, NY: State University of New York Press).
Newman, G. (1987) *The Rise of English Nationalism: A Cultural History, 1740–1830* (London: Weidenfeld & Nicolson).
Newman, K. (1983) 'Fighting the fear of crime', *Police*, September: 26–30; October: 30–2.
——(1986a) 'Police Public Relations: The Pace of Change', Police Federation Annual Lecture, 28 July.
——(1986b) *Public Order Review: Civil Disturbances 1981–85* (London: Metropolitan Police).
Newnham, A. (1986) *Employment, Unemployment and Black People* (London: Runnymede Trust).

Newton, K. (1976) *Second City Politics: Democratic Processes and Decision-Making in Birmingham* (Oxford: Clarendon Press).

Nixon, J. (1982) 'The Home Office and Race Relations Policy: Co-ordinator or Initiator?', *Journal of Public Policy*, 2, 4: 365–78.

Oakley, R. (1988) *Employment in Police Forces: A Survey of Equal Opportunities* (London: Commission for Racial Equality).

——(1996) *Race and Equal Opportunities in the Police Service* (London: Commission for Racial Equality).

OECD (1986) 'United Kingdom', National Report for the OECD Conference on the Future of Migration, Paris, February.

Offe, C. (1984) *Contradictions of the Welfare State* (London: Hutchinson).

——(1985) *Disorganised Capitalism* (Cambridge: Polity Press).

Office for Public Management (2001) *Involving Black and Ethnic Minority Communities in Local Governance* (London: Office for Public Management).

Oldham Independent Review (2001) *Panel Report* (Oldham: Oldham Independent Review).

Omi, M. and Winant, H. (1994) *Racial Formation in the United States*, 2nd edn (London: Routledge).

O Tuathaigh, M. (1985) 'The Irish in Nineteenth Century Britain: Problems of Integration', in R. Swift and S. Gilley (eds), *The Irish in the Victorian City* (London: Croom Helm).

Ouseley, H. (1981) *The System* (London: Runnymede).

——(1982) 'A Local Black Alliance', in A. Ohri, B. Manning and P. Curno, *Community Work and Racism* (London: Routledge).

——(1984) 'Local Authority Race Initiatives', in M. Boddy and C. Fudge (eds), *Local Socialism* (Basingstoke: Macmillan).

——(ed.) (1986) *A Different Reality: An Account of Black People's Experiences and their Grievances before and after the Handsworth Rebellions of September 1985* (Birmingham: West Midlands County Council).

Ouseley, H. (2001) *Community Pride, Not Prejudice: Making Diversity Work in Bradford* (Bradford: Bradford Vision).

Owen, D. (1994a) *Black People in Great Britain: Social and Economic Circumstances* (Warwick: Centre for Research in Ethnic Relations, University of Warwick).

——(1994b) *Ethnic Minority Women and the Labour Market: Analysis of the 1991 Census* (Manchester: Equal Opportunities Commission).

Owen, D. and Green, A. (1992) 'Labour Market Experience and Change among Ethnic Groups in Great Britain', *New Community*, 19, 1: 7–29.

Palmer, F. (ed.) (1986) *Anti-Racism – An Assault on Education and Value* (London: The Sherwood Press).

Panayi, P. (ed.) (1996) *Racial Violence in Britain in the Nineteenth and Twentieth Centuries*, Revd. edn. (London: Leicester University Press).

——(ed.) (1999) *The Impact of Immigration: A Documentary History of the Effects and Experiences of Immigrants in Britain since 1945* (Manchester: Manchester University Press).

Papastergiadis, N. (2000) *The Turbulence of Migration: Globalization, Deterritorialization and Hybridity* (Cambridge: Polity Press).

Parekh, B. (1987) 'The "New Right" and the Politics of Nationhood', in Runnymede Trust, *The New Right: Image and Reality* (London: Runnymede Trust).

Parekh, B. (1989) 'Between Holy Text and Moral Void', *New Statesman and Society*, 28 March, 29–32.
——(1991) 'British Citizenship and Cultural Difference', in G. Andrews (ed.), *Citizenship* (London: Lawrence and Wishart).
——(2000a) *Rethinking Multiculturalism: Cultural Diversity and Political Theory* (Basingstoke: Macmillan).
——(2000b) *The Future of Multi-Ethnic Britain: Report of the Commission on the Future of Multi-Ethnic Britain* (London: Profile Books).
Park, R. (1950) *Race and Culture* (New York: Free Press).
Parkin, F. (1979) *Marxism and Class: A Bourgeois Critique* (London: Tavistock).
Parkinson, M. and Duffy, J. (1984) 'Government's Response to Inner City Riots: The Minister for Merseyside and the Task Force', *Parliamentary Affairs*, 37, 1: 76–96.
Parmar, P. (1990) 'Black Feminism: The Politics of Articulation', in J. Rutherford (ed.), *Identity: Community, Culture, Difference* (London: Lawrence and Wishart).
Parry, B. (1998) *Delusions and Discoveries: India in the British Imagination, 1880–1930* (London: Verso).
Parsons, N. (1998) *King Khama, Emperor Joe and the Great White Queen: Victorian Britain Through African Eyes* (Chicago, Ill.: University of Chicago Press).
Patten, J. (1989) 'The Muslim Community in Britain', *The Times*, 5 July 1989.
Patterson, S. (1963) *Dark Strangers* (Harmondsworth: Penguin).
——(1969) *Immigration and Race Relations in Britain 1960–1967* (Oxford: Oxford University Press).
Paul, K. (1997) *Whitewashing Britain: Race and Citizenship in the Postwar Era* (Ithaca, NY: Cornell University Press).
Peach, C. (ed.) (1996) *Ethnicity in the 1991 Census, Volume Two, The Ethnic Minority Populations of Great Britain* (London: Office for National Statistics).
Pearson, D. (1981) *Race, Class and Political Activism* (Aldershot: Gower).
Phillips, A. (1991) *Engendering Democracy* (Cambridge: Polity Press).
——(1995) *The Politics of Presence* (Oxford: Clarendon Press).
Phillips, M. and Phillips, T. (1998) *Windrush: The Irresistible Rise of Multi-Racial Britain* (London: HarperCollins).
Philo, G. and Beattie, L. (1999) 'Race, Migration and the Media', in G. Philo (ed.), *Message Received: Glasgow Media Group Research 1993–1998* (London: Longman).
Phizacklea, A. and Miles, R. (1980) *Labour and Racism* (London: Routledge).
——(1987) 'The British trade union movement and racism', in G. Lee and R. Loveridge (eds), *The Manufacture of Disadvantage* (Milton Keynes: Open University Press).
Pieterse, J. N. (1992) *White on Black: Images of Africa and Blacks in Western Popular Culture* (New Haven, CT: Yale University Press).
Pilkington, E. (1988) *Beyond the Mother Country: West Indians and the Notting Hill White Riots* (London: I. B. Tauris).
Piven, F. F. and Cloward, R. (1977) *Poor People's Movements* (New York: Vintage Books).
Platt, C. (1991) 'The Immigration Act 1988', *Policy Paper in Ethnic Relations* (University of Warwick: Centre for Research in Ethnic Relations).
Pollins, H. (1982) *Economic History of the Jews in England* (London: Associated University Press).

Powell, E. (1969) *Still to Decide* (Kingswood: Elliot Right Way Books).
——(1972) *Still to Decide* (London: Batsford).
PREM (1956) *Immigration from the Irish Republic* PREM 11/1409 (London: Public Records Office).
Preston, M. B., Henderson, L. J. and Pureyar, P. (eds) (1982) *The New Black Politics* (New York: Longman).
Pryce, K. (1979) *Endless Pressure* (Harmondsworth: Penguin).
Pulle, S. (1973) *Police/Immigrant Relations in Ealing* (London: Runnymede Trust).
Race Relations Board (1973) *Race Relations Legislation in Britain* (London: Race Relations Board).
Ramazanoglu, C. (1989) *Feminism and the Contradictions of Oppression* (London: Routledge).
Ramdin, R. (1987) *The Making of the Black Working Class in Britain* (Aldershot: Gower).
——(1999) *Reimaging Britain: 500 Years of Black and Asian History* (London: Pluto).
Ratcliffe, P. (ed.) (1996) *Ethnicity in the 1991 Census, Volume Three, Social Geography and Ethnicity in Britain: Geographical Spread, Spatial Concentration and Internal Migration* (London: Office for National Statistics).
Rattansi, A. (1992) 'Changing the Subject? Racism, Culture and Education', in J. Donald and A. Rattansi (eds), *'Race', Culture and Difference* (London: Sage).
Rattansi, A. and Westwood, S. (eds) (1994) *Racism, Modernity and Identity* (Cambridge: Polity Press).
Redford, A. (1976) *Labour Migration in England 1800–1850* (Manchester University Press).
Reed Jr, A. (ed.) (1999) *Without Justice for All: The New Liberalism and Our Retreat from Racial Equality* (Boulder, CO: Westview Press).
Reeves, F. (1983) *British Racial Discourse* (Cambridge: Cambridge University Press).
——(1989) *Race and Borough Politics* (Avebury: Aldershot).
Reiner, R. (1985) *The Politics of the Police* (Brighton: Wheatsheaf).
Rex, J. (1973) *Race, Colonialism and the City* (London: Routledge & Kegan Paul).
——(1979) 'Black militancy and class conflict', in R. Miles and A. Phizacklea (eds), *Racism and Political Action in Britain* (London: Routledge & Kegan Paul).
——(1981) 'A Working Paradigm for Race Relations Research', *Ethnic and Racial Studies*, 4, 1: 1–25.
——(1983) *Race Relations in Sociological Theory*, 2nd edn (London: Routledge & Kegan Paul).
——(1986a) *Race and Ethnicity* (Milton Keynes: Open University Press).
——(1986b) 'The Role of Class Analysis in the Study of Race Relations – A Weberian Perspective', in J. Rex and D. Mason (eds), *Theories of Race and Ethnic Relations* (Cambridge: Cambridge University Press).
——(1988) *The Ghetto and the Underclass: Essays on Race and Social Policy* (Aldershot: Avebury).
——(1991) *Ethnic Identity and Political Mobilisation in Britain* (Warwick: Centre for Research in Ethnic Relations, University of Warwick, Monographs in Ethnic relations, no. 5).
Rex, J. and Mason, D. (eds) (1986) *Theories of Race and Ethnic Relations* (Cambridge: Cambridge University Press).

Rex, J. and Moore, R. (1967) *Race, Community and Conflict* (Oxford: Oxford University Press).

Rex, J. and Tomlinson, S. (1979) *Colonial Immigrants in a British City: A Class Analysis* (London: Routledge and Kegan Paul).

Rich, P. (1986) *Race and Empire in British Politics* (Cambridge: Cambridge University Press).

Richmond, A. (1954) *Colour Prejudice in Britain: A Study of West Indian Workers in Liverpool, 1942–51* (London: Routledge and Kegan Paul).

——(1973) *Migration and Race Relations in an English City* (Oxford: Oxford University Press).

Robinson, C. (1983) *Black Marxism* (London: Zed).

Robson, B. (1988) *Those Inner Cities* (Oxford: Clarendon Press).

Rose, E. J. B. and Associates (1969) *Colour and Citizenship: A Report on British Race Relations* (Oxford: Oxford University Press).

Rose, R. (1985) *Politics in England* (London: Faber and Faber).

Rubenstein, D. (1998) *Discrimination: A Guide to the Relevant Case Law on Race and Sex Discrimination and Equal Pay*, 11th edn (London: Industrial Relations Services).

Runnymede Trust (1992–2000) *Runnymede Trust Bulletin*, Issues 252–323 (London: Runnymede Trust).

Runnymede Trust, Commission on Antisemitism (1994) *A Very Light Sleeper: The Persistence and Danger of Antisemitism* (London: Runnymede Trust).

Rushdie, S. (1989) *The Satanic Verses* (London: Viking).

Rutherford, J. (ed.) (1990) *Identity: Community, Culture, Difference* (London: Lawrence and Wishart).

Ruthven, M. (1990) *A Satanic Affair* (London: Chatto and Windus).

Saggar, S. (1991) *Race and Public Policy* (Aldershot: Avebury).

——(1992) *Race and Politics in Britain* (London: Harvester Wheatsheaf).

——(1998a) *The General Election: Ethnic Minorities and Electoral Politics* (London: Commission for Racial Equality).

——(ed.) (1998b) *Race and British Electoral Politics* (London: UCL Press).

——(2000) *Race and Representation: Electoral Politics and Ethnic Pluralism in Britain* (Manchester: Manchester University Press).

Sahgal, G. and Yuval-Davis, N. (eds) (1992) *Refusing Holy Orders* (London: Virago).

Samad, Y. (1992) 'Book burning and race relations: Political mobilisation of Bradford Muslims', *New Community*, 18, 4: 507–19.

Samuel, R. (ed.) (1989a) *Patriotism. Volume II: Minorities and Outsiders* (London: Routledge).

——(ed.) (1989b) *Patriotism: Volume III: National Fictions* (London: Routledge).

——(1998) *Island Stories: Unravelling Britain* (London: Verso).

Saunders, P. (1981) *Social Theory and the Urban Question* (London: Hutchinson).

Scarman, Lord (1981) *The Brixton Disorders 10–12 April 1981. Report of an Inquiry by the Rt. Hon. The Lord Scarman OBE* (London: HMSO).

——(1985) 'Brixton and After' in J. Roach and J. Thomaneak (eds), *Police and Public Order in Europe* (London: Croom Helm).

Schuster, L. and Solomos, J. (1999) 'The politics of refugee and asylum policies in Britain: historical patterns and contemporary realities', in A. Bloch and C. Levy (eds), *Refugees, Citizenship and Social Policy in Europe* (Basingstoke: Macmillan).

Schwarz, B. (ed.) (1996) *The Expansion of England: Race, Ethnicity and Cultural History* (London: Routledge).

Seidel, G. (1986a) 'The Concept of Culture, "Race" and Nation in the British and French New Right', in R. Levitas (ed.), *The Ideology of the New Right* (Cambridge: Polity Press).

——(1986b) *The Holocaust Denial: Antisemitism, Racism and the New Right* (Leeds: Beyond the Pale).

Select Committee on Race Relations and Immigration (1969) *The Problems of Coloured School Leavers* (London: HMSO).

——(1972) *Police/Immigrant Relations* (London: HMSO).

——(1975) *The Organisation of Race Relations Administration* (London: HMSO).

——(1977) *The West Indian Community* (London: HMSO).

——(1978) *Immigration* (London: HMSO).

Sewell, T. (1993) *Black Tribunes: Black Political Participation in Britain* (London: Lawrence & Wishart).

Sherman, A. (1973) *Island Refuge: Britain and Refugees from the Third Reich* (London: Paul Elek).

Sherwood, M. (1984) *Many Struggles: West Indian Workers and Service Personnel in Britain 1939–45* (London: Karia Press).

Shukra, K. (1998) *The Changing Pattern of Black Politics in Britain* (London: Pluto).

Shyllon, F. O. (1974) *Black Slaves in Britain* (Oxford: Oxford University Press).

Sibbitt, R. (1997) *The Perpetrators of Racial Violence and Racial Harassment* (London: Home Office).

Silverman, J. (1986) *Independent Inquiry into the Handsworth Disturbances September 1985* (Birmingham: Birmingham City Council).

Silverman, M. (1982) *Deconstructing the Nation: Immigration, Racism and Citizenship in Modern France* (London: Routledge).

Sim, J. (1982) 'Scarman: The Police Counter Attack', *Socialist Register 1982* (London: Merlin Press).

Sivanandan, A. (1982) *A Different Hunger* (London: Pluto).

——(1985) 'RAT and the Degradation of Black Struggle', *Race and Class*, XXVI, 4: 1–33.

——(1990) *Communities of Resistance* (London: Verso).

Skolnick, R. (1969) *The Politics of Protest* (New York: Simon & Schuster).

Small, S. (1991a) 'Attaining Racial Parity in the United States and England: We Got to Go Where the Greener Grass Grows!', *Sage Race Relations Abstracts*, 16, 3: 3–55.

——(1991b) 'Racialised Relations in Liverpool: A Contemporary Anomaly', *New Community*, 11, 4: 511–37.

——(1994) *Racialised Barriers: The Black Experience in the United States and England in the 1980s* (London: Routledge).

Smith, A. M. (1994) *New Right Discourse on Race and Sexuality: Britain, 1968–1990* (Cambridge: Cambridge University Press).

Smith, B. (1999) *Imperialism, Race and Resistance: Africa and Britain 1919–1945* (London: Routledge)

Smith, D. (1987) 'Knowing your Place: Class, Politics and Ethnicity in Chicago and Birmingham 1890–1983', in N. Thrift and P. Williams (eds), *Class and Space* (Basingstoke: Macmillan).

Smith, D. J. (1977) *Racial Disadvantage in Britain* (Harmondsworth: Penguin).
——(ed.) (1992) *Understanding the Underclass* (London: Policy Studies Institute).
Smith, D. J. and Gray, J. (1987) *Police and People in London* (Aldershot: Gower).
Smith, G. (1987) *When Jim Crow Met John Bull* (London: I. B. Tauris).
Smith, S. J. (1989) *The Politics of 'Race' and Residence: Citizenship, Segregation and White Supremacy in Britain* (Cambridge: Polity Press).
Smithies, B. and Fiddick, P. (1969) *Enoch Powell on Immigration* (London: Sphere Books).
Soja, E. W. (1989) *Postmodern Geographies* (London: Verso).
Solomos, J. (1986) 'Trends in the Political Analysis of Racism', *Political Studies*, XXXIV, 2: 313–24.
——(1988) *Black Youth, Racism and the State* (Cambridge: Cambridge University Press).
——(1989) 'Equal Opportunities Policies and Racial Inequality: The Role of Public Policy', *Public Administration*, 67, 1: 79–93.
——(1991) 'Political Language and Racial Discourse', *European Journal of Intercultural Studies*, 2, 1: 21–34.
——(1998) 'Beyond Racism and Multiculturalism', *Patterns of Prejudice*, 32, 3: 45–62
——(1999) 'Social Research and the Stephen Lawrence Inquiry', *Sociological Research Online*, 4, 1 (http://www.socresonline.org.uk/socreonline/4/1/solomos.html).
Solomos, J. and Back, L. (1991) 'The Politics of Race and Social Change in Birmingham', *Research Papers No. 1* (London: Department of Politics and Sociology, Birkbeck College).
——(1993) 'Race and Racism', in J. Krieger (ed.), *The Oxford Companion to Politics of the World* (New York: Oxford University Press).
——(1995) *Race, Politics and Social Change* (London: Routledge).
——(1996) *Racism and Society* (Basingstoke: Macmillan).
Sooben, P. (1990) 'The Origins of the Race Relations Act', *Research Paper in Ethnic Relations No 12* (Warwick: Centre for Research in Ethnic Relations, University of Warwick).
Sowell, T. (1981) *Markets and Minorities* (Oxford: Basil Blackwell).
Soysal, Y. N. (1994) *Limits of Citizenship: Migrants and Postnational Membership in Europe* (Chicago, Ill.: University of Chicago Press).
Spencer, I. R. G. (1997) *British Immigration Policy Since 1939: The Making of Multi-Racial Britain* (London: Routledge).
Spencer, K., Taylor, A., Smith, B., Mawson, J., Flynn, N. and Batley, R. (1986) *Crisis in the Industrial Heartland: A Study of the West Midlands* (Oxford: Clarendon Press).
Spencer, S. (ed.) (1994) *Strangers and Citizens: A Positive Approach to Migrants and Refugees* (London: IPPR/Rivers Oram Press).
Spivak, G. C. (1987) *In Other Worlds* (London: Methuen).
Stewart, J. and Stoker, G. (eds) (1989) *The Future of Local Government* (Basingstoke: Macmillan).
Stoker, G. (1988) *The Politics of Local Government* (Basingstoke: Macmillan).
——(ed.) (2000) *The New Politics of British Local Governance* (Basingstoke: Macmillan).

Studlar, D. (1978) 'Policy Voting in Britain: The Coloured Immigration Issue in the 1964, 1966 and 1970 General Elections', *American Political Science Review*, 72, 1: 46–64.

——(1980) 'Elite Responsiveness or Elite Autonomy: British Immigration Policy Reconsidered', *Ethnic and Racial Studies*, 3, 2: 207–23.

Sudbury, J. (1998) *'Other Kinds of Dreams': Black Women's Organisations and the Politics of Transformation* (London: Routledge).

Swift R. and Gilley, S. (eds) (1985) *The Irish in the Victorian City* (London: Croom Helm).

Tabili, L. (1994) *'We Ask for British Justice': Black Workers and the Construction of Racial Difference in Late Imperial Britain* (Ithaca, NY: Cornell University Press).

Tannahill, J. A. (1958) *European Volunteer Workers in Britain* (Manchester: Manchester University Press).

Taylor, S. (1982) *The National Front in English Politics* (Basingstoke: Macmillan).

Thatcher, M. (1988) *Britain and Europe* (London: Conservative Political Centre).

Thompson, G. (1986) *The Conservatives' Economic Policy* (London: Croom Helm).

Thrift, N. and Williams, P. (eds) (1987) *Class and Space* (Basingstoke: Macmillan).

Thurlow, R. (1975) 'National Front Ideology', *Patterns of Prejudice*, 9, 1: 1–9.

——(1998) *Fascism in Britain: From Oswald Mosley's Blackshirts to the National Front* (London: I. B. Tauris).

Times, The (1968) *The Black Man in Search of Power* (London: Nelson).

Toulis, N. R. (1997) *Believing Identity: Pentecostalism and the Mediation of Jamaican Ethnicity and Gender in England* (Oxford: Berg).

Travers, M. (1999) *The British Immigration Courts* (Bristol: The Policy Press).

Troyna, B. and Williams, J. (1986) *Racism, Education and the State* (London: Croom Helm).

Twine, F. Winddance and Warren, J. W. (eds) (2000) *Racing Research, Researching Race: Methodological Dilemmas in Critical Race Studies* (New York: New York University Press).

van Dijk, T. A. (1988) *News Analysis: Case Studies of International and National News in the Press* (New Jersey: Lawrence Erlbaum).

——(1991) *Racism and the Press* (London: Routledge).

Vertovec, S. (1996) 'Multiculturalism, Culturalism and Public Incorporation', *Ethnic and Racial Studies*, 19, 1: 49–69.

Virdee, S. (1995) *Racial Violence and Harassment* (London: Policy Studies Institute).

——(2000) 'A Marxist Critique of Black Radical Theories of Trade-union Racism', *Sociology*, 34, 3: 545–65.

Visram, R. (1986) *Ayahs, Lascars and Princes* (London: Pluto).

——(2002) *Asians in Britain*, 2nd edn (London: Pluto).

Wacquant, L. J. D. (1994) 'The New Urban Colour Line: The State and Fate of the Ghetto in Post Fordist America,' in C. Calhoun (ed.), *Social Theory and the Politics of Identity* (Oxford: Blackwell).

Waddington, P. A. J. (1999) 'Police (Canteen) Sub-culture: An Appreciation', *British Journal of Criminology*, 39, 2: 286–308.

Walker, M. (1977) *The National Front* (London: Fontana).

Waller, P. J. (1981) *Democracy and Sectarianism: A Political and Social History of Liverpool 1868–1939* (Liverpool: Liverpool University Press).

Walvin, J. (1973) *Black and White: The Negro and British Society* (London: Allen & Unwin).
——(1984) *Passage to Britain* (Harmondsworth: Penguin).
——(1992) *Black Ivory: A History of British Slavery* (London: HarperCollins).
——(1999) *Making the Black Atlantic: Britain and the African Diaspora* (London: Cassell).
Wambu, O. (ed.) (1998) *Empire Windrush: Fifty Years of Writing About Black Britain* (London: Victor Gollancz).
Ward, R. (ed.) (1984) *Race and Housing in Britain* (Warwick: Centre for Research in Ethnic Relations, University of Warwick).
Ware, V. (1992) *Beyond the Pale: White Women, Racism and History* (London: Verso).
Wayland, S. V. (1997) 'Religious Expression in Public Schools: *kirpans* in Canada, *hijab* in France', *Ethnic and Racial Studies*, 20, 3: 545–61.
Werbner, P. and Anwar, M. (eds) (1991) *Black and Ethnic Leaderships* (London: Routledge).
Werbner, P. and Modood, T. (eds) (1997) *Debating Cultural Hybridity: Multi-Cultural Identities and the Politics of Anti-Racism* (London: Zed Books).
Western, J. (1992) *A Passage to England: Barbadian Londoners Speak of Home* (London: UCL Press).
Widgery, D. (1986) *Beating Time* (London: Chatto and Windus).
Wieviorka, M. (1993) 'Tendencies to Racism in Europe: Does France Represent a Unique Case, or is it Representative of a Trend', in J. Wrench and J. Solomos (eds), *Racism and Migration in Western Europe* (Oxford and New York: Berg).
Williams, F. (1995) 'Race/Ethnicity, Gender and Class in Welfare States: a Framework for Comparative Analysis', *Social Politics*, 2, 2: 127–59.
Wilpert, C. (1991) 'Migration and Ethnicity in a Non-immigration Country – Foreigners in a United Germany', *New Community*, 18, 1: 49–62.
Wilson, H. (1971) *The Labour Government 1964–70* (London: Weidenfeld & Nicolson).
Wilson, W. J. (1980) *The Declining Significance of Race* (Chicago, Ill.: University of Chicago Press).
——(1988) *The Truly Disadvantaged* (Chicago, Ill.: University of Chicago Press).
——(1996) *When Work Disappears* (New York: Alfred Knopf).
Wimmer, A. (1997) 'Explaining Xenophobia and Racism: A Critical Review of Current Research Approaches', *Ethnic and Racial Studies*, 20, 1: 17–41.
Winant, H. (2001) *The World is a Ghetto: Race and Democracy Since World War II* (New York: Basic Books).
WING (1985) *Worlds Apart: Women Under Immigration and Nationality Law* (London: Pluto).
Witte, R. (1996) *Racist Violence and the State: A Comparative Analysis of Britain, France and the Netherlands* (London: Longman).
Wolf, E. (1982) *Europe and the People Without History* (Berkeley, CA: University of California Press).
Wolpe, H. (1987) *Race, Class and the Apartheid State* (London: James Currey).
Worsthorne, P. (1978) 'Too Much Freedom', in M. Cowling (ed.), *Conservative Essays* (London: Cassell).
——(1985) 'End this Silence over Race', *Sunday Telegraph*, 26 September.

Wrench, J. and Solomos, J. (eds) (1993) *Racism and Migration in Western Europe* (Oxford and New York: Berg).

Young, I. M. (1990) *Justice and the Politics of Difference* (Princeton, NJ: Princeton University Press).

Young, K. (1985) 'Racial Disadvantage', in S. Ranson, G. Jones and K. Walsh (eds), *Between Centre and Locality* (London: Allen & Unwin).

——(1989) 'The Space Between Words: Local Authorities and the Concept of Equal Opportunities', in R. Jenkins and J. Solomos (eds), *Racism and Equal Opportunity Policies in the 1980s* (Cambridge: Cambridge University Press).

——(1990) 'Approaches to Policy Development in the Field of Equal Opportunities', in W. Ball and J. Solomos (eds), *Race and Local Politics* (Basingstoke: Macmillan).

Young, K. and Connelly, N. (1981) *Policy and Practice in the Multi-Racial City* (London: Policy Studies Institute).

——(1984) 'After the Act: Local Authority Policy Reviews under the Race Relations Act 1976', *Local Government Studies*, 10, 1: 13–25.

Young, R. (1990) *White Mythologies: Writing History and the West* (London: Routledge).

—— (ed.) (1991) *Neocolonialism*, special issue of *Oxford Literary Review*, 13, 1–2.

Zolberg, A. R. (1989) 'The Next Waves: Migration Theory for a Changing World', *International Migration Review*, 23, 3: 403–30.

Zubaida, S. (ed.) (1970) 'Introduction', *Race and Racialism* (London: Tavistock).

——(1972) 'Sociologists and Race Relations', in *Proceedings of a Seminar: Problems and Prospects of Socio-Legal Research* (Oxford: Nuffield College).

Zubrzycki, J. (1956) *Polish Immigrants to Britain* (The Hague: Martinus Nijhoff).

Index